FICTION AND ANALYSIS

FICTION AND ANALYSIS: SEVEN MAJOR THEMES

Robert Canzoneri, The Ohio State University

Page Stegner, University of California, Santa Cruz

Scott, Foresman and Company

ACKNOWLEDGMENTS

"The Guest" by Albert Camus. © Copyright 1957, 1958 by Alfred A. Knopf, Inc. Reprinted from *Exile and the Kingdom*, by Albert Camus, translated by Justin O'Brien, by permission of Alfred A. Knopf, Inc.

"Defender of the Faith" from *Goodbye, Columbus* by Philip Roth, Copyright 1959. Reprinted by permission of Houghton Mifflin Company.

"Genesis" trom *Wolf Willow* by Wallace Stegner. Copyright © 1959 by Wallace Stegner. Reprinted by permission of The Viking Press, Inc.

"The Ledge" reprinted by permission of Lawrence Sargent Hall. Copyright 1960 by Lawrence Sargent Hall. First published in *The Hudson Review*, Volume XI, No. . 4, Winter 1958-59.

"The Long March." Copyright 1952 by William Styron. Reprinted by permission of Harold Matson Co., Inc.

"Powerhouse." Copyright, 1941, by Eudora Welty. Reprinted from her volume, *A Curtain of Green and Other Stories*, by permission of Harcourt, Brace & World, Inc.

"Sonny's Blues" reprinted from *Going to Meet the Man* by James Baldwin. Copyright © 1948, 1951, 1957, 1958, 1960, 1965 by James Baldwin and used by permission of the publisher, The Dial Press, Inc. Originally published in *Partisan Review*.

"Walk Don't Run" by Robert A. Stone reprinted by permission of Russell & Volkening, Inc., for the author. Copyright © 1964 by Robert Stone.

"Patriotism," by Yukio Mishima, translated by Geoffrey W. Sargent. From Yukio Mishima, *Death in MidSummer*. Copyright © 1966 by New Directions. Reprinted by permission of New Directions Publishing Corporation.

"A Day of Old Age" from *Fever*, a collection of stories by J. M. G. LeClézio. Copyright © 1965 by Editions Gallimard. Translated from the French by Daphne Woodward, © 1966 by Hamish Hamilton, Ltd. Reprinted by permission of Atheneum Publishers.

"The Seven Who Were Hanged" by Leonid Andreyev reprinted by permission of G. P. Putnam's Sons from *Ten Modern Short Novels* edited by Leo Hamilton & Edmond Volpe. © 1958 by G. P. Putnam's Sons.

From *Pnin*, by Vladmir Nabokov. Copyright © 1953, 1955, 1957 by Vladimir Nabokov. Reprinted by permission of Doubleday & Company, Inc.

"The Lotus Eater." Copyright 1935 by W. Somerset Maugham from *The Mixture as Before*, by W. Somerset Maugham. Reprinted by permission of Doubleday & Company, Inc., and by the Literary Executor and William Heineman Ltd.

"Gusev" from *The Portable Chekhov* by Avrahm Yarmolinsky. Copyright 1947 by The Viking Press, Inc. Reprinted by permission of The Viking Press, Inc.

From *The Hamlet*. Copyright 1940 and renewed 1968 by Estelle Faulkner and Jill Faulkner Summers. Reprinted from *The Hamlet*, by William Faulkner, by permission of Random House, Inc.

"Franz F" reprinted from *Meet My Maker the Mad Molecule* by J. P. Donleavy. Copyright © 1954, 1955, 1956, 1959, 1960, 1961, 1963, 1964 by J. P. Donleavy. Copyright © 1960 by The Curtis Publishing Company. A Seymour Lawrence Book/Delacorte Press. Used by permission.

"Accomplished Desires" by Joyce Carol Oates first published in *Esquire Magazine*. © 1968 by Joyce Carol Oates. Reprinted by permission of author's agent, Blanche C. Gregory, Inc.

"The Artificial Nigger." © copyright, 1955 by Flannery O'Connor. Reprinted from her volume *A Good Man Is Hard to Find* by permission of Harcourt, Brace & World, Inc.

"First Confession." Copyright 1951 by Frank O'Connor. Reprinted from *The Stories of Frank O'Connor*, by Frank O'Connor, by permission of Alfred A. Knopf, Inc., and Cyrilly Abels.

"Gimpel the Fool" by Isaac Bashevis Singer, translated by Saul Bellow, from *A Treasury of Yiddish Stories* edited by Irving Howe and Eliezer Greenberg. Copyright 1953 by Isaac Bashevis Singer. Reprinted by permission of The Viking Press, Inc.

An introduction to fiction must assume that its readers have little acquaintance with literature and possess an undeveloped ability to read with critical insight. Our purpose in *Fiction and Analysis* is not, however, to introduce the developing reader to inferior or "easy" literature. One reason many college students need an introduction to fiction is that in high school they have been fed mindless popular stories or good novels abridged of both substance and flavor, on the assumption that ignorance is the same thing as stupidity, that because the student does not yet know what can be said about good fiction, he cannot experience it on the page. Fortunately, there is an ample body of recent fiction which requires no background knowledge of history or literary techniques to be readily accessible and immediately enjoyed. For example, it is not necessary to know the history of the short story in order to read and become powerfully involved in "The Ledge." In fact, if one is invited to read "The Ledge" as a historical document, the experience of the story will be severely damaged. It is *after* one is introduced to fiction in general or to a story in particular that one may examine it as an artifact and build toward a reading yet richer and more enjoyable. And the purpose of such an introduction as this is essentially and simply to help people learn to read—to read accurately and fully and with taste.

Taste is acquired—not legislated, not forced—and if the historical approach is debilitating at this level of development, the "plot, characters, setting, point of view, and now let us look at the symbols" method may be fatal. Again, it is only *after* the story has been read *as story* that one can with some safety do a technical analysis. Read with the conscious purpose of noting and extracting plot, a short story loses its primary "living" effect. Further, it is impossible actually to differentiate between plot and character and setting except arbitrarily. Any abstraction of *symbol* from a story must be done with the knowledge that the symbol is only one aspect and does not exist separately from the story. Whatever is lifted out of context must be somehow reinserted, grafted back in, by the reader. Often it takes a while for the incision to heal, so that the reader is incapable of reading the story "live" again. There is always danger that the critical reader will become like some inhumane surgeon whose neighbors interest him principally as clinical specimens—he would prefer to see them anesthetized upon an operating table rather than living their lives about him.

The stories which follow are grouped in terms of broad human concerns that have become traditional themes in fiction. The first three sections represent major "problems" or difficulties—Conflict, Ordeal, and Alienation. The middle section is concerned with that primary element of all our anxieties and failures, Death. The last three sections have to do with major responses to human problems—Escape, Love, and Faith.

There is no intention to limit a story to any particular concern, to provide categories into which all stories may be filed and comfortably identified, nor to suggest that these categories are the only ones possible.

Rather, the attempt is to provide a means of introduction to the works through their general thematic concerns. There can be, in literature, only new wine in old bottles. The divisions here simply identify some of the larger bottles.

Our purpose has been to indicate some of the basic ways of dealing with literary art and at the same time to avoid the sterile and unwieldy apparatus that so often accompanies a critical text. And again, there is no attempt to be all-inclusive. It is not our intention to eliminate the need for an instructor and it is hoped that he will use the critical materials presented here only as a launching pad for his own teaching.

R. C.

P. S.

CONTENTS

There are essentially two reasons for reading fiction, and both can be stated with simplicity: stories and novels extend our own boundaries by giving us greater insight into the variety of responses to human experience; and the imaginative re-creation of an experience is entertaining. It is the latter, the pleasure principle, that is most often forgotten in the shuffle of academic leaves. We read, just as we watch films or plays or television, for amusement, for entertainment—and if we are not having any fun we rest our eyes.

Reading, however, is a less passive entertainment than many of the visual arts. It requires our participation. It requires that we learn the rules of the game before we decide we do not want to play. All art forms, obviously, have their hierarchies. It is much easier to watch a Hollywood western than it is a film by Godard or Fellini. The former requires no active participation. The latter requires that you *think* about what is going on, that you make interpretations and evaluations of character and plot, that you make whatever distinctions are possible between illusion and reality. It is easier to look at photographs than at abstract paintings, for the same reason. It is easier to read The Hardy Boys books than *Ulysses.* It is easier, in short, to be the passive receptacle for formula entertainment than it is to be a participant in significant entertainment.

In art, as in any other discipline, one generally likes what one knows best, and one knows best what one takes the trouble to learn about. The explication of literary texts will undoubtedly be difficult and disenchanting at first, but it gets easier and easier, until eventually it becomes an unconscious act. Once the road signs become recognizable and the practice of exegesis a subconscious part of the reading process, the enjoyment of literature will increase immeasurably.

We must have some idea of what a piece of fiction is and is not if we are to approach it without confusion. Stories are the conscious products of man's imagination. We do not like to say that a story is a concoction, because that implies a particular method of composition which most good writers do not use. We dislike calling a story a synthesis, because it begins to smell of the laboratory. Nevertheless, a story is in a sense both a concoction and a synthesis. It is not natural, nor is it a simple reporting of nature: even in the most severe attempt at "slice of life," interpretation is a formative force—the mind of the author is the perceiver and reporter, and the words he chooses are themselves carriers of ideas.

We expect of stories something different from what we expect of nature, including the human nature which most often is their basis. One of Robert Frost's poems has a character say that there are no beginnings and endings in life, only middles. Stories, however, give form to experience. The form is not necessarily the simplest chronological sequence. Form in stories may be based upon spatial as well as temporal concepts: the story may go "full circle" as well as lineally from birth to death. The informing element may be a tone of voice as well as an action; the movement of the story may be determined as a unit of speech or a piece of music often is—by a sense of duration and completion rooted in some habit of mind or racial memory which cannot legitimately be analyzed in terms of rational development. It is a good idea for the reader to be aware of such things, and not mistake "feeling" or intuition for reason—to know, that is, what is being appealed to.

One may learn a lesson from a story, either by its rational argument or by the experience in which it involves one, or by a combination, though experience is generally the mode of fiction. Normally we do not expect fiction to *tell* us something. It is distinguished from the essay, the document, the sermon, largely in that it exists for itself, and any "good" it does is a kind of bonus. We may learn from good men by observing or by vicariously experiencing their lives; we may learn from bad and indifferent people the same way. But the life of a man does not exist essentially for its function as example. On the contrary, an example may be said to have value only if what matters essentially is living itself and the form and tone it takes.

So with fiction, which, though it is not life, is man's creation or depiction or experience of life in the imagination. It uses life and nature as its materials and strives to be true in a variety of ways to them, drawing together the pertinent and subordinating or eliminating everything which has primary relevance to some other aspect of experience. When it has done well—has found and fulfilled its form—it provides us with that aesthetic pleasure which is its excuse for being.

II

There is, fortunately, no set method of investigation that will provide the reader with a definitive statement of a story's intent. But there are certain questions one can ask, when confronted with a work of literature, that will almost always engender intelligent thought and provide a point of departure for discussion.

One can begin, for example, simply by asking, "What *kind* of story is it?" Is it an investigation of the mind of a single character, of his psychological deviation, of the limitations of his consciousness? Is it a story that examines a social situation, the conflict of manners within a society? Does it deal primarily with the relationships of individuals, of groups? Or is it a story in which a character is tested and changed, morally or intellectually, by the ordeal to which he is submitted? If one asks these questions of, say, William Styron's *The Long March,* one begins immediately to confront the main issue in the story—Mannix' mental attitude in a military situation involving other individuals and groups of people, as a result of which his relative position on the scale of human dignity is altered. Mannix pits himself against a system, undergoes a trying ordeal, and in the end wins a victory which is ambiguous at best.

Or one can begin on another tack and ask, "What kind of characters has the author drawn?" Are they individuals? Are they representatives of a specific social or economic class? Do they seem to exist primarily to depict a particular attitude or prejudice? Are they symbolic? What, for instance, of the fisherman in Lawrence Hall's "The Ledge"? Is he *only* a certain fisherman, an isolated individual caught up in a freakish incident over which he has no control and because of which he forfeits his life? Or does he take on proportions that are much greater than any one man? If he does, what then are the implications of his death? Can his death be taken as broadly symbolic of man's fate?

One can start in yet another direction and ask questions more specifically related to structure, design, mechanics. A look at the point of view in a story will very often carry one into explicative discussions. Who tells the story and, more importantly, why? Why is "Gimpel the Fool" told in the first person by Gimpel himself instead of omnisciently by the author? Why is Rusty the center of consciousness in *Genesis* instead of Spurlock or Ray Henry or Wallace Stegner? Why does Philip Roth place the narrative voice in Sergeant Marx in "Defender of the Faith" instead of Grossbart or Fishbein? And how reliable a narrator is Marx? Can we take his literal word for what he observes, or do we have to evaluate the quality of his observations—as we clearly must the lawyer's in Melville's "Bartleby the Scrivener." Is the narrative voice consistent throughout a story, or does it change, become less assertive, more qualifying—as it does again in "Bartleby." What becomes of our concept of "reality" in stories if the events are conceived by different people to have happened in different ways?

In an attempt to illustrate various ways of approaching a fictional work, for a student confronted with the writing of an analytical paper, we have included a brief explication of the first story in each section. The question generally seems to be, "How do I begin? On what critical hook do I hang my discussion?" Obviously, there are a great many possibilities. We have tried to illustrate five angles of attack that are useful in the preparation of short papers, and the student might well simplify his problems with interpretive analysis by taking a careful look at the examples. "Powerhouse" and "Bartleby the Scrivener" are dealt with in terms of *point of view,* widely differing in the two stories. In *Pnin, structural devices* are discussed; in "Patriotism," the *psychological motivations* of the main characters. The discussion of the love story from *The Hamlet* focuses upon *language.* Important dimensions of "The Artificial Nigger" are revealed through the *symbolic pattern* of the action. And because it is easy to forget that stories are born and nurtured in an artist's imagination long before they are solidified by print, we have included an interview with the author of "Genesis" on the *growth and development* of a work of fiction.

There are, quite obviously, a great many ways to approach a story and to begin articulating one's impressions of its intentions. It should be stressed, however, that focal points like structure, language, motivation, symbol, point of view, place—what have you—are useful simply in confining the scope of a paper or giving order to a discussion. Each of these may be profitably investigated, but each is, ultimately, one aspect of the larger investigation into the way in which a story embodies, through the precision of its parts, its own impetus and control. A full and lengthy analysis of a complex story might very well involve all the considerations mentioned above.

Having done however limited or complete a study, we shall hopefully have arrived at a broader or more profound comprehension of the story under examination; we shall not have provided a substitute for it.

CONFLICT

Herman Melville

BARTLEBY THE SCRIVENER

A story of wall street

I am a rather elderly man. The nature of my avocations, for the last thirty years, has brought me into more than ordinary contact with what would seem an interesting and somewhat singular set of men, of whom, as yet, nothing, that I know of, has ever been written—I mean, the law-copyists, or scriveners. I have known very many of them, professionally and privately, and, if I pleased, could relate divers histories, at which good-natured gentlemen might smile, and sentimental souls might weep. But I waive the biographies of all other scriveners, for a few passages in the life of Bartleby, who was a scrivener, the strangest I ever saw, or heard of. While, of other law-copyists, I might write the complete life, of Bartleby nothing of that sort can be done. I believe that no materials exist for a full and satisfactory biography of this man. It is an irreparable loss to literature. Bartleby was one of those beings of whom nothing is ascertainable, except from the original sources, and, in his case, those are very small. What my own astonished eyes saw of Bartleby, *that* is all I know of him, except, indeed, one vague report, which will appear in the sequel.

Ere introducing the scrivener, as he first appeared to me, it is fit I make some mention of myself, my *employés,* my business, my chambers, and general surroundings; because some such description is indispensable to an adequate understanding of the chief character about to be presented. Imprimis: I am a man who, from his youth upwards, has been filled with a profound conviction that the easiest way of life is the best. Hence, though I belong to a profession proverbially energetic and nervous, even to turbulence, at times, yet nothing of that sort have I ever suffered to invade my peace. I am one of those unambitious lawyers who never addresses a jury, or in any way draws down public applause; but, in the cool tranquillity of a snug retreat, do a snug business among rich men's bonds, and mortgages, and title-deeds. All who know me, consider me an eminently safe man. The late John Jacob Astor, a personage little given to poetic enthusiasm, had no hesitation in pronouncing my first grand point to be prudence; my next, method. I do not speak it in vanity, but simply record the fact, that I was not unemployed in my profession by the late John Jacob Astor; a name which, I admit, I love to repeat; for it hath a rounded and orbicular sound to it, and rings like unto bullion. I will freely add, that I was not insensible to the late John Jacob Astor's good opinion.

Some time prior to the period at which this little history begins, my avocations had been largely increased. The good old office, now extinct in the State of New York, of a Master in Chancery, had been conferred upon me. It was not a very arduous office, but very pleasantly remunerative. I seldom lose my temper; much more seldom indulge in dangerous indignation at wrongs and outrages; but, I must be permitted to be rash here, and declare, that I consider the sudden and violent abrogation of the office of Master in Chancery, by the new Constitution, as a —— premature act; inasmuch as I had counted upon a life-lease of the profits, whereas I only received those of a few short years. But this is by the way.

My chambers were up stairs, at No. — Wall Street. At one end, they looked upon the white wall of the interior of a spacious sky-light shaft, penetrating the building from top to bottom.

This view might have been considered rather tame than otherwise, deficient in what landscape painters call "life." But, if so, the view from the other end of my chambers offered, at least, a contrast, if nothing more. In that direction, my windows commanded an unobstructed view of a lofty brick wall, black by age and everlasting shade; which wall required no spy-glass to bring out its lurking beauties, but, for the benefit of all near-sighted spectators, was pushed up to within ten feet of my window panes. Owing to the great height of the surrounding buildings, and my chambers being on the second floor, the interval between this wall and mine not a little resembled a huge square cistern.

At the period just preceding the advent of Bartleby, I had two persons as copyists in my employment, and a promising lad as an office-boy. First, Turkey; second, Nippers; third, Ginger Nut. These may seem names, the like of which are not usually found in the Directory. In truth, they were nicknames, mutually conferred upon each other by my three clerks, and were deemed expressive of their respective persons or characters. Turkey was a short, pursy Englishman, of about my own age—that is, somewhere not far from sixty. In the morning, one might say, his face was of a fine florid hue, but after twelve o'clock, meridian—his dinner hour—it blazed like a grate full of Christmas coals; and continued blazing—but, as it were, with a gradual wane—till six o'clock P.M., or thereabouts; after which, I saw no more of the proprietor of the face, which, gaining its meridian with the sun, seemed to set with it, to rise, culminate, and decline the following day, with the like regularity and undiminished glory. There are many singular coincidences I have known in the course of my life, not the least among which was the fact, that, exactly when Turkey displayed his fullest beams from his red and radiant countenance, just then, too, at that critical moment, began the daily period when I considered his business capacities as seriously disturbed for the remainder of the twenty-four hours. Not that he was absolutely idle, or averse to business, then; far from it. The difficulty was, he was apt to be altogether too energetic. There was a strange, inflamed, flurried, flighty recklessness of activity about him. He would be incautious in dipping his pen into his inkstand. All his blots upon my documents were dropped there after twelve o'clock meridian. Indeed, not only would he be reckless, and sadly given to making blots in the afternoon, but, some days, he went further, and was rather noisy. At such times, too, his face flamed with augmented blazonry, as if cannel coal had been heaped on anthracite. He made an unpleasant racket with his chair; spilled his sand-box; in mending his pens, impatiently split them all to pieces, and threw them on the floor in a sudden passion; stood up, and leaned over his table, boxing his papers about in a most indecorous manner, very sad to behold in an elderly man like him. Nevertheless, as he was in many ways a most valuable person to me, and all the time before twelve o'clock meridian, was the quickest, steadiest creature, too, accomplishing a great deal of work in a style not easily to be matched—for these reasons, I was willing to overlook his eccentricities, though, indeed, occasionally, I remonstrated with him. I did this very gently, however, because, though the civilest, nay, the blandest and most reverential of men in the morning, yet, in the afternoon, he was disposed, upon provocation, to be slightly rash with his tongue—in fact, insolent. Now, valuing his morning services as I did, and resolved not to lose them—yet, at the same time, made uncomfortable by his inflamed ways after twelve o'clock—and being a man of peace, unwilling by my admonitions to call forth unseemly retorts from him, I took upon me, one Saturday noon (he was always worse on Saturdays) to hint to him, very kindly, that, perhaps, now that he was growing old, it might be well to abridge his labors; in short, he need not come to my chambers after twelve o'clock, but, dinner over, had best go home to his lodgings, and rest himself till tea-time. But no; he insisted upon his afternoon devotions. His countenance became intolerably fervid, as he oratorically assured me—gesticulating with a long ruler at the other end of the room—that if his services in the morning were useful, how indispensable, then, in the afternoon?

"With submission, sir," said Turkey, on this occasion, "I consider myself your right-hand man. In the morning I but marshal and deploy my columns; but in the afternoon I put myself at their head, and gallantly charge the foe, thus"—and he made a violent thrust with the ruler.

"But the blots, Turkey," intimated I.

"True; but, with submission, sir, behold these hairs! I am getting old. Surely, sir, a blot or two of a warm afternoon is not to be severely urged against gray hairs. Old age—even if it blot the page—is honorable. With submission, sir, we *both* are getting old."

This appeal to my fellow-feeling was hardly to be resisted. At all events, I saw that go he would not. So, I made up my mind to let him stay, resolving, nevertheless, to see to it that, during the afternoon, he had to do with my less important papers.

Nippers, the second on my list, was a whiskered, sallow, and, upon the whole, rather piratical-looking young man, of about five and twenty. I always deemed him the victim of two evil powers—ambition and indigestion. The ambition was evinced by a certain impatience of the duties of a mere copyist, an unwarrantable usurpation of strictly professional affairs, such as the original drawing up of legal documents. The indigestion seemed betokened in an occasional nervous testiness and grinning irritability, causing the teeth to audibly grind together over mistakes committed in copying; unnecessary maledictions, hissed, rather than spoken, in the heat of business; and especially by a continual discontent with the height of the table where he worked. Though of a very ingenious, mechanical turn, Nippers could never get this table to suit him. He put chips under it, blocks of various sorts, bits of pasteboard, and at last went so far as to attempt an exquisite adjustment, by final pieces of folded blotting-paper. But no invention would answer. If, for the sake of easing his back, he brought the table lid at a sharp angle well up towards his chin, and wrote there like a man using the steep roof of a Dutch house for his desk, then he declared that it stopped the circulation in his arms. If now he lowered the table to his waistbands, and stooped over it in writing, then there was a sore aching in his back. In short, the truth of the matter was, Nippers knew not what he wanted. Or, if he wanted anything, it was to be rid of a scrivener's table altogether. Among the manifestations of his diseased ambition was a fondness he had for receiving visits from certain ambiguous-looking fellows in seedy coats, whom he called his clients. Indeed, I was aware that not only was he, at times, considerable of a ward-politician, but he occasionally did a little business at the Justices' courts, and was not unknown on the steps of the Tombs. I have good reason to believe, however, that one individual who called upon him at my chambers, and who, with a grand air, he insisted was his client, was no other than a dun, and the alleged title-deed, a bill. But, with all his failings, and the annoyances he caused me, Nippers, like his compatriot Turkey, was a very useful man to me; wrote a neat, swift hand; and, when he chose, was not deficient in a gentlemanly sort of deportment. Added to this, he always dressed in a gentlemanly sort of way; and so, incidentally, reflected credit upon my chambers. Whereas, with respect to Turkey, I had much ado to keep him from being a reproach to me. His clothes were apt to look oily, and smell of eating-houses. He wore his pantaloons very loose and baggy in summer. His coats were execrable; his hat not to be handled. But while the hat was a thing of indifference to me, inasmuch as his natural civility and deference, as a dependent Englishman, always led him to doff it the moment he entered the room, yet his coat was another matter. Concerning his coats, I reasoned with him; but with no effect. The truth was, I suppose, that a man with so small an income could not afford to sport such a lustrous face and a lustrous coat at one and the same time. As Nippers once observed, Turkey's money went chiefly for red ink. One winter day, I presented Turkey with a highly respectable-looking coat of my own—a padded gray coat, of a most comfortable warmth, and which buttoned straight up from the knee to the neck. I thought Turkey would appreciate the favor, and abate his rashness and obstreperousness of afternoons. But no; I verily believe that buttoning himself up in so downy and blanket-like a coat had a pernicious effect upon him—upon the same principle that too much oats are bad for horses. In fact, precisely as a rash, restive horse is said to feel his oats, so Turkey felt his coat. It made him insolent. He was a man whom prosperity harmed.

Though, concerning the self-indulgent habits of Turkey, I had my own private surmises, yet, touching Nippers, I was well persuaded that, whatever might be his faults in other respects, he was, at least, a temperate young man. But, indeed, nature herself seemed to have been his vintner, and, at his birth, charged him so thoroughly with an irritable, brandy-like disposition, that all subsequent potations were needless. When I consider how, amid the stillness of my chambers, Nippers would sometimes impatiently rise from his seat, and stooping over his table, spread his arms wide apart, seize the whole desk, and move it, and jerk it, with a grim, grinding motion on the floor, as if the table were a perverse voluntary agent and vexing him, I plainly perceive that, for Nippers, brandy-and-water were altogether superfluous.

It was fortunate for me that, owing to its peculiar cause—indigestion—the irritability and consequent nervousness of Nippers were mainly observable in the morning, while in the afternoon he was comparatively mild. So that, Turkey's paroxysms only coming on about twelve o'clock, I never had to do with their eccentricities at one time. Their fits relieved each other, like guards. When Nippers's was on, Turkey's was off; and *vice versa*. This was a good natural arrangement, under the circumstances.

Ginger Nut, the third on my list, was a lad, some twelve years old. His father was a car-man, ambitious of seeing his son on the bench instead of a cart, before he died. So he sent him to my office, as student at law, errand-boy, cleaner and sweeper, at the rate of one dollar a week. He had a little desk to himself; but he did not use it much. Upon inspection, the drawer exhibited a great array of the shells of various sorts of nuts. Indeed, to this quick-witted youth, the whole noble science of the law was contained in a nutshell. Not the least among the employments of Ginger Nut, as well as one which he discharged with the most alacrity, was his duty as cake and apple purveyor for Turkey and Nippers. Copying law-papers being proverbially a dry, husky sort of business, my two scriveners were fain to moisten their mouths very often with Spitzenbergs, to be had at the numerous stalls nigh the Custom House and Post Office. Also, they sent Ginger Nut very frequently for that peculiar cake—small, flat, round, and very spicy—after which he had been named by them. Of a cold morning, when business was but dull, Turkey would gobble up scores of these cakes, as if they were mere wafers—indeed, they sell them at the rate of six or eight for a penny—the scrape of his pen blending with the crunching of the crisp particles in his mouth. Rashest of all the fiery afternoon blunders and flurried rashnesses of Turkey, was his once moistening a ginger-cake between his lips, and clapping it on to a mortgage, for a seal. I came within an ace of dismissing him then. But he mollified me by making an oriental bow, and saying—

"With submission, sir, it was generous of me to find you in stationery on my own account."

Now my original business—that of a conveyancer and title hunter, and drawer-up of recondite documents of all sorts—was considerably increased by receiving the master's office. There was now great work for scriveners. Not only must I push the clerks already with me, but I must have additional help.

In answer to my advertisement, a motionless young man one morning stood upon my office threshold, the door being open, for it was summer. I can see that figure now—pallidly neat, pitiably respectable, incurably forlorn! It was Bartleby.

After a few words touching his qualifications, I engaged him, glad to have among my corps of copyists a man of so singularly sedate an aspect, which I thought might operate beneficially upon the flighty temper of Turkey, and the fiery one of Nippers.

I should have stated before that ground glass folding-doors divided my premises into two parts, one of which was occupied by my scriveners, the other by myself. According to my humor, I threw open these doors, or closed them. I resolved to assign Bartleby a corner by the folding-doors, but on my side of them, so as to have this quiet man within easy call, in case any trifling thing was to be done. I placed his desk close up to a small side-window in that part of the room, a window which originally had afforded a lateral view of certain grimy backyards and bricks, but which, owing to subsequent erections, commanded at present no view at all, though it gave some light. Within three feet of the panes was a wall, and the light came down from far above, between two lofty buildings, as from a very small opening in a dome. Still further to a satisfactory arrangement, I procured a high green folding screen, which might entirely isolate Bartleby from my sight, though not remove him from my voice. And thus, in a manner, privacy and society were conjoined.

At first, Bartleby did an extraordinary quantity of writing. As if long famishing for something to copy, he seemed to gorge himself on my documents. There was no pause for digestion. He ran a day and night line, copying by sun-light and by candle-light. I should have been quite delighted with his application, had he been cheerfully industrious. But he wrote on silently, palely, mechanically.

It is, of course, an indispensable part of a scrivener's business to verify the accuracy of his copy, word by word. Where there are two or more scriveners in an office, they assist each other in this examination, one reading from the copy, the other holding the original. It is a very dull, wearisome, and lethargic affair. I can readily imagine that, to some sanguine temperaments, it would be altogether intolerable. For example, I cannot credit that the mettlesome poet, Byron, would have contentedly sat down with Bartleby to examine a law document of, say five hundred pages, closely written in a crimpy hand.

Now and then, in the haste of business, it had been my habit to assist in comparing some brief document myself, calling Turkey or Nippers for this purpose. One object I had, in placing Bartleby so handy to me behind the screen, was to avail myself of his services on such trivial occasions. It was on the third day, I think, of his being with me, and before any necessity had arisen for having his own writing examined, that, being much hurried to complete a small affair I had in hand, I abruptly called to Bartleby. In my haste and natural expectancy of instant compliance, I sat with my head bent over the original on my desk, and my right hand sideways, and somewhat nervously extended with the copy, so that, immediately upon emerging from his retreat, Bartleby might snatch it and proceed to business without the least delay.

In this very attitude did I sit when I called to him, rapidly stating what it was I wanted him to do—namely, to examine a small paper with me. Imagine my surprise, nay, my consternation, when, without moving from his privacy, Bartleby, in a singularly mild, firm voice, replied, "I would prefer not to."

"Prefer not to," echoed I, rising in high excitement, and crossing the room with a stride. "What do you mean? Are you moon-struck? I want you to help me compare this sheet here—take it," and I thrust it towards him.

"I would prefer not to," said he.

I looked at him steadfastly. His face was leanly composed; his gray eye dimly calm. Not a wrinkle of agitation rippled him. Had there been the least uneasiness, anger, impatience, or impertinence in his manner; in other words, had there been any thing ordinarily human about him, doubtless I should have violently dismissed him from the premises. But as it was, I should have as soon thought of turning my pale plaster-of-paris bust of Cicero out of doors. I stood gazing at him awhile, as he went on with his own writing, and then reseated myself at my desk. This is very strange, thought I. What had one best do? But my business hurried me. I concluded to forget the matter for the present, reserving it for my future leisure. So calling Nippers from the other room, the paper was speedily examined.

A few days after this, Bartleby concluded four lengthy documents, being quadruplicates of a week's testimony taken before me in my High Court of Chancery. It became necessary to examine them. It was an important suit, and great accuracy was imperative. Having all things arranged, I called Turkey, Nippers, and Ginger Nut from the next room, meaning to place the four copies in the hands of my four clerks, while I should read from the original. Accordingly, Turkey, Nippers, and Ginger Nut had taken their seats in a row, each with his document in his hand, when I called to Bartleby to join this interesting group.

"Bartleby! quick, I am waiting."

I heard a slow scrape of his chair legs on the uncarpeted floor, and soon he appeared standing at the entrance of his hermitage.

"What is wanted?" said he, mildly.

"The copies, the copies," said I, hurriedly. "We are going to examine them. There"—and I held towards him the fourth quadruplicate.

"I would prefer not to," he said, and gently disappeared behind the screen.

For a few moments I was turned into a pillar of salt, standing at the head of my seated column of clerks. Recovering myself, I advanced towards the screen, and demanded the reason for such extraordinary conduct.

"*Why* do you refuse?"

"I would prefer not to."

With any other man I should have flown outright into a dreadful passion, scorned all further words, and thrust him ignominiously from my presence. But there was something about Bartleby that not only strangely disarmed me, but in a wonderful manner, touched and disconcerted me. I began to reason with him.

"These are your own copies we are about to examine. It is labor saving to you, because one examination will answer for your four papers. It is common usage. Every copyist is bound to help examine his copy. Is it not so? Will you not speak? Answer!"

"I prefer not to," he replied in a flutelike tone. It seemed to me that, while I had been addressing him, he carefully revolved every statement that I made; fully comprehended the meaning; could not gainsay the irresistible conclusion; but, at the same time, some paramount consideration prevailed with him to reply as he did.

"You are decided, then, not to comply with my request—a request made according to common usage and common sense?"

He briefly gave me to understand, that on that point my judgment was sound. Yes: his decision was irreversible.

It is not seldom the case that, when a man is browbeaten in some unprecedented and violently unreasonable way, he begins to stagger in his own plainest faith. He begins, as it were, vaguely to surmise that, wonderful as it may be, all the justice and all the reason is on the other side. Accordingly, if any disinterested persons are present, he turns to them for some reinforcement of his own faltering mind.

"Turkey," said I, "what do you think of this? Am I not right?"

"With submission, sir," said Turkey, in his blandest tone, "I think that you are."

"Nippers," said I, "what do *you* think of it?"

"I think I should kick him out of the office."

(The reader, of nice perceptions, will here perceive that, it being morning, Turkey's answer is couched in polite and tranquil terms, but Nippers replies in ill-tempered ones. Or, to repeat a previous sentence, Nippers's ugly mood was on duty, and Turkey's off.)

"Ginger Nut," said I, willing to enlist the smallest suffrage in my behalf, "what do *you* think of it?"

"I think, sir, he's a little *luny*," replied Ginger Nut, with a grin.

"You hear what they say," said I, turning towards the screen, "come forth and do your duty."

But he vouchsafed no reply. I pondered a moment in sore perplexity. But once more business hurried me. I determined again to postpone the consideration of this dilemma to my future leisure. With a little trouble we made out to examine the papers without Bartleby, though at every page or two Turkey deferentially dropped his opinion, that this proceeding was quite out of the common; while Nippers, twitching in his chair with a dyspeptic nervousness, ground out, between his set teeth, occasional hissing maledictions against the stubborn oaf behind the screen. And for his (Nippers's) part, this was the first and the last time he would do another man's business without pay.

Meanwhile Bartleby sat in his hermitage, oblivious to everything but his own peculiar business there.

Some days passed, the scrivener being employed upon another lengthy work. His late remarkable conduct led me to regard his ways narrowly. I observed that he never went to dinner; indeed, that he never went anywhere. As yet I had never, of my personal knowledge, known him to be outside of my office. He was a perpetual sentry in the corner. At about eleven o'clock though, in the morning, I noticed that Ginger Nut would advance toward the opening in Bartleby's screen, as if silently beckoned thither by a gesture invisible to me where I sat. The boy would then leave the office, jingling a few pence, and reappear with a handful of ginger-nuts, which he delivered in the hermitage, receiving two of the cakes for his trouble.

He lives, then, on ginger-nuts, thought I; never eats a dinner, properly speaking; he must be a vegetarian, then; but no; he never eats even vegetables; he eats nothing but ginger-nuts. My mind then ran on in reveries concerning the probable effects upon the human constitution of living entirely on ginger-nuts. Ginger-nuts are so called, because they contain ginger as one of their peculiar constituents, and the final flavoring one. Now, what was ginger? A hot, spicy thing. Was Bartleby hot and spicy? Not at all. Ginger, then, had no effect upon Bartleby. Probably he preferred it should have none.

Nothing so aggravates an earnest person as a passive resistance. If the individual so resisted be of a not inhumane temper, and the resisting one perfectly harmless in his passivity, then, in the better moods of the former, he will endeavor charitably to construe to his imagination what proves impossible to be solved by his judgment. Even so, for the most part, I regarded Bartleby and his ways. Poor fellow! thought I, he means no mischief; it is plain he intends no insolence; his aspect sufficiently evinces that his eccentricities are involuntary. He is useful to me. I can get along with him. If I turn him away, the chances are he will fall in with some less-indulgent employer, and then he will be rudely treated, and perhaps driven forth miserably to starve. Yes. Here I can cheaply purchase a delicious self-approval. To befriend Bartleby; to humor him in his strange willfulness, will cost me little or nothing, while I lay up in my soul what will eventually prove a sweet morsel for my conscience. But this mood was not invariable with me. The passiveness of Bartleby sometimes irritated me. I felt strangely goaded on to encounter him in new opposition—to elicit some angry spark from him answerable to my own. But, indeed, I might as well have essayed to strike fire with my knuckles against a bit of Windsor soap. But one afternoon the evil impulse in me mastered me, and the following little scene ensued:

"Bartleby," said I, "when those papers are all copied, I will compare them with you."

"I would prefer not to."

"How? Surely you do not mean to persist in that mulish vagary?"

No answer.

I threw open the folding-doors near by, and, turning upon Turkey and Nippers, exclaimed:

"Bartleby a second time says, he won't examine his papers. What do you think of it, Turkey?"

It was afternoon, be it remembered. Turkey sat glowing like a brass boiler; his bald head steaming; his hands reeling among his blotted papers.

"Think of it?" roared Turkey; "I think I'll just step behind his screen, and black his eyes for him!"

So saying, Turkey rose to his feet and threw his arms into a pugilistic position. He was hurrying away to make good his promise, when I detained him, alarmed at the effect of incautiously rousing Turkey's combativeness after dinner.

"Sit down, Turkey," said I, "and hear what Nippers has to say. What do you think of it, Nippers? Would I not be justified in immediately dismissing Bartleby?"

"Excuse me, that is for you to decide, sir. I think his conduct quite unusual, and, indeed, unjust, as regards Turkey and myself. But it may only be a passing whim."

"Ah," exclaimed I, "you have strangely changed your mind, then—you speak very gently of him now."

"All beer," cried Turkey; "gentleness is effects of beer—Nippers and I dined together to-day. You see how gentle *I* am, sir. Shall I go and black his eyes?"

"You refer to Bartleby, I suppose. No, not to-day, Turkey," I replied; "pray, put up your fists."

I closed the doors, and again advanced towards Bartleby. I felt additional incentives tempting me to my fate. I burned to be rebelled against again. I remembered that Bartleby never left the office.

"Bartleby," said I, "Ginger Nut is away; just step around to the Post Office, won't you? (it was but a three minutes' walk), and see if there is anything for me."

"I would prefer not to."

"You *will* not?"

"I *prefer* not."

I staggered to my desk, and sat there in a deep study. My blind inveteracy returned. Was there any other thing in which I could procure myself to be ignominiously repulsed by this lean, penniless wight?—my hired clerk? What added thing is there, perfectly reasonable, that he will be sure to refuse to do?

"Bartleby!"

No answer.

"Bartleby," in a louder tone.

No answer.

"Bartleby," I roared.

Like a very ghost, agreeably to the laws of magical invocation, at the third summons, he appeared at the entrance of his hermitage.

"Go to the next room, and tell Nippers to come to me."

"I prefer not to," he respectfully and slowly said, and mildly disappeared.

"Very good, Bartleby," said I, in a quiet sort of serenely-severe, self-possessed tone, intimating the unalterable purpose of some terrible retribution very close at hand. At the moment I half intended something of the kind. But upon the whole, as it was drawing towards my dinner-hour, I thought it best to put on my hat and walk home for the day, suffering much from perplexity and distress of mind.

Shall I acknowledge it? The conclusion of this whole business was, that it soon became a fixed fact of my chambers, that a pale young scrivener, by the name of Bartleby, had a desk there; that he copied for me at the usual rate of four cents a folio (one hundred words); but he was permanently exempt from examining the work done by him, that duty being transferred to Turkey and Nippers, out of compliment, doubtless, to their superior acuteness; moreover, said Bartleby was never, on any account, to be dispatched on the most trivial errand of any sort; and that even if entreated to take upon him such a matter, it was generally understood that he would "prefer not to"—in other words, that he would refuse point-blank.

As days passed on, I became considerably reconciled to Bartleby. His steadiness, his freedom from all dissipation, his incessant industry (except when he chose to throw himself into a standing revery behind his screen), his great stillness, his unalterableness of demeanor under all circumstances, made him a valuable acquisition. One prime thing was this—*he was always there*—first in the morning, continually through the day, and the last at night. I had a singular confidence in his honesty. I felt my most precious papers perfectly safe in his hands. Sometimes, to be sure, I could not, for the very soul of me, avoid falling into sudden spasmodic passions with him. For it was exceeding difficult to bear in mind all the time those strange peculiarities, privileges, and unheard of exemptions, forming the tacit stipulations on Bartleby's part under which he remained in my office. Now and then, in the eagerness of dispatching pressing business, I would inadvertently summon Bartleby, in a short, rapid tone, to put his finger, say, on the incipient tie of a bit of red tape with which I was about compressing some papers. Of course, from behind the screen the usual answer, "I prefer not to," was sure to come; and then, how could a human creature, with the common infirmities of our nature, refrain from bitterly exclaiming upon such perverseness— such unreasonableness. However, every added repulse of this sort which I received only tended to lessen the probability of my repeating the inadvertence.

Here it must be said, that according to the custom of most legal gentlemen occupying chambers in densely-populated law buildings, there were several keys to my door. One was kept by a woman residing in the attic, which person weekly scrubbed and daily swept and dusted my apartments. Another was kept by Turkey for convenience sake. The third I sometimes carried in my own pocket. The fourth I knew not who had.

Now, one Sunday morning I happened to go to Trinity Church, to hear a celebrated preacher, and finding myself rather early on the ground I thought I would walk around to my chambers for a while. Luckily I had my key with me; but upon applying it to the lock, I found it resisted by something inserted from the inside. Quite surprised, I called out; when to my consternation a key was turned from within; and thrusting his lean visage at me, and holding the door ajar, the apparition of Bartleby appeared, in his shirt sleeves, and otherwise in a strangely tattered *déshabillé,* saying quietly that he was sorry, but he was deeply engaged just then, and—preferred not admitting me at present. In a brief word or two, he moreover added, that perhaps I had better walk around the block two or three times, and by that time he would probably have concluded his affairs.

Now, the utterly unsurmised appearance of Bartleby, tenanting my law-chambers of a Sunday morning, with his cadaverously gentlemanly *nonchalance,* yet withal firm and self-possessed, had such a strange effect upon me, that incontinently I slunk away from my own door, and did as desired. But not without sundry twinges of impotent rebellion against the mild effrontery of this unaccountable scrivener. Indeed, it was his wonderful mildness chiefly, which not only disarmed me, but unmanned me as it were. For I consider that one, for the time, is somehow unmanned when he tranquilly permits his hired clerk to dictate to him, and order him away from his own premises. Furthermore, I was full of uneasiness as to what Bartleby could possibly be doing in my office in his shirt sleeves, and in an otherwise dismantled condition of a Sunday morning. Was anything amiss going on? Nay, that was out of the question. It was not to be thought of for a moment that Bartleby was an immoral person. But what could he be doing there?—copying? Nay again, whatever might be his eccentricities, Bartleby was an eminently decorous person. He would be the last man to sit down to his desk in any state approaching to nudity. Besides, it was Sunday; and there was something about Bartleby that forbade the supposition that he would by any secular occupation violate the proprieties of the day.

Nevertheless, my mind was not pacified; and full of a restless curiosity, at last I returned to the door. Without hindrance I inserted my key, opened it, and entered. Bartleby was not to be seen. I looked round anxiously, peeped behind his screen; but it was very plain that he was gone. Upon more closely examining the place, I surmised that for an indefinite period Bartleby must have eaten, dressed, and slept in my office, and that, too, without plate, mirror, or bed. The cushioned seat of a ricketty old sofa in one corner bore the faint impress of a lean, reclining form. Rolled away under his desk, I found a blanket; under the empty grate, a blacking box and brush; on a chair, a tin basin, with soap and a ragged towel; in a newspaper a few crumbs of ginger-nuts and a morsel of cheese. Yes, thought I, it is evident enough that Bartleby has been making his home here, keeping bachelor's hall all by himself. Immediately then the thought came sweeping across me, what miserable friendlessness and loneliness are here revealed! His poverty is great; but his solitude, how horrible! Think of it. Of a Sunday, Wall Street is deserted as Petra; and every night of every day it is an emptiness. This building, too, which of weekdays hums with industry and life, at nightfall echoes with sheer vacancy, and all through Sunday is forlorn. And here Bartleby makes his home; sole spectator of a solitude which he has seen all populous—a sort of innocent and transformed Marius brooding among the ruins of Carthage!

For the first time in my life a feeling of over-powering stinging melancholy seized me. Before, I had never experienced aught but a not unpleasing sadness. The bond of a common humanity now drew me irresistibly to gloom. A fraternal melancholy! For both I and Bartleby were sons of Adam. I remembered the bright silks and sparkling faces I had seen that day, in gala trim, swan-like sailing down the Mississippi of Broadway; and I contrasted them with the pallid copyist, and thought to myself, Ah, happiness courts the light, so we deem the world is gay; but misery hides aloof, so we deem that misery there is none. These sad fancyings—chimeras, doubtless, of a sick and silly brain—led on to other and more special thoughts, concerning the eccentricities of Bartleby. Presentiments of strange discoveries hovered round me. The scrivener's pale form appeared to me laid out, among uncaring strangers, in its shivering winding sheet.

Suddenly I was attracted by Bartleby's closed desk, the key in open sight left in the lock.

I mean no mischief, seek the gratification of no heartless curiosity, thought I; besides, the desk is mine, and its contents, too, so I will make bold to look within. Everything was methodically arranged, the papers smoothly placed. The pigeon holes were deep, and removing the files of documents, I groped into their recesses. Presently I felt something there, and dragged it out. It was an old bandanna handkerchief, heavy and knotted. I opened it, and saw it was a savings' bank.

I now recalled all the quiet mysteries which I had noted in the man. I remembered that he never spoke but to answer; that, though at intervals he had considerable time to himself, yet I had never seen him reading—no, not even a newspaper; that for long periods he would stand looking out, at his pale window behind the screen, upon the dead brick wall; I was quite sure he never visited any refectory or eating house; while his pale face clearly indicated that he never drank beer like Turkey, or tea and coffee even, like other men; that he never went anywhere in particular that I could learn; never went out for a walk, unless, indeed, that was the case at present; that he had declined telling who he was, or whence he came, or whether he had any relatives in the world; that though so thin and pale, he never complained of ill health. And more than all, I remembered a certain unconscious air of pallid—how shall I call it?—of pallid haughtiness, say, or rather an austere reserve about him, which had positively awed me into my tame compliance with his eccentricities, when I had feared to ask him to do the slightest incidental thing for me, even though I might know, from his long-continued motionlessness, that behind his screen he must be standing in one of those dead-wall reveries of his.

Revolving all these things, and coupling them with the recently discovered fact, that he made my office his constant abiding place and home, and not forgetful of his morbid moodiness; revolving all these things, a prudential feeling began to steal over me. My first emotions had been those of pure melancholy and sincerest pity; but just in proportion as the forlornness of Bartleby grew and grew to my imagination, did that same melancholy merge into fear, that pity into repulsion. So true it is, and so terrible, too, that up to a certain point the thought or sight of misery enlists our best affections; but, in certain special cases, beyond that point it does not. They err who would assert that invariably this is owing to the inherent selfishness of the human heart. It rather proceeds from a certain hopelessness of remedying excessive and organic ill. To a sensitive being, pity is not seldom pain. And when at last it is perceived that such pity cannot lead to effectual succor, common sense bids the soul be rid of it. What I saw that morning persuaded me that the scrivener was the victim of innate and incurable disorder. I might give alms to his body; but his body did not pain him; it was his soul that suffered, and his soul I could not reach.

I did not accomplish the purpose of going to Trinity Church that morning. Somehow, the things I had seen disqualified me for the time from church-going. I walked homeward, thinking what I would do with Bartleby. Finally, I resolved upon this—I would put certain calm questions to him the next morning, touching his history, etc., and if he declined to answer them openly and unreservedly (and I supposed he would prefer not), then to give him a twenty dollar bill over and above whatever I might owe him, and tell him his services were no longer required; but that if in any other way I could assist him, I would be happy to do so, especially if he desired to return to his native place, wherever that might be, I would willingly help to defray the expenses. Moreover, if, after reaching home, he found himself at any time in want of aid, a letter from him would be sure of a reply.

The next morning came.

"Bartleby," said I, gently calling to him behind his screen.

No reply.

"Bartleby," said I, in a still gentler tone, "come here; I am not going to ask you to do anything you would prefer not to do—I simply wish to speak to you."

Upon this he noiselessly slid into view.

"Will you tell me, Bartleby, where you were born?"

"I would prefer not to."

"Will you tell me *anything* about yourself?"

"I would prefer not to."

"But what reasonable objection can you have to speak to me? I feel friendly towards you."

He did not look at me while I spoke, but kept his glance fixed upon my bust of Cicero, which, as I then sat, was directly behind me, some six inches above my head.

"What is your answer, Bartleby," said I, after waiting a considerable time for a reply, during which his countenance remained immovable, only there was the faintest conceivable tremor of the white attenuated mouth.

"At present I prefer to give no answer," he said, and retired into his hermitage.

It was rather weak in me I confess, but his manner, on this occasion, nettled me. Not only did there seem to lurk in it a certain calm disdain, but his perverseness seemed ungrateful, considering the undeniable good usage and indulgence he had received from me.

Again I sat ruminating what I should do. Mortified as I was at his behavior, and resolved as I had been to dismiss him when I entered my office, nevertheless I strangely felt something superstitious knocking at my heart, and forbidding me to carry out my purpose, and denouncing me for a villain if I dared to breathe one bitter word against this forlornest of mankind. At last, familiarly drawing my chair behind his screen, I sat down and said: "Bartleby, never mind, then, about revealing your history; but let me entreat you, as a friend, to comply as far as may be with the usages of this office. Say now, you will help to examine papers to-morrow or next day: in short, say now, that in a day or two you will begin to be a little reasonable:—say so, Bartleby."

"At present I would prefer not to be a little reasonable," was his mildly cadaverous reply.

Just then the folding-doors opened, and Nippers approached. He seemed suffering from an unusually bad night's rest, induced by severer indigestion than common. He overheard those final words of Bartleby.

"*Prefer not*, eh?" gritted Nippers—"I'd *prefer* him, if I were you, sir," addressing me—"I'd *prefer* him; I'd give him preferences, the stubborn mule! What is it, sir, pray, that he *prefers* not to do now?"

Bartleby moved not a limb.

"Mr. Nippers," said I, "I'd prefer that you would withdraw for the present."

Somehow, of late, I had got into the way of involuntarily using this word "prefer" upon all sorts of not exactly suitable occasions. And I trembled to think that my contact with the scrivener had already and seriously affected me in a mental way. And what further and deeper aberration might it not yet produce? This apprehension had not been without efficacy in determining me to summary measures.

As Nippers, looking very sour and sulky, was departing, Turkey blandly and deferentially approached.

"With submission, sir," said he, "yesterday I was thinking about Bartleby here, and I think that if he would but prefer to take a quart of good ale every day, it would do much towards mending him, and enabling him to assist in examining his papers."

"So you have got the word, too," said I, slightly excited.

"With submission, what word, sir," asked Turkey, respectfully crowding himself into the contracted space behind the screen, and by so doing, making me jostle the scrivener. "What word, sir?"

"I would prefer to be left alone here," said Bartleby, as if offended at being mobbed in his privacy.

"*That's* the word, Turkey," said I—"*that's* it."

"Oh, *prefer?* oh yes—queer word. I never use it myself. But, sir, as I was saying, if he would but prefer—"

"Turkey," interrupted I, "you will please withdraw."

"Oh certainly, sir, if you prefer that I should."

As he opened the folding-door to retire, Nippers at his desk caught a glimpse of me, and asked whether I would prefer to have a certain paper copied on blue paper or white. He did not in the least roguishly accent the word prefer. It was plain that it involuntarily rolled from his tongue. I thought to myself, surely I must get rid of a demented man, who already has in some degree turned the tongues, if not the heads of myself and clerks. But I thought it prudent not to break the dismission at once.

The next day I noticed that Bartleby did nothing but stand at his window in his dead-wall revery. Upon asking him why he did not write, he said that he had decided upon doing no more writing.

"Why, how now? what next?" exclaimed I, "do no more writing?"

"No more."

"And what is the reason?"

"Do you not see the reason for yourself," he indifferently replied.

I looked steadfastly at him, and perceived that his eyes looked dull and glazed. Instantly it occurred to me, that his unexampled diligence in copying by his dim window for the first few weeks of his stay with me might have temporarily impaired his vision.

I was touched. I said something in condolence with him. I hinted that of course he did wisely in abstaining from writing for a while; and urged him to embrace that opportunity of taking wholesome exercise in the open air. This, however, he did not do. A few days after this, my other clerks being absent, and being in a great hurry to dispatch certain letters by the mail, I thought that, having nothing else earthly to do, Bartleby would surely be less inflexible than usual, and carry these letters to the post-office. But he blankly declined. So, much to my inconvenience, I went myself.

Still added days went by. Whether Bartleby's eyes improved or not, I could not say. To all appearance I thought they did. But when I asked him if they did, he vouchsafed no answer. At all events, he would do no copying. At last, in reply to my urgings, he informed me that he had permanently given up copying.

"What!" exclaimed I; "suppose your eyes should get entirely well—better than ever before—would you not copy then?"

"I have given up copying," he answered, and slid aside.

He remained as ever, a fixture in my chamber. Nay—if that were possible—he became still more of a fixture than before. What was to be done? He would do nothing in the office; why should he stay there? In plain fact, he had now become a millstone to me, not only useless as a necklace, but afflictive to bear. Yet I was sorry for him. I speak less than truth when I say that, on his own account, he occasioned me uneasiness. If he would but have named a single relative or friend, I would instantly have written, and urged their taking the poor fellow away to some convenient retreat. But he seemed alone, absolutely alone in the universe. A bit of wreck in the mid Atlantic. At length, necessities connected with my business tyrannized over all other considerations. Decently as I could, I told Bartleby that in six days time he must unconditionally leave the office. I warned him to take measures, in the interval, for procuring some other abode. I offered to assist him in his endeavor, if he himself would but take the first step towards a removal. "And when you finally quit me, Bartleby," added I, "I shall see that you go not away entirely unprovided. Six days from this hour, remember."

At the expiration of that period, I peeped behind the screen, and lo! Bartleby was there.

I buttoned up my coat, balanced myself; advanced slowly towards him, touched his shoulder, and said, "The time has come; you must quit this place; I am sorry for you; here is money; but you must go."

"I would prefer not," he replied, with his back still towards me.

"You *must*."

He remained silent.

Now I had an unbounded confidence in this man's common honesty. He had frequently restored to me sixpences and shillings carelessly dropped upon the floor, for I am apt to be very reckless in such shirt-button affairs. The proceeding, then, which followed will not be deemed extraordinary.

"Bartleby," said I, "I owe you twelve dollars on account; here are thirty-two; the odd twenty are yours—Will you take it?" and I handed the bills towards him.

But he made no motion.

"I will leave them here, then," putting them under a weight on the table. Then taking my hat and cane and going to the door, I tranquilly turned and added—"After you have removed your things from these offices, Bartleby, you will of course lock the door—since every one is now gone for the day but you—and if you please, slip your key underneath the mat, so that I may have it in the morning. I shall not see you again; so good-by to you. If, hereafter, in your new place of abode, I can be of any service to you, do not fail to advise me by letter. Good-by, Bartleby, and fare you well."

But he answered not a word; like the last column of some ruined temple, he remained standing mute and solitary in the middle of the otherwise deserted room.

As I walked home in a pensive mood, my vanity got the better of my pity. I could not but highly plume myself on my masterly management in getting rid of Bartleby. Masterly I call it, and such it must appear to any dispassionate thinker. The beauty of my procedure seemed to consist in its perfect quietness. There was no vulgar bullying, no bravado of any sort, no choleric hectoring, and striding to and fro across the apartment, jerking out vehement commands for Bartleby to bundle himself off with his beggarly traps. Nothing of the kind. Without loudly bidding Bartleby depart—as an inferior genius might have done—I *assumed* the ground that depart he must; and upon that assumption built all I had to say. The more I thought over my procedure, the more I was charmed with it. Nevertheless, next morning, upon awakening, I had my doubts—I had somehow slept off the fumes of vanity. One of the coolest and wisest hours a man has, is just after he awakes in the morning. My procedure seemed as sagacious as ever—but only in theory. How it would prove in practice—there was the rub. It was truly a beautiful thought to have assumed Bartleby's departure; but, after all, that assumption was simply my own, and none of Bartleby's. The great point was, not whether I had assumed that he would quit me, but whether he would prefer so to do. He was more a man of preferences than assumptions.

After breakfast, I walked down town, arguing the probabilities *pro* and *con*. One moment I thought it would prove a miserable failure, and Bartleby would be found all alive at my office as usual; the next moment it seemed certain that I should find his chair empty. And so I kept veering about. At the corner of Broadway and Canal Street, I saw quite an excited group of people standing in earnest conversation.

"I'll take odds he doesn't," said a voice as I passed.

"Doesn't go?—done!" said I; "put up your money."

I was instinctively putting my hand in my pocket to produce my own, when I remembered that this was an election day. The words I had overheard bore no reference to Bartleby, but to the success or non-success of some candidate for the mayoralty. In my intent frame of mind, I had, as it were, imagined that all Broadway shared in my excitement, and were debating the same question with me. I passed on, very thankful that the uproar of the street screened my momentary absent-mindedness.

As I had intended, I was earlier than usual at my office door. I stood listening for a moment. All was still. He must be gone. I tried the knob. The door was locked. Yes, my procedure had worked to a charm; he indeed must be vanished. Yet a certain melancholy mixed with this: I was almost sorry for my brilliant success. I was fumbling under the door mat for the key, which Bartleby was to have left there for me, when accidentally my knee knocked against a panel, producing a summoning sound, and in response a voice came to me from within—"Not yet; I am occupied."

It was Bartleby.

I was thunderstruck. For an instant I stood like the man who, pipe in mouth, was killed one cloudless afternoon long ago in Virginia, by summer lightning; at his own warm open window he was killed, and remained leaning out there upon the dreamy afternoon, till some one touched him, when he fell.

"Not gone!" I murmured at last. But again obeying that wondrous ascendancy which the inscrutable scrivener had over me, and from which ascendancy, for all my chafing, I could not completely escape, I slowly went down stairs and out into the street, and while walking round the block, considered what I should next do in this unheard-of perplexity. Turn the man out by an actual thrusting I could not; to drive him away by calling him hard names would not do; calling in the police was an unpleasant idea; and yet, permit him to enjoy his cadaverous triumph over me—this, too, I could not think of. What was to be done? or, if nothing could be done, was there anything further that I could *assume* in the matter? Yes, as before I had prospectively assumed that Bartleby would depart, so now I might retrospectively assume that departed he was. In the legitimate carrying out of this assumption, I might enter my office in a great hurry, and pretending not to see Bartleby at all, walk straight against him as if he were air. Such a proceeding would in a singular degree have the appearance of a home-thrust. It was hardly possible that Bartleby could withstand such an application of the doctrine of assumptions. But upon second thoughts the success of the plan seemed rather dubious. I resolved to argue the matter over with him again.

"Bartleby," said I, entering the office, with a quietly severe expression, "I am seriously displeased. I am pained, Bartleby. I had thought better of you. I had imagined you of such a gentlemanly organization, that in any delicate dilemma a slight hint would suffice—in short, an assumption. But it appears I am deceived. Why," I added, unaffectedly starting, "you have not even touched that money yet," pointing to it, just where I had left it the evening previous.

He answered nothing.

"Will you, or will you not, quit me?" I now demanded in a sudden passion, advancing close to him.

"I would prefer *not* to quit you," he replied, gently emphasizing the *not.*

"What earthly right have you to stay here? Do you pay any rent? Do you pay my taxes? Or is this property yours?"

He answered nothing.

"Are you ready to go on and write now? Are your eyes recovered? Could you copy a small paper for me this morning? or help examine a few lines? or step round to the post-office? In a word, will you do anything at all, to give a coloring to your refusal to depart the premises?"

He silently retired into his hermitage.

I was now in such a state of nervous resentment that I thought it but prudent to check myself at present from further demonstrations. Bartleby and I were alone. I remembered the tragedy of the unfortunate Adams and the still more unfortunate Colt in the solitary office of the latter; and how poor Colt, being dreadfully incensed by Adams, and imprudently permitting himself to get wildly excited, was at unawares hurried into his fatal act—an act which certainly no man could possibly deplore more than the actor himself. Often it had occurred to me in my ponderings upon the subject, that had that altercation taken place in the public street, or at a private residence, it would not have terminated as it did. It was the circumstance of being alone in a solitary office, up stairs, of a building entirely unhallowed by humanizing domestic associations—an uncarpeted office, doubtless, of a dusty, haggard sort of appearance—this it must have been, which greatly helped to enhance the irritable desperation of the hapless Colt.

But when this old Adam of resentment rose in me and tempted me concerning Bartleby, I grappled him and threw him. How? Why, simply by recalling the divine injunction: "A new commandment give I unto you, that ye love one another." Yes, this it was that saved me. Aside from higher considerations, charity often operates as a vastly wise and prudent principle—a great safeguard to its possessor. Men have committed murder for jealousy's sake, and anger's sake, and hatred's sake, and selfishness' sake, and spiritual pride's sake; but no man, that ever I heard of, ever committed a diabolical murder for sweet charity's sake. Mere self-interest, then, if no better motive can be enlisted, should, especially with high-tempered men, prompt all beings to charity and philanthropy. At any rate, upon the occasion in question, I strove to drown my exasperated feelings towards the scrivener by benevolently construing his conduct. Poor fellow, poor fellow! thought I, he don't mean anything; and besides, he has seen hard times, and ought to be indulged.

I endeavored, also, immediately to occupy myself, and at the same time to comfort my despondency. I tried to fancy, that in the course of the morning, at such time as might prove agreeable to him, Bartleby, of his own free accord, would emerge from his hermitage and take up some decided line of march in the direction of the door. But no. Half-past twelve o'clock came; Turkey began to glow in the face, overturn his inkstand, and become generally obstreperous; Nippers abated down into quietude and courtesy; Ginger Nut munched his noon apple; and Bartleby remained standing at his window in one of his profoundest dead-wall reveries. Will it be credited? Ought I to acknowledge it? That afternoon I left the office without saying one further word to him.

Some days now passed, during which, at leisure intervals I looked a little into "Edwards on the Will," and "Priestley on Necessity." Under the circumstances, those books induced a salutary feeling. Gradually I slid into the persuasion that these troubles of mine, touching the scrivener, had been all predestinated from eternity, and Bartleby was billeted upon me for some mysterious purpose of an allwise Providence, which it was not for a mere mortal like me to fathom. Yes, Bartleby, stay there behind your screen, thought I; I shall persecute you no more; you are harmless and noiseless as any of these old chairs; in short, I never feel so private as when I know you are here. At last I see it, I feel it; I penetrate to the predestinated purpose of my life. I am content. Others may have loftier parts to enact; but my mission in this world, Bartleby, is to furnish you with office-room for such period as you may see fit to remain.

I believe that this wise and blessed frame of mind would have continued with me, had it not been for the unsolicited and uncharitable remarks obtruded upon me by my professional friends who visited the rooms. But thus it often is, that the constant friction of illiberal minds wears out at last the best resolves of the more generous. Though to be sure, when I reflected upon it, it was not strange that people entering my office should be struck by the peculiar aspect of the unaccountable Bartleby, and so be tempted to throw out some sinister observations concerning him. Sometimes an attorney, having business with me, and calling at my office, and finding no one but the scrivener there, would undertake to obtain some sort of precise information from him touching my whereabouts; but without heeding his idle talk, Bartleby would remain standing immovable in the middle of the room. So after contemplating him in that position for a time, the attorney would depart, no wiser than he came.

Also, when a reference was going on, and the room full of lawyers and witnesses, and business driving fast, some deeply-occupied legal gentleman present, seeing Bartleby wholly unemployed, would request him to run round to his (the legal gentleman's) office and fetch some papers for him. Thereupon, Bartleby would tranquilly decline, and yet remain idle as before. Then the lawyer would give a great stare, and turn to me. And what could I say? At last I was made aware that all through the circle of my professional acquaintance, a whisper of wonder was running round, having reference to the strange creature I kept at my office. This worried me very much. And as the idea came upon me of his possibly turning out a long-lived man, and keep occupying my chambers, and denying my authority; and perplexing my visitors; and scandalizing my professional reputation; and casting a general gloom over the premises; keeping soul and body together to the last upon his savings (for doubtless he spent but half a dime a day), and in the end perhaps outlive me, and claim possession of my office by right of his perpetual occupancy: as all these dark anticipations crowded upon me more and more, and my friends continually intruded their relentless remarks upon the apparition in my room; a great change was wrought in me. I resolved to gather all my faculties together, and forever rid me of this intolerable incubus.

Ere revolving any complicated project, however, adapted to this end, I first simply suggested to Bartleby the propriety of his permanent departure. In a calm and serious tone, I commended the idea to his careful and mature consideration. But, having taken three days to meditate upon it, he apprised me, that his original determination remained the same; in short, that he still preferred to abide with me.

What shall I do? I now said to myself, buttoning up my coat to the last button. What shall I do? what ought I to do? what does conscience say I *should* do with this man, or, rather, ghost. Rid myself of him, I must; go, he shall. But how? You will not thrust him, the poor, pale, passive mortal—you will not thrust such a helpless creature out of your door? you will not dishonor yourself by such cruelty? No, I will not, I cannot do that. Rather would I let him live and die here, and then mason up his remains in the wall. What, then, will you do? For all your coaxing, he will not budge. Bribes he leaves under your own paper-weight on your table; in short, it is quite plain that he prefers to cling to you.

Then something severe, something unusual must be done. What! surely you will not have him collared by a constable, and commit his innocent pallor to the common jail? And upon what ground could you procure such a thing to be done?—a vagrant, is he? What! he a vagrant, a wanderer, who refuses to budge? It is because he will *not* be a vagrant, then, that you seek to count him *as* a vagrant. That is too absurd. No visible means of support: there I have him. Wrong again: for indubitably he *does* support himself, and that is the only unanswerable proof that any man can show of his possessing the means so to do. No more, then. Since he will not quit me, I must quit him. I will change my offices; I will move elsewhere, and give him fair notice, that if I find him on my new premises I will then proceed against him as a common trespasser.

Acting accordingly, next day I thus addressed him: "I find these chambers too far from the City Hall; the air is unwholesome. In a word, I propose to remove my offices next week, and shall no longer require your services. I tell you this now, in order that you may seek another place."

He made no reply; and nothing more was said.

On the appointed day I engaged carts and men, proceeded to my chambers, and, having but little furniture, everything was removed in a few hours. Throughout, the scrivener remained standing behind the screen, which I directed to be removed the last thing. It was withdrawn; and, being folded up like a huge folio, left him the motionless occupant of a naked room. I stood in the entry watching him a moment, while something from within me upbraided me.

I re-entered, with my hand in my pocket—and—and my heart in my mouth.

"Good-by, Bartleby; I am going—good-by, and God some way bless you; and take that," slipping something in his hand. But it dropped upon the floor, and then—strange to say—I tore myself from him whom I had so longed to be rid of.

Established in my new quarters, for a day or two I kept the door locked, and started at every footfall in the passages. When I returned to my rooms, after any little absence, I would pause at the threshold for an instant, and attentively listen, ere applying my key. But these fears were needless. Bartleby never came nigh me.

I thought all was going well, when a perturbed-looking stranger visited me, inquiring whether I was the person who had recently occupied rooms at No. — Wall Street.

Full of forebodings, I replied that I was.

"Then, sir," said the stranger, who proved a lawyer, "you are responsible for the man you left there. He refuses to do any copying; he refuses to do anything; he says he prefers not to; and he refuses to quit the premises."

"I am very sorry, sir," said I, with assumed tranquillity, but an inward tremor, "but, really, the man you allude to is nothing to me—he is no relation or apprentice of mine, that you should hold me responsible for him."

"In mercy's name, who is he?"

"I certainly cannot inform you. I know nothing about him. Formerly I employed him as a copyist; but he has done nothing for me now for some time past."

"I shall settle him, then—good morning, sir."

Several days passed, and I heard nothing more; and, though I often felt a charitable prompting to call at the place and see poor Bartleby, yet a certain squeamishness, of I know not what, withheld me.

All is over with him, by this time, thought I, at last, when, through another week, no further intelligence reached me. But, coming to my room the day after, I found several persons waiting at my door in a high state of nervous excitement.

"That's the man—here he comes," cried the foremost one, whom I recognized as the lawyer who had previously called upon me alone.

"You must take him away, sir, at once," cried a portly person among them, advancing upon me, and whom I knew to be the landlord of No. — Wall Street. "These gentlemen, my tenants, cannot stand it any longer; Mr. B——," pointing to the lawyer, "has turned him out of his room, and he now persists in haunting the building generally, sitting upon the banisters of the stairs by day, and sleeping in the entry by night. Everybody is concerned; clients are leaving the offices; some fears are entertained of a mob; something you must do, and that without delay."

Aghast at this torrent, I fell back before it, and would fain have locked myself in my new quarters. In vain I persisted that Bartleby was nothing to me—no more than to any one else. In vain—I was the last person known to have anything to do with him, and they held me to the terrible account. Fearful, then, of being exposed in the papers (as one person present obscurely threatened), I considered the matter, and, at length, said, that if the lawyer would give me a confidential interview with the scrivener, in his (the lawyer's) own room, I would, that afternoon, strive my best to rid them of the nuisance they complained of.

Going up stairs to my old haunt, there was Bartleby silently sitting upon the banister at the landing.

"What are you doing here, Bartleby?" said I.

"Sitting upon the banister," he mildly replied.

I motioned him into the lawyer's room, who then left us.

"Bartleby," said I, "are you aware that you are the cause of great tribulation to me, by persisting in occupying the entry after being dismissed from the office?"

No answer.

"Now one of two things must take place. Either you must do something, or something must be done to you. Now what sort of business would you like to engage in? Would you like to re-engage in copying for some one?"

"No; I would prefer not to make any change."

"Would you like a clerkship in a dry-goods store?"

"There is too much confinement about that. No, I would not like a clerkship; but I am not particular."

"Too much confinement," I cried, "why you keep yourself confined all the time!"

"I would prefer not to take a clerkship," he rejoined, as if to settle that little item at once.

"How would a bar-tender's business suit you? There is no trying of the eye-sight in that."

"I would not like it at all; though, as I said before, I am not particular."

His unwonted wordiness inspirited me. I returned to the charge.

"Well, then, would you like to travel through the country collecting bills for the merchants? That would improve your health."

"No, I would prefer to be doing something else."

"How, then, would going as a companion to Europe, to entertain some young gentleman with your conversation—how would that suit you?"

"Not at all. It does not strike me that there is anything definite about that. I like to be stationary. But I am not particular."

"Stationary you shall be, then," I cried, now losing all patience, and, for the first time in all my exasperating connection with him, fairly flying into a passion. "If you do not go away from these premises before night, I shall feel bound—indeed, I *am* bound—to—to—to quit the premises myself!" I rather absurdly concluded, knowing not with what possible threat to try to frighten his immobility into compliance. Despairing of all further efforts, I was precipitately leaving him, when a final thought occurred to me—one which had not been wholly unindulged before.

"Bartleby," said I, in the kindest tone I could assume under such exciting circumstances, "will you go home with me now—not to my office, but my dwelling—and remain there till we can conclude upon some convenient arrangement for you at our leisure? Come, let us start now, right away."

"No: at present I would prefer not to make any change at all."

I answered nothing; but, effectually dodging every one by the suddenness and rapidity of my flight, rushed from the building, ran up Wall Street towards Broadway, and, jumping into the first omnibus, was soon removed from pursuit. As soon as tranquillity returned, I distinctly perceived that I had now done all that I possibly could, both in respect to the demands of the landlord and his tenants, and with regard to my own desire and sense of duty, to benefit Bartleby, and shield him from rude persecution. I now strove to be entirely care-free and quiescent; and my conscience justified me in the attempt; though, indeed, it was not so successful as I could have wished. So fearful was I of being again hunted out by the incensed landlord and his exasperated tenants, that, surrendering my business to Nippers, for a few days, I drove about the upper part of town and through the suburbs, in my rockaway; crossed over to Jersey City and Hoboken, and paid fugitive visits to Manhattanville and Astoria. In fact, I almost lived in my rockaway for the time.

When again I entered my office, lo, a note from the landlord lay upon the desk. I opened it with trembling hands. It informed me that the writer had sent to the police, and had Bartleby removed to the Tombs as a vagrant. Moreover, since I knew more about him than any one else, he wished me to appear at that place, and make a suitable statement of the facts. These tidings had a conflicting effect upon me. At first I was indignant; but, at last, almost approved. The landlord's energetic, summary disposition, had led him to adopt a procedure which I do not think I would have decided upon myself; and yet, as a last resort, under such peculiar circumstances, it seemed the only plan.

As I afterwards learned, the poor scrivener, when told that he must be conducted to the Tombs, offered not the slightest obstacle, but, in his pale, unmoving way, silently acquiesced.

Some of the compassionate and curious bystanders joined the party; and headed by one of the constables arm in arm with Bartleby, the silent procession filed its way through all the noise, and heat, and joy of the roaring thoroughfares at noon.

The same day I received the note, I went to the Tombs, or, to speak more properly, the Halls of Justice. Seeking the right officer, I stated the purpose of my call, and was informed that the individual I described was, indeed, within. I then assured the functionary that Bartleby was a perfectly honest man, and greatly to be compassionated, however unaccountably eccentric. I narrated all I knew, and closed by suggesting the idea of letting him remain in as indulgent confinement as possible, till something less harsh might be done—though, indeed, I hardly knew what. At all events, if nothing else could be decided upon, the alms-house must receive him. I then begged to have an interview.

Being under no disgraceful charge, and quite serene and harmless in all his ways, they had permitted him freely to wander about the prison, and, especially, in the inclosed grass-platted yards thereof. And so I found him there, standing all alone in the quietest of the yards, his face towards a high wall, while all around, from the narrow slits of the jail windows, I thought I saw peering out upon him the eyes of murderers and thieves.

"Bartleby!"

"I know you," he said, without looking round—"and I want nothing to say to you."

"It was not I that brought you here, Bartleby," said I, keenly pained at his implied suspicion. "And to you, this should not be so vile a place. Nothing reproachful attaches to you by being here. And see, it is not so sad a place as one might think. Look, there is the sky, and here is the grass."

"I know where I am," he replied, but would say nothing more, and so I left him.

As I entered the corridor again, a broad meat-like man, in an apron, accosted me, and, jerking his thumb over his shoulder, said—"Is that your friend?"

"Yes."

"Does he want to starve? If he does, let him live on the prison fare, that's all."

"Who are you?" asked I, not knowing what to make of such an unofficially speaking person in such a place.

"I am the grub-man. Such gentlemen as have friends here, hire me to provide them with something good to eat."

"Is this so?" said I, turning to the turnkey.

He said it was.

"Well, then," said I, slipping some silver into the grub-man's hands (for so they called him), "I want you to give particular attention to my friend there; let him have the best dinner you can get. And you must be as polite to him as possible."

"Introduce me, will you?" said the grub-man, looking at me with an expression which seemed to say he was all impatience for an opportunity to give a specimen of his breeding.

Thinking it would prove of benefit to the scrivener, I acquiesced; and, asking the grub-man his name, went up with him to Bartleby.

"Bartleby, this is a friend; you will find him very useful to you."

"Your sarvant, sir, your sarvant," said the grub-man, making a low salutation behind his apron. "Hope you find it pleasant here, sir; nice grounds—cool apartments—hope you'll stay with us some time—try to make it agreeable. What will you have for dinner to-day?"

"I prefer not to dine to-day," said Bartleby, turning away. "It would disagree with me; I am unused to dinners." So saying, he slowly moved to the other side of the inclosure, and took up a position fronting the dead-wall.

"How's this?" said the grub-man, addressing me with a stare of astonishment. "He's odd, ain't he?"

"I think he is a little deranged," said I, sadly.

"Deranged? deranged is it? Well, now, upon my word, I thought that friend of yourn was a gentleman forger; they are always pale and genteel-like, them forgers. I can't help pity 'em—can't help it, sir. Did you know Monroe Edwards?" he added, touchingly, and paused. Then, laying his hand piteously on my shoulder, sighed, "he died of consumption at Sing-Sing. So you weren't acquainted with Monroe?"

"No, I was never socially acquainted with any forgers. But I cannot stop longer. Look to my friend yonder. You will not lose by it. I will see you again."

Some few days after this, I again obtained admission to the Tombs, and went through the corridors in quest of Bartleby; but without finding him.

"I saw him coming from his cell not long ago," said a turnkey, "may be he's gone to loiter in the yards."

So I went in that direction.

"Are you looking for the silent man?" said another turnkey, passing me. "Yonder he lies—sleeping in the yard there. 'Tis not twenty minutes since I saw him lie down."

The yard was entirely quiet. It was not accessible to the common prisoners. The surrounding walls, of amazing thickness, kept off all sounds behind them. The Egyptian character of the masonry weighed upon me with its gloom. But a soft imprisoned turf grew under foot. The heart of the eternal pyramids, it seemed, wherein, by some strange magic, through the clefts, grass-seed, dropped by birds, had sprung.

Strangely huddled at the base of the wall, his knees drawn up, and lying on his side, his head touching the cold stones, I saw the wasted Bartleby. But nothing stirred. I paused; then went close up to him; stooped over, and saw that his dim eyes were open; otherwise he seemed profoundly sleeping. Something prompted me to touch him. I felt his hand, when a tingling shiver ran up my arm and down my spine to my feet.

The round face of the grub-man peered upon me now. "His dinner is ready. Won't he dine to-day, either? Or does he live without dining?"

"Lives without dining," said I, and closed the eyes.

"Eh!—He's asleep, ain't he?"

"With kings and counselors," murmured I.

. . . . .

There would seem little need for proceeding further in this history. Imagination will readily supply the meagre recital of poor Bartleby's interment. But, ere parting with the reader, let me say, that if this little narrative has sufficiently interested him, to awaken curiosity as to who Bartleby was, and what manner of life he led prior to the present narrator's making his acquaintance, I can only reply, that in such curiosity I fully share, but am wholly unable to gratify it. Yet here I hardly know whether I should divulge one little item of rumor, which came to my ear a few months after the scrivener's decease. Upon what basis it rested, I could never ascertain; and hence, how true it is I cannot now tell. But, inasmuch as this vague report has not been without a certain suggestive interest to me, however sad, it may prove the same with some others; and so I will briefly mention it. The report was this: that Bartleby had been a subordinate clerk in the Dead Letter Office at Washington, from which he had been suddenly removed by a change in the administration. When I think over this rumor, hardly can I express the emotions which seize me. Dead letters! does it not sound like dead men? Conceive a man by nature and misfortune prone to a pallid hopelessness, can any business seem more fitted to heighten it than that of continually handling these dead letters, and assorting them for the flames? For by the cart-load they are annually burned. Sometimes from out the folded paper the pale clerk takes a ring —the finger it was meant for, perhaps, moulders in the grave; a bank-note sent in swiftest charity—he whom it would relieve, nor eats nor hungers any more; pardon for those who died despairing; hope for those who died unhoping; good tidings for those who died stifled by unrelieved calamities. On errands of life, these letters speed to death.

Ah, Bartleby! Ah, humanity!

ANALYSIS

"Bartleby the Scrivener" tells of a man who, retreating inward, separates himself from a society based upon material rather than human values. Much has been written about Bartleby's withdrawal, and it is generally assumed that in his negative relationship to his surroundings he exhibits a universal failure of human beings to communicate with one another. Many Melville scholars believe also that the author, in creating Bartleby, was consciously or unconsciously reflecting his own situation in the early 1850's, when, under pressure from his family and friends to continue turning out "commercial" adventure stories, it seemed that he must succumb to material values or quit writing altogether.

Undoubtedly the questions of refusal or inability to communicate are relevant to "Bartleby." But another approach to the work reveals it to be considerably more than a somewhat enigmatic tale of social alienation: the most obvious meaning of a story is not necessarily its most important aspect. Despite surface appearances, "Bartleby the Scrivener" is not primarily about Bartleby or Bartleby's situation, but is rather about the lawyer-narrator and his education in humanity.

The story does not tell us why Bartleby withdraws; the only hint is speculation on the part of the lawyer, based upon questionable infor-mation that Bartleby had worked in a dead-letter office. The point of view is completely that of the lawyer; we know only his emotions, his actions and reactions, his observations. It quickly becomes apparent through his own account that he has himself been deliberately withdrawn from involvement in the "human" element of his own career, that he is snobbish and pompous. He belongs, he says, to a profession which is proverbially active and nervous, "even to turbulence, at times, yet nothing of that sort have I ever suffered to invade my peace." His first great point, he tells the reader, is prudence and his second, method. In the "cool tranquillity of a snug retreat," he does a fine business, not with rich men, but rich men's bonds and deeds. The only personal reference to one of his clients indicates by its phrasing removal from the client as a man ("I was not unemployed in my profession by the late John Jacob Astor") and translation of him into the commercial terms acceptable to the lawyer ("a name which, I admit, I love to repeat; for it hath a rounded and orbicular sound to it, and rings like unto bullion"). Though the lawyer "was not insensible to the late John Jacob Astor's good opinion," he obviously can speak of Astor only in negative terms ("not unemployed," "not insensible") except as the man is translated into gold.

The chambers of the lawyer are similarly cut off from humanity: "At one end, they looked upon the white wall of the interior of a spacious sky-light shaft . . ."; at the other, the "windows commanded an unobstructed view of a lofty brick wall . . . which . . . was pushed up to within ten feet of my window panes." The window at which he places Bartleby "commanded at present no view at all, though it gave some light." Between the lawyer and his scriveners there is a set of ground glass folding doors by which he may shut them off at will, and around Bartleby he places "a high green folding screen, which might entirely isolate Bartleby from my sight, though not remove him from my voice."

The lawyer is not totally unconcerned with the scriveners in his employ before the arrival of Bartleby, but he appears to have little or no interest in them outside their function in his office. If he puts up with Nippers' dyspeptic mornings, it is because Nippers works enough in the afternoon to make up for it. If he allows Turkey to stay on in spite of the misdirected energy following his noon beer, it is because Turkey is an excellent morning copyist. The lawyer's attitude is clearly evident in his own account of calling Bartleby to compare some papers: "In my haste and natural *expectancy of instant compliance,* I sat with my head bent over the original on my desk, and my right hand sideways, and somewhat nervously extended with the copy, so that, *immediately upon emerging* from his retreat, Bartleby might *snatch* it and *proceed to business without the least delay.*" (Italics added.)

At the beginning, the lawyer may not be an actively inhumane man; he is certainly unresponsive to humanity. Ironically, it is Bartleby who, by the dogged passivity of an even further removal from mankind, draws the narrator into a new and active concern for humanity. Bartleby, of course, prefers not to do anything he is asked, and eventually prefers not to do any more copying at all. The first time he refuses to comply with the lawyer's wishes, the lawyer, rather than disrupt business for a "human" response, decides to forget the matter. Several days later when the same situation occurs, the lawyer can no longer ignore it, and is turned "to a pillar of salt." At this point his education really begins. Any other man he would have fired immediately, but something about Bartleby's manner not only disarms him but, as he says, "in a wonderful manner, touched and disconcerted me."

As the days go by and the lawyer begins to wonder what Bartleby eats, where he lives, and so on, he begins to soften toward the man. "Poor fellow! thought I, he means no mischief; it is plain he intends no insolence; his aspect sufficiently evinces that his eccentricities are involuntary. . . . Here I can cheaply purchase a delicious self-approval. To befriend Bartleby; to humor him in his strange willfulness, will cost me little or nothing, while I lay up in my soul what will eventually prove a sweet morsel for my conscience." The lawyer's character has as yet undergone only the beginnings of a transformation; he justifies his wish to humor Bartleby in completely selfish terms.

Before long there is a second step in the lawyer's education, when he discovers that Bartleby is living in his chambers. "Yes, thought I, it is evident enough that Bartleby has been making his home here. . . . Immediately then the thought came sweeping across me, what miserable friendlessness and loneliness are here revealed! His poverty is great; but his solitude, how horrible!" At this point the lawyer has his first real awakening: "For the first time in my life a feeling of overpowering stinging melancholy seized me. . . . The bond of a common humanity now drew me irresistibly to gloom. A fraternal melancholy! For both I and Bartleby were sons of Adam." The lawyer's pity soon turns to repulsion, however, because of the hopelessness of Bartleby's situation: "I might give alms to his body; but his body did not pain him; it was his soul that suffered, and his soul I could not reach."

Nevertheless, the seeds have been planted and humane instincts grow in the lawyer. Although he has resolved to dismiss Bartleby, he says, "I strangely felt something superstitious knocking at my heart, and forbidding me to carry out my purpose, and denouncing me for a villain if I dared to breathe one bitter word against this forlornest of mankind." Eventually, after Bartleby quits working entirely the lawyer is forced to dismiss him, and on walking home that night suffers a serious reversion to his old self-concern. "My vanity got the better of my pity. I could not but highly plume myself on my masterly management in getting rid of Bartleby." The next morning, however, "I had my doubts—I had somehow slept off the fumes of vanity." The lawyer's humane growth continues: "When this old Adam of resentment rose in me and tempted me concerning Bartleby, I grappled him and threw him. How? Why, simply by recalling the divine injunction: 'A new commandment give I unto you, that ye love one another.'" Although he is no longer thinking in terms of "giving alms," he has not advanced beyond justifying the commandment to love one another within the typical commercial framework of enlightened self-interest.

Gradually the lawyer begins to think that his troubles with the scrivener have been predestined, set upon him for a mysterious purpose by an all-wise Providence, and he would be content to leave things as they are if the lawyer's professional friends did not begin to be irritated by Bartleby. Unable, finally, to move Bartleby, the lawyer moves his offices. His reaction on leaving Bartleby indicates clearly the change that has taken place in himself; "I re-entered, with my hand in my pocket— and—and my heart in my mouth. 'Good-bye, Bartleby; I am going— good-bye, and God some way bless you.'" The lawyer slips some money into Bartleby's hand, "and then—strange to say—I tore myself from him whom I had so longed to be rid of."

But even in his new offices the lawyer cannot forget Bartleby, and when the new tenants of his old chambers threaten to have the scrivener thrown in jail, the lawyer offers to take him into his own home. This is perhaps the principal act in his education, an act which, before his awakening, would never have entered his mind.

When Bartleby is taken away to the Tombs the lawyer visits him and does what he can to make him comfortable. The snobbish pomposity is gone by the time the lawyer is witness to Bartleby's end.

The last paragraph of the story is not so much a clue to Bartleby's withdrawal from life as it is the final chapter in the lawyer's education. He says, "When I think over this rumor [that Bartleby worked in a dead-letter office], hardly can I express the emotions which seize me. Dead letters! does it not sound like dead men?" Throughout the story Bartleby has existed as the passive agent for the narrator's discovery of human emotions which he has previously never imagined. The lawyer has come a long way from his early translation of John Jacob Astor into gold when he translates dead letters into dead men, and when he murmurs his final words: "Ah, Bartleby! Ah, humanity!"

Albert Camus

THE GUEST

The schoolmaster was watching the two men climb toward him. One was on horseback, the other on foot. They had not yet tackled the abrupt rise leading to the schoolhouse built on the hillside. They were toiling onward, making slow progress in the snow, among the stones, on the vast expanse of the high, deserted plateau. From time to time the horse stumbled. Without hearing anything yet, he could see the breath issuing from the horse's nostrils. One of the men, at least, knew the region. They were following the trail although it had disappeared days ago under a layer of dirty white snow. The schoolmaster calculated that it would take them half an hour to get onto the hill. It was cold; he went back into the school to get a sweater.

He crossed the empty, frigid classroom. On the blackboard the four rivers of France, drawn with four different colored chalks, had been flowing toward their estuaries for the past three days. Snow had suddenly fallen in mid-October after eight months of drought without the transition of rain, and the twenty pupils, more or less, who lived in the villages scattered over the plateau had stopped coming. With fair weather they would return. Daru now heated only the single room that was his lodging, adjoining the classroom and giving also onto the plateau to the east. Like the class windows, his window looked to the south too. On that side the school was a few kilometers from the point where the plateau began to slope toward the south. In clear weather could be seen the purple mass of the mountain range where the gap opened onto the desert.

Somewhat warmed, Daru returned to the window from which he had first seen the two men. They were no longer visible. Hence they must have tackled the rise. The sky was not so dark, for the snow had stopped falling during the night. The morning had opened with a dirty light which had scarcely become brighter as the ceiling of clouds lifted. At two in the afternoon it seemed as if the day were merely beginning. But still this was better than those three days when the thick snow was falling amidst unbroken darkness with little gusts of wind that rattled the double door of the classroom. Then Daru had spent long hours in his room, leaving it only to go to the shed and feed the chickens or get some coal. Fortunately the delivery truck from Tadjid, the nearest village to the north, had brought his supplies two days before the blizzard. It would return in forty-eight hours.

Besides, he had enough to resist a siege, for the little room was cluttered with bags of wheat that the administration left as a stock to distribute to those of his pupils whose families had suffered from the drought. Actually they had all been victims because they were all poor. Every day Daru would distribute a ration to the children. They had missed it, he knew, during these bad days. Possibly one of the fathers or big brothers would come this afternoon and he could supply them with grain. It was just a matter of carrying them over to the next harvest. Now shiploads of wheat were arriving from France and the worst was over. But it would be hard to forget that poverty, that army of ragged ghosts wandering in the sunlight, the plateaus burned to a cinder month after month, the earth shriveled up little by little, literally scorched, every stone bursting into dust under one's foot. The sheep had died then by thousands and even a few men, here and there, sometimes without anyone's knowing.

In contrast with such poverty, he who lived almost like a monk in his remote schoolhouse, nonetheless satisfied with the little he had and with the rough life, had felt like a lord with his whitewashed walls, his narrow couch, his unpainted shelves, his well, and his weekly provision of water and food. And suddenly this snow, without warning, without the foretaste of rain. This is the way the region was, cruel to live in, even without men—who didn't help matters either. But Daru had been born here. Everywhere else, he felt exiled.

He stepped out onto the terrace in front of the schoolhouse. The two men were now halfway up the slope. He recognized the horseman as Balducci, the old gendarme he had known for a long time. Balducci was holding on the end of a rope an Arab who was walking behind him with hands bound and head lowered. The gendarme waved a greeting to which Daru did not reply, lost as he was in contemplation of the Arab dressed in a faded blue jellaba, his feet in sandals but covered with socks of heavy raw wool, his head surmounted by a narrow, short *chèche*. They were approaching. Balducci was holding back his horse in order not to hurt the Arab, and the group was advancing slowly.

Within earshot, Balducci shouted: "One hour to do the three kilometers from El Ameur!" Daru did not answer. Short and square in his thick sweater, he watched them climb. Not once had the Arab raised his head. "Hello," said Daru when they got up onto the terrace. "Come in and warm up." Balducci painfully got down from his horse without letting go the rope. From under his bristling mustache he smiled at the schoolmaster. His little dark eyes, deep-set under a tanned forehead, and his mouth surrounded with wrinkles made him look attentive and studious. Daru took the bridle, led the horse to the shed, and came back to the two men, who were now waiting for him in the school. He led them into his room.

"I am going to heat up the classroom," he said. "We'll be more comfortable there." When he entered the room again, Balducci was on the couch. He had undone the rope tying him to the Arab, who had squatted near the stove. His hands still bound, the *chèche* pushed back on his head, he was looking toward the window. At first Daru noticed only his huge lips, fat, smooth, almost Negroid; yet his nose was straight, his eyes were dark and full of fever. The *chèche* revealed an obstinate forehead and, under the weathered skin now rather discolored by the cold, the whole face had a restless and rebellious look that struck Daru when the Arab, turning his face toward him, looked him straight in the eyes. "Go into the other room," said the schoolmaster, "and I'll make you some mint tea." "Thanks," Balducci said. "What a chore! How I long for retirement." And addressing his prisoner in Arabic: "Come on, you." The Arab got up and, slowly, holding his bound wrists in front of him, went into the classroom.

With the tea, Daru brought a chair. But Balducci was already enthroned on the nearest pupil's desk and the Arab had squatted against the teacher's platform facing the stove, which stood between the desk and the window. When he held out the glass of tea to the prisoner, Daru hesitated at the sight of his bound hands. "He might perhaps be untied." "Sure," said Balducci. "That was for the trip." He started to get to his feet. But Daru, setting the glass on the floor, had knelt beside the Arab. Without saying anything, the Arab watched him with his feverish eyes. Once his hands were free, he rubbed his swollen wrists against each other, took the glass of tea, and sucked up the burning liquid in swift little sips.

"Good," said Daru. "And where are you headed?"

Balducci withdrew his mustache from the tea. "Here, son."

"Odd pupils! And you're spending the night?"

"No. I'm going back to El Ameur. And you will deliver this fellow to Tinguit. He is expected at police headquarters."

Balducci was looking at Daru with a friendly little smile.

"What's this story?" asked the schoolmaster. "Are you pulling my leg?"

"No, son. Those are the orders."

"The orders? I'm not . . ." Daru hesitated, not wanting to hurt the old Corsican. "I mean, that's not my job."

"What! What's the meaning of that? In wartime people do all kinds of jobs."

"Then I'll wait for the declaration of war!"

Balducci nodded.

"O.K. But the orders exist and they concern you too. Things are brewing, it appears. There is talk of a forthcoming revolt. We are mobilized, in a way."

Daru still had his obstinate look.

"Listen, son," Balducci said. "I like you and you must understand. There's only a dozen of us at El Ameur to patrol throughout the whole territory of a small department and I must get back in a hurry. I was told to hand this guy over to you and return without delay. He couldn't be kept there. His village was beginning to stir; they wanted to take him back. You must take him to Tinguit tomorrow before the day is over.

Twenty kilometers shouldn't faze a husky fellow like you. After that, all will be over. You'll come back to your pupils and your comfortable life."

Behind the wall the horse could be heard snorting and pawing the earth. Daru was looking out the window. Decidedly, the weather was clearing and the light was increasing over the snowy plateau. When all the snow was melted, the sun would take over again and once more would burn the fields of stone. For days, still, the unchanging sky would shed its dry light on the solitary expanse where nothing had any connection with man.

"After all," he said, turning around toward Balducci, "what did he do?" And, before the gendarme had opened his mouth, he asked: "Does he speak French?"

"No, not a word. We had been looking for him for a month, but they were hiding him. He killed his cousin."

"Is he against us?"

"I don't think so. But you can never be sure."

"Why did he kill?"

"A family squabble, I think. One owed the other grain, it seems. It's not at all clear. In short, he killed his cousin with a billhook. You know, like a sheep, *kreezk!*"

Balducci made the gesture of drawing a blade across his throat and the Arab, his attention attracted, watched him with a sort of anxiety. Daru felt a sudden wrath against the man, against all men with their rotten spite, their tireless hates, their blood lust.

But the kettle was singing on the stove. He served Balducci more tea, hesitated, then served the Arab again, who, a second time, drank avidly. His raised arms made the jellaba fall open and the schoolmaster saw his thin, muscular chest.

"Thanks, kid," Balducci said. "And now, I'm off."

He got up and went toward the Arab, taking a small rope from his pocket.

"What are you doing?" Daru asked dryly.

Balducci, disconcerted, showed him the rope.

"Don't bother."

The old gendarme hesitated. "It's up to you. Of course, you are armed?"

"I have my shotgun."

"Where?"

"In the trunk."

"You ought to have it near your bed."

"Why? I have nothing to fear."

"You're crazy, son. If there's an uprising, no one is safe, we're all in the same boat."

"I'll defend myself. I'll have time to see them coming."

Balducci began to laugh, then suddenly the mustache covered the white teeth.

"You'll have time? O.K. That's just what I was saying. You have always been a little cracked. That's why I like you, my son was like that."

At the same time he took out his revolver and put it on the desk.

"Keep it; I don't need two weapons from here to El Ameur."

The revolver shone against the black paint of the table. When the gendarme turned toward him, the schoolmaster caught the smell of leather and horseflesh.

"Listen, Balducci," Daru said suddenly, "every bit of this disgusts me, and first of all your fellow here. But I won't hand him over. Fight, yes, if I have to. But not that."

The old gendarme stood in front of him and looked at him severely.

"You're being a fool," he said slowly. "I don't like it either. You don't get used to putting a rope on a man even after years of it, and you're even ashamed—yes, ashamed. But you can't let them have their way."

"I won't hand him over," Daru said again.

"It's an order, son, and I repeat it."

"That's right. Repeat to them what I've said to you: I won't hand him over."

Balducci made a visible effort to reflect. He looked at the Arab and at Daru. At last he decided.

"No, I won't tell them anything. If you want to drop us, go ahead; I'll not denounce you. I have an order to deliver the prisoner and I'm doing so. And now you'll just sign this paper for me."

"There's no need. I'll not deny that you left him with me."

"Don't be mean with me. I know you'll tell the truth. You're from hereabouts and you are a man. But you must sign, that's the rule."

Daru opened his drawer, took out a little square bottle of purple ink, the red wooden penholder with the "sergeant-major" pen he used for making models of penmanship, and signed. The gendarme carefully folded the paper and put it into his wallet. Then he moved toward the door.

"I'll see you off," Daru said.

"No," said Balducci. "There's no use being polite. You insulted me."

He looked at the Arab, motionless in the same spot, sniffed peevishly, and turned away toward the door. "Good-by, son," he said. The door shut behind him. Balducci appeared suddenly outside the window and then disappeared. His footsteps were muffled by the snow. The horse stirred on the other side of the wall and several chickens fluttered in fright. A moment later Balducci reappeared outside the window leading the horse by the bridle. He walked toward the little rise without turning around and disappeared from sight with the horse following him. A big stone could be heard bouncing down. Daru walked back toward the prisoner, who, without stirring, never took his eyes off him. "Wait," the schoolmaster said in Arabic and went toward the bedroom. As he was going through the door, he had a second thought, went to the desk, took the revolver, and stuck it in his pocket. Then, without looking back, he went into his room.

For some time he lay on his couch watching the sky gradually close over, listening to the silence. It was this silence that had seemed painful to him during the first days here, after the war. He had requested a post in the little town at the base of the foothills separating the upper plateaus from the desert. There, rocky walls, green and black to the north, pink and lavender to the south, marked the frontier of eternal summer. He had been named to a port farther north, on the plateau itself. In the beginning, the solitude and the silence had been hard for him on these wastelands peopled only by stones. Occasionally, furrows suggested cultivation, but they had been dug to uncover a certain kind of stone good for building. The only plowing here was to harvest rocks. Elsewhere a thin layer of soil accumulated in the hollows would be scraped out to enrich paltry village gardens. This is the way it was: bare rock covered three quarters of the region. Towns sprang up, flourished, then disappeared; men came by, loved one another or fought bitterly, then died. No one in this desert, neither he nor his guest, mattered. And yet, outside this desert neither of them, Daru knew, could have really lived.

When he got up, no noise came from the classroom. He was amazed at the unmixed joy he derived from the mere thought that the Arab might have fled and that he would be alone with no decision to make. But the prisoner was there. He had merely stretched out between the stove and the desk. With eyes open, he was staring at the ceiling. In that position, his thick lips were particularly noticeable, giving him a pouting look. "Come," said Daru. The Arab got up and followed him. In the bedroom, the schoolmaster pointed to a chair near the table under the window. The Arab sat down without taking his eyes off Daru.

"Are you hungry?"

"Yes," the prisoner said.

Daru set the table for two. He took flour and oil, shaped a cake in a frying-pan, and lighted the little stove that functioned on bottled gas. While the cake was cooking, he went out to the shed to get cheese, eggs, dates, and condensed milk. When the cake was done he set it on the window sill to cool, heated some condensed milk diluted with water, and beat up the eggs into an omelette. In one of his motions he knocked against the revolver stuck in his right pocket. He set the bowl down, went into the classroom, and put the revolver in his desk drawer. When he came back to the room, night was falling. He put on the light and served the Arab. "Eat," he said. The Arab took a piece of the cake, lifted it eagerly to his mouth, and stopped short.

"And you?" he asked.

"After you. I'll eat too."

The thick lips opened slightly. The Arab hesitated, then bit into the cake determinedly.

The meal over, the Arab looked at the schoolmaster. "Are you the judge?"

"No, I'm simply keeping you until tomorrow."

"Why do you eat with me?"

"I'm hungry."

The Arab fell silent. Daru got up and went out. He brought back a folding bed from the shed, set it up between the table and the stove, perpendicular to his own bed. From a large suitcase which, upright in a corner, served as a shelf for papers, he took two blankets and arranged them on the camp bed. Then he stopped, felt useless, and sat down on his bed. There was nothing more to do or to get ready. He had to look at this man. He looked at him, therefore, trying to imagine his face bursting with rage. He couldn't do so. He could see nothing but the dark yet shining eyes and the animal mouth.

"Why did you kill him?" he asked in a voice whose hostile tone surprised him.

The Arab looked away.

"He ran away. I ran after him."

He raised his eyes to Daru again and they were full of a sort of woeful interrogation. "Now what will they do to me?"

"Are you afraid?"

He stiffened, turning his eyes away.

"Are you sorry?"

The Arab stared at him openmouthed. Obviously he did not understand. Daru's annoyance was growing. At the same time he felt awkward and self-conscious with his big body wedged between the two beds.

"Lie down there," he said impatiently. "That's your bed."

The Arab didn't move. He called to Daru:

"Tell me!"

The schoolmaster looked at him.

"Is the gendarme coming back tomorrow?"

"I don't know."

"Are you coming with us?"

"I don't know. Why?"

The prisoner got up and stretched out on top of the blankets, his feet toward the window. The light from the electric bulb shone straight into his eyes and he closed them at once.

"Why?" Daru repeated, standing beside the bed.

The Arab opened his eyes under the blinding light and looked at him, trying not to blink.

"Come with us," he said.

In the middle of the night, Daru was still not asleep. He had gone to bed after undressing completely; he generally slept naked. But when he suddenly realized that he had nothing on, he hesitated. He felt vulnerable and the temptation came to him to put his clothes back on. Then he shrugged his shoulders; after all, he wasn't a child and, if need be, he could break his adversary in two. From his bed he could observe him, lying on his back, still motionless with his eyes closed under the harsh light. When Daru turned out the light, the darkness seemed to coagulate all of a sudden. Little by little, the night came back to life in the window where the starless sky was stirring gently. The schoolmaster soon made out the body lying at his feet. The Arab still did not move, but his eyes seemed open. A faint wind was prowling around the schoolhouse. Perhaps it would drive away the clouds and the sun would reappear.

During the night the wind increased. The hens fluttered a little and then were silent. The Arab turned over on his side with his back to Daru, who thought he heard him moan. Then he listened for his guest's breathing, become heavier and more regular. He listened to that breath so close to him and mused without being able to go to sleep. In this room where he had been sleeping alone for a year, this presence bothered him. But it bothered him also by imposing on him a sort of brotherhood he knew well but refused to accept in the present circumstances. Men who share the same rooms, soldiers or prisoners, develop a strange alliance as if, having cast off their armor with their clothing, they fraternized every evening, over and above their differences, in the ancient community of dream and fatigue. But Daru shook himself; he didn't like such musings, and it was essential to sleep.

A little later, however, when the Arab stirred slightly, the schoolmaster was still not asleep. When the prisoner made a second move, he stiffened, on the alert. The Arab was lifting himself slowly on his arms with almost the motion of a sleepwalker. Seated upright in bed, he waited motionless without turning his head toward Daru, as if he were listening attentively. Daru did not stir; it had just occurred to him that the revolver was still in the drawer of his desk. It was better to act at once. Yet he continued to observe the prisoner, who, with the same slithery motion, put his feet on the ground, waited again, then began to stand up slowly. Daru was about to call out to him when the Arab began to walk, in a quite natural but extraordinarily silent way. He was heading toward the door at the end of the room that opened into the shed. He lifted the latch with precaution and went out, pushing the door behind him but without shutting it. Daru had not stirred. "He is running away," he merely thought. "Good riddance!" Yet he listened attentively. The hens were not fluttering; the guest must be on the plateau. A faint sound of water reached him, and he didn't know what it was until the Arab again stood framed in the doorway, closed the door carefully, and came back to bed without a sound. Then Daru turned his back on him and fell asleep. Still later he seemed, from the depths of his sleep, to hear furtive steps around the schoolhouse. "I'm dreaming! I'm dreaming!" he repeated to himself. And he went on sleeping.

When he awoke, the sky was clear; the loose window let in a cold, pure air. The Arab was asleep, hunched up under the blankets now, his mouth open, utterly relaxed. But when Daru shook him, he started dreadfully, staring at Daru with wild eyes as if he had never seen him and such a frightened expression that the schoolmaster stepped back. "Don't be afraid. It's me. You must eat." The Arab nodded his head and said yes. Calm had returned to his face, but his expression was vacant and listless.

The coffee was ready. They drank it seated together on the folding bed as they munched their pieces of the cake. Then Daru led the Arab under the shed and showed him·the faucet where he washed. He went back into the room, folded the blankets and the bed, made his own bed and put the room in order. Then he went through the classroom and out onto the terrace. The sun was already rising in the blue sky; a soft, bright light was bathing the deserted plateau. On the ridge the snow was melting in spots. The stones were about to reappear. Crouched on the edge of the plateau, the schoolmaster looked at the deserted expanse. He thought of Balducci. He had hurt him, for he had sent him off in a way as if he didn't want to be associated with him. He could still hear the gendarme's farewell and, without knowing why, he felt strangely empty and vulnerable. At that moment, from the other side of the schoolhouse, the prisoner coughed. Daru listened to him almost despite himself and then, furious, threw a pebble that whistled through the air before sinking into the snow. That man's stupid crime revolted him, but to hand him over was contrary to honor. Merely thinking of it made him smart with humiliation. And he cursed at one and the same time his own people who had sent him this Arab and the Arab too who had dared to kill and not managed to get away. Daru got up, walked in a circle on the terrace, waited motionless, and then went back into the schoolhouse.

The Arab, leaning over the cement floor of the shed, was washing his teeth with two fingers. Daru looked at him and said: "Come." He went back into the room ahead of the prisoner. He slipped a hunting-jacket on over his sweater and put on walking-shoes. Standing, he waited until the Arab had put on his *chèche* and sandals. They went into the classroom and the schoolmaster pointed to the exit, saying: "Go ahead." The fellow didn't budge. "I'm coming," said Daru. The Arab went out. Daru went back into the room and made a package of pieces of rusk, dates, and sugar. In the classroom, before going out, he hesitated a second in front of his desk, then crossed the threshold and locked the door. "That's the way," he said. He started toward the east, followed by the prisoner. But, a short distance from the schoolhouse, he thought he heard a slight sound behind them. He retraced his steps and examined the surroundings of the house; there was no one there. The Arab watched him without seeming to understand. "Come on," said Daru.

They walked for an hour and rested beside a sharp peak of limestone. The snow was melting faster and faster and the sun was drinking up the puddles at once, rapidly cleaning the plateau, which gradually dried and vibrated like the air itself. When they resumed walking, the ground rang under their feet. From time to time a bird rent the space in front of them with a joyful cry. Daru breathed in deeply the fresh morning light. He felt a sort of rapture before the vast familiar expanse, now almost entirely yellow under its dome of blue sky. They walked an hour more, descending toward the south. They reached a level height made up of crumbly rocks. From there on, the plateau sloped down, eastward, toward a low plain where there were a few spindly trees and, to the south, toward outcroppings of rock that gave the landscape a chaotic look.

Daru surveyed the two directions. There was nothing but the sky on the horizon. Not a man could be seen. He turned toward the Arab, who was looking at him blankly. Daru held out the package to him. "Take it," he said. "There are dates, bread, and sugar. You can hold out for two days. Here are a thousand francs too." The Arab took the package and the money but kept his full hands at chest level as if he didn't know what to do with what was being given him. "Now look," the schoolmaster said as he pointed in the direction of the east, "there's the way to Tinguit. You have a two-hour walk. At Tinguit you'll find the administration and the police. They are expecting you." The Arab looked toward the east, still holding the package and the money against his chest. Daru took his elbow and turned him rather roughly toward the south. At the foot of the height on which they stood could be seen a faint path. "That's the trail across the plateau. In a day's walk from here you'll find pasturelands and the first nomads. They'll take you in and shelter you according to their law." The Arab had now turned toward Daru and a sort of panic was visible in his expression. "Listen," he said. Daru shook his head: "No, be quiet. Now I'm leaving you." He turned his back on him, took two long steps in the direction of the school, looked hesitantly at the motionless Arab, and started off again. For a few minutes he heard nothing but his own step resounding on the cold ground and did not turn his head. A moment later, however, he turned around. The Arab was still there on the edge of the hill, his arms hanging now, and he was looking at the schoolmaster. Daru felt something rise in his throat. But he swore with impatience, waved vaguely, and started off again. He had already gone some distance when he again stopped and looked. There was no longer anyone on the hill.

Daru hesitated. The sun was now rather high in the sky and was beginning to beat down on his head. The schoolmaster retraced his steps, at first somewhat uncertainly, then with decision. When he reached the little hill, he was bathed in sweat. He climbed it as fast as he could and stopped, out of breath, at the top. The rock-fields to the south stood out sharply against the blue sky, but on the plain to the east a steamy heat was already rising. And in that slight haze, Daru, with heavy heart, made out the Arab walking slowly on the road to prison.

A little later, standing before the window of the classroom, the schoolmaster was watching the clear light bathing the whole surface of the plateau, but he hardly saw it. Behind him on the blackboard, among the winding French rivers, sprawled the clumsily chalked-up words he had just read: "You handed over our brother. You will pay for this." Daru looked at the sky, the plateau, and, beyond, the invisible lands stretching all the way to the sea. In this vast landscape he had loved so much, he was alone.

Philip Roth

DEFENDER OF THE FAITH

In May of 1945, only a few weeks after the fighting had ended in Europe, I was rotated back to the States, where I spent the remainder of the war with a training company at Camp Crowder, Missouri. We had been racing across Germany so swiftly during the late winter and spring that when I boarded the plane that drizzly morning in Berlin, I couldn't believe our destination lay to the west. My mind might inform me otherwise, but there was an inertia of the spirit that told me we were flying to a new front where we would disembark and continue our push eastward—eastward until we'd circled the globe, marching through villages along whose twisting, cobbled streets crowds of the enemy would watch us take possession of what up till then they'd considered their own. I had changed enough in two years not to mind the trembling of the old people, the crying of the very young, the uncertain fear in the eyes of the once-arrogant. After two years I had been fortunate enough to develop an infantryman's heart which, like his feet, at first aches and swells, but finally grows horny enough for him to travel the weirdest paths without feeling a thing.

Captain Paul Barrett was to be my C. O. at Camp Crowder. The day I reported for duty he came out of his office to shake my hand. He was short, gruff, and fiery, and indoors or out he wore his polished helmet liner down on his little eyes. In Europe he had received a battlefield commission and a serious chest wound, and had been returned to the States only a few months before. He spoke easily to me, but was, I thought, unnecessarily abusive towards the troops. At the evening formation, he introduced me.

"Gentlemen," he called. "Sergeant Thurston, as you know, is no longer with this Company. Your new First Sergeant is Sergeant Nathan Marx here. He is a veteran of the European theater and consequently will take no shit."

I sat up late in the orderly room that evening, trying halfheartedly to solve the riddle of duty rosters, personnel forms, and morning reports. The CQ slept with his mouth open on a mattress on the floor. A trainee stood reading the next day's duty roster, which was posted on the bulletin board directly inside the screen door. It was a warm evening and I could hear the men's radios playing dance music over in the barracks.

The trainee, who I knew had been staring at me whenever I looked groggily into the forms, finally took a step in my direction.

"Hey, Sarge—we having a G.I. party tomorrow night?" A G.I. party is a barracks-cleaning.

"You usually have them on Friday nights?"

"Yes," and then he added mysteriously, "that's the whole thing."

"Then you'll have a G.I. party."

He turned away and I heard him mumbling. His shoulders were moving and I wondered if he was crying.

"What's your name, soldier?" I asked.

He turned, not crying at all. Instead his green-speckled eyes, long and narrow, flashed like fish in the sun. He walked over to me and sat on the edge of my desk.

He reached out a hand. "Sheldon," he said.

"Stand on your own two feet, Sheldon."

Climbing off the desk, he said, "Sheldon Grossbart." He smiled wider at the intimacy into which he'd led me.

"You against cleaning the barracks Friday night, Grossbart? Maybe we shouldn't have G.I. parties—maybe we should get a maid." My tone startled me: I felt like a Charlie McCarthy, with every top sergeant I had ever known as my Edgar Bergen.

"No, Sergeant." He grew serious, but with a seriousness that seemed only to be the stifling of a smile. "It's just G.I. parties on Friday night, of all nights . . ."

He slipped up to the corner of the desk again—not quite sitting, but not quite standing either. He looked at me with those speckled eyes flashing and then made a gesture with his hand. It was very slight, no more than a rotation back and forth of the wrist, and yet it managed to exclude from our affairs everything else in the orderly room, to make the two of us the center of the world. It seemed, in fact, to exclude everything about the two of us except our hearts. "Sergeant Thurston was one thing," he whispered, an eye flashing to the sleeping CQ, "but we thought with you here, things might be a little different."

"We?"

"The Jewish personnel."

"Why?" I said, harshly.

He hesitated a moment, and then, uncontrollably, his hand went up to his mouth. "I mean . . ." he said.

"What's on your mind?" Whether I was still angry at the "Sheldon" business or something else, I hadn't a chance to tell—but clearly I was angry.

". . . we thought you . . . Marx, you know, like Karl Marx. The Marx brothers. Those guys are all . . . M-A-R-X, isn't that how you spell it, Sergeant?"

"M-A-R-X."

"Fishbein said—" He stopped. "What I mean to say, Sergeant—" His face and neck were red, and his mouth moved but no words came out. In a moment, he raised himself to attention, gazing down at me. It was as though he had suddenly decided he could expect no more sympathy from me than from Thurston, the reason being that I was of Thurston's faith and not his. The young man had managed to confuse himself as to what my faith really was, but I felt no desire to straighten him out. Very simply, I didn't like him.

When I did nothing but return his gaze, he spoke, in an altered tone. "You see, Sergeant," he explained to me, "Friday nights, Jews are supposed to go to services."

"Did Sergeant Thurston tell you you couldn't go to them when there was a G.I. party?"

"No."

"Did he say you had to stay and scrub the floors?"

"No, Sergeant."

"Did the Captain say you had to stay and scrub the floors?"

"That isn't it, Sergeant. It's the other guys in the barracks." He leaned toward me. "They think we're goofing off. But we're not. That's when Jews go to services, Friday night. We have to."

"Then go."

"But the other guys make accusations. They have no right."

"That's not the Army's problem, Grossbart. It's a personal problem you'll have to work out yourself."

"But it's un*fair*."

I got up to leave. "There's nothing I can do about it," I said.

Grossbart stiffened in front of me. "But this is a matter of *religion,* sir."

"Sergeant."

"I mean 'Sergeant,'" he said, almost snarling.

"Look, go see the chaplain. The I.G. You want to see Captain Barrett, I'll arrange an appointment."

"No, no. I don't want to make trouble, Sergeant. That's the first thing they throw up to you. I just want my rights!"

"Damn it, Grossbart, stop whining. You have your rights. You can stay and scrub floors or you can go to *shul*—"

The smile swam in again. Spittle gleamed at the corners of his mouth. "You mean church, Sergeant."

"I mean *shul*, Grossbart!" I walked past him and outside. Near me I heard the scrunching of a guard's boots on gravel. In the lighted windows of the barracks the young men in T-shirts and fatigue pants were sitting on their bunks, polishing their rifles. Suddenly there was a light rustling behind me. I turned and saw Grossbart's dark frame fleeing back to the barracks, racing to tell his Jewish friends that they were right—that like Karl and Harpo, I was one of them.

The next morning, while chatting with the Captain, I recounted the incident of the previous evening, as if to unburden myself of it. Somehow in the telling it seemed to the Captain that I was not so much explaining Grossbart's position as defending it.

"Marx, I'd fight side by side with a nigger if the fellow proved to me he was a man. I pride myself," the Captain said looking out the window, "that I've got an open mind. Consequently, Sergeant, nobody gets special treatment here, for the good *or* the bad. All a man's got to do is prove himself. A man fires well on the range, I give him a weekend pass. He scores high in PT, he gets a weekend pass. He *earns* it." He turned from the window and pointed a finger at me. "You're a Jewish fellow, am I right, Marx?"

"Yes, sir."

"And I admire you. I admire you because of the ribbons on your chest, not because you had a hem stitched on your dick before you were old enough to even know you had one. I judge a man by what he shows me on the field of battle, Sergeant. It's what he's got *here*," he said, and then, though I expected he would point to his heart, he jerked a thumb towards the buttons straining to hold his blouse across his belly. "Guts," he said.

"Okay, sir, I only wanted to pass on to you how the men felt."

"Mr. Marx, you're going to be old before your time if you worry about how the men feel. Leave that stuff to the Chaplain—pussy, the clap, church picnics with the little girls from Joplin, that's all his business, not yours. Let's us train these fellas to shoot straight. If the Jewish personnel feels the other men are accusing them of goldbricking . . . well, I just don't know. Seems awful funny how suddenly the Lord is calling so loud in Private Grossman's ear he's just got to run to church."

"Synagogue," I said.

"Synagogue is right, Sergeant. I'll write that down for handy reference. Thank you for stopping by."

That evening, a few minutes before the company gathered outside the orderly room for the chow formation, I called the CQ, Corporal Robert LaHill, in to see me. LaHill was a dark burly fellow whose hair curled out of his clothes wherever it could. He carried a glaze in his eyes that made one think of caves and dinosaurs. "LaHill," I said, "when you take the formation, remind the men that they're free to attend church services *whenever* they are held, provided they report to the orderly room before they leave the area."

LaHill didn't flicker; he scratched his wrist, but gave no indication that he'd heard or understood.

"LaHill," I said, "*church.* You remember? Church, priest, Mass, confession . . ."

He curled one lip into a ghastly smile; I took it for a signal that for a second he had flickered back up into the human race.

"Jewish personnel who want to attend services this evening are to fall out in front of the orderly room at 1900." And then I added, "By order of Captain Barrett."

A little while later, as a twilight softer than any I had seen that year dropped over Camp Crowder, I heard LaHill's thick, inflectionless voice outside my window: "Give me your ears, troopers. Toppie says for me to tell you that at 1900 hours all Jewish personnel is to fall out in front here if they wants to attend the Jewish Mass."

At seven o'clock, I looked out of the orderly-room window and saw three soldiers in starched khakis standing alone on the dusty quadrangle. They looked at their watches and fidgeted while they whispered back and forth. It was getting darker, and alone on the deserted field they looked tiny. When I walked to the door I heard the noises of the G.I. party coming from the surrounding barracks—bunks being pushed to the wall, faucets pounding water into buckets, brooms whisking at the wooden floors. In the windows big puffs of cloth moved round and round, cleaning the dirt away for Saturday's inspection. I walked outside and the moment my foot hit the ground I thought I heard Grossbart, who was now in the center, call to the other two, "Ten-*hut!*" Or maybe when they all three jumped to attention, I imagined I heard the command.

At my approach, Grossbart stepped forward. "Thank you, sir," he said.

"Sergeant, Grossbart," I reminded him. "You call officers 'Sir.' I'm not an officer. You've been in the Army three weeks—you know that."

He turned his palms out at his sides to indicate that, in truth, he and I lived beyond convention. "Thank you, anyway," he said.

"Yes," the tall boy behind him said. "Thanks a lot."

And the third whispered, "Thank you," but his mouth barely fluttered so that he did not alter by more than a lip's movement, the posture of attention.

"For what?" I said.

Grossbart snorted, happily. "For the announcement before. The Corporal's announcement. It helped. It made it . . ."

"Fancier." It was the tall boy finishing Grossbart's sentence.

Grossbart smiled. "He means formal, sir. Public," he said to me. "Now it won't seem as though we're just taking off, goldbricking, because the work has begun."

"It was by order of Captain Barrett," I said.

"Ahh, but you pull a little weight . . ." Grossbart said. "So we thank you." Then he turned to his companions. "Sergeant Marx, I want you to meet Larry Fishbein."

The tall boy stepped forward and extended his hand. I shook it. "You from New York?" he asked.

"Yes."

"Me too." He had a cadaverous face that collapsed inward from his cheekbone to his jaw, and when he smiled—as he did at the news of our communal attachment—revealed a mouthful of bad teeth. He blinked his eyes a good deal, as though he were fighting back tears. "What borough?" he asked.

I turned to Grossbart. "It's five after seven. What time are services?"

"*Shul,*" he smiled, "is in ten minutes. I want you to meet Mickey Halpern. This is Nathan Marx, our Sergeant."

The third boy hopped forward. "Private Michael Halpern." He saluted.

"Salute officers, Halpern." The boy dropped his hand, and in his nervousness checked to see if his shirt pockets were buttoned on the way down.

"Shall I march them over, sir?" Grossbart asked, "or are you coming along?"

From behind Grossbart, Fishbein piped up. "Afterwards they're having refreshments. A Ladies' Auxiliary from St. Louis, the rabbi told us last week."

"The chaplain," whispered Halpern.

"You're welcome to come along," Grossbart said.

To avoid his plea, I looked away, and saw, in the windows of the barracks, a cloud of faces staring out at the four of us.

"Look, hurry out of here, Grossbart."

"Okay, then," he said. He turned to the others. "Double time, *march!*" and they started off, but ten feet away Grossbart spun about, and running backwards he called to me, "Good *shabus,* sir." And then the three were swallowed into the Missouri dusk.

Even after they'd disappeared over the parade grounds, whose green was now a deep twilight blue, I could hear Grossbart singing the double-time cadence, and as it grew dimmer and dimmer it suddenly touched some deep memory—as did the slant of light—and I was remembering the shrill sounds of a Bronx playground, where years ago, beside the Grand Concourse, I had played on long spring evenings such as this. Those thin fading sounds . . . It was a pleasant memory for a young man so far from peace and home, and it brought so very many recollections with it that I began to grow exceedingly tender about myself. In fact, I indulged myself to a reverie so strong that I felt within as though a hand had opened and was reaching down inside. It had to reach so very far to touch me. It had to reach past those days in the forests of Belgium and the dying I'd refused to weep over; past the nights in those German farmhouses whose books we'd burned to warm us, and which I couldn't bother to mourn; past those endless stretches when I'd shut off all softness I might feel for my fellows, and managed even to deny myself the posture of a conqueror—the swagger that I, as a Jew, might well have worn as my boots whacked against the rubble of Münster, Braunschweig, and finally Berlin.

But now one night noise, one rumor of home and time past, and memory plunged down through all I had anesthetized and came to what I suddenly remembered to be myself. So it was not altogether curious that in search of more of me I found myself following Grossbart's tracks to Chapel No. 3 where the Jewish services were being held.

I took a seat in the last row, which was empty. Two rows in front sat Grossbart, Fishbein, and Halpern, each holding a little white dixie cup. Fishbein was pouring the contents of his cup into Grossbart's, and Grossbart looked mirthful as the liquid drew a purple arc between his hand and Fishbein's. In the glary yellow light, I saw the chaplain on the pulpit chanting the first line of the responsive reading. Grossbart's prayerbook remained closed on his lap; he swished the cup around. Only Halpern responded in prayer. The fingers of his right hand were spread wide across the cover of the book, and his cap was pulled down low onto his brow so that it was round like a *yarmulke* rather than long and pointed. From time to time, Grossbart wet his lips at the cup's edge; Fishbein, his long yellow face, a dying light bulb, looked from here to there, leaning forward at the neck to catch sight of the faces down the row, in front—then behind. He saw me and his eyelids beat a tattoo. His elbow slid into Grossbart's side, his neck inclined towards his friend, and then, when the congregation responded, Grossbart's voice was among them. Fishbein looked into his book now too; his lips, however, didn't move.

Finally it was time to drink the wine. The chaplain smiled down at them as Grossbart swigged in one long gulp, Halpern sipped, meditating, and Fishbein faked devotion with an empty cup.

At last the chaplain spoke: "As I look down amongst the congregation—" he grinned at the word, "this night, I see many new faces, and I want to welcome you to Friday night services here at Camp Crowder. I am Major Leo Ben Ezra, your chaplain . . ." Though an American, the chaplain spoke English very deliberately, syllabically almost, as though to communicate, above all, to the lip-readers in the audience. "I have only a few words to say before we adjourn to the refreshment room where the kind ladies of the Temple Sinai, St. Louis, Missouri, have a nice setting for you."

Applause and whistling broke out. After a momentary grin, the chaplain raised his palms to the congregation, his eyes flicking upward a moment, as if to remind the troops where they were and Who Else might be in attendance. In the sudden silence that followed, I thought I heard Grossbart's cackle—"Let the goyim clean the floors!" Were those the words? I wasn't sure, but Fishbein, grinning, nudged Halpern. Halpern looked dumbly at him, then went back to his prayerbook, which had been occupying him all through the rabbi's talk. One hand tugged at the black kinky hair that stuck out under his cap. His lips moved.

The rabbi continued. "It is about the food that I want to speak to you for a moment. I know, I know, I know," he intoned, wearily, "how in the mouths of most of you the *trafe* food tastes like ashes. I know how you gag, some of you, and how your parents suffer to think of their children eating foods unclean and offensive to the palate. What can I tell you? I can only say close your eyes and swallow as best you can. Eat what you must to live and throw away the rest. I wish I could help more. For those of you who find this impossible, may I ask that you try and try, but then come to see me in private where, if your revulsion is such, we will have to seek aid from those higher up."

A round of chatter rose and subsided; then everyone sang "Ain Kelohanoh"; after all those years I discovered I still knew the words.

Suddenly, the service over, Grossbart was upon me. "Higher up? He means the General?"

"Hey, Shelly," Fishbein interrupted, "he means God." He smacked his face and looked at Halpern. "How high can you go!"

"Shhh!" Grossbart said. "What do you think, Sergeant?"

"I don't know. You better ask the chaplain."

"I'm going to. I'm making an appointment to see him in private.

So is Mickey."

Halpern shook his head. "No, no, Sheldon . . ."

"You have rights, Mickey. They can't push us around."

"It's okay. It bothers my mother, not me . . ."

Grossbart looked at me. "Yesterday he threw up. From the hash. It was all ham and God knows what else."

"I have a cold—that was why," Halpern said. He pushed his *yamalkah* back into a cap.

"What about you, Fishbein?" I asked. "You kosher too?"

He flushed, which made the yellow more gray than pink. "A little. But I'll let it ride. I have a very strong stomach. And I don't eat a lot anyway . . ." I continued to look at him, and he held up his wrist to re-enforce what he'd just said. His watch was tightened to the last hole and he pointed that out to me. "So I don't mind."

"But services are important to you?" I asked him.

He looked at Grossbart. "Sure, sir."

"Sergeant."

"Not so much at home," said Grossbart, coming between us, "but away from home it gives one a sense of his Jewishness."

"We have to stick together," Fishbein said.

I started to walk towards the door; Halpern stepped back to make way for me.

"That's what happened in Germany," Grossbart was saying, loud enough for me to hear. "They didn't stick together. They let themselves get pushed around."

I turned. "Look, Grossbart, this is the Army, not summer camp."

He smiled. "So?" Halpern tried to sneak off, but Grossbart held his arm. "So?" he said again.

"Grossbart," I asked, "how old are you?"

"Nineteen."

"And you?" I said to Fishbein.

"The same. The same month even."

"And what about him?" I pointed to Halpern, who'd finally made it safely to the door.

"Eighteen," Grossbart whispered. "But he's like he can't tie his shoes or brush his teeth himself. I feel sorry for him."

"I feel sorry for all of us, Grossbart, but just act like a man. Just don't overdo it."

"Overdo what, sir?"

"The sir business. Don't overdo that," I said, and I left him standing there. I passed by Halpern but he did not look up. Then I was outside, black surrounded me—but behind I heard Grossbart call, "Hey, Mickey, *liebschen*, come on back. Refreshments!"

Liebschen! My grandmother's word for me!

One morning, a week later, while I was working at my desk, Captain Barrett shouted for me to come into his office. When I entered, he had his helmet liner squashed down so that I couldn't even see his eyes. He was on the phone, and when he spoke to me, he cupped one hand over the mouthpiece.

"Who the fuck is Grossbart?"

"Third platoon, Captain," I said. "A trainee."

"What's all this stink about food? His mother called a goddam congressman about the food . . ." He uncovered the mouthpiece and slid his helmet up so I could see the curl of his bottom eyelash. "Yes, sir," he said into the phone. "Yes, sir. I'm still here, sir. I'm asking Marx here right now . . ."

He covered the mouthpiece again and looked back to me. "Lightfoot Harry's on the phone," he said, between his teeth. "This congressman calls General Lyman who calls Colonel Sousa who calls the Major who calls me. They're just dying to stick this thing on me. What's a matter," he shook the phone at me, "I don't feed the troops? What the hell is this?"

"Sir, Grossbart is strange . . ." Barrett greeted that with a mockingly indulgent smile. I altered my approach. "Captain, he's a very orthodox Jew and so he's only allowed to eat certain foods."

"He throws up, the congressman said. Every time he eats something his mother says he throws up!"

"He's accustomed to observing the dietary laws, Captain."

"So why's his old lady have to call the White House!"

"Jewish parents, sir, they're apt to be more protective than you expect. I mean Jews have a very close family life. A boy goes away from home, sometimes the mother is liable to get very upset. Probably the boy *mentioned* something in a letter and his mother misinterpreted."

"I'd like to punch him one right in the mouth. There's a goddam war on and he wants a silver platter!"

"I don't think the boy's to blame, sir. I'm sure we can straighten it out by just asking him. Jewish parents worry—"

"*All* parents worry, for Christ sake. But they don't get on their high horse and start pulling strings—"

I interrupted, my voice higher, tighter than before. "The home life, Captain, is so very important . . . but you're right, it may sometimes get out of hand. It's a very wonderful thing, Captain, but because it's so close, this kind of thing—"

He didn't listen any longer to my attempt to present both myself and Lightfoot Harry with an explanation for the letter. He turned back to the phone. "Sir?" he said. "Sir, Marx here tells me Jews have a tendency to be pushy. He says he thinks he can settle it right here in the Company . . . Yes, sir . . . I *will* call back, sir, soon as I can . . ." He hung up. "Where are the men, Sergeant?"

"On the range."

With a whack on the top, he crushed his helmet over his eyes, and charged out of his chair. "We're going for a ride."

The Captain drove and I sat beside him. It was a hot spring day and under my newly starched fatigues it felt as though my armpits were melting down onto my sides and chest. The roads were dry and by the time we reached the firing range, my teeth felt gritty with dust though my mouth had been shut the whole trip. The Captain slammed the brakes on and told me to get the hell out and find Grossbart.

I found him on his belly, firing wildly at the 500 feet target. Waiting their turns behind him were Halpern and Fishbein. Fishbein, wearing a pair of rimless G.I. glasses I hadn't seen on him before, gave the appearance of an old peddler who would gladly have sold you the rifle and cartridges that were slung all over him. I stood back by the ammo boxes, waiting for Grossbart to finish spraying the distant targets. Fishbein straggled back to stand near me.

"Hello, Sergeant Marx."

"How are you?" I mumbled.

"Fine, thank you, Sheldon's really a good shot."

"I didn't notice."

"I'm not so good, but I think I'm getting the hang of it now . . . Sergeant, I don't mean to, you know, ask what I shouldn't . . ." The boy stopped. He was trying to speak intimately but the noise of the shooting necessitated that he shout at me.

"What is it?" I asked. Down the range I saw Captain Barrett standing up in the jeep, scanning the line for me and Grossbart.

"My parents keep asking and asking where we're going. Everybody says the Pacific. I don't care, but my parents . . . If I could relieve their minds I think I could concentrate more on my shooting."

"I don't know where, Fishbein. Try to concentrate anyway."

"Sheldon says you might be able to find out—"

"I don't know a thing, Fishbein. You just take it easy, and don't let Sheldon—"

"*I'm* taking it easy, Sergeant. It's at home—"

Grossbart had just finished on the line and was dusting his fatigues with one hand. I left Fishbein's sentence in the middle.

"Grossbart, the Captain wants to see you."

He came toward us. His eyes blazed and twinkled. "Hi!"

"Don't point that goddam rifle!"

"I wouldn't shoot you, Sarge." He gave me a smile wide as a pumpkin as he turned the barrel aside.

"Damn you, Grossbart—this is no joke! Follow me."

I walked ahead of him and had the awful suspicion that behind me Grossbart was *marching*, his rifle on his shoulder, as though he were a one-man detachment.

At the jeep he gave the Captain a rifle salute. "Private Sheldon Grossbart, sir."

"At ease, Grossman." The captain slid over to the empty front seat, and crooking a finger, invited Grossbart closer.

"Bart, sir. Sheldon Gross*bart*. It's a common error." Grossbart nodded to me—*I* understand, he indicated. I looked away, just as the mess truck pulled up to the range, disgorging a half dozen K.P.'s with rolled-up sleeves. The mess sergeant screamed at them while they set up the chow line equipment.

"Grossbart, your mama wrote some congressman that we don't feed you right. Do you know that?" the Captain said.

"It was my father, sir. He wrote to Representative Franconi that my religion forbids me to eat certain foods."

"What religion is that, Grossbart?"

"Jewish."

"Jewish, *sir,*" I said to Grossbart.

"Excuse me, sir. 'Jewish, sir.'"

"What have you been living on?" the Captain asked. "You've been in the Army a month already. You don't look to me like you're falling to pieces."

"I eat because I have to, sir. But Sergeant Marx will testify to the fact that I don't eat one mouthful more than I need to in order to survive."

"Marx," Barrett asked, "is that so?"

"I've never seen Grossbart eat, sir," I said.

"But you heard the rabbi," Grossbart said. "He told us what to do, and I listened."

The Captain looked at me. "Well, Marx?"

"I still don't know what he eats and doesn't eat, sir."

Grossbart raised his rifle, as though to offer it to me. "But, Sergeant—"

"Look, Grossbart, just answer the Captain's questions!" I said sharply.

Barrett smiled at me and I resented it. "All right, Grossbart," he said, "What is it you want? The little piece of paper? You want out?"

"No, sir. Only to be allowed to live as a Jew. And for the others, too."

"What others?"

"Fishbein, sir, and Halpern."

"They don't like the way we serve either?"

"Halpern throws up, sir. I've seen it."

"I thought *you* throw up."

"Just once, sir. I didn't know the sausage was sausage."

"We'll give menus, Grossbart. We'll show training films about the food, so you can identify when we're trying to poison you."

Grossbart did not answer. Out before me, the men had been organized into two long chow lines. At the tail end of one I spotted Fishbein—or rather, his glasses spotted me. They winked sunlight back at me like a friend. Halpern stood next to him, patting inside his collar with a khaki handkerchief. They moved with the line as it began to edge up towards the food. The mess sergeant was still screaming at the K.P.'s, who stood ready to ladle out the food, bewildered. For a moment I was actually terrorized by the thought that somehow the mess sergeant was going to get involved in Grossbart's problem.

"Come over here, Marx," the Captain said to me. "Marx, you're a Jewish fella, am I right?"

I played straight man. "Yes, sir."

"How long you been in the Army? Tell this boy."

"Three years and two months."

"A year in combat, Grossbart. Twelve goddam months in combat all through Europe. I admire this man," the Captain said, snapping a wrist against my chest. "But do you hear him peeping about the food? Do you? I want an answer, Grossbart. Yes or no."

"No, sir."

"And why not? He's a Jewish fella."

"Some things are more important to some Jews than other things to other Jews."

Barrett blew up. "Look, Grossbart, Marx here is a good man, a goddam *hero*. When you were sitting on your sweet ass in high school, Sergeant Marx was killing Germans. Who does more for the Jews, you by throwing up over a lousy piece of sausage, a piece of firstcut meat—or Marx by killing those Nazi bastards? If I was a Jew, Grossbart, I'd kiss this man's feet. He's a goddam hero, you know that? And *he* eats what we give him. Why do you have to cause trouble is what I want to know! What is it you're buckin' for, a discharge?"

"No, sir."

"I'm talking to a *wall!* Sergeant, get him out of my way." Barrett pounced over to the driver's seat. "I'm going to see the chaplain!" The engine roared, the jeep spun around, and then, raising a whirl of dust, the Captain was headed back to camp.

For a moment, Grossbart and I stood side by side, watching the jeep. Then he looked at me and said, "I don't want to start trouble. That's the first thing they toss up to us."

When he spoke I saw that his teeth were white and straight, and the sight of them suddenly made me understand that Grossbart actually did have parents: that once upon a time someone had taken little Sheldon to the dentist. He was someone's son. Despite all the talk about his parents, it was hard to believe in Grossbart as a child, an heir—as related by blood to anyone, mother, father, or, above all, to me. This realization led me to another.

"What does your father do, Grossbart?" I asked, as we started to walk back towards the chow line.

"He's a tailor."

"An American?"

"Now, yes. A son in the Army," he said, jokingly.

"And your mother?" I asked.

He winked. "A *ballabusta*—she practically sleeps with a dustcloth in her hand."

"She's also an immigrant?"

"All she talks is Yiddish, still."

"And your father too?"

"A little English. 'Clean,' 'Press,' 'Take the pants in . . .' That's the extent of it. But they're good to me . . ."

"Then, Grossbart—" I reached out and stopped him. He turned towards me and when our eyes met his seemed to jump back, shiver in their sockets. He looked afraid. "Grossbart, then you were the one who wrote that letter, weren't you?"

It took only a second or two for his eyes to flash happy again. "Yes." He walked on, and I kept pace. "It's what my father *would* have written if he had known how. It was his name, though. *He* signed it. He even mailed it. I sent it home. For the New York postmark."

I was astonished, and he saw it. With complete seriousness, he thrust his right arm in front of me. "Blood is blood, Sergeant," he said, pinching the blue vein in his wrist.

"What the hell *are* you trying to do, Grossbart? I've seen you eat. Do you know that? I told the Captain I don't know what you eat, but I've seen you eat like a hound at chow."

"We work hard, Sergeant. We're in training. For a furnace to work, you've got to feed it coal."

"If you wrote the letter, Grossbart, then why did you say you threw up all the time?"

"I was really talking about Mickey there. But he would never write, Sergeant, though I pleaded with him. He'll waste away to nothing if I don't help. Sergeant, I used my name, my father's name, but it's Mickey and Fishbein too I'm watching out for."

"You're a regular Messiah, aren't you?"

We were at the chow line now.

"That's a good one, Sergeant." He smiled. "But who knows? Who can tell? Maybe you're the Messiah . . . a little bit. What Mickey says is the Messiah is a collective idea. He went to Yeshivah, Mickey, for a while. He says *together* we're the Messiah. Me a little bit, you a little bit . . . You should hear that kid talk, Sergeant, when he gets going."

"Me a little bit, you a little bit. You'd like to believe that, wouldn't you, Grossbart? That makes everything so clean for you."

"It doesn't seem too bad a thing to believe, Sergeant. It only means we should all give a little, is all . . ."

I walked off to eat my rations with the other noncoms.

Two days later a letter addressed to Captain Barrett passed over my desk. It had come through the chain of command—from the office of Congressman Franconi, where it had been received, to General Lyman, to Colonel Sousa, to Major Lamont, to Captain Barrett. I read it over twice while the Captain was at the officers' mess. It was dated May 14th, the day Barrett had spoken with Grossbart on the rifle range.

Dear Congressman:

First let me thank you for your interest in behalf of my son, Private Sheldon Grossbart. Fortunately, I was able to speak with Sheldon on the phone the other night, and I think I've been able to solve our problem. He is, as I mentioned in my last letter, a very religious boy, and it was only with the greatest difficulty that I could persuade him that the religious thing to do—what God Himself would want Sheldon to do—would be to suffer the pangs of religious remorse for the good of his country and all mankind. It took some doing, Congressman, but finally he saw the light. In fact, what he said (and I wrote down the words on a scratch pad so as never to forget), what he said was, "I guess you're right, Dad. So many millions of my fellow Jews gave up their lives to the enemy, the least I can do is live for a while minus a bit of my heritage so as to help end this struggle and regain for all the children of God dignity and humanity." That, Congressman, would make any father proud.

By the way, Sheldon wanted me to know—and to pass on to you—the name of a soldier who helped him reach this decision: SERGEANT NATHAN MARX. Sergeant Marx is a combat veteran who is Sheldon's First Sergeant. This man has helped Sheldon over some of the first hurdles he's had to face in the Army, and is in part responsible for Sheldon's changing his mind about the dietary laws. I know Sheldon would appreciate any recognition Marx could receive.

Thank you and good luck. I look forward to seeing your name on the next election ballot.

Respectfully,
SAMUEL E. GROSSBART

Attached to the Grossbart communiqué was a communiqué addressed to General Marshall Lyman, the post commander, and signed by Representative Charles E. Franconi of the House of Representatives. The communiqué informed General Lyman that Sergeant Nathan Marx was a credit to the U.S. Army and the Jewish people.

What was Grossbart's motive in recanting? Did he feel he'd gone too far? Was the letter a strategic retreat—a crafty attempt to strengthen what he considered our alliance? Or had he actually changed his mind, via an imaginary dialogue between Grossbart *père* and *fils*? I was puzzled, but only for a few days—that is, only until I realized that whatever his reasons, he had actually decided to disappear from my life: he was going to allow himself to become just another trainee. I saw him at inspection but he never winked; at chow formations but he never flashed me a sign; on Sundays, with the other trainees, he would sit around watching the noncoms' softball team, for whom I pitched, but not once did he speak an unnecessary or unusual word to me. Fishbein and Halpern retreated from sight too, at Grossbart's command I was sure. Apparently he'd seen that wisdom lay in turning back before he plunged us over into the ugliness of privilege undeserved. Our separation allowed me to forgive him our past encounters, and, finally, to admire him for his good sense.

Meanwhile, free of Grossbart, I grew used to my job and my administrative tasks. I stepped on a scale one day and discovered I had truly become a noncombatant: I had gained seven pounds. I found patience to get past the first three pages of a book. I thought about the future more and more, and wrote letters to girls I'd known before the war—I even got a few answers. I sent away to Columbia for a Law School catalogue. I continued to follow the war in the Pacific, but it was not my war and I read of bombings and battles like a civilian. I thought I could see the end in sight and sometimes at night I dreamed that I was walking on streets of Manhattan—Broadway, Third Avenue, and 116th Street, where I had lived those three years I'd attended Columbia College. I curled myself around these dreams and I began to be happy.

And then one Saturday when everyone was away and I was alone in the orderly room reading a month-old copy of *The Sporting News*, Grossbart reappeared.

"You a baseball fan, Sergeant?"

I looked up. "How are you?"

"Fine," Grossbart said. "They're making a soldier out of me."

"How are Fishbein and Halpern?"

"Coming along," he said. "We've got no training this afternoon. They're at the movies."

"How come you're not with them?"

"I wanted to come over and say hello."

He smiled—a shy, regular-guy smile, as though he and I well knew that our friendship drew its sustenance from unexpected visits, remembered birthdays, and borrowed lawnmowers. At first it offended me, and then the feeling was swallowed by the general uneasiness I felt at the thought that everyone on the post was locked away in a dark movie theater and I was here alone with Grossbart. I folded my paper.

"Sergeant," he said, "I'd like to ask a favor. It is a favor and I'm making no bones about it."

He stopped, allowing me to refuse him a hearing—which, of course, forced me into a courtesy I did not intend. "Go ahead."

"Well, actually it's two favors."

I said nothing.

"The first one's about these rumors. Everybody says we're going to the Pacific."

"As I told your friend Fishbein, I don't know. You'll just have to wait to find out. Like everybody else."

"You think there's a chance of any of us going East?"

"Germany," I said, "maybe."

"I meant New York."

"I don't think so, Grossbart. Offhand."

"Thanks for the information, Sergeant," he said.

"It's not information, Grossbart. Just what I surmise."

"It certainly would be good to be near home. My parents . . . you know." He took a step towards the door and then turned back. "Oh the other thing. May I ask the other?"

"What is it?"

"The other thing is—I've got relatives in St. Louis and they say they'll give me a whole Passover dinner if I can get down there. God, Sergeant, that'd mean an awful lot to me."

I stood up. "No passes during basic, Grossbart."

"But we're off from now till Monday morning, Sergeant. I could leave the post and no one would even know."

"I'd know. You'd know."

"But that's all. Just the two of us. Last night I called my aunt and you should have heard her. 'Come, come,' she said. 'I got gefilte fish, *chrain,* the works!' Just a day, Sergeant, I'd take the blame if anything happened."

"The captain isn't here to sign a pass."

"You could sign."

"Look, Grossbart—"

"Sergeant, for two months practically I've been eating *trafe* till I want to die."

"I thought you'd made up your mind to live with it. To be minus a little bit of heritage."

He pointed a finger at me. "You!" he said. "That wasn't for you to read!"

"I read it. So what."

"That letter was addressed to a congressman."

"Grossbart, don't feed me any crap. You *wanted* me to read it."

"Why are you persecuting me, Sergeant?"

"Are you kidding!"

"I've run into this before," he said, "but never from my own!"

"Get out of here, Grossbart! Get the hell out of my sight!"

He did not move. "Ashamed, that's what you are. So you take it out on the rest of us. They say Hitler himself was half a Jew. Seeing this, I wouldn't doubt it!"

"What are you trying to do with me, Grossbart? What are you after? You want me to give you special privileges, to change the food, to find out about your orders, to give you weekend passes."

"You even talk like a goy!" Grossbart shook his fist. "Is this a weekend pass I'm asking for? Is a Seder sacred or not?"

Seder! It suddenly occurred to me that Passover had been celebrated weeks before. I confronted Grossbart with the fact.

"That's right," he said. "Who says no? A month ago, and *I* was in the field eating hash! And now all I ask is a simple favor—a Jewish boy I thought would understand. My aunt's willing to go out of her way—to make a Seder a month later—" He turned to go, mumbling.

"Come back here!" I called. He stopped and looked at me. "Grossbart, why can't you be like the rest? Why do you have to stick out like a sore thumb? Why do you beg for special treatment?"

"Because I'm a Jew, Sergeant. I *am* different. Better, maybe not. But different."

"This is a war, Grossbart. For the time being *be* the same."

"I refuse."

"What?"

"I refuse. I can't stop being me, that's all there is to it." Tears came to his eyes. "It's a hard thing to be a Jew. But now I see what Mickey says—it's a harder thing to stay one." He raised a hand sadly toward me. "Look at you."

"Stop crying!"

"Stop this, stop that, stop the other thing! You stop, Sergeant. Stop closing your heart to your own!" And wiping his face with his sleeve, he ran out the door. "The least we can do for one another . . . the least . . ."

An hour later I saw Grossbart headed across the field. He wore a pair of starched khakis and carried only a little leather ditty bag. I went to the door and from the outside felt the heat of the day. It was quiet—not a soul in sight except over by the mess hall four K.P.'s sitting round a pan, sloped forward from the waists, gabbing and peeling potatoes in the sun.

"Grossbart!" I called.

He looked toward me and continued walking.

"Grossbart, get over here!"

He turned and stepped into his long shadow. Finally he stood before me.

"Where are you going?" I said.

"St. Louis. I don't care."

"You'll get caught without a pass."

"So I'll get caught without a pass."

"You'll go to the stockade."

"I'm in the stockade." He made an about-face and headed off.

I let him go only a step: "Come back here," I said, and he followed me into the office, where I typed out a pass and signed the Captain's name and my own initials after it.

He took the pass from me and then, a moment later, he reached out and grabbed my hand. "Sergeant, you don't know how much this means to me."

"Okay. Don't get in any trouble."

"I wish I could show you how much this means to me."

"Don't do me any favors. Don't write any more congressmen for citations."

Amazingly, he smiled. "You're right. I won't. But let me do something."

"Bring me a piece of that gefilte fish. Just get out of here."

"I will! With a slice of carrot and a little horseradish. I won't forget."

"All right. Just show your pass at the gate. And don't tell *anybody*."

"I won't. It's a month late, but a good Yom Tov to you."

"Good Yom Tov, Grossbart," I said.

"You're a good Jew, Sergeant. You like to think you have a hard heart, but underneath you're a fine decent man. I mean that."

Those last three words touched me more than any words from Grossbart's mouth had the right to. "All right, Grossbart. Now call me 'sir' and get the hell out of here."

He ran out the door and was gone. I felt very pleased with myself—it was a great relief to stop fighting Grossbart. And it had cost me nothing. Barrett would never find out, and if he did, I could manage to invent some excuse. For a while I sat at my desk, comfortable in my decision. Then the screen door flew back and Grossbart burst in again. "Sergeant!" he said. Behind him I saw Fishbein and Halpern, both in starched khakis, both carrying ditty bags exactly like Grossbart's.

"Sergeant, I caught Mickey and Larry coming out of the movies. I almost missed them."

"Grossbart, did I say tell no one?"

"But my aunt said I could bring friends. That I should, in fact."

"I'm the Sergeant, Grossbart—not your aunt!"

Grossbart looked at me in disbelief; he pulled Halpern up by his sleeve. "Mickey, tell the Sergeant what this would mean to you."

"Grossbart, for God's sake, spare us—"

"Tell him what you told me, Mickey. How much it would mean."

Halpern looked at me and, shrugging his shoulders, made his admission. "A lot."

Fishbein stepped forward without prompting. "This would mean a great deal to me and my parents, Sergeant Marx."

"No!" I shouted.

Grossbart was shaking his head. "Sergeant, I could see you denying me, but how you can deny Mickey, a Yeshivah boy, that's beyond me."

"I'm not denying Mickey anything. You just pushed a little too hard, Grossbart. *You* denied him."

"I'll give him my pass, then," Grossbart said. "I'll give him my aunt's address and a little note. At least let him go."

In a second he had crammed the pass into Halpern's pants' pocket. Halpern looked at me, Fishbein too. Grossbart was at the door, pushing it open. "Mickey, bring me a piece of gefilte fish at least." And then he was outside again.

The three of us looked at one another and then I said, "Halpern, hand that pass over."

He took it from his pocket and gave it to me. Fishbein had now moved to the doorway, where he lingered. He stood there with his mouth slightly open and then pointed to himself. "And me?" he asked.

His utter ridiculousness exhausted me. I slumped down in my seat and felt pulses knocking at the back of my eyes. "Fishbein," I said, "you understand I'm not trying to deny you anything, don't you? If it was my Army I'd serve gefilte fish in the mess hall. I'd sell kugel in the PX, honest to God."

Halpern smiled.

"You understand, don't you, Halpern?"

"Yes, Sergeant."

"And you, Fishbein? I don't want enemies. I'm just like you—I want to serve my time and go home. I miss the same things you miss."

"Then, Sergeant," Fishbein interrupted, "Why don't you come too?"

"Where?"

"To St. Louis. To Shelley's aunt. We'll have a regular Seder. Play hide-the-matzah." He gave a broad, black-toothed smile.

I saw Grossbart in the doorway again, on the other side of the screen. "Pssst!" He waved a piece of paper. "Mickey, here's the address. Tell her I couldn't get away."

Halpern did not move. He looked at me and I saw the shrug moving up his arms into his shoulders again. I took the cover off my typewriter and made out passes for him and Fishbein. "Go," I said, "the three of you."

I thought Halpern was going to kiss my hand.

That afternoon, in a bar in Joplin, I drank beer and listened with half an ear to the Cardinal game. I tried to look squarely at what I'd become involved in, and began to wonder if perhaps the struggle with Grossbart wasn't as much my fault as his. What was I that I had to *muster* generous feelings? Who was I to have been feeling so grudging, so tight-hearted? After all, I wasn't being asked to move the world. Had I a right, then, or a reason, to clamp down on Grossbart, when that meant clamping down on Halpern, too? And Fishbein, that ugly agreeable soul, wouldn't he suffer in the bargain also? Out of the many recollections that had tumbled over me these past few days, I heard from some childhood moment my grandmother's voice: "What are you making a *tsimas?*" It was what she would ask my mother when, say, I had cut myself with a knife and her daughter was busy bawling me out. I would need a hug and a kiss and my mother would moralize! But my grandmother knew—mercy overrides justice. I should have known it, too. Who was Nathan Marx to be such a pennypincher with kindness? Surely, I thought, the Messiah himself—if he should ever come—won't niggle over nickels and dimes. God willing, he'll hug and kiss.

The next day, while we were playing softball over on the Parade Grounds, I decided to ask Bob Wright, who was noncom in charge over at Classification and Assignment, where he thought our trainees would be sent when their cycle ended in two weeks. I asked casually, between innings, and he said, "They're pushing them all into the Pacific. Shulman cut the orders on your boys the other day."

The news shocked me, as though I were father to Halpern, Fishbein, and Grossbart.

That night I was just sliding into sleep when someone tapped on the door. "What is it?"

"Sheldon."

He opened the door and came in. For a moment I felt his presence without being able to see him. "How was it?" I asked, as though to the darkness.

He popped into sight before me. "Great, Sergeant." I felt my springs sag; Grossbart was sitting on the edge of the bed. I sat up.

"How about you?" he asked. "Have a nice weekend?"

"Yes."

He took a deep paternal breath. "The others went to sleep . . ." We sat silently for a while, as a homey feeling invaded my ugly little cubicle: the door was locked, the cat out, the children safely in bed.

"Sergeant, can I tell you something? Personal?"

I did not answer and he seemed to know why. "Not about me. About Mickey. Sergeant, I never felt for anybody like I feel for him. Last night I heard Mickey in the bed next to me. He was crying so, it could have broken your heart. Real sobs."

"I'm sorry to hear that."

"I had to talk to him to stop him. He held my hand, Sergeant—he wouldn't let it go. He was almost hysterical. He kept saying if he only knew where we were going. Even if he knew it *was* the Pacific, that would be better than nothing. Just to know."

Long ago, someone had taught Grossbart the sad law that only lies can get the truth. Not that I couldn't believe in Halpern's crying—his eyes *always* seemed red-rimmed. But, fact or not, it became a lie when Grossbart uttered it. He was entirely strategic. But then—it came with the force of indictment—so was I! There are strategies of aggression, but there are strategies of retreat, as well. And so, recognizing that I, myself, had not been without craft and guile, I told him what I knew. "It is the Pacific."

He let out a small gasp, which was not a lie. "I'll tell him. I wish it was otherwise."

"So do I."

He jumped on my words. "You mean you think you could do something? A change maybe?"

"No, I couldn't do a thing."

"Don't you know anybody over at C & A?"

"Grossbart, there's nothing I can do. If your orders are for the Pacific then it's the Pacific."

"But Mickey."

"Mickey, you, me—everybody, Grossbart. There's nothing to be done. Maybe the war'll end before you go. Pray for a miracle."

"But—"

"Good night, Grossbart." I settled back, and was relieved to feel the springs upbend again as Grossbart rose to leave. I could see him clearly now; his jaw had dropped and he looked like a dazed prizefighter. I noticed for the first time a little paper bag in his hand.

"Grossbart"—I smiled—"my gift?"

"Oh, yes, Sergeant. Here, from all of us." He handed me the bag. "It's egg roll."

"Egg roll?" I accepted the bag and felt a damp grease spot on the bottom. I opened it, sure that Grossbart was joking.

"We thought you'd probably like it. You know, Chinese egg roll. We thought you'd probably have a taste for—"

"Your aunt served egg roll?"

"She wasn't home."

"Grossbart, she invited you. You told me she invited you and your friends."

"I know. I just reread the letter. *Next* week."

I got out of bed and walked to the window. It was black as far off as I could see. "Grossbart," I said. But I was not calling him.

"What?"

"What are you, Grossbart? Honest to God, what are you?"

I think it was the first time I'd asked him a question for which he didn't have an immediate answer.

"How can you do this to people?" I asked.

"Sergeant, the day away did us all a world of good. Fishbein, you should see him, he *loves* Chinese food."

"But the Seder," I said.

"We took the second best, Sergeant."

Rage came charging at me. I didn't sidestep—I grabbed it, pulled it in, hugged it to my chest.

"Grossbart, you're a liar! You're a schemer and a crook! You've got no respect for anything! Nothing at all! Not for me, for the truth, not even for poor Halpern! You use us all—"

"Sergeant, Sergeant, I feel for Mickey, honest to God, I do. I *love* Mickey. I try—"

"You try! You feel!" I lurched towards him and grabbed his shirt front. I shook him furiously. "Grossbart, get out. Get out and stay the hell away from me! Because if I see you, I'll make your life miserable. *You understand that?*"

"Yes."

I let him free, and when he walked from the room I wanted to spit on the floor where he had stood. I couldn't stop the fury from rising in my heart. It engulfed me, owned me, till it seemed I could only rid myself of it with tears or an act of violence. I snatched from the bed the bag Grossbart had given me and with all my strength threw it out the window. And the next morning, as the men policed the area around the barracks, I heard a great cry go up from one of the trainees who'd been anticipating only his morning handful of cigarette butts and candy wrappers. "Egg roll!" he shouted. "Holy Christ, Chinese goddam egg roll!"

A week later when I read the orders that had come down from C & A I couldn't believe my eyes. Every single trainee was to be shipped to Camp Stoneham, California, and from there to the Pacific. Every trainee but one: Private Sheldon Grossbart was to be sent to Fort Monmouth, New Jersey. I read the mimeographed sheet several times. Dee, Farrell, Fishbein, Fuselli, Fylypowycz, Glinicki, Gromke, Gucwa, Halpern, Hardy, Helebrandt . . . right down to Anton Zygadlo, all were to be headed West before the month was out. All except Grossbart. He had pulled a string and I wasn't it.

I lifted the phone and called C & A.

The voice on the other end said smartly, "Corporal Shulman, sir."

"Let me speak to Sergeant Wright."

"Who is this calling, sir?"

"Sergeant Marx."

And to my surprise, the voice said, *"Oh."* Then: "Just a minute, Sergeant."

Shulman's *oh* stayed with me while I waited for Wright to come to the phone. Why *oh?* Who was Shulman? And then, so simply, I knew I'd discovered the string Grossbart had pulled. In fact, I could hear Grossbart the day he'd discovered Shulman, in the PX, or the bowling alley, or maybe even at services. "Glad to meet you. Where you from? Bronx? Me too. Do you know so-and-so? And so-and-so? Me too! You work at C & A? Really? Hey, how's chances of getting East? Could you do something? Change something? Swindle, cheat, lie? We gotta help each other, you know . . . if the Jews in Germany . . ."

At the other end Bob Wright answered. "How are you, Nate? How's the pitching arm?"

"Good. Bob, I wonder if you could do me a favor." I heard clearly my own words and they so reminded me of Grossbart that I dropped more easily than I could have imagined into what I had planned. "This may sound crazy, Bob, but I got a kid here on orders to Monmouth who wants them changed. He had a brother killed in Europe and he's hot to go to the Pacific. Says he'd feel like a coward if he wound up stateside. I don't know, Bob, can anything be done? Put somebody else in the Monmouth slot?"

"Who?" he asked cagily.

"Anybody. First guy on the alphabet. I don't care. The kid just asked if something could be done."

"What's his name?"

"Grossbart, Sheldon."

Wright didn't answer.

"Yeah," I said, "he's a Jewish kid, so he thought I could help him out. You know."

"I guess I can do something," he finally said. "The Major hasn't been around here for weeks—TDY to the golf course. I'll try, Nate, that's all I can say."

"I'd appreciate it, Bob. See you Sunday," and I hung up, perspiring.

And the following day the corrected orders appeared: Fishbein, Fuselli, Fylypowycz, Glinicki, Grossbart, Gucwa, Halpern, Hardy . . . Lucky Private Harley Alton was to go to Fort Monmouth, New Jersey, where for some reason or other, they wanted an enlisted man with infantry training.

After chow that night I stopped back at the orderly room to straighten out the guard duty roster. Grossbart was waiting for me. He spoke first.

"You son of a bitch!"

I sat down at my desk and while he glared down at me I began to make the necessary alterations in the duty roster.

"What do you have against me?" he cried. "Against my family? Would it kill you for me to be near my father, God knows how many months he has left to him."

"Why?"

"His heart," Grossbart said. "He hasn't had enough troubles in a lifetime, you've got to add to them. I curse the day I ever met you, Marx! Shulman told me what happened over there. There's no limit to your anti-Semitism, is there! The damage you've done here isn't enough. You have to make a special phone call! You really want me dead!"

I made the last few notations in the duty roster and got up to leave. "Good night, Grossbart."

"You owe me an explanation!" He stood in my path.

"Sheldon, you're the one who owes explanations."

He scowled. "To *you?*"

"To me, I think so, yes. Mostly to Fishbein and Halpern."

"That's right, twist things around. I owe nobody nothing, I've done all I could do for them. Now I think I've got the right to watch out for myself."

"For each other we have to learn to watch out, Sheldon. You told me yourself."

"You call this watching out for me, what you did?"

"No. For all of us."

I pushed him aside and started for the door. I heard his furious breathing behind me, and it sounded like steam rushing from the engine of his terrible strength.

"You'll be all right," I said from the door. And, I thought, so would Fishbein and Halpern be all right, even in the Pacific, if only Grossbart could continue to see in the obsequiousness of the one, the soft spirituality of the other, some profit for himself.

I stood outside the orderly room, and I heard Grossbart weeping behind me. Over in the barracks, in the lighted windows, I could see the boys in their T-shirts sitting on their bunks talking about their orders, as they'd been doing for the past two days. With a kind of quiet nervousness, they polished shoes, shined belt buckles, squared away underwear, trying as best they could to accept their fate. Behind me, Grossbart swallowed hard, accepting his. And then, resisting with all my will an impulse to turn and seek pardon for my vindictiveness, I accepted my own.

ORDEAL

Wallace Stegner

GENESIS

The summer of 1906 was very wet. It seemed to rain for weeks and the coulees ran knee keep and the Frenchman River was as high as a spring flood. The dirt roofs of the log houses of that day became so sodden that water dripped from them whether it rained or not. It stayed so wet that we had difficulty getting the hay in. The winter started early with a light snow on the 5th of November, followed by a terrific three-day blizzard that started on the 11th. From then till Christmas was a succession of bad storms. The range cattle were dying in December.

Corky Jones as an Old Man

It seemed to the young Englishman that if anyone had been watching from the bench he would have seen them like a print of Life on the Western Plains, or like a medieval procession. The sun was just rising, its dazzle not yet quite clear of the horizon, and flooding down the river valley whitened with the dust of snow, it gilded the yellow leaves that still clung to the willows, stretched the shadow of every bush and post, glazed the eastern faces of the log ranch buildings whose other side was braced with long blue shadows. And moving now, starting to roll, the outfit was strung out along the Mounted Police patrol trail. He was enclosed in it, moving with it, but in his excitement he saw it as it would look from outside and above, and it made him want to stand up in his stirrups and yell.

Leading the lithograph procession went the five hounds—the four Russian wolfhounds and the thing its owner called a staghound, a dog as big as a calf and with a head like a lioness. Across the bottoms in the morning cold they cut loose and ran for the love of running; within seconds they were out of sight among the willows by the ford. Behind them rode Schulz, the wolfer, as new to the outfit as the Englishman himself; and after him his fifteen-year-old son driving a packhorse; and after them old Jesse in the wagon pulled by a team of hairy-footed Clydesdale stallions. Then the horse herd, seventy or eighty saddle horses in a flow of dark tossing motion across the flat, and then the riders, two and two.

They carried no lances or pennons, the sun found no armor from which to strike light, but in the incandescence of being nineteen, and full of health, and assaulted in all his senses by the realization of everything splendid he had ever imagined, the English boy knew that no more romantic procession had ever set forth. The Crusades could not have thrilled him more. Though they went, and he with them, like an illumination in an old manuscript, they had their own authentic color. Among the bays and blacks and browns and buckskins and roans of the horse herd was one bright piebald; in substitution for slashed doublets and shining silks they offered two pairs of woolly goatskin chaps and Ed Spurlock's red mackinaw.

Only a week in that country, the Englishman with practically no urging would have started running with the dogs. It rattled the brains in his head like seeds in a pod to think where he was—here, in Saskatchewan, not merely on the way to the great lone land, or on its edge, but in it, and going deeper. He had lived a dream in which everything went right. Within an hour of the time he stepped off the train in Maple Creek, hesitant and a little scared, he had learned that all the big cattle outfits using the open range east of the Cypress Hills were shorthanded. Within two hours, he had found a ride with Joe Renaud, the mail driver. Within twelve, he was sleeping in the T-Down bunkhouse, an authentic cowboy. Within a week here he went, part of a company bound for adventure, on the late fall roundup to gather and bring in to feeding stations the calves that could not be expected to winter on the range.

He was face to shining face with everything new. Names he had heard here knocked and clanged in his mind—places where anything could happen, and from the sound of them, *had* happened—Jumbo's Butte, Fifty-Mile, Pinto Horse Butte, Horse Camp Coulee, the War Holes. He blew his exultant breath out between his pony's ears, and when he breathed in again he felt the cold at the root of every bared tooth. He noticed that the horses felt as he did: though they had been on the roundup and then on the long drive to Montana and then on the long drive back, and had been worked steadily since May, they were full of run; they joined him in snorting smoke.

The column turned down toward the river, and looking back the Englishman saw Molly Henry, the foreman's wife, hugging her elbows by the ranch-house door. He waved; her hand lifted. He and Ed Spurlock were the last in the line, and he saw how they would look to her, his new sheepskin and Spurlock's red mackinaw just disappearing into the willows. He thought it a lonesome piece of luck for a girl married only three weeks to be left now, with no help except a crippled handy man and no company except the Mountie on his weekly patrol from Eastend, and no woman nearer than twenty-five miles. To Spurlock, jogging beside him with his mittened hands stacked on the horn, he said with feeling, "I'm certainly glad it's not *me* being left behind!"

Spurlock glanced sideward with restless brown eyes; he said nothing; his expression did not change.

The Englishman grew aware, under Spurlock's glance, that he was posting to his pony's jogtrot. As if stretching muscles he pushed down hard into the unfamiliarly long stirrups, shoved back against the cantle, leaned a little and stacked his hands casually on the horn in imitation of Spurlock's. As soon as he had them there he felt that he seemed to be hanging on to ease the jolt of sitting the trot, and he took his hands away again. With a complex sense of being green, young, red-headed, and British—all potentially shameful—but at the same time strong, bold, high-spirited, and ready for anything, he appraised Spurlock's taciturnity and adjusted his seat in the big strange saddle and threw at random into the air a look that was cocky, self-conscious, and ingratiating all at once.

The wagon had crushed through the thin ice at the ford, and the horses waded into the broken wake and stood knee deep, bobbing away ice-pans with their noses, plunging their muzzles to suck strongly. Here and there one pulled its nose out and stood with a thoughtful, puckered, tasting expression at the corners of its dripping lips; they looked as if the water had made their teeth ache.

Then Slippers and Little Horn and Ray Henry rode in and hazed them across, and Buck and Panguingue and Spurlock and the Englishman picked up the stragglers. The cold sound of splashing became a drumming and thudding on the bank. Above and ahead, the wagon was just tilting out of sight over the dugway edge. They took the herd up after it in a rush, and burst out onto the great glittering plain.

It was tremendous, it was like a plunge over a cliff. The sun looked them straight in the eyes, the earth dazzled them. Over and under and around, above, below, behind, before, the Englishman felt the unfamiliar element, a cleanness like the blade of a knife, a distance without limits, a horizon that did not bound the world but only suggested endless space beyond. Shading his eyes with his hand while his pony rocked into a lope, he saw all ahead of him the disk of the white and yellow world, the bowl of the colorless sky unbearable with light. Squatting on the horizon right under the searchlight sun were a pair of low mounds, one far off, one nearer. The closer one must be Jumbo's Butte, the far one Stonepile. They were the only breaks he saw in the plains except when, twisting backward, he found the Cypress Hills arched across the west, showing in coulees and ravines the faded white and gold of aspen, the black of jackpines. By the time they had ridden five minutes the river valley out of which they had risen was almost invisible, sunk below the level of sight.

The wolfer and his son were already far ahead, the dogs only running specks out on the shining plain. Jesse and the pilot wagon were leading the rest of them on a beeline toward Jumbo's Butte, and as the Englishman settled down and breathed out his excitement and relaxed to the shuffle of his pony he watched the broad wheels drop and jolt into holes and burnouts and old Jesse lurch and sway on the high seat, and he let his back ache with sympathy. Then he saw Jesse's teeth flash in his face as he turned to shout something at Ray Henry riding beside the wagon, and he decided that sympathy was wasted. Jesse had been a bullwhacker with supply trains between Fort Benton and the Montana mining camps in the early days, he had known these plains when the buffalo were still shaking them, he had been jolting his kidneys loose across country like this for thirty years. If he had wanted another kind of job he could have had it. The Englishman admired him as a man who did well what he was hired to do. He believed old Jesse to be skilled, resourceful, humorous, close-mouthed, a character. Briefly he contemplated growing a mustache and trying to train it like Jesse's into a silky oxbow.

The saddle horses followed along smartly after the pilot wagon, and there was hardly any need to herd them, but the boys were fanned out in a wide semicircle, riding, as if by preference, each by himself. And among them—this was the wonder, this was what made him want to raise his face and ki-yi in pure happiness—rode Lionel Cullen, by now known as Rusty, the least of eight (as he admitted without real humility) but willing, and never more pleased with himself. That morning in early November, 1906, he would not have traded places with Sir Wilfrid Laurier.

He wanted to see everything, miss nothing, forget nothing. To make sure that he would not forget what happened to him and what he saw, he had begun a journal on the train coming west from Montreal, and every evening since then he had written in it seriously with posterity looking over his shoulder. He watched every minute of every day for the vivid and the wonderful, and he kept an alert eye on himself for the changes that were certain to occur. He had the feeling that there would be a test of some sort, that he would enter manhood—or cowboyhood, manhood in Saskatchewan terms—as one would enter a house. For the moment he was a tenderfoot, a greenhorn, on probation, under scrutiny. But at some moment there would be a door to open, or to force, and inside would be the self-assurance that he respected and envied in Jesse, Slippers, or Little Horn, the calm confidence of a top hand.

As they moved like the scattered shadow of a cloud across the face of the plain he knew practically nothing except how to sit a horse, and even that he knew in a fashion to get him laughed at. But he was prepared to serve an apprenticeship, he would prove himself as and when he must. And in the pocket of his flannel shirt he had a notebook and two pencils, ready for anything.

At noon, a little to the east of Jumbo's Butte, they stopped to boil coffee and heat a kettle of beans. The thin snow did not cover the grass; the crust that had blazed in their eyes all morning was thawing in drops that clung to the curly prairie wool. On a tarpaulin spread by the wagon they sprawled and ate the beans that Jesse might just as well not have heated, for the cold tin plates congealed them again within seconds. But the coffee burned their mouths, and the tin cups were so hot to hold that they drank with their mittens on. The steam of their coffee-heated breath was a satisfaction; Rusty tried to blow rings with it.

When he finished he lay on the tarp next to Panguingue. There was always, it seemed, room next to Panguingue: it was said of him that he took a bath every spring whether he needed it or not. In the cold, and so long as Panguingue wore a sheepskin and overshoes, Rusty did not mind. And anyway, since arriving he had seen no one take a bath, not even Buck, who was fastidious; certainly he had taken none himself. So he relaxed by Panguingue and felt the ground satisfyingly hard under the tarp, and let Panguingue thump him monotonously between the shoulder blades and dust cigarette ashes through his hair. Through half-closed eyes he heard the horses working on the curly grass all around, he saw a snowbird come boldly to pick at a scrap of salt pork by the edge of the tarp; his ears heard the sounds of ease, the scratchings, the crackle of a match; his nose smelled sour pipe, smelled Bull Durham, smelled Ray Henry's sybaritic cigar. He loved every minute, every sensation, and when, just as they were rising to tighten cinches and move on, they heard the hysterical yapping of hounds, and saw Schulz's pack, two miles away, pursue and run down a coyote, he climbed on the wagon and watched as eager as a spectator at a horse race. He thought of Schulz as belonging somehow with Jesse, the two of them survivors of an earlier stage of Plains life; he rather envied Schulz's boy, brought up to lonely cabins, skimpy cowchip campfires on the prairies, familiarity with wild animals, the knack and habit of casual killing. From high on the wagon seat, bracing himself on Jesse's shoulder, he watched Schulz ride in and scatter the hounds and dismount, while the boy gathered up the loose packhorse. He expected that the wolfers would come in and get something to eat, but he saw Schulz mount again and the three horses and the five dogs move out eastward. Even more than the cowboys, these were the wild ones; they had gone as far as it was possible to go back toward savagery. He regretted not seeing them ride in with the scalp of the coyote, the hounds bloody-muzzled from the kill. He hoped to get a chance to course a coyote or a wolf across such a marvelous plain as this on such a glorious day, when you could see for twenty miles. It was tremendous, every bit of it.

During the afternoon the country roughened, broke into coulees that opened down toward the river. They rode, it seemed, endlessly, without a break and with little talk. Rusty stiffened in the saddle, he rode lounging, stood in the stirrups, hung his feet free while under him the shaggy little horse shuffled on. The sun went down the sky toward the Cypress Hills, now no more than a faint clean lifting of the horizon. They felt the thin warmth on their necks if their collars were down; their faces felt the cold.

When they arrived at Stonepile the sun was already down. The sky back over the hills was red, the snow ahead of them lay rosy across the flats. Until they reached the coulee's rim they would not have known it was there; as for the river, it was sunk among indistinguishable rough coulees to the north, but no more than a mile away. As they dipped downward toward the Stonepile buildings, once a Mounted Police patrol post, the valley was already full of violet shadow. Rusty creaked and eased himself, letting the horse pick his way. He was stiff and chilled, his face felt like sheet metal, his eyes watered and smarted from the day's glare.

They were not talkative as they unsaddled and turned the horses loose, or during the time while they lugged bedrolls and food into the old barracks. Two or three men would be stationed here later to feed to the calves the three hundred and fifty tons of wild hay stacked in the coulee; they had brought flour, rice, oatmeal, sugar, matches and prunes, tinned corn and syrup and jam and peas, dried apples and peaches, to stock the place. There was a good deal of tracking in and out from the cold blue dusk. Jesse had stuck two tallow dips in china holders that said *Peerless Hotel.* They were all in each other's way in the narrow bunkhouse, and all in the way of Jesse, trying to get supper going. They bumped shoulders, growled. Rusty, who had thrown his bedroll forehandedly into one of the upper bunks, came in with a load later and found that Ed Spurlock had thrown it out and put his own in its place. There were only six bunks for the ten of them. In the end, Rusty spread his bed beside Panguingue's on the floor, and the wolfers, coming in a half hour after them, looked in the door briefly and decided to sleep in the stable with the Clydes, the night horses, and the dogs.

"Be careful them studs," Jesse told Schulz. "It wouldn't do if them and your lion got to mixing it."

The wolfer was a man, Rusty thought, to be noticed, perhaps to be watchful of. He still wore, in the warming barracks, a muskrat cap with earlaps. Under it his eyes were gray as agates, as sudden as an elbow in the solar plexus. His face was red, his mustache sandy. Between his eyes, even when he smiled, which was not often, he wore a deep vertical wrinkle. He had what Rusty thought of as a passionate taciturnity. He looked watchful and besieged, he would be quick to strike back, he was not a man you could make a joke with. In a low growling voice he said that he valued his hound too highly to let any forty-dollar horse kick him in the head.

Jesse looked at him, holding a stove lid half off the smoking fire, and his silky mustaches moved as if a small animal had crawled under the thatch. He said, "If one of the Clydes hit him, that wouldn't be no forty-dollar kick. That would be a genuine gold-plated eight-hundred-dollar kick guaranteed to last."

Schulz grunted and went out: Rusty told himself that he had been right in guessing him as a man with whom you did not joke. The boy, sullen-looking, with a drooping lip and eyes that looked always out their corners, went silently after him. They came back in for supper, cleaned their plates, and went out again for good.

"What's the matter with him?" Spurlock asked. "Don't he like our company?"

"Likes his dogs better," Buck said. He reared his red turkey neck up and glared out into the jammed corridor between the bunks. From the end, where he sat braced against the wall fooling with the harmonica, Rusty saw the disgust on his skinned-looking face. "What about somebody that would sleep with a God damn dog?" Buck said.

From the lower, talking around the dead cigar that poked upward from his face, Little Horn said gently, "We ain't got any right to criticize. We all been sleepin' with Panguingue for a year."

"B.S.," Panguingue said. "My feet don't smell no worse'n yours."

"Well for the love of God," Jesse said, hanging the dishpan on the wall, "let's not have any contests. There ain't a man here would survive it."

Rusty took the slick metal of the harmonica from his mouth and ventured: his feelers, tentative always to estimate his own position as one of them, told him that now, while they were criticizing the unsociable wolfer, his own position was more solid; and yet he admired the wildness and the obvious competence of the wolfer, too. The very fact that he rode in moccasins and thick German socks gave him a distinction over the rest of them in their overshoes. Rusty said, "Do you suppose it's only that he's used to living out alone, don't you know . . . that he's almost like a wild animal himself? He seems that way to me . . . or is that only fancy?"

They hooted at him, and he felt his ears grow red. "Aow, it's only fawncy, p'raps," they told each other for the next minute or two. "Deah!" they said. "Rilly?" Rusty blew into the mouth organ. He heard Little Horn saying "It's natural enough. Yell at a dog, he minds. Yell at one of you sonsofbitches, what does he do? I don't blame the guy. There's no satisfaction in a cowpuncher's company like there is in a dog's."

Spurlock said, "Can his kid talk? I never heard him say a word yet."

"Probably all he knows is 'bow-wow,'" Buck said.

Jesse pawed his yellow-white silky mustache and said with the look of foolery in his faded blue eyes, "Schulz don't look to me like he's got a steady conscience. I'd say mebbe he was a windigo."

Rusty waited, hoping someone else would take the bait, but resigning himself when no one spoke. And anyway, he was interested. "What's a windigo?"

"What the Crees used to call an Injun that had made use of man-meat," Jesse said. "Most generally seemed to sort of drive a man wild, he wasn't right afterwards. I recall hearing Bert Willoughby tell about one the Mounties had to go get up on the Swift Current, back in the early days. His tribe got suspicious, he come out of a starvin' winter lookin' so fat and slick. Also his fambly was missin'. So they collared this buck and he took 'em up to his winter camp on Bigstick Lake, and here was all these bones and skulls around, and he'd kick 'em and laugh, and say, 'This one my wife, hee hee hee,' and 'That one my mother-in-law, ho ho,' and 'This one here my father, ha ha.' He'd et the whole damn bunch, one after the other."

"Well," Little Horn said. "I wonder if somebody is settin' oncomfortable on old Schulzie's stomach?"

"Maybe we could get him to eat Panguingue before he gets too God damn high," Spurlock said.

Little Horn said regretfully, "I doubt if even a windigo would take a chance on Panguingue."

"B.S.," Panguingue said.

From the white cloud of cigar smoke that filled the enclosed space above his bunk, Ray Henry whispered, "You can all take it easy. Schulz and his boy will be stayin' here or at Bates Camp all winter, while you boys is up to your ass in dried apple pies back at the ranch."

"Good," Buck said.

"Sure, Ray," said Jesse, "I know that was the arrangement. But is it safe?"

"Safe, how?"

Jesse kicked the stove leg. "This-here my boy," he said. "Hee hee hee."

They left Schulz and his silent boy behind them at the Stonepile camp and made a hard drive eastward to the Fifty-Mile Crossing of the Whitemud, on the eastern boundary of the range that, by mutual consent among all the outfits, was called the T-Down's. Already, within a day, Rusty felt how circumstances had hardened, how what had been an adventure revealed itself as a job. He rose from his bed on the floor so stiff he hobbled like a rheumatic dog, and when he stumbled out of the foul barracks and took a breath of the morning air it was as if he had had an icicle rammed clear to his wishbone. Another cold day—colder than the one before by a good deal—and an even harder ride ahead. And leaving the Schulzes affected him unpleasantly: these two were being separated off to carry on a specific and essential duty, but no one was sorry to see them go. The outfit that he had thought of as ten was really only eight. If the others chose to find him as disagreeable as they found Schulz, it was only seven. He hung at their fringes, hoping to earn a place among them. He was painfully alert, trying to anticipate what was expected of him. What was expected was that he should climb in the saddle, on a new pony this morning—one with a trot like a springless wagon over cobblestones—and ride, and ride, and ride, straight into the blinding glare of the sun.

The night before, he had entered in his journal information on how the open range from Wood Mountain on the east to Medicine Lodge Coulee on the west was run. From the Whitemud north to the Canadian Pacific tracks the Circle Diamond and the 76, both very large outfits, divided it. South of the river there were several. Between Wood Mountain and Fifty-Mile was the Turkey Track, running about 25,000 head. Then their own outfit, the T-Down Bar, running 10,000. Between the T-Down ranch house and the Cypress Hills the Z-X ran about 2000 purebred shorthorns and whitefaces, and through the Cypress Hills to Medicine Lodge Coulee an association of small ranchers called the Whitemud Pool ran their herds together. It seemed reasonable; it even seemed neat; but it seemed terribly large when you had to ride across it at the wagon's pace.

By noon the sky had hazed over. They blessed it because of their eyes and cursed it because the wind developed a sting. Then away out on the flats in the middle of a bleak afternoon they met the wagon and four riders from the Turkey Track, bound for a camp they had on the big coulee called the War Holes. They were on the same errand as the T-Down boys: combing parts of the range missed in the spring roundup, and separating out the calves and bulls to be wintered on hay in the sheltered bottoms. Their greeting was taciturn and numb. The T-Down boys looked to them exactly as they looked to the T-Down, probably: frostbitten, with swollen watery eyes, their backs humped to the cold wind, their ponies' tails blowing between their legs as they waited out the fifteen minutes of meeting.

It had not been made clear to Rusty Cullen, until then, that they were on a belated and half-desperate job. A green hand did not inquire too closely for fear of asking foolish questions; an experienced hand volunteered nothing. And so he was surprised by the gloominess of the Turkey Track boys and their predictions of heavy losses on the range. They quoted signs and omens. They ran mittened hands against the grain of their ponies' winter hair, to show how much heavier it was than normal. They had seen muskrat houses built six feet high in the sloughs—and when the rats built high you could depend on a hard winter. Mounted Police freighters reported a steady drift of antelope from the north across the CPR tracks.

The chinook winds, he gathered, should keep the range clear enough for the stronger animals to get feed, but calves didn't winter well. Fortunately all the stock was fat: the summer range had been good. If they could get the calves in where there was feed, maybe there wouldn't be too much loss. Having exchanged omens, predictions, reassurances, and invitations to Christmas blowouts, they raised their mitts to each other and ducked each his own way into or away from the wind, and the tracks that had briefly met crawled apart again across the snow.

Somehow the brief, chilled, laconic encounter in the emptiness and cold of the flats left Rusty depressed. By the time they dragged in to camp in the willows of the river bottom at Fifty-Mile his eyes were swollen almost shut, and burned and smarted as if every little capillary and nerve in them had been twisted and tied in knots; he knew how streaked and bloodshot they were by looking at the eyes of the others. He was tired, stiff, cold; there was no immediate comfort in camp, but only more cold hard work, and the snow that was only a thin scum on the prairie was three inches deep down here. They shoveled off a space and got the tent set up in the blue dusk, and he looked it over and felt that their situation was gloomily naked and exposed. When he chopped through the river's inch of ice and watched the water well up and overflow the hole it seemed like some dark force from the ancient heart of the earth that could at any time rise around them silently and obliterate their little human noises and tracks and restore the plain to its emptiness again.

The wind dropped after sundown, the night came on clear and cold. Before turning in Rusty stepped outside and looked around. The other boys were all in their bedrolls, and the light in the tent had been blown out so that even that pale human efflorescence was gone; the tent was a misty pyramid, the wagon a shadow. Tied to the wheels, the blanketed night horses and the Clydes moved their feet uncomfortably and rustled for a last grain of oats in the seams of their nosebags.

The earth showed him nothing; it lay pallid, the willows bare sticks, the snow touched with bluish luminescence. A horn of moon was declining toward the western horizon. But in the north the lights were beginning, casting out a pale band that trembled and stretched and fell back and stretched out again until it went from horizon to horizon. Out of it streaks and flares and streamers began to reach up toward the zenith and pale the stars there as if smoke were being blown across them.

He had never felt so small, so lost, so inconsequential; his impulse was to sneak away. If anyone had asked his name and his business, inquiring what he was doing in the middle of that empty plain, he would have mumbled some foolish and embarrassed answer. In his mind's eye he saw the Turkey Track camp ten or fifteen or twenty miles out in the emptiness, the only other thing like themselves, a little lonesome spark that would soon go out and leave only the smudge of the wagon, the blur of the tent, under the cold flare of the Northern Lights. It was easy to doubt their very existence; it was easy to doubt his own.

A night horse moved again, a halter ring clinked, a sound tiny and lost. He shuddered his shoulders, worked his stiffened face, stirred up his numbed brains and shook the swimming from his eyes. When the tent flap dropped behind him and he stooped to fumble the ties shut the shiver that went through him was exultant, as if he had just been brushed by a great danger and had escaped. The warmth and the rank human odors of the tent were mystically rich with life. He made such a loud, happy, unnecessary row about the smell of Panguingue's feet when he crawled into his bedroll in their cramped head-to-foot sleeping space that three or four sleepy voices cursed him viciously and Panguingue kicked him a few good hard ones through his blankets and kicked the vapors out of him.

Sometime during that roundup they may have had a day of decent weather, but it seemed to Rusty it was a procession of trials: icy nights, days when a bitter wind lashed and stung the face with a dry sand of snow, mornings when the crust flashed up a glare so blinding that they rode with eyes closed to slits and looked at the world through their eyelashes. There was one afternoon when the whole world was overwhelmed under a white freezing fog, when horses, cattle, clothes, wagon, grew a fur of hoar frost and the herd they had gathered had to be held together in spooky white darkness mainly by ear.

On bright days they were all nearly blind, in spite of painting their cheekbones with charcoal and riding with hats pulled clear down; if they could see to work at all, they worked with tears leaking through swollen and smarting lids. Their faces grew black with sun and glare, their skin and lips cracked as crisp as the skin of a fried fish, and yet they froze. Every night the thermometer dropped near zero, and there was an almost continuous snake-tongue of wind licking out of the north or west.

The river bottom and the big rough coulees entering from the south held many cattle, and they soon collected a large herd. They were hard to move; if he had had a gun Rusty would have been tempted more than once to make immediate beef of them. The Canadian cattle, whiteface or whiteface-and-shorthorn cross, were impenetrably stupid and slow; their whole unswerving intention was to break past a rider and get back into the bottoms. The longhorns, most of which carried the Turkey Track or Circle Diamond brand and which had to be cut away from their own, were exactly the opposite: fast, agile, wicked, and smart. They could lead a man a wild chase, always in a direction he didn't want to go; they hid among other cattle and couldn't be cut out; they milled and stampeded the T-Down herd at every chance; all the boys had spills, chasing longhorns through rough country and across the icy flats; and they wore the horses, already weak and thin, to the bone.

On the third day out from Fifty-Mile, Slip, Panguingue, and Rusty were cutting out a bunch of ten or fifteen Circle Diamond longhorns from a dozen T-Down whitefaces. They wanted the whitefaces up on the bench where they could turn them into the herd; the longhorns were welcome to the coulee. Of course the whitefaces hung onto the coulee and the longhorns stampeded up onto the flats. It was astonishing how fast those cattle could move and how much noise they made. Their horns cracked; their hoofs cracked; their joints cracked; it seemed as if even their tails snapped like bullwhips. In a wild clamor they went up the coulee bank, agile as goats, with Rusty after them.

He came out onto the rim in a sting of snow and wind. The longhorns were well ahead of him, racing with their bag-of-bones clatter toward the wagon and the herd that Jesse and Spurlock were holding there. Rusty ducked his head and squinted back at Slip; he was waving and shouting: Rusty understood that he was to head the longhorns before they got too close to the herd.

The cattle, very fast for a short distance, began to slack off. His dogged little horse came up on a roan haunch, then on a brindle, then past a set of wild horns, and finally up on the leader, so close the boy could have kicked his laboring shoulder or reached out and grabbed his thirty-inch horn. He lashed him with the rope across the face; still going hard, the steer ducked and began to turn.

The next he knew, Rusty was over the pony's head like a rock shot from a slingshot. It happened so fast he knew nothing about it until he was flying through the air frantically clawing at nothing, and lit sliding, and rolled. His wind and wits went out of him together; he sat up groggily, spitting blood and snow.

And oh, how beautiful a thing it is to work with men who know their job! He sat up into a drama of danger and rescue. The steer had turned and was coming for him; Slip was riding in hard from the side to head him off. But he was too far back; Rusty saw it with the hardest sort of clarity, and he was up on hands and knees, into a crouch, his eyes estimating distances, watching the wide horns and the red eyes of the steer, noting even how the stiff ice-encased hairs sprayed back from his nostrils. While he crouched there laboring to get wind back into his lungs, Rusty saw Slip's bay in the air with all four legs stiff, coming down to a braced landing. The wide loop came snaking in the air, Slip's left hand was making a lightning dally around the horn. The timing was so close that the rope did not even sag before the steer's rush took up the slack. It simply whistled out straight and was snapped tight and humming as the pony came down stiff-legged in the snow. The steer was yanked off his feet, the horse slipped, went nearly down, recovered, the air was full of hoofs and horns, and the longhorn crashed as if he had fallen from the sky. Liquid dung rolled from under his tail; Rusty thought he had broken his neck.

Shakily he went toward the steer to unhook Slip's rope for him, but Slip warned him sharply away. His horse stepped nervously, keeping the rope tight when the steer tried to rise. A little way off, Panguingue was reaching from his saddle to catch the trailing reins of Rusty's pony. "Bust anythin'?" Slip said.

"No," Rusty said. He had sense enough to swallow his gratitude. With his cracked and blackened face, Slip looked like a dwarfish Negro jockey on that big strong horse. He was watching the herd, and Rusty turned to look too, just as Panguingue rode up and handed him his reins. All three stood a moment looking toward the wagon and listening to the uproar of shouts and curses that came from Spurlock and Jesse.

"God damn!" Panguingue said.

The longhorns, bursting into the compact herd of whitefaces, were stirring them like a great spoon. Even as they watched, the milling movement spread, the edges scattered, the whole herd was on the run back toward the coulee. Slip shook off his rope and he and Panguingue started off at a lope without a glance at Rusty. The steer rose and stood spraddling, watching him with red eyes. Limping, cursing the treacherous icy hole-pocked prairie, sorry for himself in his unregarded pain, Rusty reached his numb left arm up and took hold of the horn and mounted. Gritting his teeth, he spurred the pony into a trot, but that so agonized his arm and shoulder that in a moment he slowed to a walk. Then he swore and kicked him into a canter. He would show them. He would ride it out the whole mortal day, and they would never know until that night, after he had done without a complaint all the duty demanded of him, that he was really a stretcher case with a broken shoulder or collarbone or something. He knew he was going to be laid up, but he would stay in the saddle till he dropped. A grim campaigner, a man with the right stuff in him, he crippled along after Slip and Panguingue and the accursed cows.

He managed to get through the rest of the day, but when he was unsaddling that night at the wagon, his face skinned, his left hand helpless and his right fumbling and clumsy, no one came around with help or sympathy. One or two of them gave him bleary glances and went on past as he picked at the latigo with one freezing unmittened hand. Perhaps he dropped a tear or two of rage and weakness and pain into the snow. When he finally got the saddle off and turned the pony loose, he stumbled into the tent and lay down and turned his back to them. He heard Jesse's cooking noises, he smelled the smoke of frying meat, he felt the heat of the stove filling the canvas space. The boys talked a little, growling and monosyllabic. The wind puffed on the tent wall near his face; he cradled his aching arm the best he could and concentrated on stoicism.

Panguingue came in, crawled into his bed to warm up, and kicked Rusty companionably to get his attention. The jar shook such pain through the boy that he rose up with gritted teeth. Panguingue's astonished grin glimmered through his beard, and he said to the tent at large, "You should of seen old Rusty get piled today. How'd that feel, Rusty? You was up in the air long enough to grow feathers."

"It felt like hell, if you want to know. I think I broke my shoulder."

"Oh well," Panguingue said. "Long as it wasn't your neck."

His callousness absolutely enraged Rusty, but Spurlock enraged him more when he remarked from the other corner of the tent, "You sure chose a hell of a time to get piled, I'll say that. You fall off and we lose the whole God damn herd."

"Fall off?" Rusty said shrilly. "*Fall* off? What do *you* do when your pony steps in a hole?"

"Not what you did," Spurlock said. In the light of the two candles Jesse had stuck onto his grub box, his bloodshot eyes moved restlessly, here, there, first on Rusty, then on one of the others, never still. There was a drooping, provocative smile on his face. Rusty pulled his anger in and stayed silent.

Slippers said into the air from where he lay on his back next to Panguingue, "Rusty was doin' all right. He was headin' 'em."

"When he see his horse was too slow, he took off and flew," Panguingue said.

In imbecile good nature his rough hand jarred out, half blow and half push, and Rusty fell awkwardly on the bad shoulder. "Look out, you silly bastard!" he screamed, so much like a hysterical schoolboy that he turned again, ashamed, and gave his back to them. He knew they were watching, speculatively and with expressions of calculated neutrality. Judgment was going on in their minds, and he hated what they were thinking.

In a few minutes Ray Henry came in, the last but one into camp.

"Somebody'll have to spell Buck in an hour," he said. "After that we can take it in two-hour shifts. Little Horn, you take it first, then Panguingue, then Slip." His inflamed eyes came around to Rusty, blinked at him across the stove and candles. "Rusty, you healthy? Was that you took a spill today?"

"That was me."

"Hurt yourself?"

"I don't know. I can't move my left arm."

The foreman picked his way between the bedrolls and squatted. "Roll over and let's see." Obediently, justified and finally vindicated, Rusty helped unbutton sheepskin and both flannel shirts he wore, and the thick hands probed and squeezed and punched around his shoulder and collarbone and down the arm. Rusty flattered himself that he did not wince.

For a second or two Ray stayed squatting there, dark-faced, burly as a boulder, expressionless. "I don't think she's bust," he said. "It don't wiggle anywhere. I'll take your shift tonight, and you better lay up with the wagon tomorrow and see how it goes."

"No," Rusty said. "I can work."

"Excelsior," said Spurlock from his corner.

"What?" Ray said.

Nobody said anything.

That was always a bad time, that few minutes before supper, when they came in and lay around the tent waiting for food with their bones melting away with tiredness. But it didn't last. They were cheerful enough afterward, lying in bed, smoking, and Spurlock even went to the length of rolling Rusty a cigarette and passing it across in silence. "Oh, I say,"

Rusty said. "Thanks very much!" Spurlock threw his muzzle in the air and gave himself up to silent laughter, or to communion with his ironic gods, and shook his head in amused despair, but the edge was out of him, out of all of them.

Buck came in, cold and morose, and fussily hunted up a pan and heated water in it and washed himself before he ate the supper Jesse had kept warm. Little Horn, groaning, hunched into his sheepskin and went out. They could hear him asking the sympathy of the horse as he saddled up.

One by one the other boys made their way outside and in a few seconds came chattering in again. When it came Rusty's turn he ducked out with his arm hugged against his chest. The cold froze his teeth clear to the roots at the first breath; he shuddered and shook. It is awkward enough for a man to button and unbutton his pants with his right hand at any time, but in that freezing circumstance he might as well have tried to do it with tongs. The big pale earth was around him, the big mottled sky arched over with a slice of very white moon shining on icy-looking clouds. It was so quiet he heard his own heart thudding. For a moment he stood taking it in, and then he opened his mouth and let out a very loud yell, simply to announce himself and to crack the silence. When he went back in, hissing and shaking, he found them all staring at him.

"What in hell was that?" Buck said.

"That was me," Rusty said. "It was too quiet to suit me."

Jesse was paring a sliver of tobacco off a plug, working at it slowly and carefully as he might have peeled an apple. His faded eyes glinted up, his oxbow mustaches parted briefly. "You hadn't ought to do a thing like that, son," he said. "I reckon you don't know, though."

"Know what?"

"When it's this cold," Jesse said, "man has to be careful how loud he talks."

"What?" Rusty said. "Get too cold air into your lungs, you mean? Freeze your windpipe?"

"Tell you," Jesse said. "I used to know this feller name Dan Shields."

Rusty crept into his blankets, not willing to give any of them, even Jesse, a handle. "Anybody feel like a game of stud?" Spurlock said.

"Too damn cold," Panguingue said. "You'd freeze your hands."

"Down by where I used to work," Jesse said, in his soft insisting voice, "down there by Sheridan, there's this guy Dan Shields. He's tellin' me one time about some cold weather he seen. Said him and another guy was up on the mountain workin' a gold mine one winter, and it chilled off considerable. Man walk along outside, he'd steam like a laundry. Wood froze so hard it'd last all night in the stove—they never had a bit of fuel trouble. Go to spit, you'd have to break yourself free before you could walk away. They figured seventy-five, eighty below. Couldn't tell, the thermometer froze solid at sixty-five."

"I hope they had a steam-heated backhouse," Panguingue said. "I had to break myself free out there just now."

"Better look close, Pan," said Spurlock. "Man could make a serious mistake breakin' too careless."

"B.S.," Panguingue said. "Even broke off short I'll match you."

"Said they had them a nice warm cabin and they made out fine," Jesse said, "except the grub began to run low. One mornin' they're talkin' about what they should do, and they step outside to sort of look at the weather. They're standin' there talkin', and it seems to Dan this other guy's voice is sort of failin' him. He gets squeakier and squeakier, and finally he pinches out. The fella looks surprised and clears his throat, and spits, and breaks himself loose, and tries again. Not a whisper.

"'Is your tonsils froze, or what?' Dan says to him—and you know, *he* don't break the silence any, either. He tries his lips, and they're workin', and he wags his tongue, and *it* ain't bogged down, and he takes a big breath and tries to rip off a cussword and nothin' happens at all.

"His partner is lookin' at him very queer. He says somethin' that Dan don't get. 'By God,' says Dan at the top of his voice, 'there's somethin' almighty damn funny here!' and all he hears is nothin', just nothin'. They turn their heads and listen, and there ain't a sound.

"Dan cusses some more, thinkin' he may jar somethin' loose the way you'd kick a jammed endgate. He can't make a peep. Said he was beginnin' to get scared. Said he looks across at his partner and the sweat was up on the guy's forehead size of buckshot. The drops froze as fast as they popped out, and they roll off his face and hit the snow. You'd think they'd patter—sort of human hailstones. Not a speck, Dan says. They roll off his partner's brow and hit the ground and he can see them bounce and they don't make no more noise than feathers.

"The partner begins to get excited. His mouth is goin' like a stampmill, and yet it's just as quiet as three o'clock in the mornin'. His eyes bug out, and he makes these yellin' motions, and all of a sudden he busts inside the cabin and throws his stuff together and takes off down the mountain."

"And never was seen again," Spurlock said. "The end."

"Well, that relieves the grub situation, and after Dan has gone inside and warmed up he tries out his voice again and it works, so he stays on. The weather never lets up, though, not till way 'long in the spring. Then one mornin' the sun comes up bright and first thing Dan notices the thermometer has thawed out and begun to slide down, and she's only sixty below, and then a little later she's fifty. She's gettin' so mild he sits down on the doorstep after breakfast and smokes a pipe. While he's sitting there he hears his partner, somewhere a good ways away, but comin' closer, sayin' somethin' like, 'figger we could get down and back in three-four days if on'y it wasn't so God damn cold.'

"Said it cheered him like anythin' to hear a human voice again, and he raises up on the doorstep and looks down the trail, but ain't a sign of anybody. He's lookin' all around when his partner says, quite close, 'I don't mind bein' out of sugar, but I sure as hell don't aim to stay long where they ain't any Climax Plug.'

"'I see what you mean,' Dan says conversationally. 'I expect you get the bulk of your nourishment thataway,' and then he looks very fast behind him and all around that front yard, because it ain't him that's said it, he ain't moved his mouth or had any intention of sayin' anything. It ain't him but it's his voice.

"'My notion is we ought to go on down,' the partner says, very clear and close, and then there is a good deal of hackin' and spittin' and clearin' of the throat and the partner says, 'What in the God damn hell is happenin' to me?' and Dan hears his own voice say, 'Is your tonsils froze, or what?' and then there is a very considerable duet of cussin' and yellin', and more throat clearin' and more yellin' and a sound like a hailstorm patterin' all around, and out of this big uproar the partner says, 'By God, I'm gettin' out of here!' Well that's just what Dan does. He ducks inside that cabin and leans against the door till all the fuss dies down outside, and when she's quiet he gathers together his plunder and he hightails her off the mountain too.

"He had it figured out by then, easy enough. It was so cold out there while they was talkin' that their words froze right there in the air, froze up plumb solid and silent. Then when that quick thaw comes on they broke up all at once and come down on old Dan's head like icicles off a roof. But Dan said he didn't want to stay up there even after he figured it out. Said it made him uncomfortable to think that any time somebody might yell right in his ear three months ago. Said he never did learn to care for cold-storage conversation as well as the fresh article."

"Now ain't it funny?" Buck said. "That ain't my taste at all. I'd just as soon have everything you just said all froze up nice and solid so the coyotes could listen to it next spring and I could just lay here now with no noise going on and get some sleep."

"That's the biggest pile of cold-storage bullshit I ever heard," Spurlock said. "Jesse, you could chop that up and use it for cow-chips for a month."

"I guess," Jesse said mildly. "But I tell you, kid, don't you go yellin' so loud outside there no more. This is one of those winters when you might deefen somebody in 1907."

With his arm hanging in a sling made of a flour sack and a horse-blanket pin, and the loose sleeve of his sheepskin flapping, Rusty managed to go on riding. The weather was clear and bitter, full of signs that the boys said meant change—sundogs by day, Northern Lights by night. Even the noontime thermometer never climbed much above twenty. Flushing the stubborn cattle out of coulees and draws, they left behind them a good many cold-storage curses to startle the badgers and coyotes in the first thaw.

Day by day they worked their herd a few miles closer to Horse Camp Coulee; night by night they took turns riding around and around them, beating their arms to keep warm, and after interminable star-struck icy hours stumbled into the sighs and snores and faint warmth of the tent and shook the shoulder of the victim and benefactor who would relieve them. Some days one or another couldn't see to work, and when that happened they all suffered, for Jesse rode with the hands, instead of making camp, and in the icy evening they all had to fall to and shovel off a patch of prairie and set up the tent and fit the sooty lengths of stovepipe through the roof thimble, and anchor themselves to the earth with iron picket pins, the only thing they could drive into the frozen ground.

After an hour or two the stove would soften up the ground close around it, but near the edges and under their beds it never thawed more than just enough to moisten the tarps and freeze the beds fast, so that they pulled them up in the morning with great ripping sounds. The tent walls that they banked with snow to keep out the wind had to be chopped free every morning, and wore their clots and sheets of ice from one day to the next.

That cloth house stamped itself into Rusty's mind and memory. It spoke so plainly of the frailty and impermanence of their intrusion. And yet that frailty, and the implication of danger behind it, was what most nettled and dared and challenged him. Difficult as this job was, it was still only a job, and one done in collaboration with seven others. It called only for endurance; it had very little of the quality of the heroic that he had imagined Saskatchewan enforced upon the men who took its dare. Sometime, somehow, after he had gone through this apprenticeship in the skills of survival, he would challenge the country alone—some journey, some feat, some action that would demand of him every ounce of what he knew he had to give. There would be a real testing, and a real proof, and the certainty ever afterward of what one was. The expectation had no shape in his mind, but he thought of it in the same way he might have thought of sailing a small boat singlehanded across the Atlantic, or making a one-man expedition to climb Everest. It would be something big and it would crack every muscle and nerve and he would have to stand up to it alone, as Henry Kelsey had, wandering two years alone among unheard-of tribes in country not even rumored, or as young Alexander Mackenzie did when he took off from Fort Chippewyan to open the mysterious Northwest and track down the river that carried his name. There were even times when he thought of the wolfer Schulz with near envy. Like him or not, he didn't run in pack, he was of an older and tougher breed, he knew precisely what he was made of and what he could do, and he was the sort from whom one might learn something.

Meantime he was the greenhorn, the outcast tenderfoot of the outfit, and he would remain so until he personally turned a stampeding herd, or rode seventy-five miles and back in twenty-four hours to bring a doctor for someone critically hurt, or plucked somebody from under the horns of a crazy longhorn steer. He nursed his sore shoulder, evidence of his so-far failure to perform heroically, like a grudge that must sometime be settled, or a humiliation that must be wiped out.

The first night, when he had come out and confronted a sinking moon and a rising banner of Northern Lights, and the other one, after his fall, when he had been tempted into a yell of defiance, had several counterparts. Sometimes, riding around the dark mass of the herd, numbly aware of the click of hoofs, the sigh of a cow heaving to her feet, the flurry of movement from a scared or lost calf, the muted tramplings and mooings and lowings, it seemed he guarded all life inside his round, and heard its confusion and discomfort and dismay, and witnessed its unsleeping vigilance against the dangers that might come at it from outside the ritual circle his pony trod. The fact of living, more even than the fact of a job or a duty or the personal need to prove himself fit to call himself man in this country's own terms, bound him to the cattle. The steam that hung above them was relative to the breath that plumed before his own face. It seemed to him a fact of tremendous significance that a cow never closed its eyes in sleep in all its life. These calves were on watch against the world from the time their mothers licked away the membrane from their wet faces until the axe fell between their eyes in Kansas City or Chicago. He felt that nothing living could afford *not* to be on guard, and that the warm blood of men and cattle was in league against the forces of cold and death. Like theirs, his mortality mooed and bellowed, keeping up its courage with its voice or complaining of its discomfort. He sang to the herd, or to himself, and sometimes played them tunes on the harmonica.

They had to be content with a limited repertoire—the mouth organ had been his study for no more than ten days, on the boat coming over—so that he found himself running through a few songs many times. Sometimes, for variety, he rendered, talking aloud to himself, the pony, and the cattle, like a fool or a hermit, certain poems, especially one he had memorized in his first enthusiasm for Canada—a ballad of *coureurs de bois* and of a stranger that walked beside them and left no footprints in the snow. When he had succeeded in scaring himself with ghosts and shadows he might fall back upon a jigging Canuck tune,

> Rouli roulant, ma boule roulant,
> Rouli roulant ma boule.

But everything he said or played or sang during his hours on the night herd was meant seriously, even soberly, even ritually, for he felt in every deceptive snow-shadow and every pulse of the Northern Lights and every movement of the night wind the presence of something ancient and terrible, to which the brief stir and warmth of life were totally alien, and which must be met head on.

On those miraculously beautiful and murderously cold nights glittering with the green and blue darts from a sky like polished dark metal, when the moon had gone down, leaving the hollow heavens to the stars and the overflowing cold light of the Aurora, he thought he had moments of the clearest vision and saw himself plain in a universe simple, callous, and magnificent. In every direction from their pallid soapbubble of shelter the snow spread; here and there the implacable plain glinted back a spark—the beam of a cold star reflected in a crystal of ice.

He was young and susceptible, but he was probably not far wrong in his feeling that there never was a lonelier land, and one in which men lived more uneasily on sufferance. And he thought he knew the answer to the challenge Saskatchewan tossed him: to be invincibly strong, indefinitely enduring, uncompromisingly self-reliant, to depend on no one, to contain within himself every strength and every skill. There were evenings when he sorted through the outfit, examining models, trying on for fit Ray Henry's iron, Slip's whalebone, Little Horn's leather. Though he had ambitions beyond any of them, he admitted that there was not a man in the outfit who could not teach him something, unless it was Spurlock. And Spurlock, he perceived, was the one on whom he might have to prove himself. The others would tease him, Little Horn and Jesse would pull his leg, Panguingue would thump him in brainless good humor, but Spurlock would push his nasty little nagging persecution until he might have to be smashed. It even occurred to Rusty once or twice that that was exactly what Spurlock wanted: a test of strength. Well, so be it. Riding narrow-eyed, he compared their physical equipment. Spurlock probably had some weight on him, and Rusty had a picture in his mind of big hands, thick wrists. On the other hand, Spurlock must be at least thirty-five, and it was said that for five years he had dealt in a Butte gambling joint, an occupation to soften and weaken a man. Let him come; he might not be half as tough as he sounded or acted; and in any case, let him come.

And then, with singing stopped, and talking stopped, and harmonica stopped, riding slowly, thinking of challenges and anticipating crises and bracing himself against whatever might come, he might have word from his night companions of the prairie, and hear the *yap-yap-yap* and the shivering howl of coyotes, or the faint dark monotone of the wolves. Far more than the cattle or their protectors, they were the proper possessors of the wilderness, and their yelling was a sound more appropriate there than human curses or growls or songs, or the wheezy chords of the mouth organ, and certainly than the half-scared screech of defiance he had let off that one night. The wolves' hunting noises were always far off, back north in the river bottoms. In the eerie clarity of the white nights they seemed to cry from inexpressible distances, faint and musical and clear, and he might have been tempted to think of them as something not earthly at all, as creatures immune to cold and hunger and pain, hunting only for the wolfish joy of running and perhaps not even visible to human eyes, if he had not one afternoon ridden through a coulee where they had bloodied half an acre with a calf.

By day the labor and the cold and the stiffness of many hours in the saddle, the bawling of calves, the crackle and crunch of hoofs and wheels, the reluctant herded movement of two or three hundred cows and calves and six dozen horses, all of whom stopped at every patch of grass blown bare and had to be whacked into moving again. By night the patient circling ride around the herd, the exposure to stars and space and the eloquent speech of the wolves, and finally the crowded sleep.

Nothing between them and the stars, nothing between them and the North Pole, nothing between them and the wolves, except a twelve by sixteen house of cloth so thin that every wind moved it and light showed through it and the shadows of men hulked angling along its slope, its roof so peppered with spark holes that lying in their beds they caught squinting glimpses of the stars. The silence gulped their little disturbances, their little tinklings and snorings and sighs and the muffled noises of discomfort and weariness. The earth and the sky gaped for them like opened jaws; they lay there like lozenges on a tongue, ready to be swallowed.

In spite of his dream of a test hoped-for, met, and passed, the tenderfoot pitied himself, rather. The pain of his arm as he lay on the frozen ground kept him turning sleeplessly. Some nights his fingers throbbed as if he had smashed them with a maul, and his feet ached all night with chilblains. To be compelled to bear these discomforts and these crippling but unvaliant pains he considered privately an outrage.

They told each other that it couldn't last—and yet they half prayed it would, because cold as it was, it was working weather: they could collect and move their herd in it. Nevertheless the boys spoke of change, and said that this early in November, weather like this shouldn't last more than a few days, and that the sundogs meant something for sure. Not at all fond of what they had, they feared what might replace it.

At the end of the eighth day, with a herd of nearly four hundred cows and calves and two dozen bulls, they camped within ten miles of Horse Camp Coulee. The streaked sky of sunset hazed out in dusk. Before Jesse had supper hot the wind was whistling in the tent ropes and leaning on the roof in strange erratic patches, as if animals were jumping on the canvas. In an hour more they were outside trying to keep the tent from blowing away, half a dozen of them hauling the wagon by hand around on the windward side and anchoring the tent to it. The darkness was full of snow pebbles hard and stinging as shot, whether falling or only drifting they couldn't tell, that beat their eyes shut and melted in their beards and froze again. While they were fighting with the tent, Slip came in from the cattle herd and talked with Ray. He did not go back; it would have been risking a man's life to try to keep him riding. They did not discuss what was likely to happen to the cattle, though even Rusty could guess; they crawled into their beds to keep warm, let the fire go out to save fuel, gave at least modified thanks for the fact that they would not have to ride night herd, and because they could do nothing else, they slept.

They slept most of the time for the next two days. When the wind eased off and they dug their way out, the wagon and the tent were surrounded by a horned dune of snow. Snow lay out across the plains in the gray, overcast afternoon, long rippled drifts like an ocean petrified in mid-swell, a dull, expressionless, unlit and unshadowed sea. There was not a sign of the herd; the only horses in sight were the four they had kept miserably tied to the wagon—Jesse's Clydes and two night saddle ponies.

Slip and Little Horn hunted up the horses, far downwind, before dark. They reported bunches of cattle scattered through all the coulees in that direction for a dozen miles. They also found that range steers had drifted in among them during the storm, which meant that all of that separation of whiteface and longhorn and steer and cow and calf had to be gone through again.

The prospect appalled Rusty Cullen; he waited for them to say it couldn't be done, that they would give it up and head for the ranch. It apparently never even occurred to Ray that they might quit. They simply chased and swore and floundered through the drifts, and wore out horses and changed to others, and worked till they couldn't see, and fell into their beds after dark with about a hundred head reassembled. Next day they swung around in a big half circle to the south and east and brought together about a hundred and fifty more.

Sweeping up a few strays as they went, they moved on the third day toward the corrals at Horse Camp Coulee and made half of the ten miles they had to cover. The hard part was about over. They spoke at supper of Molly Henry's dried apple pies, disparaging Jesse's beefsteak and beans. That night, sometime between midnight and dawn, the wind reached down out of the iron north and brought them a new blizzard.

Into a night unfamiliarly black, whirling with snow, a chaos of dark and cold and the howl of a wind that sometimes all but lifted them from their feet, they struggled out stiff and clumsy with sleep, voiceless with outrage, and again anchored themselves to that unspeakable plain. While they fought and groped with ropes in their hands, ducking from the lash of wind and snow, apparitions appeared right among them, stumbled over a guy rope and almost tore the tent down, snorted and bolted blindly into the smother: range horses drifting before the storm. The cowboys cursed them and repaired their damage and got themselves as secure as they could and crawled back into their blankets, knowing sullenly what the drifting horses meant. When they dug out of this one they would have lost their herd again.

Jesse had started the fire as soon as it seemed clear that the tent would not go down. When Rusty had got back into his bed next to Buck, with Panguingue's feet jammed for a headboard against his skull, he could see the glow through the draft door and feel his stung face loosening in the warmth. The canvas roof bucked and strained, slacked off, stiffened in a blast. The wind came through in needles of cold. It was close to morning; he could make out the faint shapes inside the tent. He waited for Ray to say something—something to console them, perhaps, for their failure and their bad luck—but no one spoke at all. They lay appraising the turmoil half seen and half heard on the straining roof. Finally, after several minutes, Jesse said, "Anybody feel like a cup of coffee?"

Only then did Ray speak. His hoarse, ironic whisper croaked across the tent, "Looks like you boys could have the day off. Sleep in, if you want."

"Sleep!" Ed Spurlock said. "How could anybody sleep when he thinks where them God damn cows are going?"

"Just the same you better sleep," Ray whispered. "You'll need your rest, boy."

"You going to try rounding them up again?"

Ray said, "We're in this business to raise calves, not fertilize some prairie with their carcasses."

"*Jesus!*" Spurlock said. He rocked his head back and forth on his rolled mackinaw, glaring at the tent roof with eyes that shone oilily in the glimmer from the firebox. The wind took hold of the tent and shook it, testing every rope; they waited till the blast let go again. "You can't drive cows in this kind of weather, Ray," Spurlock said.

"I know it," Ray whispered. "That's why you get the day off."

"I bet you we end up by leaving the whole herd to scatter."

"We do, we'll lose ever' damn calf," Ray said. His face turned and craned toward Spurlock, above and across from him. His indomitable croak said, "I don't aim to lose any, if work'll save 'em."

"No, I can see," Spurlock said. "You might lose a few of us though."

Ray laughed through his nose. "Why, Ed," he said, "you sound like you thought you was more valuable than a calf."

"I'd kind of like some coffee, myself," old Jesse said. "Don't anybody else feel thataway?"

"Shut up!" said Buck's voice from under the blankets. He had a capacity for always sounding furious, even when he was talking through four layers of wool. "Shut up and let a guy get some sleep."

Panguingue produced a few exaggerated snores.

There was a brief silence. The wind gripped the tent, fell away, pounced once more; they could hear it whining and ricocheting off the guy ropes. "Good God," Ed Spurlock said restlessly, "listen to the God damn wind blow."

"I think I'll just put the pot on anyhow, long as we got that fire," Jesse's soft voice said. Rusty heard the stiff creak of his bedroll tarp and the fumbling sounds as he got on his boots. There was a grunt, and Spurlock said savagely, "God damn it to hell, Jesse, watch out where you put your feet!"

"Don't leave your face hanging out, then," Jesse said. "How can I see your face in this dark? I been huntin' for ten minutes with both hands, and I just now found my ass."

"Step on me once more and you'll find it in a sling," Spurlock said. "Why can't you stay in bed? There's nothing to get up for."

"Yes there is," Jesse said. "Coffee."

His shape reared up against the graying canvas; when he opened the lid the glow from the stove illuminated his intent face with the white bristles on cheeks and chin, and the mustache drooping in a smooth oxbow. This, Rusty thought, was all familiar to Jesse. He must have done this same thing, camped in the same brutal kind of weather, a hundred times, with Indians, with *métis hivernants,* with hide hunters, with wagon trains hauling supplies into the Montana camps, with cattle outfits like this one. His relation to the country was almost as simple as that of the wolves; no matter how fast the province changed, it remained to Jesse merely a few known forms of hardship, a known violence of weather, one or two simple but irreplaceable skills. He had the air, standing ruminatively above his stove, of a man who could conceive of no evil that a cup of hot coffee or a beefsteak fried in flour would not cure.

Daylight came as dusk and stayed that way. They dozed, and when the fire was up high for cooking they took advantage of the warmth to play poker or blackjack. When anyone had to go outside he took a look at the horses, which they had picketed to give them a little more chance to move around and keep warm, but which crowded close up against the wagon for the little shelter it gave them. Morning and evening someone hung on their noses a nosebag of their limited oat supply.

Their wood was running low too; they had been depending on getting fuel from the willows in Horse Camp Coulee. After meals they had to let the fire die, and then if they played cards they passed around a lighted candle to warm their hands by. When even that got too cold they dug down under their blankets to sleep or think. Talk flared up like matches and went out again; they cocked their ears to the howl of the wind, remoter as the tent snowed in. Once or twice one of them went out and carefully cleared the worst of the snow off the roof while the rest, inside, watched with concern the sausage-tight canvas which a careless shovel might easily slit, leaving them exposed to the storm like an out-turned nest of mice. Every hour or so Ray Henry, taciturn and expressionless, took a look outside.

When he had got his hands well warmed under the blankets, Rusty played the harmonica. There were more requests than he could gratify, with a heavy favoritism for old Red River tunes which they tried to teach him by whistling or humming. If he quit, with his hands too numb to feel the fingers and his chapped lips sore from the sliding of the little honeycomb back and forth across them, they urged him for a while, and then cursed him languidly and gave up. The afternoon waned; they yawned; they lay resting.

Once the notebook in his shirt pocket crunched as Rusty turned over, and he took it out and amused himself for a while reading the journal entries he had made. There was nothing since his catalog of information about the Stonepile Camp, but before that there was a very windy and prize-essay series of notations. He had put them down in the first place as colorful items to be incorporated into letters home: they expected him not to write very often, and he would oblige them; but they expected him, when he did write, to fill pages with cowboys and Indians and wild game and the adventures and observations of a well-educated young gentleman in the North American wilderness. In this too he had set out to oblige them. He read what he had had to say about the ranch, and the thumbnail sketches he had made of some of the cowboys, and the lyrical flights he had gone into during the days of perfect Indian Summer hay-making weather that preceded the first storm—only the night before they had set out on this belated roundup. He could imagine the family all around his mother as she read, and he cocked an inner ear to the sound of his own prose describing the apelike Panguingue with his good nature and his total disregard for cleanliness, and wry little birdy Slippers with his sore feet, as if he had walked all the way from Texas; even on roundup he wore no boots like the rest of them but elastic-sided slippers under his overshoes. Rusty told them Slip was the best bronc rider in Saskatchewan, which may have been going it a bit strong, and about how Buck kept a row of tobacco tins on the two-by-four above his bunk, with all his smaller private effects filed away in them in neat and labeled order. He described, with the proper tone of sober appraisal and respect, Ray Henry and his new wife, whom he had brought from Malta, Montana, in a buckboard, a hundred and twenty miles across country, for a wedding trip. Rusty had loaded that part of the journal with data on the country, much of it, as he saw now, in error. It was the sort of stuff which, written as a letter, would surely set his younger brother to itching, and produce another emigration from the family, but it seemed false and shrilly enthusiastic and very, very young when he read it over in the tent, while a frozen guy rope outside, within three feet of his ear, hummed like a great struck cable.

"What you got there, Rusty?" Little Horn said. "Something to read?"

"No," he said. "Oh no, just an old notebook."

"Notebook?" Spurlock said.

"Just . . . notes, don't you know," Rusty said. He was frantic with the notion that they would sit on him and take it away from him and read in it what he had said about them. If they tried it he would die fighting. He put it in his shirt pocket and buttoned it down. "Things I wanted to remember to put in letters home," he said.

"All about the cow country and the cattle business, uh?" Little Horn said.

"More or less."

"She's a real good business," Little Horn said. "You ought to think about her, Rusty." Staring at the roof, his red nose one of a half dozen projecting toward the lashed and laboring canvas, he plucked a thread from the frayed edge of his blanket and drew it dreamily between his front teeth. "Young fella from the old country could do a lot worse," he said. "There's this Englishman over on Medicine Lodge Coulee, kind of a remittance-man colony they got over there, he was tellin' me about cattle ranchin' one time. He said there was millions in it. All you do, you just get some cows and a few bulls, and you turn 'em out on the range. Say you start with a hundred cows. You get a hundred calves the first year, and fifty of them are cows and fifty you make into steers. Next year you got a hundred and fifty cows and they give you a hundred and fifty calves, and you make seventy-five steers and keep the seventy-five cows, and that builds your breeding herd to two hundred and twenty-five. That year you get two hundred and twenty-five calves, and by now you're sellin' your two-year-old and three-year-old steers, and your herd keeps growin' and you keep sellin' the bull calves, and that's all they is to her. He had it all mapped out. You ought to talk to him, Rusty."

"I'll look into it the first chance I get," Rusty said. "I've been inquiring around for a good opportunity."

"You do that," Little Horn said. "If I didn't have me this job here with Ray, I'd do somethin' about it myself. There ain't a thing to her. Once you get your herd and start them cows to calfin', all you do is set back and count the dollars rollin' in.

"They'll tell you: mange. Hell, they ain't nothin' to mange. All you got to do about that, you dip 'em twice a year. You get yourself one of them steam boilers and a tank, and you lay in some sulphur and so on. And you dig yourself a big hole in the ground, maybe a hundred feet long, say, and thirty wide, and at one end you build a couple corrals, one big one to hold maybe a couple hundred head and the other a little one to take a dozen or so. From this little one you build a chute that leads down into the hole. At the other end of the hole you make a slatted slope out of planks for the cows to climb out on, and a couple drippin' pens where the ones that has been dipped can stand, and under those pens you dig a ditch so the dip that runs off them can run back into the vat. It ain't anything, hardly. If you got ten or fifteen hands around it'll only take you a couple-three weeks' hard work altogether to build this rig.

"Then you bring your stock into the big corral, see, and feed 'em out a few at a time into the little corral and on into the chute, and on both sides of the vat you put guys with long poles with a yoke onto them, and they get the yoke over these cattle as they come down the chute and duck 'em clear under. Then you prod 'em on through the vat and up the slope and into the drippin' pens and you're done with that bunch.

"They'll tell you it's lots of work. Shucks. You got, say, ten thousand head to dip, like we would on the T-Down, and you got maybe twelve men in the outfit. You can do a dozen ever' twenty minutes, thirty-six an hour, three hundred and sixty in a ten-hour day, thirty-six hundred in ten days. You can get the whole herd through in three or four weeks, if you can get the inspector there when you want him. They'll tell you it's hell to catch the inspector, and hard to keep the herd together that long, and hard to keep the sulphur mixture strong enough and the right temperature, and a lot like that, but it ain't nothing to bother a man. Some people would talk down anything.

"Or they'll tell you it's dangerous. Shoot! Suppose one of them steers does get on the peck when he's pushed under and gets his eyes full of sulphur, what can he do? He can thrash around in the vat, maybe, and drowned himself or some other steer, or maybe he climbs out and chases you up onto the barn, or he scrambles back into the corral and gets them to millin' there till they break something down, but that ain't only a little delay. Even if some old ringy longhorn catches you before you can climb out of the corral, what can he do to you? His horns is so wide he just rams you against the fence with his forehead and holds you there till somebody twists his tail or spits Bull Durham in his eye and pulls him off, and there you are good as ever, maybe bruised up some is all.

"No, sir," Little Horn said, pulling his thread back and forth, "it's a mistake to listen to these calamity howlers about what a tough business the cow business is. Mange, that's only a sample of how they exaggerate. They'll tell you: wolves. Wolves! They won't pick off more'n one calf in ten or twenty all winter long. Sure three or four of them will pull down a cow sometimes, get her by the hind leg and a flank and pull her over and pile on, but mostly it's just calves. Say you start with two thousand head in the fall, you still got eighteen hundred in the spring. And if you want to, you can hire somebody like this Schulz to wolf your range."

"Schulz!" Buck said from down under. "I wonder if he's et his boy yet?"

"Only cost you ten dollars a scalp," Little Horn said. "If he puts out poison baits, course you might lose a few dogs. Sure a wolf is hard to poison and he's too smart to step in a trap or come within gunshot very often, but that don't have to bother you. There's other ways of handlin' wolves. You just lay around and keep an eye open and when you catch one out on the flats you can run him down on a horse. I did it once myself. I had me a little old pony that could run, and I come right up on that old white wolf and run over him. I missed him that first time, somehow, and had to come over him again, and I missed him again, but I kep' tryin'. This wolf can't get away—he's down there under the pony's feet somewhere duckin' and snarlin'. I'd of had him sure if the pony hadn't of stepped in a hole. The wolf run off then and I couldn't chase him. I was out quite a few miles, and after I shot the horse I had me quite a walk carryin' the saddle, but that experience taught me quite a bit about runnin' down wolves, and I know how it's done. I'll show you sometime, if you want."

"Oh, I say, thanks," Rusty said.

"Old Rusty, I bet he figures just like your other Englishman," Spurlock said. "Ain't it the fact, Rusty? You come out here thinking you'd get yourself a few thousand acres and a herd of cows and be a lord of the manor like Dan Tenaille, uh?"

"That's right," Rusty said. "Just now, I'm out here learning the business first hand from the experts."

"Or did you *have* to come out?" Spurlock said. "You're a remittance man too, ain't you? Tell us the story of how you happened to leave England. I bet it'd be interesting. Help pass the time, don't you know."

"I'm afraid you'd find it a bit dull."

"A bit dull?" Spurlock said heartily. "Not at all, lad, not at all. Come on, give us your reasons for trailing out to the cow country."

They were not a talking bunch, and so far as he knew they had not discussed him. He was too common a phenomenon. Unless he took pains to prove himself otherwise, any young Englishman in that country was assumed to be the second son, third son, scapegrace son, of a baronet, a KCB, a shooting partner of Edward VII. Or he was a cashiered guardsman or disgraced country vicar. Rusty was none of those, but it seemed unnecessary to insist. He said only, "I'm afraid my reasons wouldn't be as colorful as yours."

He put into his voice just the quantity of sneer that would make Spurlock rise up without realizing precisely where he was stung. Or perhaps the sneer did not do it at all, perhaps Spurlock was only bored, uncomfortable, irritable, ready to pluck any little thread that would ravel, quarrelsome out of no motive except tedium. If that was it, fine; let him come. And there he came, rearing up on one elbow and throwing across the tent a literary badman look as if he thought he was wearing black gloves and black guns like a villain in *The Virginian.* "What do you mean by that, exactly?"

From the side, Ray Henry's whisper said, "The kid's not crowding you any, Ed."

"I can tell when I'm crowded," Spurlock said.

"Pull in your elbows," Ray whispered, amused. "Then you'll have more room."

Spurlock lay down again. "Little English punks," he said. "Coming out pretending to be cowhands."

Rusty looked at Ray, but Ray only smiled. The boy said, fairly hotly, "The cows can't tell the difference."

"No," Spurlock said, "no, but a man sure can."

"I haven't heard any *men* discussing it."

Once more he reared up on his elbow. "Is its little arm sore?" he said. "Got piled, did it?"

"How are its little sore eyes?" Rusty said. Out of nothing, out of nowhere, as random and unprepared for as an August whirlwind kicking up a dust, Spurlock had produced the quarrel he evidently wanted. Rusty was angry enough to take him on, arm or no arm. He pretended to himself that he was annoyed with Ray when the foreman whispered equably, "In about a second I'm kickin' both you quarrelsome bastards out in the snow."

Rusty lay ready, smoldering, waiting for Spurlock to say something else that could not be borne, or to rise and stalk outside where it would be necessary to go out and fight him. But Spurlock did not move or speak; he only breathed through his nose in so eloquent and contemptuous a way that Rusty had to hold himself back from springing over and smashing him. The wind slammed against their canvas roof in a furious gust. Against some rope or edge or corner it howled like a wolf, and then trailed off to the steady whisper and rush again.

"They'll tell you," Little Horn said dreamily, "they'll say to you it's terrible hard work. Why, God damn, now, you just can't pay attention to that. How long we been on this-here roundup? Since first of May, more or less? And it's only November now. And they'll tell you it gets cold, but where would you find a nicer, more comfortable little tent than this one, if we only had some wood?"

Jesse crawled out and stood stretching in the narrow space among the mussed beds. Rusty noticed that he was careful to stay clear of Ed Spurlock's blankets. "Well," he said, "time for a little grub?"

Ray went past Jesse and pulled the flap aside and looked out. Beyond him the horizontal blast streaked with snow dipped and swirled; flakes settled and whirled away again; there was a curved drift building up at the tent corner. Ray's back looked bulky and solid; he was a powerful man, single-minded and devoted. A little hollow in the solar plexus from the nearness of a fight, Rusty had a wry feeling that if Spurlock and he had started something, and the foreman wanted to interfere, he could have thrashed them both. But what his hunched back and his bent head reminded Rusty of really was the burden he bore. He was foreman, he wore responsibility for both men and cattle, and he had left his bride of less than a month at the ranch house with only a crippled handy man for company. Rusty did not envy Ray, but he respected him a great deal. He wanted to do well for him; he was ashamed of having had to be reprimanded along with Spurlock. The foreman dropped the flap and came back and sat down.

"They'll tell you," Little Horn said, endless and ironic and contemplative, "they'll say, all that ridin' and brandin' and weanin' and nuttin' and chasin' cows up and down the hills and dales. How else would you want a cowpuncher to spend his time? He don't have any work to do, he just gets himself into trouble playin' cyards and fightin' and chasin' women. Lots better for him to be out in a nice tent like this, camped out comfortable in some blizzard."

Sometime before the gray afternoon howled itself out, Ray Henry shouldered into his sheepskin and went outside. The rest lay in their blankets, which they had inhabited too long for their blankets' good or their own, in their postures that were like the postures of men fallen in war. Panguingue sprawled with his drawn-up knees wide, his whiskered face glimmering a vacant grin straight upward. Little Horn and Buck were unexpected angles of arms and legs, Slip lay curled as if around a mortal body wound. Spurlock had locked his hands under the back of his head and crossed his knees under the covers. They listened to the undiminished wind. After what may have been ten minutes Jesse rose and said he guessed he'd take a look at the Clydes. He followed his jet of white breath outside, and they lay on.

Their cloth house shook, and gave way, and shuddered stiff and tight again. They heard the whistle and scream go flying through and away, and in a lull Buck said, "This one's the worst one yet." They lay considering this for quite a long time. At last Rusty heard the sound of feet, and with a relief that astonished him he cried, "Here they are!"

But no one entered. The wind pounded through and over and past. It had a curving sound; it dipped to the ear like telegraph wires to the eye. Everyone in the tent was listening for the steps Rusty had announced. At last Spurlock grumbled, "Just fawncy." Panguingue blurted a laugh.

"Christ a'mighty!" Slip said abruptly, and snapped nimble as a monkey out of his bed. He was stepping in his slippers across Ray Henry's tarp when the flap opened and Ray and Jesse stooped in on a flurry of snow. Slippers sat quietly down again on his blankets. His leathery, deeply lined, big-nosed face said nothing. Neither did any of the other smudged and whiskered faces around the tent. But they were all sitting up or half propped on their elbows; the concern that had moved Slip had been a fear in all of them. In silence they watched Ray throw down beside the cold stove three or four round cake-like chunks of ice. Rusty reached across and picked up a frozen cowchip.

"Are we burning ice now?"

With a wipe of a bare hand around on his wet, beef-red face, the foreman said, "We may be lucky to have that to burn, it's drifting pretty deep all over."

"Still from the northwest?" Buck asked.

"Oh dear," said Little Horn. "All those poor little calves and their mamas. They'll be clear the hell and gone down to Wood Mountain."

"Or else they'll be piled up in some draw," Ray said.

"You think it's pretty bad, then," Rusty said—a small, inconsequent, intrusive voice of ignorance and greenness that he himself heard with shame and dismay.

"Yes, kid," Ray said. "I think it's pretty bad."

They ebbed away into silence. With only a few sticks of wood left Jesse gave them no more for supper than warm gravy poured over frozen biscuits; not even coffee. Part of the stove, while the gravy was warming, held two of the cowchips that Ray had kicked up from under the snow, and the smell of wetted and baking manure flavored their supper. But at least the cakes dried out enough so that Jesse could use them for the breakfast fire.

The single candle gave a blotted light. When they were all still Rusty saw the humps of bedrolls fuming like a geyser basin with their eight breaths, until Little Horn said, "Well, nighty-night, kids," and blew out the candle. The wind seemed to come down on their sudden darkness with such violence that in the cold tent they lay tensely, afraid something would give. Both Slip and Little Horn had pulled their goatskin chaps over their beds for extra cover. Rusty's icy hands were folded into his armpits; he wore all his clothes except sheepskin and boots. He blew his breath into the air, moved his sore shoulder experimentally, smelled his own stale nest, thinking Holy Mother, if my people could see me now! There was a brief, vivid picture of rescuers in the spring reverently uncovering eight huddled figures, identifying each one, folding the tarp back over the frozen face. His head was full of vague heroisms related to Commodore Peary and the North Pole.

Once the thought popped whole and astonishing into his head: I might, except for one or two decisions made in excitement and stuck to through tears and argument, be sleeping in my old room right now, and if I opened my eyes I would see the model of the *Kraken* hanging from the ceiling like a ship of thanksgiving in a Danish church. Except for the excitement that his father thought wild whimsy and his mother thought heartlessness, he might be getting his exercise these days pushing a punt up and down the Cher, disturbing the swans (Swans! From here they sounded fabulous as gryphons), or drinking too much port with sporty undergraduates from his college, or sitting on some cricket pitch, or (assuming he *hadn't* chosen Oxford and the family's program) he might be guiding the tiller of the yawl with his backside while he shouted questions, jeers, comments, or other conversation at sailors leaning over the stern rails of old rustpots anchored in the stream off Spithead.

The fact that he was here in a tent on the freezing Saskatchewan plains, that one decision rashly made and stubbornly stuck to had taken him not only out of the university, out of home, out of England, but out of a whole life and culture that had been assumed for him, left him dazed. A good job he didn't have much chance to think, or he might funk it yet, and run straight home with his tail tucked. He was appalled at the effectiveness of his own will.

A numbness like freezing to death stole through him gradually, Panguingue restored him to wakefulness with a kick in the head, and he cursed Panguingue with a freedom he would not have adopted toward anyone else in the outfit. Sometime during or just after the flurry of profane protest he fell asleep.

Solitary flutes, songs from the Vienna woods, chirpings and twitterings so that he opened his eyes thinking *Birds?* and heard the awakening sounds of the outfit, and old Jesse whistling with loose lips while he stood over the stove. He lifted a can and tipped it in a quick gesture; the tent filled with the smell of kerosene. Jesse hobbled about in his boots like an old crone. His right knee crooked upward, there was a swoop and a snap, and a match popped into flame across his tight seat. The stove *whoofed* out a puff of smoke. The lids clanged on. Fire gleamed through the cracks in the ash door and Jesse shoved the coffee pot against the stovepipe. Looking, Rusty saw that Ray, Slip, and Buck were missing.

He sat up. "I say! The wind's died!"

"You say, hey?" Jesse said.

Rusty hustled to the door and looked out. Deep tracks went through the drift that curved all around them; the sky was palest blue, absolutely clear. Ray was trotting the Clydes up and down a fifty-foot trampled space, getting them warm. Their breasts and rumps and legs were completely coated in ice. Buck and Slip already had saddles on the night ponies. Whatever had been brown in the landscape had disappeared. There were no scraggly patches of bare grass in the snow waves, but packed, rippled white ran off into the southeast where the sun was just rising. He could almost see the plain move as if a current ran strongly toward where the sun squatted on the rim and sent its dazzle skipping across the million little wave crests into his eyes. Spurlock, looking over his shoulder, swore foully. "Here goes for some more God damn snowblindness." He stepped past Rusty and blew his nose with his fingers, first one nostril, then the other. Rusty shouted over to Ray, "Working weather!"

"Yeah." He laughed his dry laugh through his nose. "Come here and curry some of the ice out of these studs."

"Uh-huh!" Spurlock said behind Rusty, with I-told-you-so emphasis. The boy stared at him. "Working weather!" Spurlock said. "Jesus Christ! I guess."

His guess was right. Within minutes of the time Rusty woke he was working; they paused only long enough to bolt a steak and gulp scalding coffee and warm their hands over the fire; their last wood and all the cowchips had gone into it. Before they had more than spread their palms to the beautiful heat, Slip and Buck came in with the horse herd.

"Jesse," Ray said, "you better tear down here and get loaded and beat it on a beeline for Horse Camp. If we ain't there when you get there, which we won't be, you can improve your time and warm your blood gettin' in wood, and there ain't any such thing as too much. The rest of you is goin' to round up every cow within fifteen miles downwind, and we're going to put them all in the corrals at Horse Camp before we sleep any more. So pick you a pony with some bottom."

They looked at the shaggy, scrawny, long-maned and long-tailed herd picking at the wisps of a few forkfuls of hay that the boys had thrown out. There was not a pony among them whose ribs did not show plainly under the rough winter hair. Here and there one stood spraddled, head hanging, done in, ready to fall.

"Boneracks," Little Horn said. "Some of them ponies ain't goin' to make it, Boss."

"Then we got to leave them," Ray said. "They can maybe make out, poor as they are, but unless we get a chinook this is starvin' time for cattle."

They saddled and rode out, Ray, Slip, Panguingue, and Rusty to the southeast, straight into the sun, Spurlock and Buck and Little Horn to the northeast. They would pinch everything in to the middle and then swing and bring them back. The tent was already coming down as they rode off.

They rode a long way before they raised any cattle. When they did, down in a draw, they were humped in the deep snow, making no effort to get out. They stood and bellowed; they moved as if their blood had frozen thick, and they had among them range steers, including a few longhorns, which the boys did not want at all but had no time to cut out. They threw them all into a bunch, and attended by an intensely black and unlikely looking crow, rode on into the diamond glitter, gradually swinging eastward so that they could get some relief by ducking their heads and pulling their hats clear down on the sun side. Ray kept them pushing hard through the difficult going, knee high sometimes, hock high the next moment, crusted just enough to hold the horse's weight for a split second before he broke down through. It was hard enough in the saddle; it must have been a good deal worse under it.

"Got to hustle," Ray said. "For some reason I'm gettin' so I don't trust the damn weather." They fanned out, riding wide. Far north, across a spread of flats and one or two shallow coulees whose depressions could hardly be seen in the even glare, the black dots that were Spurlock and Little Horn and Buck were strung out across a mile or so of snow. They headed in toward the center of their loop every sad whiteface whose red hide showed. The cattle bellowed, blinking white eyelashes, and they moved reluctantly, but they moved. The crow flapped over, following companionably, flying off on some investigation of his own and returning after a few minutes to coast over and cock his wise eye down and caw with laughter to hear them talk.

About noon, far to the south and east of where they had camped, they came to the river, angling down from the northwest in its shallow valley. The willows along the banks looked thin as a Chinaman's whiskers, hardly more than weeds, but they held a surprising number of cattle, which the outfit flushed out by the dozens and scores and hazed, plunging and ducking and blindly swinging back until a horse blocked them or a rope cut across their noses, up onto the flats. They had everything in that herd: whiteface, shorthorn, longhorn, all sorts of crosses; steers, cows, bulls, calves; T-Down, Circle Diamond, Turkey Track. Ray pointed some out to Rusty when they rested their ponies for a minute on the flat and let Slip chase a half-dozen whiteface yearlings back into the bottoms. "The Seventy-Six," he said. "Their range is way up by Gull Lake, on the CPR. They've drifted twenty-five miles."

Whatever they were, whoever they belonged to, if they could not be easily cut out the riders swept them in and drove them westward, pushing them without a pause toward Horse Camp. The afternoon changed from blue-white to lavender. The crow had left them—disgusted, Rusty thought, that they never stopped to eat and threw away no scraps. The trampled waste of snow bloomed for a minute or two a pure untroubled rose, and the sun was gone as if it had stepped in a hole. Gray-blue dusk, grateful to their seared eyes, lay in every slightest hollow; the snowplain was broken with unexpected irregularities. The "drag" of cows and calves slowed, poked along, stopped and had to be cursed and flogged into starting. Their ponies, poor boneracks, plodded gamely, and if a cow tried to break away or swing back they had to gather themselves like a tired swimmer taking one last stroke. Their breath was frozen all over them, stirrups and overshoes were enameled in ice; Rusty could hear his pony wheezing in his pipes, and his skinny ewe neck was down. He stumbled in the trodden snow.

It grew dark, and they went on, following Jesse's track, or whatever track it was that Ray kept, or no track at all, but only his wild-animal's sense of direction. The faint eruption of color in the west was gone; and then as the sky darkened, the stars were there, big and frosty and glittering, bright as lamps, and Rusty found the Dipper and Cassiopeia and the Pole Star, his total astronomy. He moved in his saddle, lame and numb, his face stiff, his shoulder aching clear down across his collarbone into his chest. Ahead of him, a moving blur on the snow, the herd stumbled and clicked and mooed, the joints of their random longhorns cracked, the traveling steam went up. Off to his right he heard Buck trying to sing—a sound so strange, revelatory, and forlorn that he had to laugh, and startled himself with the voiceless croak he produced.

How much farther? Up above, the sky was pure; the Northern Lights were beginning to flare and stretch. He heard his old friend the wolf hunting down the river valleys and coulees of his ordained home and speaking his wolfish mind to the indifferent stars. Lord God, how much longer? They had been in the saddle since six, had eaten nothing since then. Neither horse nor rider could take much more of this. But nobody said, We can stop now. Nobody said, We'll camp here. They couldn't, obviously. Jesse had taken their bubble of shelter God knew how many more empty miles to Horse Camp. He thought to himself, with a qualm of panic, My God, this is *desperate*. What if we don't find him? What if a horse should give clear out?

He gave his pony clumsy mittened pats; he enlisted its loyalty with words; it plodded and stumbled on.

Eventually there was a soft orange bloom of light, and shouts cut through the luminous murk, and as he stopped, confused, Ray Henry came riding from his left and they crowded the cattle into a tighter mass. Over their moving backs and the sounds of their distress and irritation he heard poles rattle; someone ki-yi-ed. Ray pushed his horse against the rear cattle and in his almost-gone whisper drove and urged them on. They moved, they broke aside, they were turned back; the mass crawled ahead, tedious, interminable, a toss and seethe of heads and horns, until suddenly it had shrunk and dwindled and was gone, and Panguingue was down in the snow, ramming gate poles home. The whole world smelled of cow.

They sat there all together, stupid with cold and fatigue; they dismounted like skeletons tied together with wire. Ray croaked, "Let's see if Jesse ain't got a spare oat or two for these ponies," and they walked toward the wagon and the bloom of the tent. The air, which had been bright at sunset and in the first hour of dark, was blurred as if a fog were rising from the snow; beyond the tent the faint shadow of the coulee fell away, but the other side was misted out. Rusty's eyes were so longingly on Jesse's shadow as he hopped around the stove, obviously cooking, that he fell over the pile of willows stacked by the wagon: Jesse had not wasted his time; there was cooking wood for a week.

"Dad," Ray called, "you got any oats? These ponies are about done."

The white head appeared in the flap, a hand with a fork in it held the canvas back, the soft old voice said, "I got a couple-three bushel left, I guess. That has to hold the Clydes and the night horses till we get back to the ranch."

"They'll have to get along," Ray said. "I'm afraid we're going to lose some ponies anyway. They just don't have the flesh for this kind of a job."

Rusty stood with the reins in his hand, letting Jesse and Ray heave the oat bag out of the wagon. The tent with its bloom of light and its smell of frying was a paradise he yearned for as he had never yearned for anything, but he had to stand there and care for the horse first, and he hated the poor beast for its dependence. It was no tireder than he was. Nevertheless Ray's was an inescapable example. He unsaddled and threw the saddle into the wagon; he tramped a little hollow in the snow and poured out a quart or two of oats and pulled his pony's bridle and let him drop his head to them. One after the other the outfit did the same. After what seemed an hour Rusty found the tent flap and crept in. The little stove was red hot; the air was full of smoke. Jesse had unrolled their beds for them. Rusty stepped over Buck and fell full length and shut his eyes. What little strength he had left flowed out of him and was soaked up; his bones and veins and skin held nothing but tiredness and pain.

Jesse hopped around, juggling pans, going on cheerfully. He had thought by God they were never going to get in. Chopped wood till he like to bust his back. (Yeah, said somebody, *you* did a day's work!) Horse herd come all the way with him, right along behind the pilot. Those few scraps of hay the other day made tame ponies of the whole bunch. Looks like you guys got a pretty good herd of calves, considering. Anybody like a cup of coffee now?

"By God," he said after a short silence, "you fellers look *beat.*" And after another little silence in which nobody spoke, but somebody groaned or grunted, Jesse said, "Here, I don't reckon coffee has got enough nourishment for the occasion."

Beside Rusty, Buck rolled over. Rusty opened his eyes. Slip and Little Horn had rolled over too. Ray was sitting on his bed, holding a quart of whisky, shaking his head. "Jesse," he said, "by God, remind me to raise your wages."

Their common emotion while Ray worked on the cork was reverence. They sat or lay around in a ring, as bleary a crew as ever ate with its fingers or blew its nose with the same all-purpose tool, and they watched each motion of his thick wrist and big dirty hand. None of them had shaved for more than two weeks; they had all, except possibly Buck, lost any right to browbeat Panguingue about his filthiness. They felt—or at least Rusty did—that they had endured much and labored incredibly. He wondered, as the greenest hand there, how well he had done, and hoped he had done at least passably, and knew with unaccustomed humility that he could not have done more. Considering everything, the three hundred odd cattle they had finally brought to the Horse Camp corrals were an achievement. The work still to be done, the separating and weaning, and the driving of calves and bulls to the home ranch, could only be trifling after what they had been through.

The stove's heat beat on their bearded red faces, the candles gleamed in their bloodshot eyes. They watched Ray Henry's thick hands, and when the cork slipped out of the neck with a soft *pok* some of them smiled involuntarily, and Panguingue giggled, a high, falsetto sound that set off another round of smiles and made Jesse say, "Listen at old Pan, he sounds like a jack after a mare."

Ray held the bottle to the light and looked through it; he shook it and watched the bead rise. He was like a priest before an altar. He would not hurry this. "Well," he said at last, "here's looking at you, boys," and tipped the bottle to his blackened mouth. They watched the contents gurgle around the spark of candle that lived inside the amber bottle. He let the bottle down. "Whah!" he said. "Kee-rist!" and wiped the neck politely with the heel of his palm and passed it to Slip, whose bed lay beside his next to the wall. The smell of whisky cut through the smoke of the tent; they sat like Indians in the medicine lodge and passed the ceremonial vessel around, and each, as he finished, wiped the neck carefully with his palm. Slip to Jesse, Jesse to Little Horn, Little Horn to Spurlock, Spurlock to Panguingue. Panguingue drank and shook his head and wiped the neck once and started to pass the bottle and then, as if not satisfied, wiped it again. Rusty loved him for it, he loved them all; he felt that he had never known so mannerly a group of men. Buck took the bottle from Panguingue, and from Buck it came to the greenhorn, its neck flavored with all their seven mouths and hands. He raised it to his mouth and let its fire wash down his throat and felt it sting in his cracked lips. His eyes watered. He lowered the bottle and choked down a cough, and as he passed the bottle back to Ray and talk broke out all at once, he took advantage of the noise and cleared his throat and so was not shamed.

"Well, Jesse," Ray said, "what do you think? Want to save that little-bitty dab?"

"Why, I can't see it'd be much good from now on," Jesse said.

They passed it around again, and their tongues were loosened. They told each other how cold it had been and how hard they had worked. Jesse had made up a raisin-and-rice pudding, practically a pailful. It was pure ambrosia; they ate it all and scraped the kettle, and for a few minutes after supper Rusty even roused up enough strength to get out the harmonica. There was not the slightest remnant left of the irritability they had felt with one another in the snowed-in time; the boy could feel how they had been welded and riveted into a society of friends and brothers. Little Horn sang some filthy verses of "The Old Chisholm Trail." Spurlock supplied some even filthier ones from "Johnny McGraw." The whole bunch joined in a couple of songs.

Then all at once they were done in again. The talk dropped away, Rusty put the harmonica in his pocket. They went outside and walked a few steps from the tent and stood in a row and made water, lifting their faces into the night air that was mistier than ever, and warmer than any night since they had left the ranch.

"I don't know," Ray said, sniffing for wind. "I don't quite like the looks of the sky."

"Oh but hell," they said. "Feel how warm it is."

He gave in doubtfully to their optimism. The mild air might mean snow, but it also might mean a chinook coming in, and that was the best luck they could hope for. There was not enough grass bare, even out on the flats, to give the cattle a chance to feed. Rusty had never seen or felt a chinook, but he was so positive this was the birth of one that he offered to bet Little Horn and Panguingue a dollar each that it was a chinook coming. They refused, saying they did not want to hoodoo the weather. Ray remarked that such weather as they had had couldn't be hoodooed any worse. They kicked the snow around, smelling the night air soft in their faces; it smelled like a thaw, though the snow underfoot was still as dry and granular as salt. Every minute or so a hungry calf bawled over in the corral.

"Well," Ray said, "maybe this is our break."

Rusty hardly heard him. His eyes were knotted, the nerves and veins snarled together, the lids heavy with sleep. Back inside the tent there was a brief flurry of movement as they crawled in. Somebody cursed somebody else feebly for throwing his chaps across him. He heard the fire settle in the stove; after a minute or two he was not sure whether it was the stove or the first whiffling of some sleeper. Then he was asleep too, one of the first.

But not even his dead tiredness could lift from him the habits of the last ten days. In his dreams he struggled against winds, he felt the bite of cold, he heard the clamor of men and animals and he knew that he had a duty to perform, he had somehow to shout "Here!" as one did at a roll call, but he was far down under something, struggling in the dark to come up and to break his voice free. His own nightmared sounds told him he was dreaming, and moaning in his sleep, and still he could not break free into wakefulness and shove the dream aside. Things were falling on him from above; he sheltered his head with his arms, rolled, and with a wrench broke loose from tormented sleep and sat up.

Panguingue was kicking him in the head through his blankets. He was freezing cold, with all his blankets wound around his neck and shoulders like shawls. By the light of a candle stuck on the cold stove lid he saw the rest all in the same state of confused, unbelieving awakening. There was a wild sound of wind; while he sat leaning away from Panguingue's feet, stupidly groping for his wits, a screeching blast hit the tent so hard that old Jesse, standing by the flap, grabbed the pole and held it until the shuddering strain gave way a little and the screech died to a howl.

Rusty saw the look of disbelief and outrage on every face; Panguingue's grin was a wolfish baring of teeth, his ordinary dull-witted good nature shocked clear out of him. "What is it?" Rusty asked idiotically. "Is it a chinook?"

"Chinook!" Buck said furiously.

He yanked his stiff chaps on over his pants and groped chattering for his boots. They were all dressing as fast as their dazed minds and numbed fingers would let them. Jesse let go the tent pole to break some willow twigs in his hands and shove them into the stove. At that moment the wind swooped on them again and the tent came down.

Half dressed, minus mittens, boots, mackinaws, hats, they struggled under the obliterating canvas. Somebody was swearing in an uninterrupted stream. Rusty stumbled over the fallen stovepipe and his nostrils were filled with soot. Then the smothering canvas lifted a couple of feet and somebody struck a match to expose them like bugs under a kicked log, dismayed and scuttling, glaring around for whatever article they needed. He saw Jesse and Ray bracing the front pole, and as the match died he jumped to the rear one; it was like holding a fishing rod with a thousand pound fish on: the whole sail-like mass of canvas flapped and caved and wanted to fly. One or two ropes on the windward side had broken loose and the wall plastered itself against his legs, and wind and snow poured like ice water across his stockinged feet. "Somebody get outside and tie us down," Ray's grating whisper said. Little Horn scrambled past, then Spurlock. Panguingue crawled toward the front flap on hands and knees, Slip and Buck followed him. Braced against the pole, old Jesse was laughing; he lit a match on his pants and got a candle going and stuck it in its own drip on the stove. The stovepipe lay in sooty sections across the beds.

Ropes outside jerked; the wall came away from Rusty's legs, the tent rose to nearly its proper position, the strain on the pole eased. Eventually it reached a wobbly equilibrium so that he could let go and locate his boots in the mess of his bed. The five outsiders came in gasping, beating their numbed hands. In the gray light of storm and morning, they all looked like old men; the blizzard had sown white age in their beards.

"*God* A'mighty!" Slip said, and wiped away an icicle from under his nose.

"Cold, uh?" Ray whispered.

"Must be thirty below."

"Will the tent hold?"

"I dunno," Slip said. "Corner ropes is onto the wheels, but one of the middle ones is pulled plumb out."

They stood a second or two, estimating the strain on the ropes, and as if to oblige their curiosity the wind lit on them and heeled them halfway over again. The whole middle of the windward wall bellied inward; the wind got under the side and for an instant they were a balloon; Rusty thought for certain they would go up in the air. He shut his eyes and hung on, and when he looked again three of the boys had grappled the uplifting skirt of the cloth and pinned it down.

"We got to get in off these flats," Jesse said.

"I guess," Ray said. "The question is how. It's three-four miles to the river."

"We could keep the wind on our left and drift a little with it. That'd bring us in somewhere below Bates Camp."

"Well," Ray said, and looked at the rest of them, holding the tent down, "we haven't got much choice. Slip, you reckon we could find any horses in this?"

"I reckon we could try."

"No," Ray said. "It'd be too risky. We couldn't drive them against this wind if we found them."

"What about the cattle?" Buck said.

"Yeah," said Little Horn. "What about them?"

"D'you suppose," Ray whispered, and a spasm like silent mirth moved his iron face, "after we get things ready to go, you boys could pull about three poles out of the corral gate?"

"You mean turn 'em loose?"

"I mean turn 'em loose."

Ed Spurlock said, "So after all this, we wind up without a single God damn calf?" and Ray said, "You rather have a corral full of dead ones?"

Rusty leaned against the swaying pole while the furious wind whined and howled down out of the Arctic, and he listened to them with a bitterness that was personal and aggrieved. It seemed to him atrocious, a wrong against every principle and every expectation, that the devoted and herculean labors of eight good men should be thwarted by a blind force of nature, a meteorological freak, a mere condition of wind and cold.

Now on with the boots over feet bruised and numb from walking stocking-footed on the frozen ground, and on with the overshoes, and stamp to get life going. Now button the sheepskin collar close and pull the fur cap down, earlaps and forehead piece, leaving exposed only the eyes, the chattering jaw, the agonized spuming of the breath, *huh-huh-huh, huh-huh-huh-huh.* Clumsy with clothing, beat mittened hands in armpits, stoop with the others to get the stovepipe together, the grub box packed, the beds rolled. "Keep out a blanket apiece," Ray Henry says.

The tent tugs and strains, wanting to be off. In the gray light, snow sifts dry as sand down through the open stovepipe thimble and onto the stove—a stove so useless that if anyone touched it with a bare hand he would freeze fast.

As in a nightmare where everything is full of shock and terror and nothing is ever explained, Rusty looks around their numb huddle and sees only a glare of living eyes, and among them Panguingue's eyes that roll whitely toward the tent roof to ask a question.

"We'll leave it up till we get set," Ray says. "It ain't a hell of a lot, but it's something."

They duck outside, and shielding faces behind shoulders and collars, drive into the wind. The paralyzing wind hammers drift against eyelids, nose, and lips, and their breath comes in gasps and sobs as they throw things into the wagon. Jesse and Ray are harnessing the Clydes over their yellow blankets, Slip pounds ice off the blanket of the night pony getting ready to throw the saddle on. From their feet plumes of drift streak away southward. Beyond the figures in the squirming dusk the whole visible world moves—no sky, no horizon, no earth, no air, only this gray-white streaming, with a sound like a rush of water, across and through it other sounds like howling and shouting far off, high for a moment and lost again in the whistle and rush.

The cheek Rusty has exposed feels scorched as if by flame. Back in the icy, half-cleared tent, the hollow of quiet amid the wind seems a most extravagant sanctuary, and he heaves a great breath as if he has been running. He does not need to be told that what moves them now is not caution, not good judgment, not anything over which they have any control, but desperation. The tent will not stand much more, and no tent means no fire. With no horses left but the Clydes and one night pony, they will have to walk, and to reach either of the possible shelters, either Stonepile or Bates Camp, they will have to go north and west, bucking the wind that just now, in the space of a dozen breaths, has seared his face like a blowtorch. He has a feeling outraged and self-pitying and yet remotely contemplating a deserved punishment, a predicted retribution, the sort of feeling that he used to have in childhood when something tempted him beyond all caution and all warnings and he brought himself to a caning in the iodine- and carbolic-smelling office where his father, the doctor, used to look him down into shame before laying the yardstick around his legs. They have got what they deserved for daring Authority; the country has warned them three separate times. Now the punishment.

Into the wagon, jumbled any old way, goes everything the tent holds—grub box, saddles, stove, stovepipe, kerosene can, and again they gather in the still, icy hollow, strangely empty without the stove. Ray Henry has two lariats in his hands, Buck an axe, and Jesse a lighted lantern. The foreman wipes his nose on the back of his mitt and squints at old Jesse. "Dad, you sure you want to drive? It'll be colder up there than walkin'."

The old-timer shakes the lantern, and his eyes gleam and his square teeth gleam. "Lantern between m'feet, buffler robe over the top," he says, "I don't care how cold I get upstairs if I'm warm from the tail down."

"Long as you don't set yourself afire," Ray says. "How about somebody ridin' up there with you?"

"Dee-lighted!" Jesse says, flashing his teeth like Teddy Roosevelt, and they laugh as if they were all short of wind. The foreman's gray thinking eyes go over them. When his look pauses on Rusty Cullen, the boy's breath is held for a moment in sneaking hope, for he has never been so miserable or so cold; the thought of going out there and fighting across six miles of snowflats in the terrible wind has paralyzed his nerve. Also, he tells himself, he is the injured one; his arm still hurts him. The possibility pictures itself seductively before him: to ride, bundled under the buffalo robe and with the lantern's warmth. Like a child pretending sleep when a night emergency arises and the rain beats in an open window or the wind has blown something loose, to sit snug beside old Jesse, relieved of responsibility, while the grownups take care of it . . . He cannot read the foreman's gray eyes; he feels his own wavering down. A crawl of shame moves in his guts, and he thinks, if he picks me it will be because I'm the weakest as well as the greenest.

The thinking eye moves on. "Slip," Ray says, "you ain't got the feet for walkin'. You can spell Dad with the lines. It'll be bad on the hands."

To cover his relief Rusty is beating his hands rhythmically in his armpits and jiggling on nerveless feet. He watches Ray pass the lariats to Little Horn. "If you're tied together, we won't lose nobody."

"Where'll you be?"

"I'll be ridin' pilot."

They are all moving constantly, clumsily. Spurlock has wrapped a woolen muffler around his mouth so that only his restless eyes show. Buck and Panguingue already have hung blankets over their heads and shoulders. Little Horn pulls off a mitt to pat the chimney of Jesse's lantern with a bare hand. "Well," Ray says, "I guess it's time she came down."

They lurch outside. Rusty, unsure of what to do, astonished at their instant obedience, finds himself standing stupidly while Buck with the butt of the axe knocks out one picket pin, then another, and chops off the ropes that tie the tent to the wheels. Jesse and Panguingue, at the ends, reach inside the flaps and lift and yank at the poles, and down it comes in a puddle of frozen canvas that they fall upon and grapple together and heave into the wagon. They curse and fight the wind, pushing and folding the tent down, throwing the poles and two saddles on it to hold it, hauling and lashing the wagon cover tight. Rusty looks back at where their shelter has been and his insides are pinched by cold panic. Drift is already streaking across the patch of thawed and refrozen grass; the little space their living warmth has thawed there in the midst of the waste looks as passionately and finally abandoned as the fresh earth of a grave.

Little Horn is tying them together, using the rope to snug and hold the blankets they have wrapped around themselves, when out of the tattered edge of storm cattle appear, longhorns that swerve away at a stumbling half-trot. After them and among them, a streaming miserable horde, come the whiteface and shorthorns, cows and calves, some steers, a few bulls, with no noise except an occasional desperate blat from a calf, and the clicking of longhorn hoofs and joints carried headlong southward by the wind. Well fleshed and round-bellied no more than a week ago, they stream and flinch past, gaunt ghosts of themselves, and Rusty thinks sullenly, while Little Horn ties the rope tight around him and their four hands tuck the blanket under, that it has been human foolishness that has brought the cattle to this condition. Driven all day by cowboys, and every other night by blizzards, they have eaten hardly anything for days. Left alone, yarding up in the coulees and river bottoms, they could at least have gnawed willows.

He is furious at their violent futile effort, and at Ray Henry for insisting upon it. Inhuman labor, desperate chances, the risk of death itself, for what? For a bunch of cattle who would be better off where their instinct told them to go, drifting with the storm until they found shelter. For owners off in Aberdeen or Toronto or Calgary or Butte who would never come out themselves and risk what they demanded of any cowboy for twenty dollars a month and found.

The tip of his mitt is caught under the rope; he tears it loose, and for a moment Little Horn's barely exposed eyes glint sideways, surprised. Out of the storm behind the last straggling cattle rides Ray Henry, already plastered white. He waves, somebody shouts, the wind tears the sound away and flings it across the prairie, the Clydes jerk sideways, the frozen wheels of the wagon crackle loose and crush through a crested foot-deep drift. The five walkers bunch up to get the protection of the wagon for their faces and upper bodies; the wind under the box and through the spokes tears at their legs as they swing half around and jolt off angling across the storm—northeast, Rusty judges, if the wind is northwest— following the stooped figure of the foreman on the horse. As they pass the corrals, Rusty sees the stained ground humped with carcasses already whitening under the blast of snow and wind.

He huddles his blanket across his chest, clenching and unclenching his numb hands; he crowds close to the others, eager to conform; he plants his feet carefully, clumsily, in the exact footprints of Ed Spurlock, and he tries to keep the rope between them just slack enough so that it does not drag and trip him. His face, unless he carelessly falls behind, is out of the worst lash of the wind; with walking, he has begun to feel his feet again. It seems possible after all—they can walk under these conditions the necessary five or six miles to shelter. He is given confidence by the feel of the rope around his waist, and the occasional tug when Spurlock or someone else up ahead stumbles or lurches, or when he feels Little Horn coming behind. Beside his cheek the wheel pours dry snow, and every turning spoke is a few inches gained toward safety.

Once, as they bounced across the flats, Slippers leaned out and shouted something down to Buck, leading the single-file walkers. An unintelligible word came down the line, the wheels beside them rolled faster, and they were forced into a trot to keep up. Rusty staggered sideways in the broken snow, kept himself from falling under the wheel by a wild shove against the wagon box, lurched and was yanked forward into step so roughly that it kinked his neck. The line of them jogged, grunting in cadence, trotting awkwardly armless, wrapped in their blankets, beside the ponderous wagon. Eventually Buck shouted up at the seat, and they slowed to a walk, but the run had done them good. The blood was out at their edges and extremities again. Rusty felt it sharp and stinging in his cheeks.

Up ahead, revealed and half covered, and revealed and nearly obscured, moving steadily through the lateral whip and crawl of the storm, went the whitened horse, the humped white figure of Ray Henry. Once when Rusty looked he was down, walking and leading the pony. A few minutes later he was up again. The plain stretched on, interminable. Rusty dropped his head turtle-fashion, wiped an edge of the blanket across his leaking and freezing nose, concentrated on putting his feet precisely into the tracks of Ed Spurlock. Dreamlike and hypnotic, body moved, brain moved, but both sluggishly, barely awake. Life was no more than movement, than dull rhythm. Eyes were aware only of the drooping rope, the alternating feet ahead, and once in a while the glimpse of Ray Henry moving through the blizzard out at the edge of visibility. Walking or riding, he went with the inevitability of a cloud driving across the sky; to look up and find him not there would have been a shock and a dismay. And yet he went ambiguously too, something recognized or remembered from an old charade or pantomime or tableau, Leader or Betrayer, urgent, compulsive, vaguely ominous, so that one hurried to keep him in sight and cursed him for the way he led on, and on.

In the thudding hollows of the skull, deep under the layered blanket, the breath-skimmed sheepskin, inside the stinging whiskered face and the bony globe that rode jolting on the end of the spine, deep in there as secret as the organs at the heart of a flower or a nut inside shell and husk, the brain plodded remotely at a heart's pace or a walking pace, saying words that had been found salutary for men or cattle on a brittle and lonesome night, words that not so much expressed as engendered what the mind felt: sullenness, fear, doubt.

Up ahead the foreman moved steadily, dusky stranger, silent companion, and if he did not "bend upon the snowshoe with a long and limber stride," he had a look as tireless and unstoppable as if he had in fact been that Spirit Hunter, that Walker of the Snow, one of the shapes with which the country deluded frightened men.

The wind had changed, and instead of driving at their legs under the box between the spokes was coming much more from behind them. Rusty felt Little Horn's hand on his back, but when he turned to see what was wanted, Little Horn shook his head at him from under the blanket hood: only a stumble, or the wind hustling him along too fast. The pour of dry snow from the wheel blew on forward instead of sideward into their faces. Except for his hands and his impossible leaky nose, he was not cold. They must have come more than half of the three miles that would bring them to the river, where there would be protection among the willows and under the cutbanks, and where they might even choose to make some sort of shelter of the wagon and the tent—build a big wood fire and thaw out and wait for the storm to blow by. He hoped they would; he did not relish the thought of turning into the wind, even in the more sheltered river valley.

He saw The Walker coming back, bent double, his face turned aside. When he reached them his pony turned tail to wind and Jesse cramped the Clydes around and they stood for a brief conference. It seemed that the wind had not changed. The horses simply wouldn't head across it, and kept swinging. That meant they would hit the river lower down, and have a longer upwind pull to Bates.

Only Ray's eyes showed through the mask-like slot of a felt cap that came clear down around his throat. To Jesse and Slip he whisper-shouted something that Rusty could not hear, and mounted and rode off again. The wagon crunched after him, the segmented ten-footed worm beside it took up its lockstep. Deafened by fur and wool, anesthetized by cold and the monotony of walking, the next-to-last segment, joined to the segments before and behind by a waist of half-inch hard-twist rope, plodded on, thinking its own dim thoughts, which were concerned with cosmic injustice and the ways of God to man.

Why couldn't there be, just at this moment, the lucky loom of an unknown or unexpected cowcamp, the whiff of lignite smoke on the wind? Why, just once, could not rescue come from Heaven, instead of having to be earned foot by foot? He dreamed of how warmth would feel in the face, the lovely stink of four or five shut-in cowboys in a hot shack, and he sucked and sniffed at the drooling of his mouth and nose, a hateful, inescapable oozing that turned to ice in his beard and on his lips.

Head down, he plodded on, one step and then another. Once as he put his foot in the print that Spurlock's foot had just left, he caught the heel of Spurlock's overshoe with his toe, and saw Spurlock fling an irritable snarl over the shoulder. Oh, the hell, he thought. Can't you be decent even when we're like this? The rope tugged tight around him, he hopped to get in step again, walking carefully, left, right, left, right, wiping his leaking nose against the blanket's edge and feeling slick ice there.

Sancta Maria, speed us!
The sun is falling low;
Before us lies the valley
Of the Walker of the Snow!

Later—hours or days, for time whipped and snaked past in unceasing movement like the wind and the trails of drift, and all its proportions were lost—Rusty bumped into Spurlock and an instant later felt Little Horn bump into him in turn. The wagon had stopped, and Ray was back, leading his pony by the bridle. His visor of felt was iron-stiff with ice, so that he pulled it down and craned his neck and lifted his chin to shout over it to Jesse, perched on the high seat beside Slip with the buffalo robe folded up around him under the armpits. Rusty, squinting to see what they were looking at, felt the sticky drag of ice on his lashes as if his eyes were fringed with crickets' legs, and saw that ahead of them the land fell away beyond an edge where the grass was blown bare. Ahead or below, the ground-hugging trails of drift were gone, leaving only air murky as dusk, with fitful swirls and streaks of dark at its bottom which he realized were brush. He dragged at his wet nose. The river.

But the brief, gratified expectation he had that this would be an easier stage lasted no more than two minutes. The hills dipping down to the floodplain were gullied and washed, and drifted deep. Even with Ray riding ahead to try the going, the wheels dropped into holes and hollows, rose over knobs; the wagon canted at perilous angles, groaning and jolting its way slanting, with the wind almost dead behind it. Pulling out wide from the rocking wagon, the men were caught in the open wind and blown along. Rusty saw the Clydes braced back in the breeching, their hairy fetlocks coming up out of the snow rattling with balls of ice, and their muscular haunches bunching under the blankets, and then here came Slip digging out from under the buffalo robe to throw his weight on the brake. Ice against ice, shoe slid on tire and held nothing; the wagon rolled heavily down upon the Clydes, who braced lower, slipping. The walkers jumped aside and then, as the wagon lumbered past them, jumped to the endgate to try to hold it back. Its ponderous weight yanked them along, their dug heels plowed up snow. They could feel it under their hands getting away, they knew it without Jesse's yell that snapped off on the wind above their heads. Jesse rose half to his feet, braced between seat and box. The wagon jackknifed sharply as he swung the Clydes along the sidehill to slow them. The left side dropped down, the right heaved up, and with a neat final motion like the end of a crack-the-whip the wagon tipped over and cast off Slip in a spidery leap down the hillside. Jesse, hanging to the tilted seat to the end, slid off it to land on his feet with the reins in one hand and the lantern in the other. By the time Ray discovered what had happened and rode back, he had unhooked the Clydes and got them quiet. The wagon lay with its load bulging out of the lashed cover, the busy wind already starting to cover it with snow.

Rusty would not have believed that in that wind and cold it was possible to work up a sweat, but he did. It was a blind and furious attack they launched on the tipped wagon, unloading almost everything and carrying it down to more level ground where the abrupt hill aproned off, stacking it there while they floundered back to dig and pry at the jackknifed wheels. Ray hitched on with his saddle horse, they heaved while their held breath burst out of them in grunts and straining curses, until they righted it, and straightened the wheels, and a spoke at a time got them turning; three of them carrying the tongue and the others ready to push or hold back, they angled it down onto leveler and smoother ground.

There they wasted not a second, but hitched up and loaded as if they raced against time. When the muffled-up figure of Spurlock started to heave a saddle up, and slipped and fell flat on its back with the saddle on its chest, Rusty coughed out one abrupt bark of laughter, but no one else laughed. Panguingue and Buck picked the saddle off Spurlock's chest and tossed it aboard, and before Spurlock was back on his feet Little Horn and Buck were starting to tie together the worm of walkers. Up where Jesse and Slip were fussily folding the buffalo robe around and under them it looked bitterly cold, but down where Rusty stood it was better. He could feel his hands all the way, his feet all but the tips of the toes. Where the fur cap covered it, his forehead was damp, and under the ponderous layers of clothing and blanket his body itched a little with warmth. He was winded, and dead tired, and his shoulder ached as if the fierce haul and heave of the unloading and loading had pulled it from its socket, but the dismay of the accident was worked off. They were all right, they would make it yet.

He twisted to help Little Horn tuck the blanket-ends under the rope, and at that moment Spurlock, moving awkwardly in front, put his foot down crooked, reeled against him, landed on his foot and anchored him there, and bore him helplessly over in the drift. If it had been anyone else, Rusty might have laughed, reassured and warmed by work as he was; but since it was Spurlock he rose to one knee anticipating trouble. He was not wrong; the hand he put on Spurlock's arm was knocked off angrily, and through the layers of the muffler the words were savage: ". . . the Christ you're doing!"

The boy's anger blew up instant and hot, and he bounded to his feet freeing his elbows from the blanket. They faced each other, tied together by four feet of rope like gladiators coupled to fight to the death, and then the shadow above them made itself felt and Rusty looked up to see Ray Henry sitting hands-on-horn and looking down on them.

"What's trouble?" the foreman said.

The unintelligible growl that came out of Spurlock's muffled mouth could have told him nothing, but Rusty pulled the collar away from his chin and said passionately, "Look, put me somewhere else in this line! I'm not going to stand for . . ."

"What's trouble?" Ray said again.

"He keeps stumbling around and falling down and then blaming me . . ."

"If he falls down, help him up," Ray croaked, and kneed his frosted pony around and rode off in front. The wheels jerked, the icy axles shrieked, their feet automatically hopped to get in step, and they were walking again. Rusty pulled his chin back inside the collar and went sullenly, furious at the injustice of the rebuke, and alert to make the most of any slightest slip or stumble ahead of him.

Down in the bottoms among the willows the wind was less, and they could bring the horses to turn halfway into it, feeling for the river. But if the wind was less, the snow was deeper; the Clydes floundered belly deep and the wagon box scraped up a great drift that piled up over the doubletree and against the stallions' rumps and finally stopped them dead. They shoveled it away and cleared the Clydes' feet, never quite sure whether or not they would have their brains kicked out. Then they fell into two lines out in front and tramped a way for the horses and the wagon wheels down through smothered rosebushes and between clumps of willow whose bark gleamed red under the hood of snow. Ten feet of it was enough to wind a man; they panted their way ahead, turned to tramp backward and deepen the track, stopped every twenty yards to dig away the snow that the wagon box scooped up. They worked like people fighting a fire, exhausted themselves and stood panting a minute and fell to it again, frenzied for the easy going on the river ice.

The wagon eased over the edge of a bushy bank, the Clydes plunged as Jesse took them over straight on. The front wheels went down, pushing the stallions out onto the ice. Just as Rusty saw them lunging to pull the wagon through, a jerk from behind dragged him over in the drift and the whole line of walkers came down. When they got to their feet there was the wagon on the river.

Getting up watchfully, Rusty thought he felt Spurlock yanking at the rope, and he yanked back harshly. Sunk between the muskrat cap and the muffler, and blindered on both sides by the wings of the mackinaw collar, Spurlock's eyes peered out like the eyes of a fierce animal peering from a crack in the rock, but he turned away without a word, giving Rusty at least the smoldering satisfaction of having yanked last, of having finished something that the other had started.

The cutbank partially shielded them from the wind. Upriver was a straight reach with an irregular streak of clear, blown ice down its center, grading up to the shelving drifts against both banks. Drift skated and blew down it like dust down an alley. The last lap of the road to shelter lay before them as smooth as a paved highway.

Ray Henry, leading his pony down the broken bank, stopped by them a moment where they hung panting on the wagon. "Everybody all right?"

They looked at him from among their wrappings.

"Ed?" Ray said.

It seemed to Rusty terribly unjust that particular attention should have been paid to Spurlock rather than to himself. It meant that the foreman still looked upon Spurlock as in the right, himself in the wrong. It meant that he had no concern for the one of his men who was hurt, and might be in trouble. He saw Ray's eyes within the visor that was like the helmet of a hero, and his unhappiness that he had lost prestige and respect drove words to his lips, impulsive and too eager, anything to be recognized and accepted again. He did not care about Spurlock, actually; he was already ashamed of that quarrel. But he wanted Ray Henry to notice him, and so he said, "What do we do now, Ray? Camp here till it's over?"

"Not hardly," Ray said. "The Clydes have had all the fresh air they need."

"How much farther?"

"Three miles, maybe four."

"Do we ride from here?"

The gray, thinking eye examined him from within the helmet of ice-hardened felt. The foreman said, "You reckon you're any more petered than them studs?"

He went stooping and slipping out in front to confer with Jesse and Slip, and Rusty, avoiding Little Horn's eyes and with his back to Spurlock and the others, watched the smothered rosebushes on the bank quiver in a gust. The slow warmth under all his wrappings might have come from the heavy work of getting the wagon through the brush and the drifts, but it might just as well have been shame, and he hated them all for never giving a man a chance, for taking things wrong, for assuming what should not be assumed. He hadn't been wanting to quit, he had asked only for information. Sullenly he waited, resolved to keep his mouth shut and plod it out. Once they got back to the ranch, he could simply leave the job; he was under no obligation to stay at it any longer than he pleased to. Neither Ray nor anyone else could compel a man to stick it through months of this kind of thing, no matter how short-handed the T-Down was. There was sure to be a great change as soon as he announced he was leaving. He could see Ray Henry's face—all their faces. Every man who left, left more for the remaining ones to do. Too late, chaps. Sorry. Ta-ta, gentlemen. Enjoy the winter.

In the river bottom the wind was louder, though he felt it less. The bare willows and the rosebushes, bent like croquet wickets into the drifts, whistled with it, the cutbank boomed it back in hollow eddies, every corner and edge and groove of the valley gave it another tongue. More than out on the flats, even, it echoed with hallucinatory voices, shouts, screams, whistles, moans, jeers. Rusty concentrated on it. He had only been asking a perfectly reasonable question, considering that they were running for their lives and still had an unknown distance to go. Would it be so terrible to climb up and let those big strong horses pull them for a little while along the level ice? Would it, for that matter, be entirely unheard of to sacrifice the Clydes, if necessary, to save eight lives? He asked himself what about a leader who thought more of his horses than of his men.

The blood in his veins was sluggish with cold, his mind was clogged with sullen hatred. Ray, shouting up to Jesse and Slip, and Spurlock, weaving bearlike from one foot to the other, were both part of a nightmare which he loathed and wanted to escape, but the numbness held him and he stood spraddling, squinting from behind the wagon box, hearing the shouts of those ahead torn from their lips and flung streaming down the ice to become part of the headlong illusory wailing that blew and moaned around the river's bends. His mind, groping among images, was as clumsy as his mittened unfeeling hands would have been, trying to pick up a coin from the snow. He thought of old Jesse's friend down by Sheridan, with his frozen conversation, and of how others had explained, not so humorously, the voices that haunted the wind in this country.

> For I saw by the sickly moonlight
> As I followed, bending low,
> That the walking of the stranger
> Left no footmarks on the snow.

The voices of all the lost, all the Indians, *métis,* hunters, Mounted Police, wolfers, cowboys, all the bundled bodies that the spring uncovered and the warming sun released into the stink of final decay; all the starving, freezing, gaunt, and haunted men who had challenged this country and failed; all the ghosts from smallpox-stilled Indian camps, the wandering spirits of warriors killed in their sleep on the borders of the deadly hills, all the skeleton women and children of the starving winters, all the cackling, maddened cannibals, every terrified, lonely, crazed, and pitiful outcry that these plains had ever wrung from human lips, went wailing and moaning over him, mingled with the living shouts of the foreman and the old-timer, and he said, perhaps aloud, remembering the legend of the Crying River, and the voices that rode the wind there as here, *Qu'appelle? Qu'appelle?*

Heartless and inhuman, older than earth and totally alien, as savage and outcast as the windigo, the cannibal spirit, the wind dipped and swept upon them down the river channel, tightening the lightly sweating inner skin with cold and the heart with fear. Rusty watched Ray hump his back and shake off the worst of the blast, saw the arm wave. The wagon rolled again. Ed Spurlock, unready, was pulled sideways a stumbling step or two by the tightening of the rope, and Rusty got one clear look into the brown, puckered eyes. Out of his fear and misery and anger he sneered, "Learn to walk!" But if Spurlock heard he made no sign. In a moment he was only the hooded, blanketed, moving stoop, not human, not anything, that Rusty imitated movement for movement, step for step, plodding up the river after the wagon.

Exhaustion and cold are a kind of idiocy, the mind moves as numbly as the body, the momentary alertness that a breathing spell brings is like the sweat that can be raised under many clothes even in the bitterest weather; when the breathing spell is over and the hard work past, mind and body are all the worse for the brief awakening. The sweaty skin chills, the images that temporary alertness has caught scrape and rasp in the mind like edged ice and cannot be dislodged or thought away or emptied out, but slowly coagulate there.

For Rusty they were the images of fear. No matter how much he tried to tie his mind to the plod-plod-plod of foot after foot, he heard the spirit of that bitter country crying for cold and pain. Under his moving feet the ice passed, now clear, with coin-like bubbles in it, now coated with a pelt of dry smooth snow, now thinly drifted. The world swung slowly, the dry snow under their feet blew straight sideward, then quartered backward; his quickly lifted eyes saw that the right bank had dropped to a bar and the left curved up in a cutbank. The wind lashed his face so that he hunched and huddled the blanket closer, leaving only the slightest hole, and still the wind got in, filled the blanket, threatened to blow it off his back. His eyes were full of water and he wiped them free, terrified that they would freeze shut. With his head bowed clear over, almost to the rope, he stumbled on. Through the slits of sight remaining to him he saw that the drift now was blowing straight backward from Spurlock's feet. The river had swung them directly into the wind. The line of walkers huddled to the left until they were walking bunched behind the feeble protection of the wagon.

The wagon stopped, the line of walkers bumped raggedly to a halt. Rusty had forgotten them: he was surprised to find them there, glaring from the frozen crevices of their clothes. From out in front Ray Henry came looming, a huge indomitable bulk, leading the pony whose bony face was covered with a shell of ice, the hairy ears pounded full of snow, the breast of the blanket sheathed. He unlooped the halter rope and tied it to the endgate, pulled the bridle and hung it on the saddle horn. For a minute he rubbed and worked at the pony's face, turned grunting, and said from inside his visor, "They just can't buck it. We're gonna have to lead 'em." He helped Little Horn pull open the loose, frozen knot in the rope and free himself from the others. "Rusty," he said, "see if you can find a blanket up in the load somewhere."

Rusty found the blanket, the foreman and Little Horn flapped off with it, the walkers huddled back to the wagon, eying the miserable pony which now took half their shelter. After a minute or two the yell came back, they turned, they stirred their stiffened legs and moved their wooden feet. The wind shrieked around the wagon, between the spokes, along the axles and the snow-clogged reach, and Rusty, colder now than at any time since he had awakened half frozen in his blankets, heard the blizzardy bottoms wild with voices. *Qu'appelle? . . . Qu'appelle? . . . Qu'appelle?*

In an hour, or four hours, or ten minutes, the river blessedly bent rightward, and the wind went screaming and flying above them but touched them only in swoops and gusts. There was a stretch where the inshore drifts let them go close up under the bank, and for a brief time the air was almost still, the snow settling almost gently as on any winter's day, a day to put roses in the cheeks.

Sancta Maria, speed us!

During that brief, numbed lull Spurlock tangled his feet and fell again, pulling over Panguingue ahead of him. Rusty, hopping awkwardly to keep from getting entangled with the sliding, swiveling figures, saw Buck squat and grab the rope to maintain his balance against the drag of the fallen ones. There went the three of them, helplessly dragged along on back or feet, and here came Rusty, a lead-footed dancer, prancing and shouting in their wake until those up ahead heard and they stopped.

Ray was back again. Panguingue and Buck stood up and cleared the rope, but Spurlock sat on the ice with his head down, pawing at his face and heaving his shoulders under the blanket. Rusty stayed back in scorn and contempt, sure that the blame would somehow be pinned on him. He was the proper scapegoat; everything that happened was caused by his awkwardness.

Ray was stooping, shaking Spurlock's shoulder. His hand worked at the muffler around Spurlock's face. Then he straightened up fierce and ready and with so much power left that Rusty moved a step back, astonished. "'The lantern!" Ray shouted, and lunged around the line of walkers to reach and take the lantern from Jesse's hand. Back at Spurlock, stooping to hold the lantern directly against the muffler, he said over his shoulder, "Rusty, unhitch yourself and rustle some wood. We're gonna have to stop and thaw out."

The knot was stiff with ice, his fingers like sticks, but he got loose and stumped around in the deep snow breaking dead stalks out of willow clumps. Slip appeared to help him, and Rusty said, pausing a second in his fumbling, "What's the matter with Spurlock?"

"Smotherin'," Slip said. "God damn muffler froze to his whiskers."

"Are we going to camp here?"

"Why?" said Slip in surprise. "Do you *want* to?"

Rusty floundered down the bank with his handful of twigs, watched Panguingue cone them on the ice and souse them with kerosene. The smell cut his nostrils, and he sniffed back the wetness and spat in the snow. It was that drooling that had got Spurlock in trouble. Drool and freeze fast. Dully curious, he watched Ray moving the lantern glass around on the frozen wool, while Buck pulled on the unfrozen ends. Spurlock's head was pulled out of his collar; he looked like a fish on a hook. Then Panguingue found a match and reached across Buck to scratch it on the dry bottom of the lantern. The little cone of sticks exploded in bright flame.

"More," Panguingue said thickly.

Little Horn, who had led the Clydes around in a half circle, was already up over the endgate, unlashing the wagon cover. Stupidly Rusty watched as he loosened it all across the windward side and dropped it in the lee, and then, comprehending, he helped tie it to the spokes to make a windbreak. The fire had burned out its splash of kerosene, and was smoldering in the snow until Panguingue swished it again and it blazed up. "More!" he said. "We need wood."

"In the wagon," Jesse said. "What do you think I chopped all that wood for yesterday?"

He climbed the wheel to burrow into the uncovered load, and his face with its bowed mustaches emerged from under the tangled tent like a walrus at a waterhole and he winked in Rusty's face, handing him out wood two and three sticks at a time. His manner was incredible to the boy. He acted as if they were out on a picnic or a berry-picking and were stopping for lunch. Buck and Ray were holding Spurlock's face close to the little fire and working away at the muffler. The wind, here, was only a noise: they squatted in their bivouac with the fire growing and sputtering in the water of its melting, and they gathered close around it, venturing their faces a little out of their coverings.

Spurlock cursed clearly for the first time, the muffler came loose in Buck's hands. Ray set the lantern aside while Spurlock breathed deeply and passed his hands around on his face.

"Stick her right in," Jesse said. "That's the quickest way to thaw her. Set those weeds on fire."

They sat knee to knee, they put their mittens on sticks of wood in the snow and held stiff red hands in the very flames, they opened collars and exposed smarting faces. Life returned as pain: far down his legs Rusty felt a deep, passionate ache beginning in his feet. He knew from the burn of his cheeks and the chilblain feel of his fingers that he would have some frostbite to doctor. But he loved the snug out-of-the-wind shelter, the fire, even the pain that was beginning now and would get worse. For no matter how they came out, or whether they camped here to wait out the storm or went on after a rest to Bates, which couldn't be more than another mile or two, he would go with a knowledge that warmed him like Jesse's lantern under the robe: it hadn't been *he* that cracked. And what a beautiful and righteous and just thing it was that the one who did crack should be Spurlock! In triumph and justification he looked across the fire at the sagging figure, but he couldn't make the restless reddened eyes hold still. Spurlock hadn't said a word since they released him from the smothering scarf.

A half hour later, when Ray said they must go on, Rusty received the words like a knife in his guts. He had been sitting and secretly willing that they should stay. But he glanced again across the fire and this time caught Ed Spurlock's moving eyes, and the eyes ducked like mice. He told himself that if he was unwilling, Spurlock was scared to death. When they lashed the wagon cover back on and tied themselves together again and hooded the Clydes in the red Hudson's Bay blanket and Little Horn and Ray swung them by the bits and the forlorn night pony stretched his neck and came unwillingly, Rusty had a feeling that the moving line literally tore Spurlock from the side of the fire, now sunk into the crust and sizzling out blackly at the edges in steam and smoke.

The river swung, and the wind got at them. It swung wider, and they were plucked and shoved and blinded so that they walked sideward with their backs to the bar and their faces turned to the fantastic pagoda-roof of snow along the cutbank. In fury and anguish they felt how the river turned them. Like things with an identical electrical charge, their faces bent and flinched away, but in the end there was no evading it. The wagon stopped and started, stopped and started. The feet that by the fire had felt renewed life began to go dead again, the hands were going back to wood, the faces, chafed and chapped and sore, were pulled deep into the wool and fur. Gasping, smelling wet sheepskin and the tallowy smell of muskrat fur, feeling the ice at their very beards and the wind hunting for their throats, they hunched and struggled on.

Rusty, bent like a bow, with every muscle strained to the mindless plod, plod, plod of one foot after the other, and his eyes focused through the blanket's crack on Spurlock's heels, saw the feet turn sideward, the legs go out of sight. Apparently Spurlock had simply sat down, but the rope, tightening on him, pulled him over. Sliding on the ice, hauled after the backward-walking, braced, and shouting Panguingue, he was trying to untie the rope around his waist with his mittened hands.

Again their yells were torn away downwind, voices to blend with the blizzard's crying, or thaw out to haunt hunters or cowboys in some soft spring. They dragged Spurlock a hundred feet before those up in front heard. Then Rusty stood furiously over him and cursed him for his clumsiness and cried for him to get up, but Spurlock, straightening to sit with his arms hung over his knees, neither looked up nor stood up. He mumbled something with his head down.

"Lone," he mumbled, "rest minute."

Rusty's leg twitched: he all but kicked the miserable bundle. Slip and Jesse or both were shouting from the wagon seat, Ray Henry was coming back—for how many'th time? They were utterly exposed, the wind whistled and the drift blinded them. He dropped his mouth again to Spurlock's ear, shouted again. Panguingue was hauling at Spurlock's armpits. "Can't sit down," he said. "Got to keep him movin'."

Not until then did the understanding grow into Rusty's mind, a slow ache of meaning like the remote feeling in his feet. Spurlock was done. It wasn't just awkwardness, he wasn't just quitting, he was exhausted. The danger they had been running from, a possibility in which Rusty had never thoroughly believed, was right among them. This was how a man died.

His hands found an arm under blanket and coat, and he and Panguingue helped Spurlock's feeble scrambling until they had him on his feet. They held him there, dragged down by his reluctant weight, while Ray peered grimly into his face. "He's played out," Panguingue said, and Rusty said, "Couldn't we put him in the wagon? He can't walk any farther."

Ray said, "Put him in the wagon he'd be froze stiff in twenty minutes." His hands went out to Spurlock's shoulders and he shook him roughly. "Ed! You hear? You got to keep movin'. It's only another mile. Just keep comin'."

"'mall right," Spurlock said. "Just rest minute."

"Not a damn minute," Ray said. "You rest a minute and you're dead."

Spurlock hung between Rusty and Panguingue until they were holding almost his whole weight. "You hear, Ed?" Ray said, glaring from his visor like a hairy animal. "You stop to rest, you're dead. Come on now, stand up and walk."

Somehow he bullied strength into the legs and a glitter of life into the eyes. Then he drove back against the wind to take the bridle of the off horse, and the halting, laborious crawl moved on. But now Rusty and Panguingue had hitched their ropes around and walked one on each side of Ed Spurlock, each with a hand under the rope around his waist to haul him along, and to support him if he started to go down. He came wobbling, and he murmured through the blanket they had wrapped over his whole head, but he came.

Rusty's shoulder ached—he ached all over, in fact, whenever he had any feeling at all—and the strain of half supporting Spurlock twisted his body until he had a stabbing stitch in his side. The hand he kept in Spurlock's waist rope was as unfeeling as an iron hook.

A mile more, Ray said. But the river led them a long time around an exposed loop. He had all he could do to force himself into the blast of snow and wind that faded and luffed only to howl in their faces again more bitterly than ever. When Spurlock, stumbling like a sleepwalker, hung back or sagged, trying to sit down, Rusty felt Panguingue's strength and heard Panguingue's stout cursing. His own face was so stiff that he felt he could not have spoken, even to curse, if he tried; he had lost all feeling in his lips and chin. His inhuman hook dragged at Spurlock's waist rope, he threw his shoulder across to meet Panguingue's when the weight surged too far forward, and he put foot after foot, not merely imbecilic now with cold and exhaustion, but nearly mindless, watching not the feet ahead, for there were none now, with three of them abreast and Buck trailing them behind, but the roll of the broad iron tire with the snow spume hissing from it.

He watched it hypnotically, revolving slowly like the white waste of his mind where a spark of awareness as dim as the consciousness of an angleworm glimmered. His body lived only in its pain and weariness. The white waste on which the wheel moved broke into dark angles, was overspread by blackness that somehow rose and grew, strangely fluid and engulfing, and the air was full of voices wild and desolate and terrible as the sound of hunting wolves. The led pony reared and broke its halter rope and vanished somewhere. Then Rusty felt himself yanked sideward, falling into Spurlock and Panguingue in an encumbered tangle, seeing even as he fell, shocked from his stupor, that the endgate was clear down, the hub drowned in black water that spread across the snow. Kicking crabwise, he fled it on his back, helped by someone hauling on the rope behind, until they stood at the edge of the little shallow rapid and saw Jesse and Slip in the tilted wagon ready to jump, and the round wet heads of stones among the broken ice, and the Clydes struggling, one half down and then up again, Little Horn hanging from the bits, hauled clear of the ice as they plunged. There was a crack like a tree coming down, the stallions plunged and steadied, and then Ray was working back along the broken tongue to get at the singletrees and unhook the tugs and free them.

Ray was standing on the broken tongue and calming the stallions with a hand on each back while he yelled downwind. Rusty pulled at his cap, exposed one brittle ear, and heard the foreman shouting, "Get him on up to the cabin . . . two or three hundred yards . . . right after you."

So with hardly a pause longer than the pause of their falling sideward away from the crunch of ice and the upwelling of water from the broken shell of the rapid, he and Panguingue were walking again, cast free from the rope and supporting Spurlock each with one arm around his shoulders, the other hands locked in front of him. He drooped and wobbled, mumbling and murmuring about rest. He tricked them with sudden lurches to left or right; when he staggered against them his weight was as hard to hold as a falling wall. Twice he toppled them to the ice. Compelled to watch where he walked, Rusty had to let the blanket blow from head and face, and without its protection he flinched and gasped, blinded, and felt the ice forming stickily along his eyelashes, and peered and squinted for the sight of the dugway that would lead them out of the channel and up the cutbank and across a little flat to the final security, so close now and so much more desperately hard to reach with every step.

The river bent, they dragged their burden along, they yielded to his murmurings and to their own exhaustion and let him sag a minute onto the ice, and then hauled and dragged him onto his feet and staggered on. The right bank was low and brushy; the wind came across it so that they leaned and fought across its whipping edge. Rusty freed his left hand and scoured the wrist of the mitten across his eyes and looked into the blast for the slant of the dugway, and saw nothing but the very throat of the blizzard. It was more than muscle and will could endure; panic was alive in his insides again. Even a hundred yards was too much; they could fall and die before the others could overtake them, right here within a few rods of safety. He gasped and sucked at his drooling lip, lost his hold on Panguingue's hand, felt with anguish how Spurlock slid away and went down.

Somehow they got him up again; somehow they struggled another hundred feet along the ice, and now a cutbank curving into a left-hand bend cut off some of the wind, and Rusty heard Panguingue grunt and. felt the veer and stagger as he turned in toward the bank. Rusty still could not see it, but starting up, slipping, he put a hand down to stay himself and felt the dugway. Strengthless, they leaned into the bank; Spurlock tried to lie back; they held him with difficulty, and lifting the blanket to look into his face Rusty saw his eyes frozen wholly shut with teardrops of ice on the lashes. Above the dark beard the cheekbones were dead white.

When they tried to move him again, he sagged back against the bank and gave them his limp arms to haul at, and their combined strength was not enough to get him onto his feet, much less to start him up the steep dugway. They tried to drag him and stopped exhausted after six feet. The glare of uncertainty, fear, helplessness, was in Panguingue's glimmer of eyes and teeth. Rusty understood him well enough. Leave him? The others would soon come along. But if they didn't come in a few minutes he would be dead. Again they lifted and hauled at Spurlock, got him halfway, and felt him slip and go comfortably down again. Panguingue let go. "We better try to get up to the cabin. Schulz might be there."

"Suppose he isn't?"

He heard the forlorn, hopeless sound of Panguingue's snuffing. The face looked at him, bearded clear to the eyes.

"You go," Rusty said. "I'll wait here with him."

A snuffle, a momentary look, and Panguingue ducked away, scrambling with hands and feet, to disappear over the dugway edge.

For a while Rusty lay beside Spurlock on the slope, his blanket huddled over to cover both their faces, and simply waited, without mind or thought, no longer afraid, not hopeful, not even aware or sentient, but simply waiting while the gasp of breath and hammer of heart labored toward some slowing-point. He could not feel his feet at all; his hands were clubs of wood. Driven inward from its frontiers, his life concentrated itself in his chest where heart and lungs struggled.

A little later there was a stage in which his consciousness hung above him, like the consciousness in a dream where one is both actor and observer, and saw him lying there, numb already nearly to the knees, nearly to the elbows, nose and lips and forehead and the tender sockets of the eyes gone feelingless, ears as impersonal as paper ears pinned to his head. What he saw was essentially a corpse huddling over another corpse. He recognized the fact without surprise or alarm. This was the way it ended, this was the way they would be found.

Under the blanket's hood was a darkness and stillness. He felt how absurd it was, really. Absurd for men to chase around an arctic prairie wearing themselves and their cattle to death. Absurd. Take a rest, now, and . . .

Coming? Who? *Qu'appelle?* Old wolf, old walker of the snow, old windigo, *qu'appelle?* He smiled. It was a joke between them.

He heard now neither the wind nor the dry rustle of his mind. Inside the blanket the air was still, red-dusky, not cold. But as he moved to make his legs more comfortable the hillside toppled, a dull anguish of unwilling sensation spread in his throat, and he struggled back up, straightening the elbow that had given way and let him fall across Spurlock's up-jutting face. A powder flash of terror lighted up his whole head. The imprint of Spurlock's chin, unyielding as stone, ached in his Adam's apple. The face of a corpse—his too? But it was not his own pain so much as the appalling rigidity of Spurlock's jaw that shocked him. The man was dying, if not dead. Something had to be done, he couldn't just wait for help from Panguingue or the others.

His hands clutched and shook the stiffening bundle, the unfeeling hooks tried to close, to lift. "Ed! Ed, come on! We're almost there, man! Get up, you can't lie here. Only a little way farther. Ed! *Ed!* You hear? God damn it, Ed, get up! Come on, move!"

His eyes were full of catastrophic tears; he dashed them away with a fold of the blanket and threw a look up the dugway and gulped a burning throatful of the wind. He heard the voices wail and howl around the eaves of the riverbank, and he bent and slapped and pounded and tugged, screaming at the clownish, bearded, ice-eyed, and white-cheekboned face that turned and whimpered under his attack.

Gasping, he stopped a moment, threw another look upward. The top of the bank was less than thirty feet above him. Beyond that, within two hundred feet, should be the cabin. Five minutes, no more than ten even on hands and knees. He looked in anguish for the outfit, possibly coming up the river ice, and saw only trails of drift vanishing around the bend. The boys rendering their fantastic duty to the horses could not possibly come in time. And Panguingue must have found the shack deserted or he would have been back by now. Was he stopping to build a fire, or was he too exhausted to come back? Or was he lying in the snow himself, somewhere between the cutbank and the cabin?

"Ed! Wake up! Get up and walk! It's only a little way!"

Hopeless; inert and hopeless. He could not help the tears, though he knew they would be his blindness and his death. "Please, Ed! Please, come on!"

In a clumsy frenzy he hauled and yanked and dragged; his frantic strength skidded Spurlock a yard or two up the dugway, and when Spurlock began mumblingly to resist with arms and legs, Rusty attacked him with three times more fury and by slaps and kicks and blows reinforced his resistance until, miraculously, Spurlock was on his feet. With hooks and shoulder Rusty helped him, braced him, shoved him upward, moved him a step, and another; and crying encouragement, panting, winded and dead-armed and dead-legged, forced the man foot by foot up the dugway path until he felt the ground level off and the wind fling itself full against them.

They toppled and almost fell. Spurlock sagged and started to sit down and Rusty barely managed to hold him. He could not see more than a bleared half-light—no objects at all. His tears were already ice, his lashes stitched together, and he could make no move to clear his sight without letting Spurlock slip away, probably for the last time. Savagely he rasped his face across the snow-slick wool of Spurlock's blanketed shoulder; with what little vision he could gain he glared straight into the wind for the dark wall or icicled eaves that would be the cabin. The wind drove down his throat; his shouting was strangled and obliterated; it was like trying to look and shout up a waterfall. The wilderness howled at him in all its voices. He was brought to a full stop, sightless, breathless, deafened, and with no strength to move and barely enough to stand, not enough—frantically not enough—to hold the weight of Ed Spurlock that despite every effort he could make slid away and down.

With a groan Rusty let him go. Both hands rose to rub the wristlets of his mittens across his sealed eyes. Pain stabbed through his eyeballs as if he had run across them with sandpaper but he broke the threads of ice that stitched him shut, and looked again into the gray and howling wind, saw a square darkness, a loom of shadow in the murk, and thought in wonder, My God, we've been right against the shack all the time, and then the darkness moved and the wind's voice fell from whine and howl to a doglike barking, and Panguingue was there shouting in his face.

Relief was such pure bliss to him that he was rendered imbecilic by it, and stood mouth open and cheeks stretched to force open his eyes, watching Panguingue try to pull Spurlock erect. He loved Panguingue, the stoutest and decentest and bravest and most dependable man alive. Merely his presence brought not only hope but assurance. It would be no trouble now. And even while he was bending to help he heard the unmistakable dig and clump of the Clydes behind him, and turned to see them clear the dugway with tennis balls of ice rattling in their fetlocks and Jesse hanging to the lines behind them, and then the others—one, then another, then another, leading the pony.

What had been impossible was suddenly easy, was nothing. Among them they hoisted Spurlock to his feet. Rusty felt an arm around him, the urge of someone else's undiminished strength helping him along through a thigh-deep drift that gave way abruptly to clear ground. His head sounded with hollow kickings and poundings and with one last defeated howl of wind, and he saw icicles under the shack's eaves like yard-long teeth, and the wind stopped, the noises fell, the light through his sticky eyelids darkened, his nostrils filled with smells of mice, kerosene, sheepskins, ham rind, sardines, and a delirious tropical odor of cinnamon and cloves like his mother's spice cupboard, and someone steered him and turned him and pushed on his shoulders, and Ray Henry's whisper said, "O.K., kid, take a load off your feet." He felt safety with his very buttocks as he eased himself down on the rustly hay-stuffed tick of a bunk.

Later he sat with his aching feet in a dishpan of snow and water, and when the pain in his hands swelled until it seemed the fingers would split like sausages, he stooped and numbed the ache into bearability in the same dishpan. His eyes were inflamed and sore; in each cheek a spot throbbed with such violence that he thought the pulse must be visible in the skin like a twitching nerve. His ears were swollen red-hot fungi, his nose that had run and drooled incontinently all the way through the blizzard was now so stuffed and swollen that he gurgled for air. He knew how he looked by looking at Little Horn, who had got wet to the knees when the Clydes went through the rapid, and who sat now on an apple box with first one foot and then the other in a bucket of snow. Little Horn's skin showed like a flaming sunburn through his reddish beard. He had innocent blue eyes like Jesse's, and the same blunt chin. When he was twenty years older he would look a good deal like Jesse—they were members of the same tribe. Now he lifted one tallowy foot from the deep snowprint in the pail and set it tenderly on the floor and lifted the other into its place, and looked across at Rusty with his mild ironic eye and shook his head in acknowledgment of something.

Ray and Jesse were squatting by the bunk against the side wall where Spurlock lay. Each had a blotched foot in his hands, each was massaging it and sousing it with snow. At the head of the bunk Buck worked on Spurlock's hands. Spurlock's fiery face looked straight upward; his teeth were set; he said nothing. Back by the door Slip and Panguingue had just finished washing each other's faces with snow. All of them, emerged from their cumbersome wrappings, looked disheveled as corpses dredged from a river. Rusty marveled at their bony hairless feet, their red hands, their vulnerable throats. They were making a good deal of talkative noise, their skins were full of the happiness of rescue, and not yet quite full of pain.

Little Horn looked at Panguingue's wet face. He said to Rusty, "Ain't that the way it goes? Of all the people that might of froze their feet and got a good wash out of it, who is the one God damn boy in the outfit without even a frozen toe but old Pan?"

Jesse said from the end of Spurlock's bunk, "Cold couldn't get through that crust."

"B.S.," Panguingue said. "I'm just tougher than you. And besides, I froze my face damn good."

"Snow washed some of the protective layer off," Little Horn said. "No, more I think of it, more I think you shouldn't make any mistake and wash them feet till spring, Pan. We'll need somebody around to do the chores while we get well."

"Hey, by God," Panguingue said. "How about my face?"

"Just leave it go. A little proud flesh would improve it."

"B.S.," said Slip, in imitation of Panguingue's growl, and he and Panguingue threatened each other with pans of snow. From the other bunk Ray Henry said, "Feelin' 'em yet?"

"You're damn right," Ed Spurlock said through his teeth.

"Better let 'em set in the water for a while," Ray said. "The slower they come back the better." He stood up, looking at Rusty. "Rusty, you needin' that dishpan for a while?"

"No, take it." He moved his feet carefully out onto the dirty board floor, and the foreman shoved the pan under Spurlock's dangling feet. Standing over Rusty, burly, matted-haired, grave-eyed, totally enigmatic to the boy but restored to his position of authority and respect, he said, "How you doin'? Feelin' yours?"

"Enough," Rusty said. He raised his head a little. "What's the cure for frostbite?"

"Whiskey," Jesse said from beside Spurlock.

"Fine," said Little Horn. "Just what we ain't got."

"If we had some rocks we could have some rock and rye," Slip said. "If we had some rye."

"No particular cure," Ray said to Rusty. "Thaw it out slow, keep away from heat, little arnica if you get sores, cut it out if you get gangrene. And wait."

"How long?"

"Depends how bad you are. You and Little Horn, maybe a week, ten days. Ed maybe two-three weeks. It's the hands and feet that lay you up."

"What do we do, stay here till we're well?"

"I expect we'll cobble up that tongue and beat it for the ranch soon as it clears off."

"Vacation with pay," Little Horn said. "Peach pies. Whiskey every hour, while Panguingue does the chores. I tell you, Rusty, there's no life like a cowboy's."

But Rusty was thinking of the two weeks they had just gone through, and of the cattle that had gone streaming miserably downwind from the Horse Camp corrals, the gaunt exhausted horses that had hung around the tent and wagon until the wind literally blew them away. "What about the calves?" he asked. "And what about the horses?"

"Horses we'll have to round up, some of them anyway. They'll winter out all right, but we need work ponies."

"You mean—ride out there and hunt through all that country and drive them on back to the ranch?"

"Uh-huh."

"I tell you," Little Horn said, and lifted his left foot out of the bucket and raised his right tenderly in, "there's no business like the cow business to make a man healthy and active. There's hardly a job you can work at that'll keep you more in the open air."

Rusty smelled the coffee that Jesse had put on the fire as soon as he got it going. He saw the flaw of moisture the spout cast on the stovepipe, and he moved his pain-distended hands cautiously, cradling them in his lap. The shack's growing warmth burned in his cheeks. Over on the other side of the stove Slippers' face, purple in the bare patches, black where the beard grew, brooded with its eyes on the floor. This was the leathery little man who would ride out to bring the ponies back across sixty miles of rough country. And maybe one or two others—maybe himself—with him. The very notion, at that moment, moved the boy to something like awe.

"What about the calves?" he said.

For the first time expression—disgust? anger? ironic resignation?— flickered across Ray's chapped, bearded mouth. "The calves. Well, the ones that ain't dead by the time this one blows out may find some willows to gnaw in a coulee, and if we get a chinook they'll have feed and come through all right. If we don't get a chinook the wolves are gonna be very fat by spring."

"But we aren't going to try rounding them up again."

Ray turned away with the flicker widening momentarily on his mouth. "I wouldn't worry about it," he said.

"Don't be impatient," Little Horn said, and hissed sharply as he moved his foot and bumped the pail. He set the heel on the floor and looked at the swollen toes, looked at his sausage-like fingers, shook his head. On the bunk Spurlock raised one foot from the dishpan. "Wait a minute," Jesse said. "Got enough of that footbath for a while?"

He helped the legs with their rolled-up pants to straighten out in the bunk. In the silence that came down as the pain of returning blood preoccupied them Rusty heard the undiminished wind shriek along the icicled eaves of the shack and swoop away. Smoke puffed out around the rings of the stove lids, lay there for a minute like fat white circular worms, and was sucked in again. Shaggy as cavemen, weather-beaten and battered, they huddled back against the walls and away from the stove and contemplated each in his own way the discomforts of the outraged flesh. Each retired within his skinful of pain and weariness, and among them Rusty Cullen, as weary as any, as full of pain as any—pain enough to fill him to the chin and make him lock his jaw for fear of whimpering. He made note that none whimpered, not even Spurlock; the worst was an occasional querulous growl when one moved too fast. Jesse, the old-timer, the knowing one, Nestor and patriarch, unfrozen except for a touch on the fingers and ears, moved between them in stockinged feet and flipped the coffeepot lid with the edge of his palm, saving his tender fingertips, and looked in. The mystic smells of brotherhood were strong in the shack. The stove lids puffed out worms of smoke once more, and once more sucked them inward. The wind went over and around them, the ancient implacable wind, and tore away balked and shrill.

The Rusty Cullen who sat among them was a different boy, outside and inside, from the one who had set out with them two weeks before. He thought that he knew enough not to want to distinguish himself by heroic deeds: singlehanded walks to the North Pole, incredible journeys, rescues, what not. Given his way, he did not think that he would ever want to do anything alone again, not in this country. Even a trip to the privy was something a man might want to take in company.

The notion insinuated itself into his head, not for the first time, that his sticking with Spurlock after Panguingue left was an act of special excellence, that the others must look upon him with a new respect because of it. But the tempting thought did not stand up under the examination he gave it. Special excellence? Why hadn't anyone praised him for it, then? He knew why: because it was what any of them would have done. To have done less would have been cowardice and disgrace. It was probably a step in the making of a cowhand when he learned that what would pass for heroics in a softer world was only chores around here.

Around him he heard the hiss of air drawn between clenched teeth, he saw the careful, excruciating slowness of hands and feet being moved in search of more comfortable positions, he saw and smelled and felt how he was indistinguishable from the other seven. His greenness did not show, was perhaps not quite so green as it had been. And he did not take it ill, but understood it as a muffled acceptance of acknowledgment, when Spurlock sniffed thickly and said to the sagging springs above his nose, "Is that coffee I smell, Jesse, or is it only fawncy?"

AN INTERVIEW WITH WALLACE STEGNER

Interviewer: The theme of "Genesis," as its title implies, is one of the oldest in literature—the trial by ordeal through which a boy, a greenhorn, an innocent, becomes a tested and proven man. It is the story, one might say, of the birth of an individual into experience and knowledge. Generally speaking, how conscious is an author of his themes *before* he sets out to write a story?

Stegner: It is impossible to say as a general thing. Different writers work differently, and different stories find their way onto the page in different ways. Some writers—Hawthorne is an example—seem to start from a question or a theme, and find characters and situation to dramatize it. Others just as clearly start with characters, situation, even complete story, and let the theme reveal itself in the telling. The more "intellectual" the writer is, the likelier it is that his stories will resemble *exempla,* even equations, and the more likely it is that ideas will dominate characters and that characters will illustrate ideas. A less intellectual writer may be content to leave his meanings diffused, implicit, hardly formulated, as in life. That way, they seem less like a formal intention than like a by-product.

In practice, of course, a writer probably, through the course of a number of drafts, is working from both directions at once, trying to make characters *live* and *mean* simultaneously. It is not at all unusual that he should not be conscious of his theme in the beginning, but by the end he had better be.

Interviewer: In "Genesis," did the theme come first? Or the situation? How soon, in other words, does tradition begin to intrude upon the imagination and begin to direct the course of a story?

Stegner: In "Genesis" situation definitely came before theme. For one thing, the story was planned as part of a larger whole, the book *Wolf Willow,* which covered the historical panorama of the Cypress Hills country. Whatever this cowboy story developed into would have to be subordinate to the theme of the book. The form and length of the story were as vague as the theme, and of course I did not have the title until the theme had been discovered and worked out in actions which suggested not only the beginning of manhood but the beginnings of a new country.

What I began with was a notion of writing a story about the winter of 1906, which put the open range cattle outfits out of business and opened the way for homesteaders. I was telling the story of a disaster. Tradition, as you suggest, may have steered the story into becoming, as well, the story of a testing. Perhaps the plain logic of my materials forced me in that direction. Perhaps memory played a part in it, since I was remembering places and events close to my own childhood, and the childhood of a somewhat frail child on a rough frontier is full of testings.

But the testing theme did not insist upon itself at once. When I began writing I had no tenderfoot hero—I had the exact reverse, for I started telling it from the point of view of Ray Henry, the foreman, who had already won his manhood and didn't need to prove anything. All I began with were the specific events of the belated roundup, in which all the cattle outfits in that country fought to save their stock, and lost. I began with the story of a physical defeat; the theme of a spiritual gain as a consequence of the struggle came in later.

Interviewer: Writers write out of their experience. But how much out of their experience? And isn't there a danger, sometimes, in relying too much on the facts of actual experience and not allowing the imagination to operate on a given situation?

Stegner: Of course writers write out of their experience, but rarely out of their unmodified experience. The closer to fact one's materials are, the greater the danger of being strait-jacketed by them. That doesn't mean one should strain for the fantastic or bizarre. I am a realist, essentially; I believe fiction should reflect actual life, and distort it only for the purpose of reflecting it better. But when remembered events have a certain internal logic and the story that grows out of them keeps wanting to have another, historical fact has to bend. Isak Dinesen used to say that the story should be given its head. It should. For when the story wants its head, it is a sign that the imagination is working; you are not simply reporting something that happened, you are creating something absolutely new. In those parts of *Wolf Willow* where I was writing history or autobiography, I had no choice but to put down accurately the selected facts I felt the narrative needed. But in "Genesis," where I was after another sort of truth, I had no hesitation in diverting, recombining, reversing, compressing, doing anything I wanted to the facts I knew from historical accounts. Which is only another way of saying that I let the story find its own channel, like running water.

Interviewer: How much of your own experience went into "Genesis," both in its characters and its events?

Stegner: Very little of my own experience went into "Genesis" except sensuous experience—remembered places, colors, sensations, the look of yellow grassland under a scurf of snow, the sound and feel of blizzardy weather, that sort of thing. I knew, and know, little about cowboying, but I do know how it feels to be half frozen, I do know how it feels to be near complete exhaustion, I do know what it is like to be numb and nearly mindless with cold and fatigue. So I didn't have to do much imagining to reproduce how those T-Down cowboys would have felt. But it should be remarked that in that very act of remembering sensations I was falsifying a little for art's sake. Perhaps that was where my tenderfoot protagonist first came in. For the seasoned cowboys lived by a code that would have told them to make as little as possible of their hardships. The first-hand accounts on which I was drawing were as laconic as weather reports. For the sake of readers who had never lived by that code, I needed both characters who took hardships for granted, like chores, and at least one who would look upon his sufferings as a personal outrage. So I began putting into my young Englishman some of the uncowboy-like vividness of sensation that I might have felt myself.

As for the characters, two of them were drawn freely from the writers of the two first-hand recollections that were available to me. Some others, notably Slip, Rusty, and Little Horn, bear names that were once worn by cowboys I knew when I was seven or eight years old, but they are in no sense portraits of those men. They couldn't be. About all I remember of them is their names and the fact that Rusty, reputed to be the third son of an English earl, played the mouth organ.

Interviewer: When you sit down to write a story like "Genesis" does it automatically fall into a particular pattern of telling or does it take a great deal of experimenting until you find the right way?

Stegner: Sometimes a story finds its channel easily, sometimes not. "Genesis" took a lot of trial and error, despite the fact that it finally emerged as a relatively simple, even mythic, sort of tale. Remember that I did not know where I was going, except that I was writing of the disastrous winter of 1906. I did not know what the story would *say,* I only knew what it was going to be *about.* For the events of that winter, as well as for invaluable details of life on the Whitemud range in the early days, I had two manuscripts, the reminiscences of Corky Jones, who had been foreman of the Z Bar X, and of Harry Otterson, who had been foreman of either the T-Down or the Turkey Track, I forget which. And here was a case of fact getting somewhat in the way of fiction. Harry Otterson's memoir, though he dwelt hardly at all on his personal feelings and sufferings, was so factually vivid that I was bent by it. I started to tell the story from his point of view, and it led me into events that eventually I had to cut out of the story. I began with his marriage in Malta, Montana, in the fall of 1906, and I spent two long chapters on his honeymoon trip, by buckboard and across country utterly without roads, from Malta to the T-Down ranch on the Whitemud. They got lost, they were marooned three nights in a sheep-herder's shack, they picnicked by a slough where the ducks kept coming in and sliding end over end on the slick ice. All of that I wrote and then threw away, though I saved scraps of it in a later story called "Carrion Spring." Of the figure of Molly Henry, nothing remains in "Genesis" except her figure waving goodbye as the outfit leaves for the roundup at the beginning of the story. In the same way, the figures of the wolfer and his son, prominent in Otterson's narrative and prominent in my original notions of the story, got whittled back and drop out early, though they too were salvaged for another story, called "The Wolfer," which never got into the book *Wolf Willow* at all.

The point is that both Molly Henry and the wolfers threatened to lead the story in a direction that for some stubborn internal reason it did not want to take. Neither of the Henrys, and certainly neither of the wolfers, was a tenderfoot. And the blizzardy winter of 1906 kept wanting, in my imagination, to try someone's soul, preferably someone likely to break. So after my first try, I turned back to the reminiscences of Corky Jones, who had come out a good many years before as a green eighteen-year-old Englishman, and had found himself a cowboy only a few days after his arrival. The minute I started with him as the central figure I knew that I was on the track that the story wanted to follow, and I knew that it wanted to confine itself, for action and event, to that single thread of the belated roundup.

One thing that I didn't at first realize kept me from finishing the story promptly. I had thought it would go chronologically straight through the winter until the proportions of the disaster were apparent with the spring thaw. I had the suspicion that I might be writing a full-length novel. But when I got the outfit to safety in the shack, with the herd blown a hundred miles downwind, I couldn't seem to get things going again. I tried, and it died on me two or three times, so I put the manuscript away. Then I came back to it after a year and read it through, and understood why it had not wanted to go on. It was finished. It didn't want to be anything but the concentrated story of that roundup and the testing of the tenderfoot Rusty. So I used scraps of what I had tried to add on, and made them into the two short stories "The Wolfer" and "Carrion Spring." Instead of a novel, I wound up with a *nouvelle* and two stories.

It seems very accidental and unplanned. Actually, however, it was not unplanned at all: it simply wouldn't conform to the plan I had for it; it wanted its head. Even the point of view wouldn't work as I had planned it. I had tried first with Ray Henry; then I made a try using Molly Henry (I kept her point of view in "Carrion Spring"); then I shifted to Rusty, in the first person singular. On the fourth try I shifted to Rusty as protagonist, but in the third person, because I found that I wanted a little more distance on this boy, a little more chance for irony than the first person permitted.

Planning, in the writing of fiction, is likely to take the form of trial and error.

Interviewer: How much does the *author* discover as he goes along—about his characters and events? Is the creative process a learning process?

Stegner: What I have just said about trial and error indicates that, at least for me, the creative process is in good part a learning process. The story finds a way it can be told, a compass of actions it can deal with, a set of people it will involve, a meaning that it can arrive at. Sometimes all of this is mental, but often it has to be tried out on paper before we believe it. I doubt that most of us write what we know; we write what we want to find out. A story is an imaginative model of experience, starting with a tentative "What if . . . ?" and ending (if it works) with a "yes, it would have to go that way."

Interviewer: Do you think that certain kinds of stories, by their very thematic nature, limit or control the form in which they can be contained? "Genesis" is really a *nouvelle.* Is this, in your opinion, the ideal form for the "ordeal" story, or does length make any difference?

Stegner: I do think that certain kinds of stories control or dictate the form in which they can be told. The story of an ordeal most particularly does. That is one reason why the novel I thought I was working on never came off: everything after the end of the "Genesis" section would have been anticlimactic. As an ordeal, this roundup had to be single, separate, and its own proper length. It wanted to be over when it was over. It could not have been a short story, for at story length the ordeal would not have been sufficiently excruciating, it would not have tested either the top hands or the tenderfoot enough, and would consequently not sufficiently have defined manhood in Saskatchewan terms. An ordeal must be long enough to be nearly unbearable, not long enough to become either dispersed or tiresome. The typical ordeal story is a very long short story or a pretty short novel—in short, a *nouvelle.* Styron's *The Long March* is such a story. Conrad wrote some of the great ones—*Youth, Typhoon, The Nigger of the Narcissus.* And if I were to confess the full truth I would have to admit that all the time I was writing "Genesis" I felt a good deal like Conrad on a cowhorse.

Lawrence Sargent Hall

THE LEDGE

On Christmas morning before sunup the fisherman embraced his warm wife and left his close bed. She did not want him to go. It was Christmas morning. He was a big, raw man, with too much strength, whose delight in winter was to hunt the sea ducks that flew in to feed by the outer ledges, bare at low tide.

As his bare feet touched the cold floor and the frosty air struck his nude flesh, he might have changed his mind in the dark of this special day. It was a home day, which made it seem natural to think of the outer ledges merely as some place he had shot ducks in the past. But he had promised his son, thirteen, and his nephew, fifteen, who came from inland. That was why he had given them his present of an automatic shotgun each the night before, on Christmas Eve. Rough man though he was known to be, and no spoiler of boys, he kept his promises when he understood what they meant. And to the boys, as to him, home meant where you came for rest after you had had your Christmas fill of action and excitement.

His legs astride, his arms raised, the fisherman stretched as high as he could in the dim privacy of his bedroom. Above the snug murmur of his wife's protest he heard the wind in the pines and knew it was easterly as the boys had hoped and he had surmised the night before. Conditions would be ideal, and when they were, anybody ought to take advantage of them. The birds would be flying. The boys would get a man's sport their first time outside on the ledges.

His son at thirteen, small but steady and experienced, was fierce to grow up in hunting, to graduate from sheltered waters and the blinds along the shores of the inner bay. His nephew at fifteen, an overgrown farm boy, had a farm boy's love of the sea, though he could not swim a stroke and was often sick in choppy weather. That was the reason his father, the fisherman's brother, was a farmer and chose to sleep in on the holiday morning at his brother's house. Many of the ones the farmer had grown up with were regularly seasick and could not swim, but they were unafraid of the water. They could not have dreamed of being anything but fishermen. The fisherman himself could swim like a seal and was never sick, and he would sooner die than be anything else.

He dressed in the cold and dark, and woke the boys gruffly. They tumbled out of bed, their instincts instantly awake while their thoughts still fumbled slumbrously. The fisherman's wife in the adjacent bedroom heard them apparently trying to find their clothes, mumbling sleepily and happily to each other, while her husband went down to the hot kitchen to fry eggs—sunny-side up, she knew, because that was how they all liked them.

Always in winter she hated to have them go outside, the weather was so treacherous and there were so few others out in case of trouble. To the fisherman these were no more than woman's fears, to be taken for granted and laughed off. When they were first married they fought miserably every fall because she was after him constantly to put his boat up until spring. The fishing was all outside in winter, and though prices were high the storms made the rate of attrition high on gear. Nevertheless he did well. So she could do nothing with him.

People thought him a hard man, and gave him the reputation of being all out for himself because he was inclined to brag and be disdainful. If it was true, and his own brother was one of those who strongly felt it was, they lived better than others, and his brother had small right to criticize. There had been times when in her loneliness she had yearned to leave him for another man. But it would have been dangerous. So over the years she had learned to shut her mind to his hard-driving, and take what comfort she might from his unsympathetic competence. Only once or twice, perhaps, had she gone so far as to dwell guiltily on what it would be like to be a widow.

The thought that her boy, possibly because he was small, would not be insensitive like his father, and the rattle of dishes and smell of frying bacon downstairs in the kitchen shut off from the rest of the chilly house, restored the cozy feeling she had had before she was alone in bed. She heard them after a while go out and shut the back door.

Under her window she heard the snow grind drily beneath their boots, and her husband's sharp, exasperated commands to the boys. She shivered slightly in the envelope of her own warmth. She listened to the noise of her son and nephew talking elatedly. Twice she caught the glimmer of their lights on the white ceiling above the window as they went down the path to the shore. There would be frost on the skiff and freezing suds at the water's edge. She herself used to go gunning when she was younger; now, it seemed to her, anyone going out like that on Christmas morning had to be incurably male. They would none of them think about her until they returned and piled the birds they had shot on top of the sink for her to dress.

Ripping into the quiet pre-dawn cold she heard the hot snarl of the outboard taking them out to the boat. It died as abruptly as it had burst into life. Two or three or four or five minutes later the big engine broke into a warm reassuring roar. He had the best of equipment, and he kept it in the best of condition. She closed her eyes. It would not be too long before the others would be up for Christmas. The summer drone of the exhaust deepened. Then gradually it faded in the wind until it was lost at sea, or she slept.

The engine had started immediately in spite of the temperature. This put the fisherman in a good mood. He was proud of his boat. Together he and the two boys heaved the skiff and outboard onto the stern and secured it athwartships. His son went forward along the deck, iridescent in the ray of the light the nephew shone through the windshield, and cast the mooring pennant loose into darkness. The fisherman swung to starboard, glanced at his compass, and headed seaward down the obscure bay.

There would be just enough visibility by the time they reached the headland to navigate the crooked channel between the islands. It was the only nasty stretch of water. The fisherman had done it often in fog or at night—he always swore he could go anywhere in the bay blindfolded—but there was no sense in taking chances if you didn't have to. From the mouth of the channel he could lay a straight course for Brown Cow Island, anchor the boat out of sight behind it, and from the skiff set their tollers off Devil's Hump three hundred yards to seaward. By then the tide would be clearing the ledge and they could land and be ready to shoot around half-tide.

It was early, it was Christmas, and it was farther out than most hunters cared to go in this season of the closing year, so that he felt sure no one would be taking possession ahead of them. He had shot thousands of ducks there in his day. The Hump was by far the best hunting. Only thing was you had to plan for the right conditions because you didn't have too much time. About four hours was all, and you had to get it before three in the afternoon when the birds left and went out to sea ahead of nightfall.

They had it figured exactly right for today. The ledge would not be going under until after the gunning was over, and they would be home for supper in good season. With a little luck the boys would have a skiff-load of birds to show for their first time outside. Well beyond the legal limit, which was no matter. You took what you could get in this life, or the next man made out and you didn't.

The fisherman had never failed to make out gunning from Devil's Hump. And this trip, he had a hunch, would be above ordinary. The easterly wind would come up just stiff enough, the tide was right, and it was going to storm by tomorrow morning so the birds would be moving. Things were perfect.

The old fierceness was in his bones. Keeping a weather eye to the murk out front and a hand on the wheel, he reached over and cuffed both boys playfully as they stood together close to the heat of the exhaust pipe running up through the center of the house. They poked back at him and shouted above the drumming engine, making bets as they always did on who would shoot the most birds. This trip they had the thrill of new guns, the best money could buy, and a man's hunting ground. The black retriever wagged at them and barked. He was too old and arthritic to be allowed in December water, but he was jaunty anyway at being brought along.

Groping in his pocket for his pipe the fisherman suddenly had his high spirits rocked by the discovery that he had left his tobacco at home. He swore. Anticipation of a day out with nothing to smoke made him incredulous. He searched his clothes, and then he searched them again, unable to believe the tobacco was not somewhere. When the boys inquired what was wrong he spoke angrily to them, blaming them for being in some devious way at fault. They were instantly crestfallen and willing to put back after the tobacco, though they could appreciate what it meant only through his irritation. But he bitterly refused. That would throw everything out of phase. He was a man who did things the way he set out to do.

He clamped his pipe between his teeth, and twice more during the next few minutes he ransacked his clothes in disbelief. He was no stoic. For one relaxed moment he considered putting about and gunning somewhere nearer home. Instead he held his course and sucked the empty pipe, consoling himself with the reflection that at least he had whiskey enough if it got too uncomfortable on the ledge. Peremptorily he made the boys check to make certain the bottle was really in the knapsack with the lunches where he thought he had taken care to put it. When they reassured him he despised his fate a little less.

The fisherman's judgment was as usual accurate. By the time they were abreast of the headland there was sufficient light so that he could wind his way among the reefs without slackening speed. At last he turned his bow toward open ocean, and as the winter dawn filtered upward through long layers of smoky cloud on the eastern rim his spirits rose again with it.

He opened the throttle, steadied on his course, and settled down to the two hour run. The wind was stronger but seemed less cold coming from the sea. The boys had withdrawn from the fisherman and were talking together while they watched the sky through the windows. The boat churned solidly through a light chop, flinging spray off her flaring bow. Astern the headland thinned rapidly till it lay like a blackened sill on the grey water. No other boats were abroad.

The boys fondled their new guns, sighted along the barrels, worked the mechanisms, compared notes, boasted, and gave each other contradictory advice. The fisherman got their attention once and pointed at the horizon. They peered through the windows and saw what looked like a black scum floating on top of gently agitated water. It wheeled and tilted, rippled, curled, then rose, strung itself out and became a huge raft of ducks escaping over the sea. A good sign.

The boys rushed out and leaned over the washboards in the wind and spray to see the flock curl below the horizon. Then they went and hovered around the hot engine, bewailing their lot. If only they had been already set out and waiting. Maybe these ducks would be crazy enough to return later and be slaughtered. Ducks were known to be foolish.

In due course and right on schedule they anchored at mid-morning in the lee of Brown Cow Island. They put the skiff overboard and loaded it with guns, knapsacks, and tollers. The boys showed their eagerness by being clumsy. The fisherman showed his in bad temper and abuse which they silently accepted in the absorbed tolerance of being boys. No doubt they laid it to lack of tobacco.

By outboard they rounded the island and pointed due east in the direction of a ridge of foam which could be seen whitening the surface three hundred yards away. They set the decoys in a broad, straddling vee opening wide into the ocean. The fisherman warned them not to get their hands wet, and when they did he made them carry on with red and painful fingers, in order to teach them. Once the last toller was bobbing among his fellows, brisk and alluring, they got their numbed fingers inside their oilskins and hugged their warm crotches. In the meantime the fisherman had turned the skiff toward the patch of foam where as if by magic, like a black glossy rib of earth, the ledge had broken through the belly of the sea.

Carefully they inhabited their slippery nub of the North American continent, while the unresting Atlantic swelled and swirled as it had for eons round the indomitable edges. They hauled the skiff after them, established themselves as comfortably as they could in a shallow sump on top, lay on their sides a foot or so above the water, and waited, guns in hand.

In time the fisherman took a thermos bottle from the knapsack and they drank steaming coffee, and waited for the nodding decoys to lure in the first flight to the rock. Eventually the boys got hungry and restless. The fisherman let them open the picnic lunch and eat one sandwich apiece, which they both shared with the dog. Having no tobacco the fisherman himself would not eat.

Actually the day was relatively mild, and they were warm enough at present in their woolen clothes and socks underneath oilskins and hip boots. After a while, however, the boys began to feel cramped. Their nerves were agonized by inactivity. The nephew complained and was severely told by the fisherman—who pointed to the dog, crouched unmoving except for his white-rimmed eyes—that part of doing a man's hunting was learning how to wait. But he was beginning to have misgivings of his own. This could be one of those days where all the right conditions masked an incalculable flaw.

If the fisherman had been alone, as he often was, stopping off when the necessary coincidence of tide and time occurred on his way home from hauling trawls, and had plenty of tobacco, he would not have fidgeted. The boys' being nervous made him nervous. He growled at them again. When it came it was likely to come all at once, and then in a few moments be over. He warned them not to slack off, never to slack off, to be always ready. Under his rebuke they kept their tortured peace, though they could not help shifting and twisting until he lost what patience he had left and bullied them into lying still. A duck could see an eyelid twitch. If the dog could go without moving so could they.

"Here it comes!" the fisherman said tersely at last.

The boys quivered with quick relief. The flock came in downwind, quartering slightly, myriad, black, and swift.

"Beautiful—" breathed the fisherman's son.

"All right," said the fisherman, intense and precise. "Aim at singles in the thickest part of the flock. Wait for me to fire and then don't stop shooting till your gun's empty." He rolled up onto his left elbow and spread his legs to brace himself. The flock bore down, arrowy and vibrant, then a hundred yards beyond the decoys it veered off.

"They're going away!" the boys cried, sighting in.

"Not yet!" snapped the fisherman. "They're coming round."

The flock changed shape, folded over itself, and drove into the wind in a tight arc. "Thousands—" the boys hissed through their teeth. All at once a whistling storm of black and white broke over the decoys.

"Now!" the fisherman shouted. "Perfect!" And he opened fire at the flock just as it hung suspended in momentary chaos above the tollers. The three pulled at their triggers and the birds splashed into the water, until the last report went off unheard, the last smoking shell flew unheeded over their shoulders, and the last of the routed flock scattered diminishing, diminishing, diminishing in every direction.

Exultantly the boys dropped their guns, jumped up and scrambled for the skiff.

"I'll handle that skiff!" the fisherman shouted at them. They stopped. Gripping the painter and balancing himself he eased the skiff into the water stern first and held the bow hard against the side of the rock shelf the skiff had rested on. "You stay here," he said to his nephew. "No sense in all three of us going in the boat."

The boy on the reef gazed at the grey water rising and falling hypnotically along the glistening edge. It had dropped about a foot since their arrival. "I want to go with you," he said in a sullen tone, his eyes on the streaming eddies.

"You want to do what I tell you if you want to gun with me," answered the fisherman harshly. The boy couldn't swim, and he wasn't going to have him climbing in and out of the skiff any more than necessary. Besides he was too big.

The fisherman took his son in the skiff and cruised round and round among the decoys picking up dead birds. Meanwhile the other boy stared unmoving after them from the highest part of the ledge. Before they had quite finished gathering the dead birds, the fisherman cut the outboard and dropped to his knees in the skiff. "Down!" he yelled. "Get down!" About a dozen birds came tolling in. "Shoot—shoot!" his son hollered from the bottom of the boat to the boy on the ledge.

The dog, who had been running back and forth whining, sank to his belly, his muzzle on his forepaws. But the boy on the ledge never stirred. The ducks took late alarm at the skiff, swerved aside and into the air, passing with a whirr no more than fifty feet over the head of the boy, who remained on the ledge like a statue, without his gun, watching the two crouching in the boat.

The fisherman's son climbed onto the ledge and held the painter. The bottom of the skiff was covered with feathery black and white bodies with feet upturned and necks lolling. He was jubilant. "We got twenty-seven!" he told his cousin. "How's that? Nine apiece. Boy—" he added, "what a cool Christmas!"

The fisherman pulled the skiff onto its shelf and all three went and lay down again in anticipation of the next flight. The son, reloading, patted his shotgun affectionately. "I'm going to get me ten next time," he said. Then he asked his cousin, "Whatsamatter—didn't you see the strays?"

"Yeah," the boy said.

"How come you didn't shoot at 'em?"

"Didn't feel like it," replied the boy, still with a trace of sullenness.

"You stupid or something?" The fisherman's son was astounded. "What a highlander!" But the fisherman, though he said nothing, knew that the older boy had had an attack of ledge fever. .

"Cripes!" his son kept at it. "I'd at least of tried."

"Shut up," the fisherman finally told him, "and leave him be."

At slack water three more flocks came in, one right after the other, and when it was over, the skiff was half full of clean, dead birds. During the subsequent lull they broke out the lunch and ate it all and finished the hot coffee. For a while the fisherman sucked away on his cold pipe. Then he had himself a swig of whiskey.

The boys passed the time contentedly jabbering about who shot the most—there were ninety-two all told—which of their friends they would show the biggest ones to, how many each could eat at a meal provided they didn't have to eat any vegetables. Now and then they heard sporadic distant gunfire on the mainland, at its nearest point about two miles to the north. Once far off they saw a fishing boat making in the direction of home.

At length the fisherman got a hand inside his oilskins and produced his watch.

"Do we have to go now?" asked his son.

"Not just yet," he replied. "Pretty soon." Everything had been perfect. As good as he had ever had it. Because he was getting tired of the boys' chatter he got up, heavily in his hip boots, and stretched. The tide had turned and was coming in, the sky was more ashen, and the wind had freshened enough so that whitecaps were beginning to blossom. It would be a good hour before they had to leave the ledge and pick up the tollers. However, he guessed they would leave a little early. On account of the rising wind he doubted there would be much more shooting. He stepped carefully along the back of the ledge, to work his kinks out. It was also getting a little colder.

The whiskey had begun to warm him, but he was unprepared for the sudden blaze that flashed upward inside him from belly to head. He was standing looking at the shelf where the skiff was. Only the foolish skiff was not there!

For the second time that day the fisherman felt the deep vacuity of disbelief. He gaped, seeing nothing but the flat shelf of rock. He whirled, started toward the boys, slipped, recovered himself, fetched a complete circle, and stared at the unimaginably empty shelf. Its emptiness made him feel as if everything he had done that day so far, his life so far, he had dreamed. What could have happened? The tide was still nearly a foot below. There had been no sea to speak of. The skiff could hardly have slid off by itself. For the life of him, consciously careful as he inveterately was, he could not now remember hauling it up the last time. Perhaps in the heat of hunting, he had left it to the boy. Perhaps he could not remember which was the last time.

"Christ—" he exclaimed loudly, without realizing it because he was so entranced by the invisible event.

"What's wrong, Dad?" asked his son, getting to his feet.

The fisherman went blind with uncontainable rage. "Get back down there where you belong!" he screamed. He scarcely noticed the boy sink back in amazement. In a frenzy he ran along the ledge thinking the skiff might have been drawn up at another place, though he knew better. There was no other place.

He stumbled, half falling, back to the boys who were gawking at him in consternation, as though he had gone insane. "God damn it!" he yelled savagely, grabbing both of them and yanking them to their knees. "Get on your feet!"

"What's wrong?" his son repeated in a stifled voice.

"Never mind what's wrong," he snarled. "Look for the skiff—it's adrift!" When they peered around he gripped their shoulders, brutally facing them about. "Downwind—" He slammed his fist against his thigh. "Jesus!" he cried, struck to madness at their stupidity.

At last he sighted the skiff himself, magically bobbing along the grim sea like a toller, a quarter of a mile to leeward on a direct course for home. The impulse to strip himself naked was succeeded instantly by a queer calm. He simply sat down on the ledge and forgot everything except the marvellous mystery.

As his awareness partially returned he glanced toward the boys. They were still observing the skiff speechlessly.Then he was gazing into the clear young eyes of his son.

"Dad," asked the boy steadily, "what do we do now?"

That brought the fisherman upright. "The first thing we have to do," he heard himself saying with infinite tenderness as if he were making love, "is think."

"Could you swim it?" asked his son.

He shook his head and smiled at them. They smiled quickly back, too quickly. "A hundred yards maybe, in this water. I wish I could," he added. It was the most intimate and pitiful thing he had ever said. He walked in circles round them, trying to break the stall his mind was left in.

He gauged the level of the water. To the eye it was quite stationary, six inches from the shelf at this second. The fisherman did not have to mark it on the side of the rock against the passing of time to prove to his reason that it was rising, always rising. Already it was over the brink of reason, beyond the margins of thought—a senseless measurement. No sense to it.

All his life the fisherman had tried to lick the element of time, by getting up earlier and going to bed later, owning a faster boat, planning more than the day would hold, and tackling just one other job before the deadline fell. If, as on rare occasions he had the grand illusion, he ever really had beaten the game, he would need to call on all his reserves of practice and cunning now.

He sized up the scant but unforgivable three hundred yards to Brown

Cow Island. Another hundred yards behind it his boat rode at anchor, where, had he been aboard, he could have cut in a fathometer to plumb the profound and occult seas, or a ship-to-shore radio on which in an interminably short time he would have heard his wife's voice talking to him over the air about homecoming.

"Couldn't we wave something so somebody would see us?" his nephew suggested.

The fisherman spun round. "Load your guns!" he ordered. They loaded as if the air had suddenly gone frantic with birds. "I'll fire once and count to five. Then you fire. Count to five. That way they won't just think it's only somebody gunning ducks. We'll keep doing that."

"We've only got just two-and-a-half boxes left," said his son.

The fisherman nodded, understanding that from beginning to end their situation was purely mathematical, like the ticking of the alarm clock in his silent bedroom. Then he fired. The dog, who had been keeping watch over the decoys, leaped forward and yelped in confusion. They all counted off, fired the first five rounds by threes, and reloaded. The fisherman scanned first the horizon, then the contracting borders of the ledge, which was the sole place the water appeared to be climbing. Soon it would be over the shelf.

They counted off and fired the second five rounds. "We'll hold off a while on the last one," the fisherman told the boys. He sat down and pondered what a trivial thing was a skiff. This one he and the boy had knocked together in a day. Was a gun, manufactured for killing.

His son tallied up the remaining shells, grouping them symmetrically in threes on the rock when the wet box fell apart. "Two short," he announced. They reloaded and laid the guns on their knees.

Behind thickening clouds they could not see the sun going down. The water, coming up, was growing blacker. The fisherman thought he might have told his wife they would be home before dark since it was Christmas day. He realized he had forgotten about its being any particular day. The tide would not be high until two hours after sunset. When they did not get in by nightfall, and could not be raised by radio, she might send somebody to hunt for them right away. He rejected this arithmetic immediately, with a sickening shock, recollecting it was a two-and-a-half hour run at best. Then it occurred to him that she might send somebody on the mainland who was nearer. She would think he had engine trouble.

He rose and searched the shoreline, barely visible. Then his glance dropped to the toy shoreline at the edges of the reef. The shrinking ledge, so sinister from a boat, grew dearer minute by minute as though the whole wide world he gazed on from horizon to horizon balanced on its contracting rim. He checked the water level and found the shelf awash.

Some of what went through his mind the fisherman told to the boys. They accepted it without comment. If he caught their eyes they looked away to spare him or because they were not yet old enough to face what they saw. Mostly they watched the rising water. The fisherman was unable to initiate a word of encouragement. He wanted one of them to ask him whether somebody would reach them ahead of the tide. He would have found it possible to say yes. But they did not inquire.

The fisherman was not sure how much, at their age, they were able to imagine. Both of them had seen from the docks drowned bodies put ashore out of boats. Sometimes they grasped things, and sometimes not. He supposed they might be longing for the comfort of their mothers, and was astonished, as much as he was capable of any astonishment except the supreme one, to discover himself wishing he had not left his wife's dark, close, naked bed that morning.

"Is it time to shoot now?" asked his nephew.

"Pretty soon," he said, as if he were putting off making good on a promise. "Not yet."

His own boy cried softly for a brief moment, like a man, his face averted in an effort neither to give nor show pain.

"Before school starts," the fisherman said, wonderfully detached, "we'll go to town and I'll buy you boys anything you want."

With great difficulty, in a dull tone as though he did not in the least desire it, his son said after a pause, "I'd like one of those new thirty-horse outboards."

"All right," said the fisherman. And to his nephew, "How about you?"

The nephew shook his head desolately. "I don't want anything," he said.

After another pause the fisherman's son said, "Yes he does, Dad. He wants one too."

"All right—" the fisherman said again, and said no more.

The dog whined in uncertainty and licked the boys' faces where they sat together. Each threw an arm over his back and hugged him. Three strays flew in and sat companionably down among the stiff-necked decoys. The dog crouched, obedient to his training. The boys observed them listlessly. Presently, sensing something untoward, the ducks took off, splashing the wave tops with feet and wingtips, into the dusky waste.

The sea began to make up in the mounting wind, and the wind bore a new and deathly chill. The fisherman, scouring the somber, dwindling shadow of the mainland for a sign, hoped it would not snow. But it did. First a few flakes, then a flurry, then storming past horizontally. The fisherman took one long, bewildered look at Brown Cow Island three hundred yards dead to leeward, and got to his feet.

Then it shut in, as if what was happening on the ledge was too private even for the last wan light of the expiring day.

"Last round," the fisherman said austerely.

The boys rose and shouldered their tacit guns. The fisherman fired into the flying snow. He counted methodically to five. His son fired and counted. His nephew. All three fired and counted. Four rounds.

"You've got one left, Dad," his son said.

The fisherman hesitated another second, then he fired the final shell. Its pathetic report, like the spat of a popgun, whipped away on the wind and was instantly blanketed in falling snow.

Night fell all in a moment to meet the ascending sea. They were now barely able to make one another out through driving snowflakes, dim as ghosts in their yellow oilskins. The fisherman heard a sea break and glanced down where his feet were. They seemed to be wound in a snowy sheet. Gently he took the boys by the shoulders and pushed them in front of him, feeling with his feet along the shallow sump to the place where it triangulated into a sharp crevice at the highest point of the ledge. "Face ahead," he told them. "Put the guns down."

"I'd like to hold mine, Dad," begged his son.

"Put it down," said the fisherman. "The tide won't hurt it. Now brace your feet against both sides and stay there."

They felt the dog, who was pitch black, running up and down in perplexity between their straddled legs. "Dad," said his son, "what about the pooch?"

If he had called the dog by name it would have been too personal. The fisherman would have wept. As it was he had all he could do to keep from laughing. He bent his knees, and when he touched the dog hoisted him under one arm. The dog's belly was soaking wet.

So they waited, marooned in their consciousness, surrounded by a monstrous tidal space which was slowly, slowly closing them out. In this space the periwinkle beneath the fisherman's boots was king. While hovering airborne in his mind he had an inward glimpse of his house as curiously separate, like a June mirage.

Snow, rocks, seas, wind the fisherman had lived by all his life. Now he thought he had never comprehended what they were, and he hated them. Though they had not changed. He was deadly chilled. He set out to ask the boys if they were cold. There was no sense. He thought of the whiskey, and sidled backward, still holding the awkward dog, till he located the bottle under water with his toe. He picked it up squeamishly as though afraid of getting his sleeve wet, worked his way forward and bent over his son. "Drink it," he said, holding the bottle against the boy's ribs. The boy tipped his head back, drank, coughed hotly, then vomited.

"I can't," he told his father wretchedly.

"Try—try—" the fisherman pleaded, as if it meant the difference between life and death.

The boy obediently drank, and again he vomited hotly. He shook his head against his father's chest and passed the bottle forward to his cousin, who drank and vomited also. Passing the bottle back, the boys dropped it in the frigid water between them.

When the waves reached his knees the fisherman set the warm dog loose and said to his son, "Turn around and get up on my shoulders." The boy obeyed. The fisherman opened his oilskin jacket and twisted his hands behind him through his suspenders, clamping the boy's booted ankles with his elbows.

"What about the dog?" the boy asked.

"He'll make his own way all right," the fisherman said. "He can take the cold water." His knees were trembling. Every instinct shrieked for gymnastics. He ground his teeth and braced like a colossus against the sides of the submerged crevice.

The dog, having lived faithfully as though one of them for eleven years, swam a few minutes in and out around the fisherman's legs, not knowing what was happening, and left them without a whimper. He would swim and swim at random by himself, round and round in the blinding night, and when he had swum routinely through the paralyzing water all he could, he would simply, in one incomprehensible moment, drown. Almost the fisherman, waiting out infinity, envied him his pattern.

Freezing seas swept by, flooding inexorably up and up as the earth sank away imperceptibly beneath them. The boy called out once to his cousin. There was no answer. The fisherman, marvelling on a terror without voice, was dumbly glad when the boy did not call again. His own boots were long full of water. With no sensation left in his straddling legs he dared not move them. So long as the seas came sidewise against his hips, and then sidewise against his shoulders, he might balance—no telling how long. The upper half of him was what felt frozen. His legs, disengaged from his nerves and his will, he came to regard quite scientifically. They were the absurd, precarious axis around which reeled the surged universal tumult. The waves would come on and on; he could not visualize how many tossing reinforcements lurked in the night beyond—inexhaustible numbers, and he wept in supernatural fury at each because it was higher, till he transcended hate and took them, swaying like a convert, one by one as they lunged against him and away aimlessly into their own undisputed, wild realm.

From his hips upward the fisherman stretched to his utmost as a man does whose spirit reaches out of dead sleep. The boy's head, none too high, must be at least seven feet above the ledge. Though growing larger every minute, it was a small light life. The fisherman meant to hold it there, if need be, through a thousand tides.

By and by the boy, slumped on the head of his father, asked, "Is it over your boots, Dad?"

"Not yet," the fisherman said. Then through his teeth he added, "If I fall—kick your boots off—swim for it—downwind—to the island. . . ."

"You . . . ?" the boy finally asked.

The fisherman nodded against the boy's belly. "—Won't see each other," he said.

The boy did for the fisherman the greatest thing that can be done. He may have been too young for perfect terror, but he was old enough to know there were things beyond the power of any man. All he could do he did, by trusting his father to do all he could, and asking nothing more.

The fisherman, rocked to his soul by a sea, held his eyes shut upon the interminable night.

"Is it time now?" the boy said.

The fisherman could hardly speak. "Not yet," he said. "Not just yet. . . ."

As the land mass pivoted toward sunlight the day after Christmas, a tiny fleet of small craft converged off shore like iron filings to a magnet. At daybreak they found the skiff floating unscathed off the headland, half full of ducks and snow. The shooting *had* been good, as someone hearing on the nearby mainland the previous afternoon had supposed. Two hours afterward they found the unharmed boat adrift five miles at sea. At high noon they found the fisherman at ebb tide, his right foot jammed cruelly into a glacial crevice of the ledge beside three shotguns, his hands tangled behind him in his suspenders, and under his right elbow a rubber boot with a sock and a live starfish in it. After dragging unlit depths all day for the boys, they towed the fisherman home in his own boat at sundown, and in the frost of evening, mute with discovering purgatory, laid him on his wharf for his wife to see.

She, somehow, standing on the dock as in her frequent dream, gazing at the fisherman pure as crystal on the icy boards, a small rubber boot still frozen under one clenched arm, saw him exaggerated beyond remorse or grief, absolved of his mortality.

William Styron

THE LONG MARCH

I

One noon, in the blaze of a cloudless Carolina summer, what was left of eight dead boys lay strewn about the landscape, among the poison ivy and the pine needles and loblolly saplings. It was not so much as if they had departed this life but as if, sprayed from a hose, they were only shreds of bone, gut, and dangling tissue to which it would have been impossible ever to impute the quality of life, far less the capacity to relinquish it. Of course, though, these had really died quickly, no doubt before the faintest flicker of recognition, of wonder, apprehension, or terror had had time to register in their minds. But the shock, it occurred to Lieutenant Culver, who stood in the shady lee of an ambulance and watched the scene, must have been fantastic to those on the periphery of the explosion, those fifteen or so surviving marines who now lay on the ground beneath blankets, moaning with pain and fright, and who, not more than half an hour before, had been waiting patiently in line for their lunch before the two mortar shells, misfired—how? why? the question already hung with a buzzing, palpable fury in the noontime heat—had plummeted down upon the chow-line and had deadened their ears and senses and had hurled them earthward where they lay now, alive but stricken in a welter of blood and brain, scattered messkits and mashed potatoes, and puddles of melting ice cream. Moments ago in the confusion—just before he had stolen off from the Colonel's side to go behind a tree and get sick—Lieutenant Culver had had a glimpse of a young sweaty face grimed with dust, had heard the boy's voice, astonishing even in that moment of nausea because of its clear, unhysterical tone of explanation: "Major, I tell you I was on the field phone and I tell you as soon as they come out the tube I knew they were short rounds and so I hollered . . ." Of course it had been an accident. But why? He heard the Major shout something, then Culver had heard no more, retching on the leaves with a sound that, for the moment, drowned out the cries and whines of the wounded and the noise of trucks and ambulances crashing up through the underbrush.

It was not that he had a weak stomach or that he was unacquainted with carnage that allowed him to lose control. If anything, he prided himself on his stomach, and as for blood he had seen a lot spilled on Okinawa and had himself (although through no act of valor whatever) received a shrapnel wound—in the buttocks, a matter which even in retrospect, as he had often been forced to remind his wife, possessed no elements of comedy at all. In this case it was simply that on the one hand he himself had been shocked. The sight of death was the sort of thing which in wartime is expected, which one protects oneself against, and which is finally excused or at least ignored, in the same way that a beggar is ignored, or a head cold, or a social problem. But in training here in the States in peacetime (or what, this sweltering summer in the early 1950s, passed as peacetime) one had felt no particular need for that type of self-defense, and the slick nude litter of intestine and shattered blue bones, among which forks and spoons peeked out like so many pathetic metal flowers, made a crazy, insulting impact at Culver's belly, like the blow of a fist. And on the other hand (and the pulsing ache at his brow now as he vomited helplessly onto his shoes lent confirmation to what he'd been trying to deny to himself for months): he was too old, he was no longer an eager kid just out of Quantico with a knife between his teeth. He was almost thirty, he was old, and he was afraid.

Lieutenant Culver had been called back to the marines early that spring. When, one Saturday morning, his wife had thrown the brown envelope containing his orders onto the bed where he lay sleeping, he experienced an odd distress which kept him wandering about, baffled and mumbling to himself, for days. Like most of his fellow reserves he had retained his commission after the last war. It was an insouciant gesture which he had assumed would in some way benefit him in case of an all-out conflict, say, thirty years hence, but one which made no provisions for such an eventuality as a police action in Korea. It had all come much too soon and Culver had felt weirdly as if he had fallen asleep in some barracks in 1945 and had awakened in a half-dozen years or so to find that the intervening freedom, growth, and serenity had been only a glorious if somewhat prolonged dream. A flood of protest had welled up in him, for he had put the idea of war out of his mind entirely, and the brief years since Okinawa had been the richest of his life. They had produced, among lesser things, a loving, tenderly passionate wife who had passed on to their little girl both some of her gentle nature and her wealth of butter-colored hair; a law degree, the fruits of which he had just begun to realize, even though still somewhat impecuniously, as one of the brightest juniors in a good New York law firm; a friendly beagle named Howard whom he took for hikes in Washington Square; a cat, whom he did not deign to call by name, and despised; and a record-player that played Haydn, Mozart and Bach.

Up until the day that his orders came—the day that he tried to forget and the one that Betsy, his wife, soon bitterly referred to as "the day the roof fell in"—they had been living in a roomy walk-up in the Village and experiencing the prosaic contentment that comes from eating properly, indulging themselves with fair moderation in the pleasures of the city, and watching the growth of a child. This is not to say that they were either smug or dull. They had a bright circle of friends, mostly young lawyers and newspapermen and doctors and their wives. There were parties and occasional week ends in the country, where everyone became frankly drunk. There were the usual household skirmishes, too, but these were infrequent and petered out quickly. Both of them were too sensible to allow some domestic misdemeanor to develop into anything horrible; they were well adjusted and each of them found it easy to admit, long after the honeymoon, that they were deeply in love. Months later at camp, ensnared futilely in the coils of some administrative flypaper, Culver would find himself gazing up from his work and out across the smoky hot barrens of pine and sand, relieving his vast boredom in a daydream of that vanished simplicity and charm. His mind seemed to drift toward one recurrent vision. This was of the afternoons in winter when—bundled to the ears, the baby-carriage joggling bravely in the van and the melancholy beagle scampering at their heels—they took their Sunday stroll. On such days the city, its frantic heartbeat quieted and clothed in the sooty white tatters of a recent snow, seemed to have an Old World calm, and the people that passed them in the twilight appeared to be, like themselves, pink-cheeked and contented, no matter what crimson alarms flowered at the newsstands or what evil rumors sounded from distant radios. For Culver the waning Sunday light had not spelled out the promise of Monday morning's gloom but of Monday's challenge—and this was not because he was a go-getter but because he was happy. He was happy to walk through the chill and leafless dusk with his wife and his child and his dog. And he was happy to return home to warmth and peanut butter and liverwurst, to the familiar delight of the baby's good-night embrace, to the droll combat between beagle and cat, to music before sleep. Sometimes in these reveries Culver thought that it was the music, more than anything, which provided the key, and he recalled himself at a time which already seemed dark ages ago, surrounded by beer cans and attuned, in the nostalgic air of a winter evening, to some passage from some forgotten Haydn. It was one happy and ascending bar that he remembered, a dozen bright notes through which he passed in memory to an earlier, untroubled day at the end of childhood. There, like tumbling flowers against the sunny grass, their motions as nimble as the music itself, two lovely little girls played tennis, called to him voicelessly, as in a dream, and waved their arms.

The sordid little town outside the camp possessed the horror of recognition, for Culver had been there before. They left the baby with a sister and headed South where, on the outskirts of the town, they found a cramped room in a tourist cabin. They were there for two weeks. They searched vainly for a place to live, there was no more room at the camp. They turned away from bleak cell-like rooms offered at five times their value, were shown huts and chicken-coops by characters whose bland country faces could not hide the sparkle, in their calculating eyes, of venal lust. The aging proprietress of the tourist camp was a scold and a cheat. And so they finally gave up. Betsy went home. He kissed her good-by late one rainy afternoon in the bus station, surrounded by a horde of marines and by cheap suitcases and fallen candy wrappers and the sound of fretful children—all of the unlovely mementoes, so nightmarishly familiar, of leave-taking and of anxiety. Of war. He felt her tears against his cheek. It had been an evil day, and the rain that streamed against the windows, blurring a distant frieze of gaunt gray pines, had seemed to nag with both remembrance and foreboding—of tropic seas, storm-swept distances and strange coasts.

II

He had heard the explosion himself. They had been eating at their own chow-line in a command post set up in a grove of trees, when the noise came from off to the right, distant enough but still too close: a twin quick earthshaking sound—*crump crump.* Then seconds later in the still of noon when even the birds had become quiet and only a few murmured voices disturbed the concentration of eating, a shudder had passed through the surrounding underbrush, like a faint hot wind. It was premonitory, perhaps, but still no one knew. The leaves rustled, ceased, and Culver had looked up from where he squatted against a tree to see fifty scattered faces peering toward the noise, their knives and forks suspended. Then from the galley among the trees a clatter broke the silence, a falling pan or kettle, and someone laughed, and the Colonel, sitting nearby, had said to the Major—what had he said? Culver couldn't remember, yet there had been something uneasy in his tone, even then, before anyone had known, and at least ten minutes before the radio corporal, a tobacco-chewing clown from Oklahoma named Hobbs, came trotting up brushing crumbs from his mouth, a message book clutched in one fat paw. He was popular in battalion headquarters, one of those favored men who, through some simplicity or artlessness of nature, can manage a profane familiarity which in another would be insubordinate; the look of concern on his clown's face, usually so whimsical, communicated an added dread.

"I gotta flash red from Plumbob, Colonel, and it ain't no problem emergency. All hell's broke loose over in Third Battalion. They dropped in some short rounds on a chow-line and they want corpsmen and a doctor and the chaplain. Jesus, you should hear 'em down there."

The Colonel had said nothing at first. The brief flicker of uneasiness in his eyes had fled, and when he put down his mess-kit and looked up at Hobbs it was only to wipe his hands on his handkerchief and squint casually into the sun, as if he were receiving the most routine of messages. It was absolutely typical of the man, Culver reflected. Too habitual to be an act yet still somehow too faintly self-conscious to be entirely natural, how many years and what strange interior struggle had gone into the perfection of such a gesture? It was good, Grade-A Templeton, perhaps not a distinctly top-notch performance but certainly, from where the critic Culver sat, deserving of applause: the frail, little-boned, almost pretty face peering upward with a look of attitudinized contemplation; the pensive bulge of tongue sliding inside the rim of one tanned cheek to gouge out some particle of food; small hands working calmly in the folds of the handkerchief—surely all this was more final, more commanding than the arrogant loud mastery of a Booth, more like the skill of Bernhardt, who could cow men by the mystery of her smallest twitch. Perhaps fifteen seconds passed before he spoke. Culver became irritated—at his own suspense, throbbing inside him like a heartbeat, and at the awesome silence which, as if upon order, had fallen over the group of five, detached from the bustle of the rest of the command post: the Colonel; Hobbs; Major Lawrence, the executive officer, now gazing at the Colonel with moist underlip and deferential anxiety; Captain Mannix; himself. Back off in the bushes a mockingbird commenced a shrill rippling chant and far away, amidst the depth of the silence, there seemed to be a single faint and terrible scream. Hobbs spat an auburn gob of tobacco-juice into the sand, and the Colonel spoke: "Let me have that radio, Hobbs, and get me Plumbob One," he said evenly, and then with no change of tone to the Major: "Billy, send a runner over for Doc Patterson and you two get down there with the chaplain. Take my jeep. Tell the Doc to detach all his corpsmen. And you'd better chop-chop."

The Major scrambled to his feet. He was youthful and handsome, a fine marine in his polished boots, his immaculate dungarees—donned freshly clean, Culver had observed, that morning. He was of the handsomeness preferred by other military men—regular features, clean-cut, rather athletic—but there was a trace of peace-time fleshiness in his cheeks which often lent to the corners of his mouth a sort of petulance, so that every now and again, his young uncomplicated face in deep concentration over some operations map or training schedule or order, he looked like a spoiled and arrogant baby of five. "Aye-aye, sir," he said and bent over the Colonel, bestowing upon him that third-person flattery which to Culver seemed perilously close to bootlicking and was thought to be considerably out of date, especially among the reserves. "Does the Colonel want us to run our own problem as ordered, sir?" He was a regular.

Templeton took the headset from Hobbs, who lowered the radio down beside him in the sand. "Yeah, Billy," he said, without looking up, "yeah, that'll be all right. We'll run her on time. Tell O'Leary to tell all companies to push off at thirteen-hundred."

"Aye-aye, sir." And the Major, boots sparkling, was off in a puff of pine needles and dust.

"Jesus," Mannix said. He put down his messkit and nudged Culver in the ribs. Captain Mannix, the commanding officer of headquarters company, was Culver's friend and, for five months, his closest one. He was a dark heavy-set Jew from Brooklyn, Culver's age and a reserve, too, who had had to sell his radio store and leave his wife and two children at home. He had a disgruntled sense of humor which often seemed to bring a spark of relief not just to his own, but to Culver's, feeling of futility and isolation. Mannix was a bitter man and, in his bitterness, sometimes recklessly vocal. He had long ago given up genteel accents, and spoke like a marine. It was easier, he maintained. "Je-*sus*," he whispered again, too loud, "what'll Congress do about this? Look at Billy chop-chop."

Culver said nothing. His tension eased off a bit, and he looked around him. The news had not seemed yet to have spread around the command post; the men began to get up and walk to the chow-line to clean their messgear, strolled back beneath the trees and flopped down, heads against their packs, for a moment's nap. The Colonel spoke in an easy, confidential voice with the other battalion commander: the casualties were confined, Culver gathered, to that outfit. It was a battalion made up mostly of young reserves and it was one in which, he suddenly thanked God, he knew no one. Then he heard the Colonel go on calmly—to promise more aid, to promise to come down himself, shortly. "Does it look rough, Luke?" Culver heard him say, "Hold on tight, Luke boy"— all in the cool and leisurely, almost bored, tones of a man to whom the greatest embarrassment would be a show of emotion, and to whom, because of this quality, had been given, in the midst of some strained and violent combat situation long ago, the name "Old Rocky." He was not yet forty-five, yet the adjective "old" applied, for there was a gray sheen in his hair and a bemused, unshakable look in his tranquil eyes that made him seem, like certain young ecclesiastics, prematurely aged and perhaps even wise. Culver saw him put the headset down and get up, walking off toward the operations tent with a springy, slim-hipped, boyish stride, calling out over his shoulder as he went: "Mannix." Simply that: Mannix. A voice neither harsh nor peremptory nor, on the other hand, particularly gentle. It was merely a voice which expected to be obeyed, and Culver felt Mannix's big weight against him as the Captain put a hand on his shoulder and pried himself up from the ground, muttering, "Jesus, lemme digest a bit, Jack."

Mannix despised the Colonel. Yet, Culver thought, as the Captain hulked stiff-kneed behind the Colonel and disappeared after him into the operations tent, Mannix despised everything about the Marine Corps. In this attitude he was like nearly all the reserves, it was true, but Mannix was more noisily frank in regard to his position. He detested Templeton not because of any slight or injustice, but because Templeton was a lieutenant colonel, because he was a regular, and because he possessed over Mannix—after six years of freedom—an absolute and unquestioned authority. Mannix would have hated any battalion commander, had he the benignity of Santa Claus, and Culver, listening to Mannix's frequently comical but often too audible complaints, as just now, was kept in a constant state of mild suspense—half amusement, half horror. Culver settled himself against the tree. Apparently there was nothing, for the moment at least, that he could do. Above him an airplane droned through the stillness. A truck grumbled across the clearing, carrying a group of languid hospital corpsmen, was gone; around him the men lay against their packs in crumpled attitudes of sleep. A heavy drowsiness came over him, and he let his eyes slide closed. Suddenly he yearned, with all of the hunger of a schoolboy in a classroom on a May afternoon, to be able to collapse into slumber. For the three days they had been on the problem he had averaged only four hours of sleep a night—almost none last night—and gratefully he knew he'd be able to sleep this evening. He began to doze, dreaming fitfully of home, of white cottages, of a summer by the sea. *Long walk tonight.* And his eyes snapped open then—on what seemed to be the repeated echo, from afar, of that faint anguished shriek he had heard before—in the horrid remembrance that there would be no sleep tonight. For anyone at all. Only a few seconds had passed.

"Long walk tonight," the voice repeated. Culver stared upward through a dazzling patchwork of leaves and light to see the broad pink face of Sergeant O'Leary, smiling down.

"Christ, O'Leary," he said, "don't remind me."

The Sergeant, still grinning, gestured with his shoulder in the direction of the operations tent. "The Colonel's really got a wild hair, ain't he?" He chuckled and reached down and clutched one of his feet, with an elaborate groan.

Culver abruptly felt cloaked in a gloom that was almost tangible, and he was in no mood to laugh. "You'll be really holding that foot tomorrow morning," he said, "and that's no joke."

The grin persisted. "Ah, Mister Culver," O'Leary said, "don't take it so hard. It's just a little walk through the night. It'll be over before you know it." He paused, prodding with his toe at the pine needles. "Say," he went on, "what's this I heard about some short rounds down in Third Batt?"

"I don't know from nothing, O'Leary. I just read the papers." Another truck came by, loaded with corpsmen, followed by a jeep in which sat the helmeted Major Lawrence, a look of sulky arrogance on his face, his arms folded at his chest like a legionnaire riding through a conquered city. "But from what I understand," Culver went on, turning back, "quite a few guys got hurt."

"That's tough," O'Leary said. "I'll bet you they were using that old stuff they've had stored on Guam ever since '45. Jesus, you'd think they'd have better sense. Why, I seen those shells stacked up high as a man out there just last year, getting rained on every day and getting the jungle rot and Jesus, they put tarps over 'em but five years is one hell of a long time to let 81-shells lay around. I remember once . . ." Culver let him talk, without hearing the words, and drowsed. O'Leary was an old-timer (though only a few years older than Culver), a regular who had just signed over for four more years, and it was impossible to dislike him. On Guadalcanal he had been only a youngster, but in the intervening years the Marine Corps had molded him—perhaps by his own unconscious choice—in its image, and he had become as inextricably grafted to the system as any piece of flesh surgically laid on to arm or thigh. There was great heartiness and warmth in him but at the same time he performed all infantry jobs with a devoted, methodical competence. He could say sarcastically, "The Colonel's really got a wild hair, ain't he?" but shrug his shoulders and grin, and by that ambivalent gesture sum up an attitude which only a professional soldier could logically retain: I doubt the Colonel's judgment a little, but I will willingly do what he says. He also shared with Hobbs, the radio-man, some sort of immunity. And thus it had been last night, Culver recalled, that upon the Colonel's announcement about this evening's forced march—which was to take thirteen hours and extend the nearly thirty-six miles back to the main base—O'Leary had been able to give a long, audible, incredulous whistle, right in the Colonel's face, and elicit from the Colonel an indulgent smile; whereas in the same blackout tent and at virtually the same instant Mannix had murmured, "Thirty-six miles, Jesus Christ," in a tone, however, laden with no more disbelief or no more pain than O'Leary's whistle, and Culver had seen the Colonel's smile vanish, replaced on the fragile little face by a subtle, delicate shadow of irritation.

"You think that's too long?" the Colonel had said to Mannix then, turning slightly. There had been no hostility in his voice, or even reproof; it had, in fact, seemed merely a question candidly stated—although this might have been because two enlisted men had been in the tent, O'Leary, and some wizened, anonymous little private shivering over the radio. It was midsummer, but nights out in the swamps were fiercely, illogically cold, and from where they had set up the operations tent that evening— on a tiny patch of squashy marshland—the dampness seemed to ooze up and around them, clutching their bones in a chill which extra sweaters and field jackets and sweatshirts could not dislodge. A single kerosene pressure-lamp dangled from overhead—roaring like a pint-sized, en-capsuled hurricane; it furnished the only light in the tent, and the negligible solace of a candlelike heat. It had the stark, desperate, manufactured quality of the light one imagines in an execution chamber; under it the Colonel's face, in absolute repose as he stared down for a brief, silent instant and awaited Mannix's reply, looked like that of a mannequin, chalky, exquisite, solitary beneath a store-window glare.

"No, sir," Mannix said. He had recovered quickly. He peered up at the Colonel from his camp stool, expressionless. "No, sir," he repeated, "I don't think it's too long, but it's certainly going to be some hike."

The Colonel did something with his lips. It seemed to be a smile. He said nothing—bemused and mystifying—wearing the enigma of the moment like a cape. In the silence the tempestuous little lamp boiled and raged; far off in the swamp somewhere a mortar flare flew up with a short, sharp crack. O'Leary broke the quietness in the tent with a loud sneeze, followed, almost like a prolongation of the sneeze, by a chuckle, and said: "Oh boy, Colonel, there're gonna be some sore feet Saturday morning."

The Colonel didn't answer. He hooked his thumbs in his belt. He turned to the Major, who was brooding upward from the field desk, cheeks propped against his hands. "I was sitting in my tent a while ago, Billy," the Colonel said, "and I got to thinking. I got to thinking about a lot of things. I got to thinking about the Battalion. I said to myself, 'How's the Battalion doing?' I mean, 'What kind of an outfit do I have here? Is it in good combat shape? If we were to meet an Aggressor enemy tomorrow would we come out all right?' Those were the queries I posed to myself. Then I tried to formulate an answer." He paused, his eyes luminous and his lips twisted in a wry, contemplative smile as if he were indeed, again, struggling with the weight of the questions to which he had addressed himself. The Major was absorbed; he looked up at Templeton with an intent baby-blue gaze and parted mouth, upon which, against a pink cleft of the lower lip, there glittered a bead of saliva. "Reluctantly," the Colonel went on slowly, "reluctantly, I came to this conclusion: the Battalion's been doping off." He paused again. "Doping off. Especially," he said, turning briefly toward Mannix with a thin smile, "a certain component unit known as Headquarters and Service Company." He leaned back on the camp stool and slowly caressed the pewter-colored surface of his hair. "I decided a little walk might be in order for tomorrow night, after we secure the problem. Instead of going back to the base on the trucks. What do you think, Billy?"

"I think that's an excellent idea, sir. An excellent idea. In fact I've been meaning to suggest something like that to the Colonel for quite some time. As a means of inculcating a sort of group *esprit*."

"It's what they need, Billy."

"Full marching order, sir?" O'Leary put in seriously.

"No, that'd be a little rough."

"Aaa-h," O'Leary said, relieved.

Suddenly Culver heard Mannix's voice: "Even so—"

"Even so, what?" the Colonel interrupted. Again, the voice was not hostile, only anticipatory, as if it already held the answer to whatever Mannix might ask or suggest.

"Well, even so, Colonel," Mannix went on mildly, while Culver, suddenly taut and concerned, held his breath, "even without packs thirty-six miles is a long way for anybody, much less for guys who've gone soft for the past five or six years. I'll admit my company isn't the hottest outfit in the world, but most of them are reserves—"

"Wait a minute, Captain, wait a minute," the Colonel said. Once more the voice—as cool and as level as the marshy ground upon which they were sitting—carefully skirted any tone of reproach and was merely explicit: "I don't want you to think I'm taking it out on the Battalion merely because of you, or rather H & S Company. But they aren't reserves. They're *marines. Comprend?*" He arose from the chair. "I think," he went on flatly, almost gently, "that there's one thing that we are all tending to overlook these days. We've been trying to differentiate too closely between two particular bodies of men that make up the Marine Corps. Technically it's true that a lot of these new men are reserves—that is, they have an 'R' affixed at the end of the 'USMC.' But it's only a technical difference, you see. Because first and foremost they're *marines*. I don't want my marines doping off. They're going to *act* like marines. They're going to be *fit*. If they meet an Aggressor enemy next week they might have to march a long, long way. And that's what I want this hike to teach them. *Comprend?*" He made what could pass for the token of a smile and laid his hand easily and for a lingering second on Mannix's shoulder, in a sort of half-gesture of conciliation, understanding—something—it was hard to tell. It was an odd picture because from where he sat Culver was the only one in the tent who could see, at the same instant, both of their expressions. In the morbid, comfortless light they were like classical Greek masks, made of chrome or tin, reflecting an almost theatrical disharmony: the Colonel's fleeting grin sculpted cleanly and prettily in the unshadowed air above the Captain's darkened, downcast face where, for a flicker of a second, something outraged and agonized was swiftly graven and swiftly scratched out. The Colonel's smile was not complacent or unfriendly. It was not so much as if he had achieved a triumph but merely equilibrium, had returned once more to that devout, ordered state of communion which the Captain's words had ever so briefly disturbed. At that moment Culver almost liked the Colonel, in some negative way which had nothing to do with affection, but to which "respect," though he hated the word, was the nearest approach. At least it was an honest smile, no matter how faint. It was the expression of a man who might be fatuous and a ham of sorts, but was not himself evil or unjust—a man who would like to overhear some sergeant say, "He keeps a tight outfit, but he's straight." In men like Templeton all emotions—all smiles, all anger—emanated from a priestlike, religious fervor, throbbing inwardly with the cadence of parades and booted footfalls. By that passion rebels are ordered into quick damnation but simple doubters sometimes find indulgence—depending upon the priest, who may be one inclined toward mercy, or who is one ever rapt in some litany of punishment and court-martial. The Colonel was devout but inclined toward mercy. He was not a tyrant, and his smile was a sign that the Captain's doubts were forgiven, probably even forgotten. But only Culver had seen the Captain's face: a quick look of both fury and suffering, like the tragic Greek mask, or a shackled slave. Then Mannix flushed. "Yes, sir," he said.

The Colonel walked toward the door. He seemed already to have put the incident out of his mind. "Culver," he said, "if you can ever make radio contact with Able Company tell them to push off at 0600. If you can't, send a runner down before dawn to see if they've got the word." He gave the side of his thigh a rather self-conscious, gratuitous slap. "Well, good night."

There was a chorus of "Good night, sirs," and then the Major went out, too, trailed by O'Leary. Culver looked at his watch: it was nearly three o'clock.

Mannix looked up. "You going to try and get some sleep, Tom?"

"I've tried. It's too cold. Anyway, I've got to take over the radio watch from Junior here. What's your name, fellow?"

The boy at the radio looked up with a start, trembling with the cold. "McDonald, sir." He was very young, with pimples and a sweet earnest expression; he had obviously just come from boot camp, for he had practically no hair.

"Well, you can shove off and get some sleep, if you can find a nice warm pile of pine needles somewhere." The boy sleepily put down his earphones and went out, fastening the blackout flap behind him.

"I've tried," Culver repeated, "but I just can't get used to sleeping on the ground any more. I'm getting old and rheumatic. Anyway, the Old Rock was in here for about two hours before you came, using up my sack time while he told the Major and O'Leary and me all about his Shanghai days."

"He's a son of a bitch." Mannix morosely cupped his chin in his hands, blinking into space, at the bare canvas wall. He was chewing on the butt of a cigar. The glare seemed to accentuate a flat Mongoloid cast in his face; he looked surly and tough and utterly exhausted. Shivering, he pulled his field jacket closer around his neck, and then, as Culver watched, his face broke out into the comical, exasperated smile which always heralded his bitterest moments of outrage—at the Marine Corps, at the system, at their helpless plight, the state of the world—tirades which, in their unqualified cynicism, would have been intolerable were they not always delivered with such gusto and humor and a kind of grisly delight. "Thirty . . . six . . . *miles,*" he said slowly, his eyes alive and glistening, *thirty. . . six . . . miles!* Christ on a crutch! Do you realize how far that is? Why that's as far as it is from Grand Central to Stamford, Connecticut! Why, man, I haven't walked a hundred consecutive yards since 1945. I couldn't go thirty-six miles if I were sliding downhill the whole way on a sled. And a *forced* march, mind you. You just don't stroll along, you know. That's like running. That's a regulation two-and-a-half miles per hour with only a ten-minute break each hour. So H & S Company is fouled up. So maybe it is. He can't take green troops like these and do that. After a couple of seven- or ten- or fifteen-mile conditioning hikes, maybe so. If they were young. And rested. Barracks-fresh. But this silly son of a bitch is going to have all these tired, flabby old men flapping around on the ground like a bunch of fish after the first two miles. Christ on a frigging crutch!"

"He's not a bad guy, Al," Culver said, "he's just a regular. Shot in the ass with the Corps. A bit off his nut, like all of them."

But Mannix had made the march seem menacing, there was no doubt about that, and Culver—who for the moment had been regarding the hike as a sort of careless abstraction, a prolonged evening's stroll—felt a solid dread creep into his bones, along with the chill of the night. Involuntarily, he shuddered. He felt suddenly unreal and disoriented, as if through some curious second sight or seventh sense his surroundings had shifted, ever so imperceptibly, into another dimension of space and time. Perhaps he was just so tired. Freezing marsh and grass instead of wood beneath his feet, the preposterous cold in the midst of summer, Mannix's huge distorted shadow cast brutishly against the impermeable walls by a lantern so sinister that its raging noise had the sound of a typhoon at sea—all these, just for an instant, did indeed contrive to make him feel as if they were adrift at sea in a dazzling, windowless box, ignorant of direction or of any points of the globe, and with no way of telling. What he had had for the last years—wife and child and home—seemed to have existed in the infinite past or, dreamlike again, never at all, and what he had done yesterday and the day before, moving wearily with this tent from one strange thicket to a stranger swamp and on to the green depths of even stranger ravine, had no sequence, like the dream of a man delirious with fever. All time and space seemed for a moment to be enclosed within the tent, itself unmoored and unhelmed upon a dark and compassless ocean.

And although Mannix was close by, he felt profoundly alone. Something that had happened that evening—something Mannix had said, or suggested, perhaps not even that, but only a fleeting look in the Captain's face, the old compressed look of torment mingled with seething outrage—something that evening, without a doubt, had added to the great load of his loneliness an almost intolerable burden. And that burden was simply an anxiety, nameless for the moment and therefore the more menacing. It was not merely the prospect of the hike. Exhaustion had just made him vulnerable to a million shaky, anonymous fears—fears which he might have resisted had he felt strong and refreshed, or younger. His age was showing badly. All this would have been easy at twenty-three. But he was thirty, and seventy-two virtually sleepless hours had left him feeling bushed and defeated. And there was another subtle difference he felt about his advanced age—a new awakening, an awareness—and therein lay the reason for his fears.

It was simply that after six years of an ordered and sympathetic life—made the more placid by the fact that he had assumed he had put war forever behind him—it was a shock almost mystically horrifying, in its unreality, to find himself in this new world of frigid nights and blazing noons, of disorder and movement and fanciful pursuit. He was insecure and uprooted and the prey of many fears. Not for days but for weeks, it seemed, the battalion had been on the trail of an invisible enemy who always eluded them and kept them pressing on—across swamps and blasted fields and past indolent, alien streams. This enemy was labeled Aggressor, on maps brightly spattered with arrows and symbolic tanks and guns, but although there was no sign of his aggression he fled them nonetheless and they pushed the sinister chase, sending up shells and flares as they went. Five hours' pause, five hours in a tent somewhere, lent to the surrounding grove of trees a warm, homelike familiarity that was almost like permanence, and he left each command post feeling lonely and uprooted, as they pushed on after the spectral foe into the infinite strangeness of another swamp or grove. Fatigue pressed down on his shoulders like strong hands, and he awoke in the morning feeling weary, if he ever slept at all. Since their constant movement made the sunlight come from ever-shifting points of the compass, he was often never quite sure—in his steady exhaustion— whether it was morning or afternoon. The displacement and the confusion filled him with an anxiety which would not have been possible six years before, and increased his fatigue. The tent itself, in its tiny, momentary permanence, might have had all of the appeal of the home which he so desperately hungered for, had it not been so cold, and had it not seemed, as he sat there suddenly shivering with fear, so much more like a coffin instead.

Then it occurred to him that he was actually terrified of the march, of the thirty-six miles: not because of the length—which was beyond comprehension—but because he was sure he'd not be able to make it. The contagion of Mannix's fear had touched him. And he wondered then if Mannix's fear had been like his own: that no matter what his hatred of the system, of the Marine Corps, might be, some instilled, twisted pride would make him walk until he dropped, and his fear was not of the hike itself, but of dropping. He looked up at Mannix and said, "Do you think you can make it, Al?"

Mannix heavily slapped his knee. He seemed not to have heard the question. The giddy sensation passed, and Culver got up to warm his hands at the lamp.

"I'll bet if Regiment or Division got wind of this they'd lower the boom on the bastard," Mannix said.

"They have already. They said fine."

"What do you mean? How do you know?"

"He said so, before you came in. He radioed to the base for permission, or so he said."

"The bastard."

"He wouldn't dare without it," Culver said. "What I can't figure out is why Regiment gave him the O.K. on it."

"The swine. The little swine. It's not on account of H & S Company. You know that. It's because it's an exploit. He wants to be known as a tough guy, a boondocker."

"There's one consolation, though," said Culver, after a pause, "if it'll help you any."

"What, for God's sake?"

"Old Rocky, or whatever they call him, is going to hike along, too."

"You think so?" Mannix said doubtfully.

"I know so. So do you. He wouldn't dare not push along with his men."

Mannix was silent for a moment. Then he said viciously, as if obsessed with the idea that no act of Templeton's could remain untainted by a prime and calculated evil: "But the son of a bitch! He's made for that sort of thing. He's been running around the boondocks for six years getting in shape while sane people like you and me were home living like humans and taking it easy. Billy Lawrence, too. They're both gung ho. These fat civilians can't take that sort of thing. My God! Hobbs! Look at that radioman, Hobbs. That guy's going to keel over two minutes out—" He rose suddenly to his feet and stretched, his voice stifled by the long, indrawn breath of a yawn. "Aaa-h, fuck it. I'm going to hit the sack."

"Why don't you?"

"Fine bed. A poncho in a pile of poison ivy. My ass looks like a chessboard from chigger bites. Jesus, if Mimi could see me now." He paused and pawed at his red-rimmed eyes. "Yeah," he said, blinking at his watch, "I think I will." He slapped Culver on the back, without much heartiness. "I'll see you tomorrow, sport. Stay loose." Then he lumbered from the tent, mumbling something: *be in for fifty years.*

Culver turned away from the lamp. He sat down at the field desk, strapping a black garland of wires and earphones around his skull. The wild, lost wail of the radio signal struck his ears, mingling with the roar, much closer now, of the lamp; alone as he was, the chill and cramped universe of the tent seemed made for no one more competent than a blind midget, and was on the verge of bursting with a swollen obbligato of demented sounds. He felt almost sick with the need for sleep and, with the earphones still around his head, he thrust his face into his arms on the field desk. There was nothing on the radio except the signal; far off in the swamp the companies were sleeping wretchedly in scattered squads and platoons, tumbled about in the cold and the dark, and dreaming fitful dreams. The radios were dead everywhere, except for their signals: a crazy, tortured multitude of wails on which his imagination played in exhaustion. They seemed like the cries of souls in the anguish of hell, if he concentrated closely enough, shrill cracklings, whines, barks and shrieks—a whole jungle full of noise an inch from his eardrum and across which, like a thread of insanity, was strung the single faint fluting of a dance-band clarinet—blown in from Florida or New York, someplace beyond reckoning. His universe now seemed even more contained: not merely by the tiny space of the tent, but by the almost tangible fact of sound. And it was impossible to sleep. Besides, something weighed heavily on his mind; there was something he had forgotten, something he was supposed to do . . .

Then suddenly he remembered the Colonel's instructions. He cleared his throat and spoke drowsily into the mouthpiece, his head still resting against his arms. "This is Bundle Three calling Bundle Able. This is Bundle Three calling Bundle Able. This . . . Able. This is Bundle Three calling Bundle Able. Do you hear me? Over . . ." He paused for a moment, waiting. There was no answer. He repeated: "This is Bundle Three calling Bundle Able, this is Bundle Three calling Bundle Able, this is. . . ." And he snapped abruptly erect, thinking of Mannix, thinking: to hell with it: simply because the words made him feel juvenile and absurd, as if he were reciting Mother Goose.

He *would* stay awake. And he thought of Mannix. Because Mannix would laugh. Mannix appreciated the idiocy of those radio words, just as in his own crazy way he managed to put his finger on anything which might represent a symbol of their predicament. Like the radio code. He had a violent contempt for the gibberish, the boy-scout passwords which replaced ordinary conversation in the military world. To Mannix they were all part of the secret language of a group of morons, morons who had been made irresponsibly and dangerously clever. He had despised the other side, also—the sweat, the exertion, and the final danger. It had been he, too, who had said, "None of this Hemingway crap for me, Jack"; he was nobody's lousy hero, and he'd get out of this outfit some way. Yet, Culver speculated, who really was a hero anyway, any more? Mannix's disavowal of faith put him automatically out of the hero category, in the classical sense, yet if suffering was part of the hero's role, wasn't Mannix as heroic as any? On his shoulder there was a raw, deeply dented, livid scar, made the more conspicuous and, for that matter, more ugly, by the fact that its evil slick surface only emphasized the burly growth of hair around it. There were smaller scars all over his body. About them Mannix was neither proud nor modest, but just frank, and once while they were showering down after a day in the field, Mannix told him how he had gotten the scars, one day on Peleliu. "I was a buck sergeant then. I got pinned down in a shell hole out in front of my platoon. Christ knows how I got there but I remember there was a telephone in the hole and—whammo!—the Nips began laying in mortar fire on the area and I got a piece right here." He pointed to a shiny, triangular groove just above his knee. "I remember grabbing that phone and hollering for them to for Christ's sake get the 81s up and knock out that position, but they were slow, Jesus they were slow! The Nips were firing for effect, I guess, because they were coming down like rain and every time one of the goddam things went off I seemed to catch it. All I can remember is hollering into that phone and the rounds going off and the zinging noise that shrapnel made. I hollered for 81s and I caught a piece in my hand. Then I hollered for at least a goddam rifle grenade and I caught a piece in the ass, right here. I hollered for 60s and guns and airplanes. Every time I hollered for something I seemed to catch some steel. Christ, I was scared. And hurting! Jesus Christ, I never hurt so much in my life. Then I caught this one right here"—he made a comical, contorted gesture, with a bar of soap, over his shoulder—"man, it was lights out then. I remember thinking, 'Al, you've had it,' and just before I passed out I looked down at that telephone. You know, that frigging wire had been blasted right out of sight all that time."

No, perhaps Mannix wasn't a hero, any more than the rest of them, caught up by wars in which, decade by half-decade, the combatant served peonage to the telephone and the radar and the thunderjet—a horde of cunningly designed, and therefore often treacherous, machines. But Mannix had suffered once, that "once" being, in his own words, "once too goddam many, Jack." And his own particular suffering had made him angry, had given him an acute, if cynical, perception about their renewed bondage, and a keen nose for the winds that threatened to blow up out of the oppressive weather of their surroundings and sweep them all into violence. And he made Culver uneasy. His discontent was not merely peevish; it was rocklike and rebellious, and thus this discontent seemed to Culver to be at once brave and somehow full of peril.

He had first seen Mannix the revolutionary five months ago, soon after they had been called back to duty. He hadn't known him then. There were compulsory lectures arranged at first, to acquaint the junior officers with recent developments in what had been called "the new amphibious doctrine." The outlines of these lectures were appallingly familiar: the stuffy auditorium asprawl with bored lieutenants and captains, the brightly lit stage with its magnified charts and graphs, the lantern slides (at which point, when the lights went out, it was possible to sneak a moment's nap, just as in officers' school seven years ago), the parade of majors and colonels with their maps and pointers, and their cruelly tedious, doggedly memorized lectures: the whole scene, with its grave, professorial air, seemed seedily portentous, especially since no one cared, save the majors and colonels, and no one listened. When Culver sat down, during the darkness of a lantern slide, next to the big relaxed mass which he dimly identified as a captain, he noticed that it was snoring. When the lights went up, Mannix still slept on, filling the air around him with a loud, tranquil blubber. Culver aroused him with a nudge. Mannix grumbled something, but then said "Thanks, Jack." A young colonel had come onto the stage then. He had made many of the lectures that week. He had a curiously thick, throaty voice which would have made him sound like a yokel, except that his words were coolly, almost passionately put, and he bent forward over the lectern with a bleak and solemn attitude—a lean, natty figure with hair cut so close to his head that he appeared to be, from that distance, nearly bald. "An SS man," Mannix whispered, "he's gonna come down here and cut your balls off. You Jewish?" He grinned and collapsed back, forehead against his hand, into quiet slumber. Culver couldn't recall what the colonel talked about: the movement of supplies, logistics, ship-to-shore movement, long-range planning, all abstract and vast, and an ardent glint came to his eyes when he spoke of the "grandiose doctrine" which had been formulated since they, the reserves, had been away. "You bet your life, Jack," Mannix had whispered out of the shadows then. He seemed to have snapped fully awake and, following the lecture intently, he appeared to address his whispers not to Culver, or the colonel, but to the air. "You bet your life they're grandiose," he said, "even if you don't know what grandiose means. I'll bet you'd sell your soul to be able to drop a bomb on somebody." And then, aping the colonel's instructions to the corporal— one of the enlisted flunkies who, after each lecture, passed out the reams of printed and mimeographed tables and charts and résumés, which everyone promptly, when out of sight, threw away—he whispered in high, throaty, lilting mockery: "Corporal, kindly pass out the atom bombs for inspection." He smacked the arm of his seat, too hard; it could be heard across the auditorium, and heads turned then, but the colonel had not seemed to have noticed. "Jesus," Mannix rumbled furiously, "Jesus Christ almighty," while the colonel droned on, in his countrified voice: "Our group destiny," he said, "amphibiously integrated, from any force thrown against us by Aggressor enemy."

Later—toward the end of that week of lectures, after Mannix had spoken the calm, public manifesto which at least among the reserves had made him famous, and from then on the object of a certain awe, though with a few doubts about his balance, too—Culver had tried to calculate how he had gotten by with it. Perhaps it had to do with his size, his bearing. There was at times a great massive absoluteness in the way he spoke. He was huge, and the complete honesty and candor of his approach seemed to rumble forth, like notes from a sounding board, in direct proportion to his size. He had suffered, too, and this suffering had left a persistent, unwhipped, scornful look in his eyes, almost like a stain, or rather a wound, which spells out its own warning and cautions the unwary to handle this tortured parcel of flesh with care. And he was an enormous man, his carriage was formidable. That skinny, bristle-haired colonel, Culver finally realized, had been taken aback past the point of punishment, or even reprimand, merely because of the towering, unavoidable, physical fact that he was facing not a student or a captain or a subordinate, but a stubborn and passionate man. So it was that, after a lecture on transport of supplies, when the colonel had called Mannix's name at random from a list to answer some generalized, hypothetical question, Mannix had stood up and said merely, "I don't know, sir." A murmur of surprise passed over the auditorium then, for the colonel, early in the hour, had made it plain that he had wanted at least an attempt at an answer—a guess—even though they might be unacquainted with the subject. But Mannix merely said, "I don't know, sir," while the colonel, as if he hadn't heard correctly, rephrased the question with a little tremor of annoyance. There was a moment's silence and men turned around in their seats to look at the author of this defiance. "I don't know, sir," he said again, in a loud but calm voice. "I don't know what my first consideration would be in making a space table like that. I'm an infantry officer. I got an 0302." The colonel's forehead went pink under the glare of the lights. "I stated earlier, Captain, that I wanted some sort of answer. None of you gentlemen is expected to know this subject pat, but you can essay *some kind of an answer.*" Mannix just stood there, solid and huge, blinking at the colonel. "I just have to repeat, sir," he said finally, "that I don't have the faintest idea what my first consideration would be. I never went to cargo-loading school. I'm an 0302. And I'd like to respectfully add, sir, if I might, that there's hardly anybody in this room who knows that answer, either. They've forgotten everything they ever learned seven years ago. Most of them don't even know how to take an M-1 apart. They're too old. They should be home with their family." There was passion in his tone but it was controlled and straightforward—he had managed to keep out of his voice either anger or insolence—and then he fell silent. His words had the quality, the sternness, of an absolute and unequivocal fact, as if they had been some intercession for grace spoken across the heads of a courtroom by a lawyer so quietly convinced of his man's innocence that there was no need for gesticulations or frenzy. The colonel's eyes bulged incredulously at Mannix from across the rows of seats, but in the complete, astounded hush that had followed he was apparently at a loss for words. A bit unsteadily, he called out another name and Mannix sat down, staring stonily ahead.

It had been perhaps a court-martial offense, at least worthy of some reprimand, but that was all there was to it. Nothing happened, no repercussions, nothing. The thing had been forgotten; either that, or it had been stored away in the universal memory of colonels, where all such incidents are sorted out for retribution, or are forgotten. Whatever effect it had on the colonel, or whatever higher, even more important sources got wind of it, it had its effect on Mannix. And the result was odd. Far from giving the impression that he had been purged, that he had blown off excess pressure, he seemed instead more tense, more embittered, more in need to scourge something—his own boiling spirit, authority, anything.

Culver's vision of him at this time was always projected against Heaven's Gate, which was the name—no doubt ironically supplied at first by the enlisted men—of the pleasure-dome ingeniously erected amid a tangle of alluvial swampland, and for officers only. He and Mannix lived in rooms next to each other, in the bachelor quarters upstairs. The entire area was a playground which had all the casual opulence of a Riviera resort and found its focus in the sparkling waters of a swimming pool, set like an oblong sapphire amid flowered walks and a fanciful growth of beach umbrellas. There, at ten minutes past four each day, Mannix could be found, his uniform shed in an instant and a gin fizz in his hand—a sullen, mountainous figure in a lurid sportshirt, across which a squadron of monstrous butterflies floated in luminous, unmilitary files. Both Mannix and Culver hated the place—its factitious luxury, its wanton atmosphere of alcohol and torpid ease and dances, the vacant professional talk of the regular officers and the constant teasing presence of their wives, who were beautiful and spoke in tender drawls and boldly flaunted at the wifeless reserves—in a proprietary, Atlanta-debutante fashion—their lecherous sort of chastity. The place seemed to offer up, like a cornucopia, the fruits of boredom, of footlessness and dissolution. It was, in Mannix's words, like a prison where you could have anything you wanted except happiness, and once, in a rare midnight moment when he allowed himself to get drunk, he got paper and wood together from his room and announced to Culver in an unsteady but determined voice that he was going to burn the place down. Culver held him off, but it was true: they were bound to the pleasures of the place by necessity—for there was no place to go for a hundred miles, even if they had wanted to go—and therefore out of futility. "Goddam, it's degrading," Mannix had said, making use of an adjective which indeed seemed to sum it all up. "It's like sex now. Or the lack of it. Now maybe it's all right for a kid to go without sex, but it's degrading for someone like me almost thirty to go without making love for so long. It's simply degrading, that's all. I'd go for one of these regulars' pigs if it wasn't for Mimi. . . . This whole mess is degrading. I know it's my own fault I stayed in the reserves, Jack, you don't have to tell me that. I was a nut. I didn't know I was going to get called out for every frigging international incident that came along. But, goddam, it's degrading"—and with a glum, subdued gesture he'd down the dregs of his drink—"it's degrading for a man my age to go sniffing around on my belly in the boondocks like a dog. And furthermore—" He looked scornfully about him, at the glitter and chrome, at the terrace by the pool where Japanese lanterns hung like a grove of pastel moons, and a girl's shrill and empty laugh uncoiled as bright as tinsel through the sluggish coastal dusk. It was a silent moment in a night sprinkled with a dusty multitude of Southern stars, and the distant bleating saxophone seemed indecisive and sad, like the nation and the suffocating summer, neither at peace nor at war. "Furthermore, it's degrading to come out of the field each day and then be *forced* to go to a night club like this, when all you want to do is go home to your wife and family. Goddam, man, I've *gotta* get out!"

But underneath his rebellion, Culver finally knew, Mannix—like all of them—was really resigned. Born into a generation of conformists, even Mannix (so Culver sensed) was aware that his gestures were not symbolic, but individual, therefore hopeless, maybe even absurd, and that he was trapped like all of them in a predicament which one personal insurrection could, if anything, only make worse. "You know," he said once, "I think I was really afraid just one time last war." The phrase "last war" had had, itself, a numb, resigned quality, in its lack of any particular inflection, like "last week end," or "last movie I went to see." They had been lying on the beach to which they fled each hot week end. In that setting of coast and sea and lugubrious solitude they felt nearly peaceful, in touch with a tranquil force more important, and more lasting (or so it seemed on those sunlit afternoons), than war. Mannix had been, almost for the first time since Culver had known him, rested and subdued, and the sound of his voice had been a surprise after long, sun-laden hours of sleep and silence. "That's the goddam truth," he said thoughtfully, "I was only afraid once. Really afraid, I mean. It was at a hotel in San Francisco. I think I really came closer to dying that night than I ever have in my life. We were drunk, you see, polluted, all of us. I think there were five of us, all of us boots just out of Dago. Kids. We were on the tenth floor of this hotel and in this room and I believe we were about as drunk as anyone could get. I remember going in to take a shower in the bathroom. It was late at night, past midnight, and after I took this shower, you see, I came out into the room buck naked. Two of those drunk guys were waiting for me. They grabbed me and pushed me toward the window. I was so loaded I couldn't battle. Then they pushed me out the window and held me by the heels while I dangled upside-down buck naked in space, ten floors above the street." He paused and sucked at a beer can. "Can you imagine that?" he went on slowly. "How I felt? I got stone-sober in a second. Imagine being that high upside-down in space with two drunks holding onto your heels. I was heavy, man, just like now, you see. All I can remember is those teeny-weeny lights below and the tiny little people like ants down there and those two crazy drunk guys holding onto my wet slippery ankles, laughing like hell and trying to decide whether to let go or not. I just remember the cold wind blowing on my body and that dark, man, infinite darkness all around me, and my ankles beginning to slip out of their hands. I really saw Death then, and I think that all I could think of was that I was going to fall and smash myself on that hard, hard street below. That those crazy bastards were going to let me fall. I was praying, I guess. I remember the blood rushing to my brain and my ankles slipping, and that awful strange noise. And I was reaching out, man, clutching at thin air. Then I wondered what that noise was, that high loud noise, and then I realized it was me, screaming at the top of my voice, all over San Francisco." He stopped talking then and scuffed at the sand with one calloused heel. "They hauled me up somehow. It was those sober guys—I guess they were sober—the other two. They got me up. But every time I remember that moment a great big cold shudder runs up and down my spine." He chuckled and chewed on his cigar but the laugh was half-hearted and listless, and he dug his elbows into the sand and resumed his quiet, placid gaze toward the horizon. Culver watched him: his bitterness dissolved in the hot salty air, slumped in the sand gazing wistfully out to sea, sun-glassed, hairy-chested, a cigar protruding from his face and a beer can warming in his hand, he seemed no longer the man who could sicken himself with resentment, but relaxed, pliable even, like a huge hairy baby soothed by the wash of elemental tides, ready to receive anything, all, into that great void in his soul which bitterness and rebellion had briefly left vacant—all—the finality of more suffering, or even death. War was in the offing. A promenade of waves, snow-crowned like lovely garlands in the dark hair of girls, swelled eastward toward Africa: past those smoky heights, more eastward still, the horizon seemed to give back repeated echoes of the sea, like far-off thunder, or guns. Culver remembered making a quick, contorted motion in the sand with his body, and being swept by a hot wave of anguish. It was loneliness and homesickness, but it was also fright. Across the rim of his memory two little girls playing on the sunny grass waved to him, were gone, pursued by a shower of uncapturable musical sounds. Mannix's resigned silence fed his loneliness. Suddenly he felt, like Mannix, upturned drunkenly above the abyss, blood rushing to his head, in terror clutching at the substanceless night. . . .

In the noonday light Sergeant O'Leary, his face brightly pink, was still talking. Culver snapped awake with a start. O'Leary grinned down at him—"Damn, Lieutenant, you're gonna crap out tonight if you're that tired now"—and Culver struggled for speech; time seemed to have unspooled past him in a great spiral, and for an instant—his mind still grappling with the memory of a hurried, chaotic nightmare—he was unable to tell where he was. He had the feeling that it should be the night before, and that he was still in the tent. "Did I go to sleep, O'Leary?" he said, blinking upward.

"Yes, sir," O'Leary said, and chuckled, "you sure did."

"How long?"

"Oh, just a second."

"Christ, I *am* tired. I dreamt it was last night," Culver said. He got to his feet. A truck moved through the clearing in a cloud of dust. There seemed to be new activity in the command post, and new confusion. Culver and O'Leary turned together then toward the operations tent; the Colonel had come out and was striding toward them, followed by Mannix.

"Culver, get your jeep and driver," he said, walking toward the road, not looking up. His voice was briskly matter-of-fact; he strode past them with short, choppy steps and the swagger stick in his hand made a quick tattoo, *slap-slap*-slapping against his dungaree pants. "I want you and Captain Mannix to go with me down to Third Batt. See if we can help." His voice faded; Mannix trailed behind him, saying nothing, but his face seemed to Culver even more exhausted, and even more grimly taut, than it had been an hour before.

The road was a dusty cart-path that rambled footlessly across scrubby, fallow farmland. Shacks and cabins, long ago abandoned, lay along its way. They piled into the jeep, Mannix and Culver in the back, the Colonel in front next to the driver. They hadn't far to go—less than a mile—but the trip felt endless to Culver because the day, by now a fitful carrousel of sleepy sounds, motions without meaning, seemed wildly, almost dangerously abstracted, as if viewed through drug-glazed eyes or eyes, like those of a mole, unacquainted with light. Dust billowed past them as they went. Above them a blue cloudless sky in which the sun, pitched now at its summit, beat fearfully down, augured no rain for the day, or for the evening. Mannix said nothing; his silence prompted Culver to turn and look at him. He was gazing straight ahead with eyes that seemed to bore through the Colonel's neck. Tormented beast in the cul-de-sac, baffled fury, a grief at the edge of defeat—his eyes made Culver suddenly aware of what they were about to see, and he turned dizzily away and watched the wreck of a Negro cabin float past through the swirling dust: shell-shattered doors and sagging walls, blasted facade—a target across which for one split second in the fantastic noon there seemed to crawl the ghosts of the bereaved and the departed, mourning wraiths come back to reclaim from the ruins some hot scent of honeysuckle, smell of cooking, murmurous noise of bees. Culver closed his eyes and drowsed, slack-jawed, limp, his stomach faintly heaving.

One boy's eyes lay gently closed, and his long dark lashes were washed in tears, as though he had cried himself to sleep. As they bent over him they saw that he was very young, and a breeze came up from the edges of the swamp, bearing with it a scorched odor of smoke and powder, and touched the edges of his hair. A lock fell across his brow with a sort of gawky, tousled grace, as if preserving even in that blank and mindless repose some gesture proper to his years, a callow charm. Around his curly head grasshoppers darted among the weeds. Below, beneath the slumbering eyes, his face had been blasted out of sight. Culver looked up and met Mannix's gaze. The Captain was sobbing helplessly. He cast an agonized look toward the Colonel, standing across the field, then down again at the boy, then at Culver. "Won't they ever let us alone, the sons of bitches," he murmured, weeping. "Won't they ever let us alone?"

III

That evening at twilight, just before the beginning of the march, Mannix found a nail in his shoe. "Look at it," he said to Culver, "what lousy luck." They were sitting on an embankment bordering the road. The blue dusk was already scattered with stars, but evening had brought no relief to the heat of the day. It clung to them still, damp and stifling, enveloping them like an overcoat. The battalion, over a thousand men, was ready for the march. It stretched out in two files on either side of the road below them for more than a mile. Culver turned and looked down into Mannix's shoe: sure enough, a nail-end had penetrated the lining at the base of the heel, a sharp pinpoint of torture. Mannix inspected the bottom of his big dirty foot. He pulled off a flake of skin which the nail had already worn away. "Of all the lousy luck," he said, "gimme a band-aid."

"It'll wear right through, Al," Culver said, "you'd better get another pair of shoes. Try flattening it out with the end of your bayonet."

Mannix hammered for a moment at the nail and then looked up in exasperation. "It won't go all the way. Gimme that band-aid." A rusty spatter of blood he had picked up at noon was still on the sleeve of his dungarees. He had become nervous and touchy. All that afternoon, after they had come back, he had seemed, like Culver, still shaken by the slaughter, still awed, and rather despondent. Finally, he had alternated moments of remote abstraction with quick outbursts of temper. The shock of the explosion seemed to have set something off in him. His mood had become vague and unpredictable, and he was able to shift from sour, uncommunicative gloom to violent anger in an instant. Culver had never seen him quite so cranky before, nor had he ever seen him so testily at odds with his men, to whom he usually had shown the breeziest good will. All afternoon he'd been after them, nagging, bellowing orders—only to fall suddenly into a profound and brooding silence. As he squatted in the weeds eating his evening meal two hours before, he had hardly said a word, except to murmur—irrelevantly, Culver thought—that his company "had better goddam well shape up." It puzzled Culver; the explosion seemed to have stripped off layers of skin from the Captain, leaving only raw nerves exposed.

Now he had become fretful again, touchily alert, and his voice was heavy with impatience. He mumbled as he plastered the band-aid on his foot. "I wish they'd get this show on the road. That's the trouble with the Marine Corps, you always stand frigging around for half the night while they think up some grandiose doctrine. I wish to Christ I'd joined the Army. Man, if I'd have known what I was getting in for when I went down to that recruiting office in 1941, I'd have run off at the door." He looked up from his foot and down toward the command group nearly at the head of the column. Three or four officers were clustered together on the road. The Colonel was among them, neat, almost jaunty, in new dungarees and boots. On his head there was a freshly clean utility cap with a spruce uptilted bill and a shiny little silver leaf. At his side he wore a pearlhandled .38 revolver, glistening with silver inlay. It was, as usual, loaded, though no one knew why, for he was never known to shoot it; the general feeling seemed to be that it was his emblematic prerogative, no more an affectation, certainly, than a visored hat encrusted with gilt, or grenades worn at the shoulder. The pistol—like the swagger stick; the nickname; the quizzical, almost tenderly contemplative air of authority—was part of the act, and to be sure, Culver reflected, the act was less offensive, less imperious than it might be. One simply learned soon to believe that the pistol "belonged," just as the name "Old Rocky" belonged; if such an act finally did no harm, if it only flattered his vanity, was the Colonel to be blamed, Culver asked himself, if he did nothing to mitigate the total impression?

Mannix watched him, too, watched the Colonel toe at the sand, thumbs hooked rakishly in his belt, a thin gentle smile on his face, adumbrated by the fading light: he looked youthful and fresh, nonchalant, displaying the studied casualness of an athlete before the stadium throng, confident of his own victory long before the race begins. Mannix gnawed at the end of a cigar, spat it out viciously. "Look at the little jerk. He thinks he's gonna have us pooped out at the halfway mark—"

Culver put in, "Look Al, why don't you do something about that nail? If you told the Colonel he'd let you ride in—"

Mannix went fiercely on, in a husky whisper: "Well he's not. He's a little sadist, but he's not gonna have Al Mannix crapped out. I'll walk anywhere that son of a bitch goes and a mile further. He thinks H & S Company's been doping off. Well, I'll show him. I wouldn't ask him to ride in if I'd been walking over broken glass. I'll—"

He paused. Culver turned and looked at him. They were both silent, staring at each other, embarrassed by the common understanding of their gaze. Each turned away; Mannix murmured something and began to tie his shoe. "You're right, Al," Culver heard himself saying. It seemed it was almost more than he could bear. Night was coming on. As in a stupor, he looked down the road at the battalion, the men lounging along the embankments with their rifles, smoking and talking in tired, subdued voices, smoke rising in giant blue clouds through the dusk, where swarms of gnats rose and fell in vivacious, panicky flight. In the swamp, frogs had begun a brainless chorale; their noise seemed perfectly suited to his sense of complete and final frustration. It was almost more than he could bear. So Mannix had felt it, too: not simply fear of suffering, nor exhaustion, nor the lingering horror, which gripped both of them, of that bloody wasteland in the noonday heat. But the other; the old atavism that clutched them, the voice that commanded, once again, *you will.* How stupid to think they had ever made their own philosophy; it was as puny as a house of straw, and at this moment—by the noise in their brains of those words, *you will*—it was being blasted to the winds like dust. They were as helpless as children. Another war, and years beyond reckoning, had violated their minds irrevocably. For six years they had slept a cataleptic sleep, dreaming blissfully of peace, awakened in horror to find that, after all, they were only marines, responding anew to the old commands. They were marines. Even if they were old. Bank clerks and salesmen and lawyers. Even if, right now, they were unutterably tired. They could no more *not* be determined to walk the thirty-six miles than they could, in the blink of an eye, turn themselves into beautiful nymphs. Culver was afraid he wasn't going to make it, and now he knew Mannix was afraid, and he didn't know what to feel—resentment or disgust—over the fact that his fear was mingled with a faint, fugitive pride.

Mannix looked up from his shoe and at the Colonel. "You're goddam right, Jack, we're going to make it," he said. "My company's going to make it if I have to *drag in their bodies.*" There was a tone in his voice that Culver had never heard before.

Suddenly the Colonel's flat voice broke through the stillness: "All right, Billy, let's saddle up."

"'Tallion saddle up!" The Major's words were eager and shrill, became multiplied down the long mile. "Smoking lamps out!" The blue cloud dissolved on the air, the gnats descended in a swarm and the voices passed on—*Saddle up, saddle up*—while the battalion rose to its feet, not all at once but in a steady gradual surge, like rows of corn snapping back erect after the passing of a wind. Mannix got to his feet, began to sideslip in a cloud of dust down the embankment toward his company directly below. It was at the head of the column, right behind the command group. Culver, moving himself now down the hill, heard Mannix's shout. It rang out in the dusk with deliberate authority, hoarse blunt command: "All right, H & S Company, saddle up, saddle up! You people get off your asses and straighten up!" Culver passed by him on his way to the command group: he stood surrounded by a cloud of gnats, hulking enormously above the company, hands balanced lightly on his hips, poised forward badgering the men like some obsessed, rakehell Civil War general before a battle: "All right, you people, we're gonna walk thirty-six miles tonight and I mean walk! First man I see drop out's gonna get police duty for two weeks, and that goes for everybody. You think I'm kidding you wait and see. There's gonna be trucks going in for those that can't make it but I don't want to see anyone from H & S Company climbing on! If an old man with as much flab as I've got can make it you people can too . . ." There was a note, almost, of desperation in his voice.

Culver, passing along the line of bedraggled, mournful-looking men, so few of whom looked like fabled marines, heard the voice rise to a taut pitch close to frenzy; it was too loud, it worried Culver, and he wished to caution him: no longer just admonishing the men to a simple duty, it was the voice of a man wildly fanatic with one idea: to last. "I want to hear no bitching out of you people! Take it easy on the water. You get shinsplints or blisters you see the corpsman, don't come crying to me. When we get in I want to see all of you people . . ." Not because the hike was good or even sensible, Culver thought, but out of hope of triumph, like a chain-gang convict who endures a flogging without the slightest whimper, only to spite the flogger. Culver joined the command group, heard the Colonel say to the Major: "Looks like H & S Company's going to make it *en masse*, Billy." It was just as Culver feared, for although his words were pleasant enough, his face, regarding Mannix for a brief moment, had a look of narrow scrutiny, as if he, too, had detected in the Captain's tone that note of proud and willful submission, rebellion in reverse. But there was no emotion in his voice as he turned quickly, with a glance at his watch, and said, "Let's move out, Billy."

They started out without delay. A jeep, its headlamps lit, preceded them. The Colonel, in the lead, abreast of the Major and just ahead of Culver, plunged off into the deep dust of the road. He walked with a slinky-hipped, athletic stride, head down between his shoulders and slightly forward, arms bent and moving methodically; nothing broke the rhythm of his steps—ruts in the road or the deeply grooved tire tracks— and Culver became quickly amazed, and rather appalled, at the pace he was setting. It was the pace of a trained hiker—determined, unhesitant, much closer to a trot now than a walk—and only a few minutes passed before Culver was gasping for breath. Sand lay thick in the road, hindering a natural step. They had not gone more than a couple of hundred yards; already he felt sweat trickling down his forehead and beneath his arms. For a moment fear surged up in him unnaturally, and a crazy panic. He had been afraid of the march before, but his fear had been abstract and hazy; now so quickly fatigued, in what seemed a matter of seconds, he felt surely (as Mannix had predicted) that he'd be unable to last the first hour. A panicky wash of blood came to his face and he struggled for breath, wanting to cry out—it passed. His mind groped for reason and the terror receded: once he adjusted to the shock of this pace, he realized, he'd be all right. Then the panic went away; as it did so, he found himself breathing easier, freed of that irrational fright. The Colonel pushed ahead in front of him with the absolute mechanical confidence of a wound-up, strutting tin soldier on a table top. Culver, panting a bit, heard his voice, as calm and unwinded as if he were sitting at a desk somewhere, addressed to the Major: "We shoved off at nine on the dot, Billy. We should make the main road at ten and have a break." "Yes, sir," he heard the Major say, "we'll be ahead of the game." Culver made a calculation then; by the operations map, which he knew so well, that was three and a half miles—a mile farther than the regulation distance for an hour's march. It was, indeed, like running. Pushing on through the sand, he felt a wave of hopelessness so giddy and so incomprehensible that it was almost like exhilaration—and he heard a noise—half-chuckle, half-groan—escape between his labored breaths. Three and a half miles: the distance from Greenwich Village almost to Harlem. In his mind he measured that giddy parade of city blocks, an exhausting voyage even on wheels. It was like twisting a knife in his side but he went on with the mental yardstick—to imagine himself plodding that stretch up the sandless, comfortably receptive pavements of Fifth Avenue, past Fourteenth Street and the bleak vistas of the Twenties and the Thirties, hurrying onward north by the Library, twenty blocks more to the Plaza, and pressing still onward along the green acres of the Park . . . his thoughts recoiled. Three and a half miles. In an hour. With more than thirty-two still to go. A vision of Mannix came swimming back; Culver stumbled along after the dauntless Colonel, thinking, Christ on a crutch.

They hastened on. Night had fallen around them, tropic and sudden, lit now, as they descended across a thicket of swampy ground, only by the lights of the jeep. Culver had regained his wind but already his chest and back were awash in sweat, and he was thirsty. He took a vague comfort in the fact that others felt the same way, for behind him he heard canteens being unsnapped from their cases, rattling out of their cups, and the noise, in mid-march, of drinking—a choked, gurgling sound—then, faint to the rear, Mannix's angry voice: "All right, goddammit, I told you people to hold onto your water! Put those goddam canteens back until the break!" Culver, craning his neck around, saw nothing—no Mannix, who had apparently dropped behind—nothing except a shadowy double line of men laboring through the sand, fading off far down the road into the general blackness. To the rear some marine made a joke, a remark; there was laughter and a snatch of song—*on top of old Smo-oky, all covered. . .* Then Mannix's voice again out of the dark: "O.K. you people can grabass all you want but I'm telling you you'd better save your wind. If you want to talk all the way it's O.K. with me but you're gonna crap out if you do, and remember what I said . . ." His tone had become terse and vicious; it could have been the sound of a satrap of Pharaoh, a galley master. It had the forbidding quality of a strand of barbed wire or a lash made of thorns, and the voices, the song, abruptly ceased, as if they had been strangled. Still his words continued to sting and flay them—already, in this first hour, with the merciless accents of a born bully—and Culver, suddenly angered, had an impulse to drop back and try to make him let up.

"You people close it up now! Dammit, Shea, keep those men closed up there. They fall back they're gonna have to run to catch up! Goddammit, close it up now, you hear me! I mean *you,* Thompson, goddammit you aren't deaf! Close it up! *Close it up,* I said!" So it was that the voice, brutal and furious, continued the rest of the way.

And so it was that those first hours Culver recollected as being the most harrowing of all, even though the later hours brought more subtle refinements of pain. He reasoned that this was because during the first few miles or so he was at least in rough possession of his intellect, his mind lashing his spirit as pitilessly as his body. Later, he seemed to be involved in something routine, an act in which his brain, long past cooperation, played hardly any part at all. But during these early hours there was also the fact of Mannix. Superimposed upon Culver's own fantasies, his anger, his despair (and his own calm moments of rationalization, too) was his growing awareness of what was happening to the Captain. Later, Mannix's actions seemed to become mixed up and a part of the general scheme, the nightmare. But here at first Culver's mind was enough in focus for Mannix's transformation to emerge clearly, even if with the chill, unreal outlines of coming doom—like a man conversing, who might turn around briefly to a mirror and see behind him in the room no longer his familiar friend, but something else—a shape, a ghost, a horror—a wild and threatful face reflected from the glass.

They made the highway at ten o'clock, almost to the minute. When the Colonel looked at his watch and stopped and the Major raised his arm, shouting, "Breather! Ten minutes!" Culver went over to the side of the road and sat down in the weeds. Blood was knocking angrily at his temples, behind his eyes, and he was thirsty enough to drink, with a greedy recklessness, nearly a third of his canteen. He lit a cigarette; it tasted foul and metallic and he flipped it away. His knees and thighs, unaccustomed to so much pounding, were stiff and fatigued; he stretched them out slowly into the dewy underbrush, looking upward at a placid cloud of stars. He turned. Up the road, threading its way through a barrier of outstretched legs and rifles, came a figure. It was Mannix. He was still muttering as he lumbered up and sank down beside him. "Those goddam people, they won't keep it closed up. I have to dog them every minute. They're going to find themselves running the whole way if they don't keep closed up. Gimme a butt." He was breathing heavily, and he passed the back of his hand over his brow to wipe the sweat away.

"Why don't you leave them alone?" Culver said. He gave the Captain a cigarette, which he lit, blowing the smoke out in a violent sort of choked puff.

"Dammit," he replied, coughing, "you *can't* leave them alone! They don't want to make this lousy hike. They'd just as soon crap out on the side and let the trucks haul them in. They'd just as soon take police duty. Man, they're reserves. They don't care who sees them crap out—me, anybody." He fell back with a sigh into the weeds, arms over his eyes. "Fuck it," he said. Culver looked down at him. From the jeep's head-lamps an oblong of yellow slanted across the lower part of his face. One corner of his mouth jerked nervously—a distasteful grimace, as if he had been chewing something sour. Exhausted, completely bushed, there was something in his manner—even in repose—which refused to admit his own exhaustion. He clenched his teeth convulsively together. It was as if his own fury, his own obsession now, held up, Atlas-like, the burden of his great weariness. "Jesus," he murmured, almost irrelevantly, "I can't help thinking about those kids today, lying out there in the weeds."

Culver rested easily for a moment, thinking too. He looked at his watch, with a sinking sensation: six of their ten minutes had already passed—so swiftly that they seemed not to have existed at all. Then he said, "Well, for Christ's sake, Al, why don't you let them crap out? If you were getting screwed like these enlisted men are you'd crap out too, you wouldn't care. You don't have to chew them out like you've been doing. Let's face it, you don't really care if they make it. You. Me, maybe. But these guys . . . anybody else. What the hell." He paused, fumbling for words, went on feebly, "*Do* you?"

Mannix rose up on his elbows then. "You're damn right I do," he said evenly. They turned toward the Colonel standing not far away; he and the Major, pointing a flashlight, were bent together over a map. Mannix hawked something up and spat. His voice became more controlled. "You see that little jerk standing there?" he said. "He thinks he's pulling something on us. Thirty-six miles. *N*obody walks that far, stateside. *N*obody. We never walked that far even with Edson, last war. See, that little jerk wants to make a name for himself—Old Rocky Templeton. Led the longest forced march in the history of the Corps—"

"But—" Culver started.

"He'd just love to see H & S Company crap out," he went on tensely, "he'd *love* it. It'd do something to his ego. Man, I can see him now"—and his voice lifted itself in a tone of sour mockery— " 'Well, Cap'n Mannix, see where you had a little trouble last night getting your men in. Need a little bit more *esprit,* huh?' " His voice lowered, filled with venom. "Well, screw *him,* Jack. I'll get my company in if I have to carry them on my back—"

It was useless to reason with him. Culver let him go on until he had exhausted his bitter spurt of hatred, of poison, and until finally he lay back again with a groan in the weeds—only a moment before the cry came again: "Saddle up! Saddle up!"

They pushed off once more. It was just a bit easier now, for they were to walk for two miles on the highway, where there was no sand to hinder their steps, before turning back onto the side roads. Yet there was a comfortless feeling at the outset, too: legs cramped and aching from the moment's rest, he walked stooped and bent over, at the start, like an arthritic old man, and he was sweating again, dry with thirst, after only a hundred yards. How on earth, he wondered, gazing up for a second at the dim placid landscape of stars, would they last until the next morning, until nearly noon? A car passed them—a slick convertible bound for the North, New York perhaps—wherever, inevitably, for some civilian pleasure—and its fleet, almost soundless passage brought, along with the red pinpoint of its vanishing taillights, a new sensation of unreality to the night, the march: dozing, shrouded by the dark, its people seemed unaware of the shadowy walkers, had sped unceasingly on, like ocean voyagers oblivious of all those fishy struggles below them in the night, submarine and fathomless.

They plodded on, the Colonel pacing the march, but slower now, and Culver played desperately with the idea that the man would, somehow, tire, become exhausted himself. A wild fantasia of hopes and imaginings swept through his mind: that Templeton *would* become fatigued, having overestimated his own strength, *would* stop the march after an hour or so and load them on the trucks—like a stern father who begins a beating, only to become touched with if not remorse then leniency, and stays his hand. But Culver knew it was a hollow desire. They pushed relentlessly ahead, past shadowy pine groves, fields dense with the fragrance of alfalfa and wild strawberries, shuttered farmhouses, deserted rickety stores. Then this brief civilized vista they abandoned again, and for good, when without pause they plunged off again onto another road, into the sand. Culver had become bathed in sweat once more; they all had, even the Colonel, whose neat dungarees had a black triangular wet spot plastered at their back. Culver heard his own breath coming hoarsely again, and felt the old panic: He'd never be able to make it, he knew, he'd fall out on the side like the old man he was—but far back to the rear then he heard Mannix's huge voice, dominating the night: "All right, goddammit, move out! We got sand here now. Move out and close it up! Close it up, I say, goddammit! Leadbetter, get that barn out of your ass and close it up! *Close it up,* I say!" They spurred Culver on, after a fashion, but following upon those shouts, there was a faint, subdued chorus, almost inaudible, of moans and protests. They came only from Mannix's company, a muffled, sullen groan. To them Culver heard his own fitful breath add a groan—expressing something he could hardly put a name to: fury, despair, approaching doom—he scarcely knew. He stumbled on behind the Colonel, like a ewe who follows the slaughterhouse ram, dumb and undoubting, too panicked by the general chaos to hate its leader, or care.

At the end of the second hour, and three more miles, Culver was sobbing with exhaustion. He flopped down in the weeds, conscious now of a blister beginning at the bottom of his foot, as if it had been scraped by a razor.

Mannix was having trouble, too. This time when he came up, he was limping. He sat down silently and took off his shoe; Culver, gulping avidly at his canteen, watched him. Both of them were too winded to smoke, or to speak. They were sprawled beside some waterway—canal or stream; phosphorescent globes made a spooky glow among shaggy Spanish moss, and a rank and fetid odor bloomed in the darkness—not the swamp's decay, Culver realized, but Mannix's feet. "Look," the Captain muttered suddenly, "that nail's caught me right in the heel." Culver peered down by the glare of Mannix's flashlight to see on his heel a tiny hole, bleeding slightly, bruised about its perimeter and surrounded by a pasty white where the band-aid had been pulled away. "How'm I going to do it with that?" Mannix said.

"Try beating that nail down again."

"I tried, but the point keeps coming out. I'd have to take the whole frigging shoe apart."

"Can't you put a piece of cloth over it or something?"

"I tried that, too, but it puts my foot off balance. It's worse than the nail." He paused. "Jesus Christ."

"Look," Culver said, "try taking this strip of belt and putting it over it." They debated, operated, talked hurriedly, and neither of them was aware of the Colonel, who had walked over through the shadows and was standing beside them. "What's the matter, Captain?" he said.

They looked up, startled. Hands hooked as usual—Culver wanted to say "characteristically"—in his belt, he stood serenely above them. In the yellow flashlight glow his face was red from exertion, still damp with sweat, but he appeared no more fatigued than a man who had sprinted a few yards to catch a bus. The faint smile hovered at the corners of his lips. Once more it was neither complacent nor superior but, if anything, almost benevolent, so that by the unnatural light, in which his delicate features became fiery red and again now, along the borders of his slim tapering fingers, nearly transparent, he looked still not so much the soldier but the priest in whom passion and faith had made an alloy, at last, of only the purest good intentions; above meanness or petty spite, he was leading a march to some humorless salvation, and his smile—his solicitous words, too—had at least a bleak sincerity.

"I got a nail in my shoe," Mannix said.

The Colonel squatted down and inspected Mannix's foot, cupping it almost tenderly in his hand. Mannix appeared to squirm at the Colonel's touch. "That looks bad," he said after a moment, "did you see the corpsman?"

"No, sir," Mannix replied tensely, "I don't think there's anything can be done. Unless I had a new pair of boondockers."

The Colonel ruminated, rubbing his chin, his other hand still holding the Captain's foot. His eyes searched the dark reaches of the surrounding swamp, where now the rising moon had laid a tranquil silver dust. Frogs piped shrilly in the night, among the cypress and the shallows and closer now, by the road and the stagnant canal, along which danced shifting pinpoints of fire—cigarettes that rose and fell in the hidden fingers of exhausted men. "Well," the Colonel finally said, "well—" and paused. Again the act: indecision before decision, the waiting. "Well," he said and paused again. The waiting. At that moment—in a wave that came up through his thirst, his throbbing lips, his numb sense of futility—Culver felt that he knew of no one on earth he had ever loathed so much before. And his fury was heightened by the knowledge that he did not hate the man—the Templeton with his shrewd friendly eyes and harmless swagger, that fatuous man whose attempt to convey some impression of a deep and subtle wisdom was almost endearing—not this man, but the Colonel, the marine: that was the one he despised. He didn't hate him for himself, nor even for his brutal march. Bad as it was, there were no doubt worse ordeals; it was at least a peaceful landscape they had to cross. But he did hate him for his perverse and brainless gesture: squatting in the sand, gently, almost indecently now, stroking Mannix's foot, he had too long been conditioned by the system to perform with grace a human act. Too ignorant to know that with this gesture—so nakedly human in the midst of a crazy, capricious punishment which he himself had imposed—he lacerated the Captain by his very touch. Then he spoke. Culver knew what he was going to say. Nothing could have been worse.

"Well," he said, "maybe you'd better ride in on one of the trucks."

If there had been ever the faintest possibility that Mannix would ride in, those words shattered it. Mannix drew his foot away abruptly, as if the Colonel's hand were acid, or fire. "No, sir!" he said fiercely—too fiercely, the note of antagonism, now, was unmistakable—"No, sir! I'll make this frigging march." Furiously, he began to put on his shoe. The Colonel rose to his feet, hooked his thumbs in his belt and gazed carelessly down.

"I think you're going to regret it," he said, "with that foot of yours."

The Captain got up, limping off toward his company, over his retreating shoulder shot back a short, clipped burst of words at the Colonel—whose eyeballs rolled white with astonishment when he heard them—and thereby joined the battle.

"Who cares what you think," he said.

IV

Had the Colonel entertained any immediate notions of retribution, he held them off, for at a quarter past four that morning—halfway through the march, when the first green light of dawn streaked the sky—Culver still heard Mannix's hoarse, ill-tempered voice, lashing his troops from the rear. For hours he had lost track of Mannix. As for the Colonel, the word had spread that he was no longer pacing the march but had gone somewhere to the rear and was walking there. In his misery, a wave of hope swelled up in Culver: if the Colonel had become fagged, and was walking no longer but sitting in his jeep somewhere, at least they'd all have the consolation of having succeeded while their leader failed. But it was a hope, Culver knew, that was ill-founded. He'd be back there slogging away. The bastard could outmarch twenty men, twenty raging Mannixes.

The hike had become disorganized, no slower but simply more spread out. Culver—held back by fatigue and thirst and the burning, enlarging pain in his feet—found himself straggling behind. From time to time he managed to catch up; at one point he discovered himself at the tail end of Mannix's company, but he no longer really cared. The night had simply become a great solitude of pain and thirst, and an exhaustion so profound that it enveloped his whole spirit, and precluded thought.

A truck rumbled past, loaded with supine marines, so still they appeared unconscious. Another passed, and another—they came all night. But far to the front, long after each truck's passage, he could hear Mannix's cry: "Keep on, Jack! This company's walking in." They pushed on through the night, a shambling horde of zombies in drenched dungarees, eyes transfixed on the earth in a sort of glazed, avid concentration. After midnight it seemed to Culver that his mind only registered impressions, and these impressions had no sequence but were projected upon his brain in a scattered, disordered riot, like a movie film pieced together by an idiot. His memory went back no further than the day before; he no longer thought of anything so unattainable as home. Even the end of the march seemed a fanciful thing, beyond all possibility, and what small aspirations he now had were only to endure this one hour, if just to attain the microscopic bliss of ten minutes' rest and a mouthful of warm water. And bordering his memory was ever the violent and haunting picture of the mangled bodies he had seen—when? where? it seemed weeks, years ago, beneath the light of an almost prehistoric sun;

try as he could, to dwell upon consoling scenes—home, music, sleep—his mind was balked beyond that vision: the shattered youth with slumbering eyes, the blood, the swarming noon.

Then at the next halt, their sixth—or seventh, eighth, Culver had long ago lost count—he saw Mannix lying beside a jeep-towed water-cart at the rear of his company. O'Leary was sprawled out next to him, breath coming in long asthmatic groans. Culver eased himself painfully down beside them and touched Mannix's arm. The light of dawn, a feverish pale green, had begun to appear, outlining on Mannix's face a twisted look of suffering. His eyes were closed.

"How you doing, Al?" Culver said, reaching up to refill his canteen.

"Hotsy-totsy," he breathed, "except for my frigging foot. How you making it, boy?" His voice was listless. Culver looked down at Mannix's shoe; he had taken it off, to expose heel and sock, where, soaked up like the wick of a lantern, rose a dark streak of blood.

"Jesus," Culver said, "Al, for Christ sake now, you'd better ride in on a truck."

"Nail's out, sport. I finally stole me a pair of pliers, some radioman. Had to run like hell to catch up."

"Even so—" Culver began. But Mannix had fallen into an impervious silence. Up the road stretched a line of squatting men, Mannix's company. Most were sprawled in the weeds or the dust of the road in attitudes as stiff as death, yet some nearby sat slumped over their rifles, drinking water, smoking; there was a thin resentful muttering in the air. And the men close at hand—the faces he could see in the indecisive light—wore looks of agonized and silent protest. They seemed to be mutely seeking for the Captain, author of their misery, and they were like faces of men in bondage who had jettisoned all hope, and were close to defeat. In the weeds Mannix breathed heavily, mingling his with the tortured wheezes of O'Leary, who had fallen sound asleep. It was getting hot again. No one spoke. Then a fitful rumbling filled the dawn, grew louder, and along the line bodies stirred, heads turned, gazing eastward down the road at an oncoming, roaring cloud of dust. Out of the dust came a machine. It was a truck, and it passed them, and it rattled to a stop up in the midst of the company.

"Anyone crapped out here?" a voice called. "I got room for ten more."

There was a movement toward the truck; nearby, half a dozen men got to their feet, slung their rifles, and began to hobble up the road. Culver watched them tensely, hearing Mannix stir beside him, putting his shoe back on. O'Leary had awakened and sat up. Together the three of them watched the procession toward the truck: a straggle of limping men plodding as wretchedly as dogpound animals toward that yawning vehicle in the smoky dawn, huge, green, and possessed of wheels—which would deliver them to freedom, to sleep, oblivion. Mannix watched them without expression, through inflamed eyes; he seemed so drugged, so dumb with exhaustion, that he was unaware of what was taking place. "What happened to the Colonel?" he said absently.

"He went off in a jeep a couple of hours ago," O'Leary said, "said something about checking on the column of march."

"What?" Mannix said. Again, he seemed unaware of the words, as if they—like the sight of this slow streaming exodus toward the truck—were making no sudden imprint on his mind, but were filtering into his consciousness through piles and layers of wool. A dozen more men arose and began a lame procession toward the truck. Mannix watched them, blinking. "What?" he repeated.

"To check the column, sir," O'Leary repeated. "That's what he said."

"He *did?*" Mannix turned with an angry, questioning look. "Who's pacing the march, then?"

"Major Lawrence is."

"He *is?*" Mannix rose to his feet, precariously, stiffly and in pain balancing himself not on the heel, but the toe only, of his wounded foot. He blinked in the dawn, gazing at the rear of the truck and the cluster of marines there, feebly lifting themselves into the interior. He said nothing and Culver, watching him from below, could only think of the baffled fury of some great bear cornered, bloody and torn by a foe whose tactics were no braver than his own, but simply more cunning. He bit his lips—out of pain perhaps, but as likely out of impotent rage and frustration, and he seemed close to tears when he said, in a tone almost like grief: "*He* crapped out! *He* crapped out!"

He came alive like a somnambulist abruptly shocked out of sleep, and he abruptly lunged forward onto the road with a wild and tormented bellow. "Hey, you people, get off that goddam truck!" He sprang into the dust with a skip and a jump, toiling down the road with hobbled leg and furious flailing arms. By his deep swinging gait, his terrible limp, he looked no more capable of locomotion than a wheel-chair invalid, and it would have been funny had it not seemed at the same time so full of threat and disaster. He pressed on. "Off that truck, goddammit, I say! Off that truck. Saddle up. Saddle up now, I say! On your feet!" he yelled. "Get off that goddam truck before I start kicking you people in the ass!" His words flayed and cowed them; a long concerted groan arose in the air, seemed to take possession of the very dawn; yet they debarked from the truck in terrified flight, scuttling down like mice from a sinking raft. "Move the hell out of here!" he shouted at the truck driver, a skinny corporal, eyes bulging, who popped back into the cab in fright. "Get that heap out of here!" The truck leaped off with a roar, enveloping the scene in blue smoke and a tornado of dust. Mannix, with windmilling arms, stood propped on his toe in the center of the road, urged the men wildly on "Saddle up now! Let somebody else crap out O.K., but not you people, hear me! Do you hear me! Goddammit, I mean it! Shea, get those people moving out up there! You people better face it, you got eighteen more miles to go . . ." Culver tried to stop him, but they had already begun to run.

Panic-stricken, limping with blisters and with exhaustion, and in mutinous despair, the men fled westward, whipped on by Mannix's cries. They pressed into the humid, sweltering light of the new day. Culver followed; O'Leary, without a murmur, puffed along beside him, while to the rear, with steady slogging footsteps, trailed the remnants of the battalion. Dust billowed up and preceded them, like Egypt's pillar of cloud, filling the air with its dry oppressive menace. It coated their lips and moist brows with white powdery grit, like a spray of plaster, and gave to the surrounding trees, the underbrush and vacant fields, a blighted pallor, as if touched by unseasonable frost. The sun rose higher, burning down at their backs so that each felt he bore on his shoulders not the burden of a pack but, almost worse, a portable oven growing hotter and hotter as the sun came up from behind the sheltering pines. They walked automatically, no longer with that light and tentative step in order to ease the pain in their feet, but with the firm, dogged tread of robots; and if they were all like Culver they had long since parted with a sensation of motion below the hips, and felt there only a constant throbbing pain—of blisters and battered muscles and the protest of exhausted bones.

Then one time Culver saw the Colonel go by in a jeep, boiling along in a cloud of dust toward the head of the column. He caught a glimpse of him as he passed: he looked sweaty and tired, far from rested, and Culver wondered how justified Mannix's outrage had been, assigning to the Colonel that act of cowardice. So he hadn't been pacing the march, but God knows he must have been hiking along to the rear; and his doubts were bolstered by O'Leary's voice, coming painfully beside him: "Old Captain Mannix's mighty pissed off at the Colonel." He paused, wheezing steadily. "Don't know if he's got a right to be that way. Old Colonel ain't gonna crap out without a reason. Colonel's kind of rough sometimes but he'll go with the troops." Culver said nothing. They plodded ahead silently. Culver felt like cursing the Sergeant. How could he be so stupid? How could he, in the midst of this pain, yield up still only words of accord and respect and even admiration for the creator of such a wild and lunatic punishment? Only a man so firmly cemented to the system that all doubts were beyond countenance could say what O'Leary did—and yet—and yet God knows, Culver thought wearily, he could be right and himself and Mannix, and the rest of them, inescapably wrong. His mind was confused. A swarm of dust came up and filled his lungs. Mannix was screwing everything up horribly, and Culver wanted suddenly to sprint forward—in spite of the effort it took—reach the Captain, take him aside and tell him: *Al, Al, let up, you've already lost the battle.* Defiance, pride, endurance—none of these would help. He only mutilated himself by this perverse and violent rebellion; no matter what the Colonel was—coward and despot or staunch bold leader—he had him beaten, going and coming. Nothing could be worse than what Mannix was doing—adding to a disaster already ordained (Culver somehow sensed) the burden of his vicious fury. At least let up, the men had had enough. But his mind was confused. His kidneys were aching as if they had been pounded with a mallet, and he walked along now with his hands on his waist, like a professor lecturing in a classroom, coattails over his arms.

And for the first time he felt intolerably hot—with a heat that contributed to his mounting fury. At night they had sweated more from exertion; the coolness of the evening had been at least some solace, but the morning's sun began to flagellate him anew, adding curious sharp blades of pain to the furious frustration boiling inside him. Frustration at the fact that he was not independent enough, nor possessed of enough free will, was not *man* enough to say, to hell with it and crap out himself; that he was not man enough to disavow all his determination and endurance and suffering, cash in his chips, and by that act flaunt his contempt of the march, the Colonel, the whole bloody Marine Corps. But he was *not* man enough, he knew, far less simply a free man; he was just a marine—as was Mannix, and so many of the others—and they had been marines, it seemed, all their lives, would go on being marines forever; and the frustration implicit in this thought brought him suddenly close to tears. Mannix. A cold horror came over him. Far down, profoundly, Mannix was so much a marine that it could make him casually demented. The corruption begun years ago in his drill-field feet had climbed up, overtaken him, and had begun to rot his brain. Culver heard himself sobbing with frustration and outrage. The sun beat down against his back. His mind slipped off into fevered blankness, registering once more, on that crazy cinematic tape, chaos, vagrant jigsaw images: Mannix's voice far ahead, hoarse and breaking now, then long spells of silence; halts beside stifling, windless fields, then a shady ditch into which he plunged, feverish and comatose, dreaming of a carnival tent where one bought, from a dozen barrels, all sorts of ice, chipped, crushed, and cubed, in various shapes and sizes. He was awakened by that terrible cry—*Saddle up, saddle up!*—and he set out again. The sun rose higher and higher. O'Leary, with a groan, dropped behind and vanished. Two trucks passed loaded with stiff, green-clad bodies motionless as corpses. The canteen fell off Culver's belt, somewhere, sometime; now he found though, to his surprise, that he was no longer thirsty and no longer sweating. This was dangerous, he recalled from some lecture, but at that moment the young marine vomiting at the roadside seemed more important, even more interesting. He stopped to help, thought better of it, passed on—through a strange crowd of pale and tiny butterflies, borne like bleached petals in shimmering slow-motion across the dusty road. At one point Hobbs, the radioman, cruised by in a jeep with a fishpole antenna; he was laughing, taunting the marchers with a song—*I got romance in my pants*—and he waved a jolly fat hand. A tanager rose, scarlet and beautiful, from a streaming thicket and pinwheeled upward, down again, and into the meadow beyond: there Culver thought, for a brief terrified moment, that he saw eight butchered corpses lying in a row, blood streaming out against the weeds. But it passed. Of course, he remembered, that was yesterday—or was it?—and then for minutes he tried to recall Hobbs' name, gave up the effort; it was along about this time, too, that he gazed at his watch, neither pleased nor saddened to find that it was not quite nine o'clock, began to wind it with careful absorption as he trudged along, and looked up to see Mannix looming enormously at the roadside.

"Get up," the Captain was saying. He had hardly any voice left at all; whatever he spoke with gave up only a rasp, a whisper. "Get your ass off the deck," he was saying, "get up, I say."

Culver stopped and watched. The marine lay back in the weeds. He was fat and he had a three-day growth of beard. He held up one bare foot, where there was a blister big as a silver dollar and a dead, livid white, the color of a toadstool; as the Captain spoke, the marine blandly peeled the skin away, revealing a huge patch of tender, pink, virgin flesh. He had a patient hillbilly voice and he was explaining softly, "Ah just cain't go on, Captain, with a foot like this. Ah just cain't do it, and that's all there is to it."

"You *can*, goddammit," he rasped. "I walked ten miles with a nail in my foot. If I can do it you can, too. Get up, I said. You're a marine . . ."

"Captain," he went on patiently, "Ah cain't help it about your nail. Ah may be a marine and all that but Ah ain't no goddam fool . . ."

The Captain, poised on his crippled foot, made a swift, awkward gesture toward the man, as if to drag him to his feet; Culver grabbed him by the arm, shouting furiously: "Stop it, Al! Stop it! Stop it! Stop it! Enough!" He paused, looking into Mannix's dull hot eyes. "Enough!" he said, more quietly. "Enough." Then gently, "That's enough, Al. They've just had enough." The end was at hand, Culver knew, there was no doubt of that. The march had come to a halt again, the men lay sprawled out on the sweltering roadside. He looked at the Captain, who shook his head dumbly and suddenly ran trembling fingers over his eyes. "O.K.," he murmured, "yeah . . . yes"—something incoherent and touched with grief—and Culver felt tears running down his cheeks. He was too tired to think—except: old Al. Mannix. Goddam. "They've had enough," he repeated.

Mannix jerked his hand away from his face. "O.K.," he croaked, "Christ sake, I hear you. O.K. They've had enough, they've had enough. O.K. I heard you the first time. Let 'em crap out! I've did—done—" He paused, wheeled around. "To hell with them all."

He watched Mannix limp away. The Colonel was standing nearby up the road, thumbs hooked in his belt, regarding the Captain soberly. Culver's spirit sank like a rock. Old Al, he thought. You just couldn't win. Goddam. Old great soft scarred bear of a man.

If in defeat he appeared despondent, he retained one violent shred of life which sustained him to the end—his fury. It would get him through. He was like a man running a gauntlet of whips, who shouts outrage and defiance at his tormentors until he falls at the finish. Yet—as Culver could have long ago foretold—it was a fury that was uncontained; the old smoking bonfire had blazed up in his spirit. And if it had been out of control hours ago when he had first defied the Colonel, there was no doubt at all that now it could not fail to consume both of them. At least one of them. Culver, prone on his belly in the weeds, was hot with tension, and he felt blood pounding at his head when he heard the Colonel call, in a frosty voice: "Captain Mannix, will you come here a minute?"

Culver was the closest at hand. There were six more miles to go. The break had extended this time to fifteen minutes—an added rest because, as Culver had heard the Colonel explain to the Major, they'd walk the last six miles without a halt. Another break, he'd said, with a wry weary grin, and they'd never be able to get the troops off the ground. Culver had groaned—another senseless piece of sadism—then reasoned wearily that it *was* a good idea. Probably. Maybe. Who knew? He was too tired to care. He watched Mannix walk with an awful hobbling motion up the road, face screwed up in pain and eyes asquint like a man trying to gaze at the sun. He moved at a good rate of speed but his gait was terrible to behold—jerks and spasms which warded off, reacted to, or vainly tried to control great zones and areas of pain. Behind him most of his men lay in stupefied rows at the edge of the road and waited for the trucks to come. They knew Mannix had finished, and they had crumpled completely. For the last ten minutes, in a listless fashion, he had assembled less than a third of the company who were willing to continue the march—die-hards, athletes, and just those who, like Mannix himself, would make the last six miles out of pride and spite. Out of fury. It was a seedy, bedraggled column of people: of hollow, staring eyes and faces green with slack-jawed exhaustion; and behind them the remnants of the battalion made hardly more than two hundred men. Mannix struggled on up the road, approached the Colonel, and stood there propped on his toe, hands on his hips for balance.

The Colonel looked at him steadily for a moment, coldly. Mannix was no longer a simple doubter but the heretic, and was about to receive judgment. Yet there was still an almost paternal reluctance in Templeton's voice as he spoke, slowly and very softly, out of the troops' hearing: "Captain Mannix, I want you to go in on the trucks."

"No, sir," Mannix said hoarsely, "I'm going to make this march."

The Colonel looked utterly whipped; gray bags of fatigue hung beneath his eyes. He seemed no longer to have strength enough to display his odd theatrical smile; his posture was taut and vaguely stooped, the unmistakable bent-kneed stance of a man with blisters, and Culver was forced to concede—with a sense of mountainous despair—that he *had* made the march after all, somewhere toward the rear and for legitimate reasons of his own, even if Mannix now was too blind, too outraged, to tell. *Goddam,* Culver heard himself moaning aloud, *if just he only hadn't made it,* but he heard the Colonel go on coolly: "Not with that foot you aren't." He glanced down. The Captain's ankle had swollen to a fat milky purple above the top of his shoe; he was unable to touch his heel to the ground even if he had wanted to. "Not with that foot," he repeated.

Mannix was silent, panting deeply—not as if taken aback at all, but only as if gathering wind for an outburst. He and the Colonel gazed at each other, twin profiles embattled against an escarpment of pines, the chaste blue sky of morning. "Listen, Colonel," he rasped, "you ordered this goddam hike and I'm going to walk it even if I haven't got one goddam man left. You can crap out yourself for half the march—" Culver wanted desperately, somehow, by any means to stop him—not just because he was pulling catastrophe down on his head but because it was simply no longer worth the effort. Couldn't he see? That the Colonel didn't care and that was that? That with him the hike had had nothing to do with courage or sacrifice or suffering, but was only a task to be performed, that whatever he was he was no coward, he had marched the whole way—or most of it, any idiot could see that—and that he was as far removed from the vulgar battle, the competition, which Mannix had tried to promote as the frozen, remotest stars. He just didn't care. Culver strove, in a sick, heaving effort, to rise, to go and somehow separate them, but Mannix was charging on: "You run your troops. Fine. O.K. But what's all this about crapping out—"

"Wait a minute, Captain, now—" the Colonel blurted ominously. "For your information—"

"*Fuck* you and your information," said Mannix in a hoarse, choked voice. He was almost sobbing. "If you think—"

But he went no further, for the Colonel had made a curious, quick gesture—stage-gesture, fantastic and subtle, and it was like watching an old cowboy film to see the Colonel's hand go swiftly back to the handle of his pistol and rest there, his eyes cool and passionate and forbidding. It was a gesture of force which balked even the Captain. Mannix's face went pale—as if he had only just then realized the words which had erupted so heedlessly from his mouth—and he said nothing, only stood there sullen and beaten and blinking at the glossy white handle of the pistol as the Colonel went on: "For your information, Captain, you aren't the only one who made this march. But I'm not *interested* in your observations. You quiet down now, hear? You march in, see? I order you confined to your quarters, and I'm going to see that you get a court-martial. Do you understand? I'm going to have you tried for gross insubordination. I'll have you sent to Korea. *Keep your mouth shut.* Now get back to your company!" He was shaking with wrath; the hot morning light beat with piety and with vengeance from his gray, outraged eyes. "Get back to your men," he whispered, *"get back to your men!"*

Then he turned his back to the Captain and called down the road to the Major: "All right, Billy, let's saddle up!"

So it was over, but not quite all. The last six miles took until past noon. Mannix's perpetual tread on his toe alone gave to his gait a ponderous, bobbing motion which resembled that of a man wretchedly spastic and paralyzed. It lent to his face too—whenever Culver became detached from his own misery long enough to glance at him—an aspect of deep, almost prayerfully passionate concentration—eyes thrown skyward and lips fluttering feverishly in pain—so that if one did not know he was in agony one might imagine that he was a communicant in rapture, offering up breaths of hot desire to the heavens. It was impossible to imagine such a distorted face; it was the painted, suffering face of a clown, and the heaving gait was a grotesque and indecent parody of a hopeless cripple, with shoulders gyrating like a seesaw and with flapping, stricken arms. The Colonel and the Major had long since out-distanced them, and Culver and Mannix walked alone. When the base came into sight, he was certain they were not going to make it. They trudged into the camp. Along the barren, treeless streets marines in neat khaki were going to lunch, and they turned to watch the mammoth gyrating Captain, so tattered and soiled—who addressed convulsive fluttering prayers to the sky, and had obviously parted with his senses. Then Mannix stopped suddenly and grasped Culver's arm. "What the hell," he whispered, "we've made it."

V

For a long while Culver was unable to sleep. He had lain naked on his bed for what seemed hours, but unconsciousness would not come; his closed eyes offered up only vistas of endless roads, steaming thickets, fields, tents—sunshine and darkness illogically commingled—and the picture, which returned to his mind with the unshakable regularity of a scrap of music, of the boys who lay dead beneath the light of another noon. Try as he could, sleep would not come. So he dragged himself erect and edged toward the window, laboriously, because of his battered feet; it took him a full minute to do so, and his legs, like those of an amputee which possess the ghost of sensation, felt as if they were still in motion, pacing endless distances. He lowered himself into a chair and lighted a cigarette. Below, the swimming pool was grotto-blue, a miniature of the cloudless sky above, lit with shapes of dancing light as shiny as silver dimes. A squad of sunsuited maidens, officers' wives, splashed at its brink or ate ice-cream sundaes on the lawn, and filled the noontime with their decorous sunny laughter. It was hot and still. Far off above the pines, in the hot sunlight and over distant peace and civilization, brewed the smoky and threatful beginnings of a storm.

Culver let his head fall on his arm. Yes, they had had it—those eight boys—he thought, there was no doubt of that. In mindless slumber now, they were past caring, though diadems might drop or Doges surrender. They were ignorant of all. And that they had never grown old enough to know anything, even the tender miracle of pity, was perhaps a better ending—it was hard to tell. Faint warm winds came up from the river, bearing with them a fragrance of swamp and pine, and a last whisper of air passed through the trees, shuddered, died, became still; suddenly Culver felt a deep vast hunger for something he could not explain, nor ever could remember having known quite so achingly before. He only felt that all of his life he had yearned for something that was as fleeting and as incommunicable, in its beauty, as that one bar of music he remembered, or those lovely little girls with their ever joyful, ever sprightly dance on some far and fantastic lawn—serenity, a quality of repose—he could not call it by name, but only knew that, somehow, it had always escaped him. As he sat there, with the hunger growing and blossoming within him, he felt that he had hardly ever known a time in his life when he was not marching or sick with loneliness or afraid.

And so, he thought, they had all had it, in their various fashions. The Colonel had had his march and his victory, and Culver could not say still why he was unable to hate him. Perhaps it was only because he was a different kind of man, different enough that he was hardly a man at all, but just a quantity of attitudes so remote from Culver's world that to hate him would be like hating a cannibal, merely because he gobbled human flesh. At any rate, he had had it. And as for Mannix—well, *he'd* certainly had it, there was no doubt of *that*. Old Al, he thought tenderly. The man with the back unbreakable, the soul of pity—where was he now, great unshatterable vessel of longing, lost in the night, astray at mid-century in the never-endingness of war?

His hunger faded and died. He raised his head and gazed out the window. Over the pool a figure swan-dived against the sky, in crucified, graceless descent broke the water with a lumpy splash. A cloud passed over the day, darkening the lawn with a moment's somber light. The conversation of the girls became subdued, civilized, general. Far off above the trees, on the remotest horizon, thunderheads bloomed, a squall. Later, toward sundown, they would roll landward over a shadowing reach of waves, borne nearer, ever more darkly across the coast, the green wild desolation of palmetto and cypress and pine—and here, where the girls pink and scanty in sunsuits would slant their tar-black eyes skyward in the gathering night, abandon pool and games and chatter and with shrill cries of warning flee homeward like gaudy scraps of paper on the blast, voices young and lovely and lost in the darkness, the onrushing winds. One thing, Culver thought, was certain—they were in for a blow. Already there would be signals up and down the coast.

Abruptly he was conscious of a dry, parched thirst. He rose to his feet, put on a robe, and hobbled out into the hallway toward the water cooler. As he rounded the corner he saw Mannix, naked except for a towel around his waist, making his slow and agonized way down the hall. He was hairy and enormous and as he inched his way toward the shower room, clawing at the wall for support, his face with its clenched eyes and taut, drawn-down mouth was one of tortured and gigantic suffering. The swelling at his ankle was the size of a grapefruit, an ugly blue, and his leg he dragged behind him, a dead weight no longer capable of motion.

Culver started to limp toward him, said, "Al—" in an effort to help him along, but just then one of the Negro maids employed in the place came swinging along with a mop, stopped, seeing Mannix, ceased the singsong little tune she was humming, too, and said, "Oh my, you poor man. What you been doin'? Do it hurt?" Culver halted.

"Do it hurt?" she repeated. "Oh, I bet it does. Deed it does." Mannix looked up at her across the short yards that separated them, silent, blinking. Culver would remember this: the two of them communicating across that chasm one unspoken moment of sympathy and understanding before the woman, spectacled, bandannaed, said again, "Deed it does," and before, almost at precisely the same instant, the towel slipped away slowly from Mannix's waist and fell with a soft plop to the floor; Mannix then, standing there, weaving dizzily and clutching for support at the wall, a mass of scars and naked as the day he emerged from his mother's womb, save for the soap which he held feebly in one hand. He seemed to have neither the strength nor the ability to lean down and retrieve the towel and so he merely stood there huge and naked in the slanting dusty light and blinked and sent toward the woman, finally, a sour, apologetic smile, his words uttered, it seemed to Culver, not with self-pity but only with the tone of a man who, having endured and lasted, was too weary to tell her anything but what was true.

"Deed it does," he said.

ALIENATION

Eudora Welty

POWERHOUSE

Powerhouse is playing!

He's here on tour from the city—"Powerhouse and His Keyboard"—
"Powerhouse and His Tasmanians"—think of the things he calls himself!
There's no one in the world like him. You can't tell what he is. "Nigger
man"?—he looks more Asiatic, monkey, Jewish, Babylonian, Peruvian,
fanatic, devil. He has pale gray eyes, heavy lids, maybe horny like a
lizard's, but big glowing eyes when they're open. He has African feet of
the greatest size, stomping, both together, on each side of the pedals. He's
not coal black—beverage colored—looks like a preacher when his mouth
is shut, but then it opens—vast and obscene. And his mouth is going
every minute: like a monkey's when it looks for something. Improvising,
coming on a light and childish melody—*smooch*—he loves it with his
mouth.

Is it possible that he could be this! When you have him there
performing for you, that's what you feel. You know people on a
stage—and people of a darker race—so likely to be marvelous, frightening.

This is a white dance. Powerhouse is not a show-off like the Harlem
boys, not drunk, not crazy—he's in a trance; he's a person of joy, a fanatic.
He listens as much as he performs, a look of hideous, powerful rapture on
his face. Big arched eyebrows that never stop traveling, like a Jew's—
wandering-Jew eyebrows. When he plays he beats down piano and seat
and wears them away. He is in motion every moment—what could be
more obscene? There he is with his great head, fat stomach, and little
round piston legs, and long yellow-sectioned strong big fingers, at rest
about the size of bananas. Of course you know how he sounds—you've
heard him on records—but still you need to see him. He's going all the
time, like skating around the skating rink or rowing a boat. It makes
everybody crowd around, here in this shadowless steel-trussed hall with
the rose-like posters of Nelson Eddy and the testimonial for the mind-
reading horse in handwriting magnified five hundred times. Then all

quietly he lays his finger on a key with the promise and serenity of a sibyl touching the book.

Powerhouse is so monstrous he sends everybody into oblivion. When any group, any performers, come to town, don't people always come out and hover near, leaning inward about them, to learn what it is? What is it? Listen. Remember how it was with the acrobats. Watch them carefully, hear the least word, especially what they say to one another, in another language—don't let them escape you; it's the only time for hallucination, the last time. They can't stay. They'll be somewhere else this time tomorrow.

Powerhouse has as much as possible done by signals. Everybody, laughing as if to hide a weakness, will sooner or later hand him up a written request. Powerhouse reads each one, studying with a secret face: that is the face which looks like a mask—anybody's; there is a moment when he makes a decision. Then a light slides under his eyelids, and he says, "92!" or some combination of figures—never a name. Before a number the band is all frantic, misbehaving, pushing, like children in a schoolroom, and he is the teacher getting silence. His hands over the keys, he says sternly, "You-all ready? You-all ready to do some serious walking?"—waits—then, STAMP. Quiet. STAMP, for the second time. This is absolute. Then a set of rhythmic kicks against the floor to communicate the tempo. Then, O Lord! say the distended eyes from beyond the boundary of the trumpets, Hello and good-bye, and they are all down the first note like a waterfall.

This note marks the end of any known discipline. Powerhouse seems to abandon them all—he himself seems lost—down in the song, yelling up like somebody in a whirlpool—not guiding them—hailing them only. But he knows, really. He cries out, but he must know exactly. "Mercy! . . . What I say! . . . Yeah!" And then drifting, listening—"Where that skin beater?"—wanting drums, and starting up and pouring it out in the greatest delight and brutality. On the sweet pieces such a leer for everybody! He looks down so benevolently upon all our faces and whispers the lyrics to us. And if you could hear him at this moment on "Marie, the Dawn is Breaking"! He's going up the keyboard with a few fingers in some very derogatory triplet-routine, he gets higher and higher, and then he looks over the end of the piano, as if over a cliff. But not in a show-off way—the song makes him do it.

He loves the way they all play, too—all those next to him. The far section of the band is all studious, wearing glasses, every one—they don't count. Only those playing around Powerhouse are the real ones. He has a bass fiddler from Vicksburg, black as pitch, named Valentine, who plays with his eyes shut and talking to himself, very young: Powerhouse has to keep encouraging him. "Go on, go on, give it up, bring it on out there!" When you heard him like that on records, did you know he was really pleading?

He calls Valentine out to take a solo.

"What you going to play?" Powerhouse looks out kindly from behind the piano; he opens his mouth and shows his tongue, listening.

Valentine looks down, drawing against his instrument, and says without a lip movement, "'Honeysuckle Rose.'"

He has a clarinet player named Little Brother, and loves to listen to anything he does. He'll smile and say, "Beautiful!" Little Brother takes a step forward when he plays and stands at the very front, with the whites of his eyes like fishes swimming. Once when he played a low note, Powerhouse muttered in dirty praise, "He went clear downstairs to get that one!"

After a long time, he holds up the number of fingers to tell the band how many choruses still to go—usually five. He keeps his directions down to signals.

It's a bad night outside. It's a white dance, and nobody dances, except a few straggling jitterbugs and two elderly couples. Everybody just stands around the band and watches Powerhouse. Sometimes they steal glances at one another, as if to say, Of course, you know how it is with *them*—Negroes—band leaders—they would play the same way, giving all they've got for an audience of one. . . . When somebody, no matter who, gives everything, it makes people feel ashamed for him.

Late at night they play the one waltz they will ever consent to play—by request, "Pagan Love Song." Powerhouse's head rolls and sinks like a weight between his waving shoulders. He groans, and his fingers drag into the keys heavily, holding on to the notes, retrieving. It is a sad song.

"You know what happened to me?" says Powerhouse.

Valentine hums a response, dreaming at the bass.

"I got a telegram my wife is dead," says Powerhouse, with wandering fingers.

"Uh-huh?"

His mouth gathers and forms a barbarous O while his fingers walk up straight, unwillingly, three octaves.

"Gypsy? Why how come her to die, didn't you just phone her up in the night last night long distance?"

"Telegram say—here the words: Your wife is dead." He puts 4/4 over the 3/4.

"Not but four words?" This is the drummer, an unpopular boy named Scoot, a disbelieving maniac.

Powerhouse is shaking his vast cheeks. "What the hell was she trying to do? What was she up to?"

"What name has it got signed, if you got a telegram?" Scoot is spitting away with those wire brushes.

Little Brother, the clarinet player, who cannot now speak, glares and tilts back.

"Uranus Knockwood is the name signed." Powerhouse lifts his eyes open. "Ever heard of him?" A bubble shoots out on his lip like a plate on a counter.

Valentine is beating slowly on with his palm and scratching the strings with his long blue nails. He is fond of a waltz, Powerhouse interrupts him.

"I don't know him. Don't know who he is." Valentine shakes his head with the closed eyes.

"Say it agin."

"Uranus Knockwood."

"That ain't Lenox Avenue."

"It ain't Broadway."

"Ain't ever seen it wrote out in any print, even for horse racing."

"Hell, that's on a star, boy, ain't it?" Crash of the cymbals.

"What the hell was she up to?" Powerhouse shudders. "Tell me, tell me, tell me." He makes triplets, and begins a new chorus. He holds three fingers up.

"You say you got a telegram." This is Valentine, patient and sleepy, beginning again.

Powerhouse is elaborate. "Yas, the time I go out, go way downstairs along a long cor-ri-dor to where they puts us: coming back along the cor-ri-dor: steps out and hands me a telegram: Your wife is dead."

"Gypsy?" The drummer like a spider over his drums.

"Aaaaaaaaa!" shouts Powerhouse, flinging out both powerful arms for three whole beats to flex his muscles, then kneading a dough of bass notes. His eyes glitter. He plays the piano like a drum sometimes—why not?

"Gypsy? Such a dancer?"

"Why you don't hear it straight from your agent? Why it ain't come from headquarters? What you been doing, getting telegrams in the *corridor,* signed nobody?"

They all laugh. End of that chorus.

"What time is it?" Powerhouse calls. "What the hell place is this? Where is my watch and chain?"

"I hang it on you," whimpers Valentine. "It still there."

There it rides on Powerhouse's great stomach, down where he can never see it.

"Sure did hear some clock striking twelve while ago. Must be *midnight.*"

"It going to be intermission," Powerhouse declares, lifting up his finger with the signet ring.

He draws the chorus to an end. He pulls a big Northern hotel towel out of the deep pocket in his vast, special-cut tux pants and pushes his forehead into it.

"If she went and killed herself!" he says with a hidden face. "If she up and jumped out that window!" He gets to his feet, turning vaguely, wearing the towel on his head.

"Ha, ha!"

"Sheik, sheik!"

"She wouldn't do that." Little Brother sets down his clarinet like a precious vase, and speaks. He still looks like an East Indian queen, implacable, divine, and full of snakes. "You ain't going to expect people doing what they says over long distance."

"Come on!" roars Powerhouse. He is already at the back door, he has pulled it wide open, and with a wild, gathered-up face is smelling the terrible night.

Powerhouse, Valentine, Scoot and Little Brother step outside into the drenching rain.

"Well, they emptying buckets," says Powerhouse in a mollified voice. On the street he holds his hands out and turns up the blanched palms like sieves.

A hundred dark, ragged, silent, delighted Negroes have come around from under the eaves of the hall, and follow wherever they go.

"Watch out Little Brother don't shrink," says Powerhouse. "You just the right size now, clarinet don't suck you in. You got a dry throat, Little Brother, you in the desert?" He reaches into the pocket and pulls out a paper of mints. "Now hold 'em in your mouth—don't chew 'em. I don't carry around nothing without limit."

"Go in that joint and have beer," says Scoot, who walks ahead.

"Beer? Beer? You know what beer is? What do they say is beer? What's beer? Where I been?"

"Down yonder where it say World Café—that do?" They are in Negrotown now.

Valentine patters over and holds open a screen door warped like a sea shell, bitter in the wet, and they walk in, stained darker with the rain and leaving footprints. Inside, sheltered dry smells stand like screens around a table covered with a red-checkered cloth, in the center of which flies hang onto an obelisk-shaped ketchup bottle. The midnight walls are checkered again with admonishing "Not Responsible" signs and black-figured, smoky calendars. It is a waiting, silent, limp room. There is a burned-out-looking nickelodeon and right beside it a long-necked wall instrument labeled "Business Phone, Don't Keep Talking." Circled phone numbers are written up everywhere. There is a worn-out peacock feather hanging by a thread to an old, thin, pink, exposed light bulb, where it slowly turns around and around, whoever breathes.

A waitress watches.

"Come here, living statue, and get all this big order of beer we fixing to give."

"Never seen you before anywhere." The waitress moves and comes forward and slowly shows little gold leaves and tendrils over her teeth. She shoves up her shoulders and breasts. "How I going to know who you might be? Robbers? Coming in out of the black of night right at midnight, setting down so big at my table?"

"Boogers," says Powerhouse, his eyes opening lazily as in a cave.

The girl screams delicately with pleasure. O Lord, she likes talk and scares.

"Where you going to find enough beer to put out on this here table?" She runs to the kitchen with bent elbows and sliding steps.

"Here's a million nickels," says Powerhouse, pulling his hand out of his pocket and sprinkling coins out, all but the last one, which he makes vanish like a magician.

Valentine and Scoot take the money over to the nickelodeon, which looks as battered as a slot machine, and read all the names of the records out loud.

"Whose 'Tuxedo Junction'?" asks Powerhouse.

"You know whose."

"Nickelodeon, I request you please to play 'Empty Red Blues' and let Bessie Smith sing."

Silence: they hold it like a measure.

"Bring me all those nickels on back here," says Powerhouse. "Look at that! What you tell me the name of this place?"

"White dance, week night, raining, Alligator, Mississippi, long ways from home."

"Uh-huh."

"Sent for You Yesterday and Here You Come Today" plays.

The waitress, setting the tray of beer down on a back table, comes up taut and apprehensive as a hen. "Says in the kitchen, back there putting their eyes to little hole peeping out, that you is Mr. Powerhouse. . . . They knows from a picture they seen."

"They seeing right tonight, that is him," says Little Brother.

"You him?"

"That is him in the flesh," says Scoot.

"Does you wish to touch him?" asks Valentine. "Because he don't bite."

"You passing through?"

"Now you got everything right."

She waits like a drop, hands languishing together in front.

"Little-Bit, ain't you going to bring the beer?"

She brings it, and goes behind the cash register and smiles, turning different ways. The little fillet of gold in her mouth is gleaming.

"The Mississippi River's here," she says once.

Now all the watching Negroes press in gently and bright-eyed through the door, as many as can get in. One is a little boy in a straw sombrero which has been coated with aluminum paint all over.

Powerhouse, Valentine, Scoot and Little Brother drink beer, and their eyelids come together like curtains. The wall and the rain and the humble beautiful waitress waiting on them and the other Negroes watching enclose them.

"Listen!" whispers Powerhouse, looking into the ketchup bottle and slowly spreading his performer's hands over the damp, wrinkling cloth with the red squares. "Listen how it is. My wife gets missing me. Gypsy. She goes to the window. She looks out and sees you know what. Street. Sign saying Hotel. People walking. Somebody looks up. Old man. She looks down, out the window. Well? . . . Sssst! Plooey! What she do? Jump out and bust her brains all over the world."

He opens his eyes.

"That's it," agrees Valentine. "You gets a telegram."

"Sure she misses you," Little Brother adds.

"No, it's night time." How softly he tells them! "Sure. It's the night time. She say, What do I hear? Footsteps walking up the hall? That him? Footsteps go on off. It's not me. I'm in Alligator, Mississippi, she's crazy. Shaking all over. Listens till her ears and all grow out like old music-box horns but still she can't hear a thing. She says, All right! I'll jump out the window then. Got on her nightgown. I know that nightgown, and her thinking there. Says, Ho hum, all right, and jumps out the window. Is she mad at me! Is she crazy! She don't leave *nothing* behind her!"

"Ya! Ha!"

"Brains and insides everywhere, Lord, Lord."

All the watching Negroes stir in their delight, and to their higher delight he says affectionately, "Listen! Rats in here."

"That must be the way, boss."

"Only, naw, Powerhouse, that ain't true. That sound too *bad.*"

"Does? I even know who finds her," cries Powerhouse. "That no-good pussyfooted crooner creeper, that creeper that follow around after me, coming up like weeds behind me, following around after me everything I do and messing around on the trail I leave. Bets my numbers, sings my songs, gets close to my agent like a Betsy-bug; when I going out he just coming in. I got him now! I got my eye on him."

"Know who he is?"

"Why, it's that old Uranus Knockwood!"

"Ya! Ha!"

"Yeah, and he coming now, he going to find Gypsy. There he is, coming around that corner, and Gypsy kadoodling down, oh-oh, watch out! *Sssst! Plooey!* See, there she is in her little old nightgown, and her insides and brains all scattered round."

A sigh fills the room.

"Hush about her brains. Hush about her insides."

"Ya! Ha! You talking about her brains and insides—old Uranus Knockwood," says Powerhouse, "look down and say Jesus! He say, Look here what I'm walking round in!"

They all burst into halloos of laughter. Powerhouse's face looks like a big hot iron stove.

"Why, he picks her up and carries her off!" he says.

"Ya! Ha!"

"Carries her *back* around the corner. . . ."

"Oh, Powerhouse!"

"You know him."

"Uranus Knockwood!"

"Yeahhh!"

"He take our wives when we gone!"

"He come in when we goes out!"

"Uh-huh!"

"He go out when we comes in!"

"Yeahhh!"

"He standing behind the door!"

"Old Uranus Knockwood."

"You know him."

"Middle-size man."

"Wears a hat."

"That's him."

Everybody in the room moans with pleasure. The little boy in the fine silver hat opens a paper and divides out a jelly roll among his followers.

And out of the breathless ring somebody moves forward like a slave, leading a great logy Negro with bursting eyes, and says, "This here is Sugar-Stick Thompson, that dove down to the bottom of July Creek and pulled up all those drownded white people fall out of a boat. Last summer, pulled up fourteen."

"Hello," says Powerhouse, turning and looking around at them all with his great daring face until they nearly suffocate.

Sugar-Stick, their instrument, cannot speak; he can only look back at the others.

"Can't even swim. Done it by holding his breath," says the fellow with the hero.

Powerhouse looks at him seekingly.

"I his half brother," the fellow puts in.

They step back.

"Gypsy say," Powerhouse rumbles gently again, looking at *them*, "'What is the use? I'm gonna jump out so far—so far. . . .' *Sssst—!*"

"Don't, boss, don't do it agin," says Little Brother.

"It's awful," says the waitress. "I hates that Mr. Knockwoods. All that the truth?"

"Want to see the telegram I got from him?" Powerhouse's hand goes to the vast pocket.

"Now wait, now wait, boss." They all watch him.

"It must be the real truth," says the waitress, sucking in her lower lip, her luminous eyes turning sadly, seeking the windows.

"No, babe, it ain't the truth." His eyebrows fly up, and he begins to whisper to her out of his vast oven mouth. His hand stays in his pocket. "Truth is something worse, I ain't said what, yet. It's something hasn't come to me, but I ain't saying it won't. And when it does, then want me to tell you?" He sniffs all at once, his eyes come open and turn up, almost too far. He is dreamily smiling.

"Don't, boss, don't, Powerhouse!"

"Oh!" the waitress screams.

"Go on git out of here!" bellows Powerhouse, taking his hand out of his pocket and clapping after her red dress.

The ring of watchers breaks and falls away.

"*Look* at that! Intermission is up," says Powerhouse.

He folds money under a glass, and after they go out, Valentine leans back in and drops a nickel in the nickelodeon behind them, and it lights up and begins to play "The Goona Goo." The feather dangles still.

"Take a telegram!" Powerhouse shouts suddenly up into the rain over the street. "Take a answer. Now what was that name?"

They get a little tired.

"Uranus Knockwood."

"You ought to know."

"Yas? Spell it to me."

They spell it all the ways it could be spelled. It puts them in a wonderful humor.

"Here's the answer. I got it right here. 'What in the hell you talking about? Don't make any difference: I gotcha.' Name signed: Powerhouse."

"That going to reach him, Powerhouse?" Valentine speaks in a maternal voice.

"Yas, yas."

All hushing, following him up the dark street at a distance, like old rained-on black ghosts, the Negroes are afraid they will die laughing.

Powerhouse throws back his vast head into the steaming rain, and a look of hopeful desire seems to blow somehow like a vapor from his own dilated nostrils over his face and bring a mist to his eyes.

"Reach him and come out the other side."

"That's it, Powerhouse, that's it. You got him now."

Powerhouse lets out a long sigh.

"But ain't you going back there to call up Gypsy long distance, the way you did last night in that other place? I seen a telephone. . . . Just to see if she there at home?"

There is a measure of silence. That is one crazy drummer that's going to get his neck broken some day.

"No," growls Powerhouse. "No! How many thousand times tonight I got to say No?"

He holds up his arm in the rain.

"You sure-enough unroll your voice some night, it about reach up yonder to her," says Little Brother, dismayed.

They go on up the street, shaking the rain off and on them like birds.

Back in the dance hall, they play "San" (99). The jitterbugs start up like windmills stationed over the floor, and in their orbits—one circle, another, a long stretch and a zigzag—dance the elderly couples with old smoothness, undisturbed and stately.

When Powerhouse first came back from intermission, no doubt full of beer, they said, he got the band tuned up again in his own way. He didn't strike the piano keys for pitch—he simply opened his mouth and gave falsetto howls—in A, D and so on—they tuned by him. Then he took hold of the piano, as if he saw it for the first time in his life, and tested it for strength, hit it down in the bass, played an octave with his elbow, lifted the top, looked inside, and leaned against it with all his might. He sat down and played it for a few minutes with outrageous force and got it under his power—a bass deep and coarse as a sea net—then produced something glimmering and fragile, and smiled. And who could ever remember any of the things he says? They are just inspired remarks that roll out of his mouth like smoke.

They've requested "Somebody Loves Me," and he's already done twelve or fourteen choruses, piling them up nobody knows how, and it will be a wonder if he ever gets through. Now and then he calls and shouts, "'Somebody loves me! Somebody loves me, I wonder who!'" His mouth gets to be nothing but a volcano. "I wonder who!"

"Maybe . . ." He uses all his right hand on a trill.

"Maybe . . ." He pulls back his spread fingers, and looks out upon the place where he is. A vast, impersonal and yet furious grimace transfigures his wet face.

". . . Maybe it's you!"

ANALYSIS

If we read "Powerhouse" with the expectation of a standard plot, we are likely to protest that although Miss Welty has captured a mood she has not given us a story. A story, we have learned to say, consists of a development and resolution of conflict or tension. Its conclusion should register a change which settles the issues raised. The protagonist should be altered in character or situation, or the reader should come into knowledge which alters his view of the protagonist.

The principal issue raised by "Powerhouse" seems to be alienation. The isolation of an artist from his audience is the clearest line of melody around which many variations are improvised. Yet it appears that the conflict and tension—the alienation and "impersonality" of artist and audience—are as strong at the end as at the beginning. Why is it, then, that when we read "Powerhouse" without trying to force it into a pattern we feel that it does resolve?

Certainly, the conflict and resolution are less obvious—less external—than in the usual story. One reason may be found in the role of the reader in "Powerhouse." Of course, the reader is involved in any good story—he conquers with the hero, rejoices with the heroine, blinks back tears with the old man reconciled to death. But the reader is involved in "Powerhouse" far more intimately than in most stories: he is, in a sense, a central figure. It is in the reader—not in any character or situation on the page—that the vital change takes place.

The unique pattern of point of view is important to an understanding of the reader's role in "Powerhouse." First we are being told about Powerhouse by (apparently) a white person at the dance: "Of course you know how he sounds—you've heard him on records. . . . He looks down so benevolently upon all our faces and whispers the lyrics to us." Here the reader is, in effect, the "you" addressed—and is presumably expected to see things much as the narrator does.

Next we seem to be among (but not one of) the musicians as they play the last song before intermission, go to the beer joint in Negrotown, and return. We see from the vantage point, in effect, of an unbodied observer. Finally, back in the dance hall, we are looking on again as Powerhouse plays, but certainly not from among the musicians, and apparently not from the white audience. Both musicians and audience are referred to as "they"; no narrator is telling us now that "you" would have to see him pile up choruses. We seem still to be looking on as an unbodied observer, but quite a different one. As we move through these three points of view, we come to a fuller identification with Powerhouse than can any audience (white at the dance, Negro at the beer joint)—into the same sort of relationship as the musicians "playing around Powerhouse . . . the real ones."

In a sense, "Powerhouse" is a love story, but the retention of a certain vital distance is necessary to the kind of love involved. We have seen a similar situation in "Bartleby the Scrivener," in which a change toward love of fellowman takes place because of distance; and that story is complicated by the fact that the real protagonist is not the apparent main character, but rather the narrator-antagonist. "Powerhouse" goes a step further. The "character" who changes is never physically on the scene. In the first section of the story, this important person is known only as "you," the one to whom the account is being given. Removal from the scene is specific, here. The reader must keep his distance. Distance is insisted upon by the secondhand nature of the account as well as by direct statements about separateness, about looking on without being able to look into: "You can't tell what he is. . . . Of course, you know how it is with *them*. . . ."

From the moment when Powerhouse and his group begin to play the last number before intermission, the white audience is ignored. Now there is an intimate group (only "those next to him. The far section of the band is all studious, wearing glasses, every one—they don't count") improvising a story-within-the-story which will continue until the return after intermission. At the beer hall another audience gathers: The Negroes look on, listen, are fascinated and entertained, but the distance between them and Powerhouse is evident through the encounter with Sugar-Stick. Sugar-Stick, the local hero, is brought out and introduced, but "Sugar-Stick, their instrument, cannot speak," and "Powerhouse looks at him seekingly."

Finally, when the musicians return to the dance hall, the tone of the account is even less personal than before—and Powerhouse himself is described at the end as looking "impersonal."

Distance between the artist and the audience is necessary to art. The artist performing "Pagan Love Song" cannot at the same time be involved in pagan love with the audience. Involvement in the one is physical; involvement in the other, aesthetic. Powerhouse's story of Gypsy and Uranus Knockwood is such a case. It rises from fact—the fact of being on the road and lonely, of having left the wife behind, of being at least the potential prey of such "creepers" as Uranus Knockwood. Out of the actual circumstances, however, the artist creates an imaginative story in which isolation and fear take such shape that they can be faced and even enjoyed—because of distance. The intricate network of "distance" in the story is complicated by the dual nature of Powerhouse. He is a performer and he is a person. The onlookers can deal with the personality; the fact of a person behind the mask embarrasses them: "When somebody, no matter who, gives everything, it makes people feel ashamed for him." It is between person and person that the greatest distance lies, and only love can bridge it.

Love in the first section of the story is reserved to Powerhouse's love for the music and for the artistic enactment of love: "Improvising, coming on a light and childish melody—*smooch*—he loves it with his mouth."

While playing "Pagan Love Song," Powerhouse begins his blues-type love story about Gypsy, largely by means of which, as it is continued through intermission, the reader comes to know him as an artist-person rather than as a performer-personality. We watch the story grow and change as it rises from the situation and feelings of Powerhouse, and quite subtly we are brought into sympathy with him. Now he is no longer a "mask," so that "you can't tell what he is." We no longer look upon him from the point of view of the white audience; we are more nearly within his "impersonal" face looking out than on the dance floor looking on. At the beginning of the story the reader has identified with the "you" being told,

Is it possible that he could be this! When you have him there performing for you, that's what you feel. You know people on a stage—and people of a darker race—so likely to be marvelous, frightening.

At the end, the reader comes very near identifying with the "you" to whom Powerhouse sings,

"'Somebody loves me! Somebody loves me, I wonder who!'" His mouth gets to be nothing but a volcano. "I wonder who!"
"Maybe . . ." He uses all his right hand on a trill.
"Maybe . . ." He pulls back his spread fingers, and looks out upon the place where he is. A vast, impersonal and yet furious grimace transfigures his wet face.
". . . Maybe it's you!"

The protagonist has not changed; his audience has not changed; the reader has not come upon essentially new knowledge—but through an emotional experience similar to that of music, the reader has changed, and the story has come to its proper resolution.

James Baldwin

SONNY'S BLUES

I read about it in the paper, in the subway, on my way to work. I read it, and I couldn't believe it, and I read it again. Then perhaps I just stared at it, at the newsprint spelling out his name, spelling out the story. I stared at it in the swinging lights of the subway car, and in the faces and bodies of the people, and in my own face, trapped in the darkness which roared outside.

It was not to be believed and I kept telling myself that, as I walked from the subway station to the high school. And at the same time I couldn't doubt it. I was scared, scared for Sonny. He became real to me again. A great block of ice got settled in my belly and kept melting there slowly all day long, while I taught my classes algebra. It was a special kind of ice. It kept melting, sending trickles of ice water all up and down my veins, but it never got less. Sometimes it hardened and seemed to expand until I felt my guts were going to come spilling out or that I was going to choke or scream. This would always be at a moment when I was remembering some specific thing Sonny had once said or done.

When he was about as old as the boys in my classes his face had been bright and open, there was a lot of copper in it; and he'd had wonderfully direct brown eyes, and great gentleness and privacy. I wondered what he looked like now. He had been picked up, the evening before, in a raid on an apartment downtown, for peddling and using heroin.

I couldn't believe it; but what I mean by that is that I couldn't find any room for it anywhere inside me. I had kept it outside me for a long time. I hadn't wanted to know. I had had suspicions, but I didn't name them, I kept putting them away. I told myself that Sonny was wild, but he wasn't crazy. And he'd always been a good boy, he hadn't ever turned hard or evil or disrespectful, the way kids can, so quick, so quick, especially in Harlem. I didn't want to believe that I'd ever see my brother going down, coming to nothing, all that light in his face gone out, in the condition I'd already seen so many others. Yet it had happened and here I was, talking about algebra to a lot of boys who might, every one of them for all I knew, be popping off needles every time they went to the head. Maybe it did more for them than algebra could.

I was sure that the first time Sonny had ever had horse, he couldn't have been much older than these boys were now. These boys, now, were living as we'd been living then, they were growing up with a rush and their heads bumped abruptly against the low ceiling of their actual possibilities. They were filled with rage. All they really knew were two darknesses, the darkness of their lives, which was now closing in on them, and the darkness of the movies, which had blinded them to that other darkness, and in which they now, vindictively, dreamed, at once more together than they were at any other time, and more alone.

When the last bell rang, the last class ended, I let out my breath. It seemed I'd been holding it for all that time. My clothes were wet—I may have looked as though I'd been sitting in a steam bath, all dressed up, all afternoon. I sat alone in the classroom a long time. I listened to the boys outside, downstairs, shouting and cursing and laughing. Their laughter struck me for perhaps the first time. It was not the joyous laughter which—God knows why—one associates with children. It was mocking and insular, its intent was to denigrate. It was disenchanted, and in this, also, lay the authority of their curses. Perhaps I was listening to them because I was thinking about my brother and in them I heard my brother. And myself.

One boy was whistling a tune, at once very complicated and very simple, it seemed to be pouring out of him as though he were a bird, and it sounded very cool and moving through all that harsh, bright air, only just holding its own through all those other sounds.

I stood up and walked over to the window and looked down into the courtyard. It was the beginning of the spring and the sap was rising in the boys. A teacher passed through them every now and again, quickly, as though he or she couldn't wait to get out of that courtyard, to get those boys out of their sight and off their minds. I started collecting my stuff. I thought I'd better get home and talk to Isabel.

The courtyard was almost deserted by the time I got downstairs. I saw this boy standing in the shadow of a doorway, looking just like Sonny. I almost called his name. Then I saw that it wasn't Sonny, but somebody we used to know, a boy from around our block. He'd been Sonny's friend. He'd never been mine, having been too young for me, and, anyway, I'd never liked him. And now, even though he was a grown-up man, he still hung around that block, still spent hours on the street corners, was always high and raggy. I used to run into him from time to time and he'd often work around to asking me for a quarter or fifty cents. He always had some real good excuse, too, and I always gave it to him, I don't know why.

But now, abruptly, I hated him. I couldn't stand the way he looked at me, partly like a dog, partly like a cunning child. I wanted to ask him what the hell he was doing in the school courtyard.

He sort of shuffled over to me, and he said, "I see you got the papers. So you already know about it."

"You mean about Sonny? Yes, I already know about it. How come they didn't get you?"

He grinned. It made him repulsive and it also brought to mind what he'd looked like as a kid. "I wasn't there. I stay away from them people."

"Good for you." I offered him a cigarette and I watched him through the smoke. "You come all the way down here just to tell me about Sonny?"

"That's right." He was sort of shaking his head and his eyes looked strange, as though they were about to cross. The bright sun deadened his damp dark brown skin and it made his eyes look yellow and showed up the dirt in his kinked hair. He smelled funky. I moved a little away from him and I said, "Well, thanks. But I already know about it and I got to get home."

"I'll walk you a little ways," he said. We started walking. There were a couple of kids still loitering in the courtyard and one of them said goodnight to me and looked strangely at the boy beside me.

"What're you going to do?" he asked me. "I mean, about Sonny?"

"Look. I haven't seen Sonny for over a year, I'm not sure I'm going to do anything. Anyway, what the hell *can* I do?"

"That's right," he said quickly, "ain't nothing you can do. Can't much help old Sonny no more, I guess."

It was what I was thinking and so it seemed to me he had no right to say it.

"I'm surprised at Sonny, though," he went on—he had a funny way of talking, he looked straight ahead as though he were talking to himself—"I thought Sonny was a smart boy, I thought he was too smart to get hung."

"I guess he thought so too," I said sharply, "and that's how he got hung. And how about you? You're pretty goddamn smart, I bet."

Then he looked directly at me, just for a minute. "I ain't smart," he said. "If I was smart, I'd have reached for a pistol a long time ago."

"Look. Don't tell *me* your sad story, if it was up to me, I'd give you one." Then I felt guilty—guilty, probably, for never having supposed that the poor bastard *had* a story of his own, much less a sad one, and I asked, quickly, "What's going to happen to him now?"

He didn't answer this. He was off by himself some place. "Funny thing," he said, and from his tone we might have been discussing the quickest way to get to Brooklyn, "when I saw the papers this morning, the first thing I asked myself was if I had anything to do with it. I felt sort of responsible."

I began to listen more carefully. The subway station was on the corner, just before us, and I stopped. He stopped, too. We were in front of a bar and he ducked slightly, peering in, but whoever he was looking for didn't seem to be there. The juke box was blasting away with something black and bouncy and I half watched the barmaid as she danced her way from the juke box to her place behind the bar. And I watched her face as she laughingly responded to something someone said to her, still keeping time to the music. When she smiled one saw the little girl, one sensed the doomed, still-struggling woman beneath the battered face of the semi-whore.

"I never *give* Sonny nothing," the boy said finally, "but a long time ago I come to school high and Sonny asked me how it felt." He paused, I couldn't bear to watch him, I watched the barmaid, and I listened to the music which seemed to be causing the pavement to shake. "I told him it felt great." The music stopped, the barmaid paused and watched the juke box until the music began again. "It did."

All this was carrying me some place I didn't want to go. I certainly didn't want to know how it felt. It filled everything, the people, the houses, the music, the dark, quicksilver barmaid, with menace; and this menace was their reality.

"What's going to happen to him now?" I asked again.

"They'll send him away some place and they'll try to cure him." He shook his head. "Maybe he'll even think he's kicked the habit. Then they'll let him loose"—he gestured, throwing his cigarette into the gutter. "That's all."

"What do you mean, that's *all?*"

But I knew what he meant.

"I *mean,* that's *all.*" He turned his head and looked at me, pulling down the corners of his mouth. "Don't you know what I mean?" he asked, softly.

"How the hell *would* I know what you mean?" I almost whispered it, I don't know why.

"That's right," he said to the air, "how would he know what I mean?" He turned toward me again, patient and calm, and yet I somehow felt him shaking, shaking as though he were going to fall apart. I felt that ice in my guts again, the dread I'd felt all afternoon; and again I watched the barmaid, moving about the bar, washing glasses, and singing. "Listen. They'll let him out and then it'll just start all over again. That's what I mean."

"You mean—they'll let him out. And then he'll just start working his way back in again. You mean he'll never kick the habit. Is that what you mean?"

"That's right," he said, cheerfully. "*You* see what I mean."

"Tell me," I said at last, "why does he want to die? He must want to die, he's killing himself, why does he want to die?"

He looked at me in surprise. He licked his lips. "He don't want to die. He wants to live. Don't nobody want to die, ever."

Then I wanted to ask him—too many things. He could not have answered, or if he had, I could not have borne the answers. I started walking. "Well, I guess it's none of my business."

"It's going to be rough on old Sonny," he said. We reached the subway station. "This is your station?" he asked. I nodded. I took one step down. "Damn!" he said, suddenly. I looked up at him. He grinned again. "Damn it if I didn't leave all my money home. You ain't got a dollar on you, have you? Just for a couple of days, is all."

All at once something inside gave and threatened to come pouring out of me. I didn't hate him any more. I felt that in another moment I'd start crying like a child.

"Sure," I said. "Don't sweat." I looked in my wallet and didn't have a dollar, I only had a five. "Here," I said. "That hold you?"

He didn't look at it—he didn't want to look at it. A terrible, closed look came over his face, as though he were keeping the number on the bill a secret from him and me. "Thanks," he said, and now he was dying to see me go. "Don't worry about Sonny. Maybe I'll write him or something."

"Sure," I said. "You do that. So long."

"Be seeing you," he said. I went on down the steps.

And I didn't write Sonny or send him anything for a long time. When I finally did, it was just after my little girl died, he wrote me back a letter which made me feel like a bastard.

Here's what he said:

Dear brother,

You don't know how much I needed to hear from you. I wanted to write you many a time but I dug how much I must have hurt you and so I didn't write. But now I feel like a man who's been trying to climb up out of some deep, real deep and funky hole and just saw the sun up there, outside. I got to get outside.

I can't tell you much about how I got here. I mean I don't know how to tell you. I guess I was afraid of something or I was trying to escape from something and you know I have never been very strong in the head (smile). I'm glad Mama and Daddy are dead and can't see what's happened to their son and I swear if I'd known what I was doing I would never have hurt you so, you and a lot of other fine people who were nice to me and who believed in me.

I don't want you to think it had anything to do with me being a musician. It's more than that. Or maybe less than that. I can't get anything straight in my head down here and I try not to think about what's going to happen to me when I get outside again. Sometime I think I'm going to flip and *never* get outside and sometime I think I'll come straight back. I tell you one thing, though, I'd rather blow my brains out than go through this again. But that's what they all say, so they tell me. If I tell you when I'm coming to New York and if you could meet me, I sure would appreciate it. Give my love to Isabel and the kids and I was sure sorry to hear about little Gracie. I wish I could be like Mama and say the Lord's will be done, but I don't know it seems to me that trouble is the one thing that never does get stopped and I don't know what good it does to blame it on the Lord. But maybe it does some good if you believe it.

Your brother,
Sonny

Then I kept in constant touch with him and I sent him whatever I could and I went to meet him when he came back to New York. When I saw him many things I thought I had forgotten came flooding back to me. This was because I had begun, finally, to wonder about Sonny, about the life that Sonny lived inside. This life, whatever it was, had made him older and thinner and it had deepened the distant stillness in which he had always moved. He looked very unlike my baby brother. Yet, when he smiled, when we shook hands, the baby brother I'd never known looked out from the depths of his private life, like an animal waiting to be coaxed into the light.

"How you been keeping?" he asked me.

"All right. And you?"

"Just fine." He was smiling all over his face. "It's good to see you again."

"It's good to see you."

The seven years' difference in our ages lay between us like a chasm: I wondered if these years would ever operate between us as a bridge. I was remembering, and it made it hard to catch my breath, that I had been there when he was born; and I had heard the first words he had ever spoken. When he started to walk, he walked from our mother straight to me. I caught him just before he fell when he took the first steps he ever took in this world.

"How's Isabel?"

"Just fine. She's dying to see you."

"And the boys?"

"They're fine, too. They're anxious to see their uncle."

"Oh, come on. You know they don't remember me."

"Are you kidding? Of course they remember you."

He grinned again. We got into a taxi. We had a lot to say to each other, far too much to know how to begin.

As the taxi began to move, I asked, "You still want to go to India?"

He laughed. "You still remember that. Hell, no. This place is Indian enough for me."

"It used to belong to them," I said.

And he laughed again. "They damn sure knew what they were doing when they got rid of it."

Years ago, when he was around fourteen, he'd been all hipped on the idea of going to India. He read books about people sitting on rocks, naked, in all kinds of weather, but mostly bad, naturally, and walking barefoot through hot coals and arriving at wisdom. I used to say that it sounded to me as though they were getting away from wisdom as fast as they could. I think he sort of looked down on me for that.

"Do you mind," he asked, "if we have the driver drive alongside the park? On the west side—I haven't seen the city in so long."

"Of course not," I said. I was afraid that I might sound as though I were humoring him, but I hoped he wouldn't take it that way.

So we drove along, between the green of the park and the stony, lifeless elegance of hotels and apartment buildings, toward the vivid, killing streets of our childhood. These streets hadn't changed, though housing projects jutted up out of them now like rocks in the middle of a boiling sea. Most of the houses in which we had grown up had vanished, as had the stores from which we had stolen, the basements in which we had first tried sex, the rooftops from which we had hurled tin cans and bricks. But houses exactly like the houses of our past yet dominated the landscape, boys exactly like the boys we once had been found themselves smothering in these houses, came down into the streets for light and air and found themselves encircled by disaster. Some escaped the trap, most didn't. Those who got out always left something of themselves behind, as some animals amputate a leg and leave it in the trap. It might be said, perhaps, that I had escaped, after all, I was a school teacher; or that Sonny had, he hadn't lived in Harlem for years. Yet, as the cab moved uptown through streets which seemed, with a rush, to darken with dark people, and as I covertly studied Sonny's face, it came to me that what we both were seeking through our separate cab windows was that part of ourselves which had been left behind. It's always at the hour of trouble and confrontation that the missing member aches.

We hit 110th Street and started rolling up Lenox Avenue. And I'd known this avenue all my life, but it seemed to me again, as it had seemed on the day I'd first heard about Sonny's trouble, filled with a hidden menace which was its very breath of life.

"We almost there," said Sonny.

"Almost." We were both too nervous to say anything more.

We live in a housing project. It hasn't been up long. A few days after it was up it seemed uninhabitably new, now, of course, it's already rundown. It looks like a parody of the good, clean, faceless life—God knows the people who live in it do their best to make it a parody. The beat-looking grass lying around isn't enough to make their lives green, the hedges will never hold out the streets, and they know it. The big windows fool no one, they aren't big enough to make space out of no space. They don't bother with the windows, they watch the TV screen instead. The playground is most popular with the children who don't play at jacks, or skip rope, or roller skate, or swing, and they can be found in it after dark. We moved in partly because it's not too far from where I teach, and partly for the kids; but it's really just like the houses in which Sonny and I grew up. The same things happen, they'll have the same things to remember. The moment Sonny and I started into the house I had the feeling that I was simply bringing him back into the danger he had almost died trying to escape.

Sonny has never been talkative. So I don't know why I was sure he'd be dying to talk to me when supper was over the first night. Everything went fine, the oldest boy remembered him, and the youngest boy liked him, and Sonny had remembered to bring something for each of them; and Isabel, who is really much nicer than I am, more open and giving, had gone to a lot of trouble about dinner and was genuinely glad to see him. And she's always been able to tease Sonny in a way that I haven't. It was nice to see her face so vivid again and to hear her laugh and watch her make Sonny laugh. She wasn't, or, anyway, she didn't seem to be, at all uneasy or embarrassed. She chatted as though there were no subject which had to be avoided and she got Sonny past his first, faint stiffness. And thank God she was there, for I was filled with that icy dread again. Everything I did seemed awkward to me, and everything I said sounded freighted with hidden meaning. I was trying to remember everything I'd heard about dope addiction and I couldn't help watching Sonny for signs. I wasn't doing it out of malice. I was trying to find out something about my brother. I was dying to hear him tell me he was safe.

"Safe!" my father grunted, whenever Mama suggested trying to move to a neighborhood which might be safer for children. "Safe, hell! Ain't no place safe for kids, nor nobody."

He always went on like this, but he wasn't, ever, really as bad as he sounded, not even on weekends, when he got drunk. As a matter of fact, he was always on the lookout for "something a little better," but he died before he found it. He died suddenly, during a drunken weekend in the middle of the war, when Sonny was fifteen. He and Sonny hadn't ever got on too well. And this was partly because Sonny was the apple of his father's eye. It was because he loved Sonny so much and was frightened for him, that he was always fighting with him. It doesn't do any good to fight with Sonny. Sonny just moves back, inside himself, where he can't be reached. But the principal reason that they never hit it off is that they were so much alike. Daddy was big and rough and loud-talking, just the opposite of Sonny, but they both had—that same privacy.

Mama tried to tell me something about this, just after Daddy died. I was home on leave from the army.

This was the last time I ever saw my mother alive. Just the same, this picture gets all mixed up in my mind with pictures I had of her when she was younger. The way I always see her is the way she used to be on a Sunday afternoon, say, when the old folks were talking after the big Sunday dinner. I always see her wearing pale blue. She'd be sitting on the sofa. And my father would be sitting in the easy chair, not far from her. And the living room would be full of church folks and relatives. There they sit, in chairs all around the living room, and the night is creeping up outside, but nobody knows it yet. You can see the darkness growing against the windowpanes and you hear the street noises every now and again, or maybe the jangling beat of a tambourine from one of the churches close by, but it's real quiet in the room. For a moment nobody's talking, but every face looks darkening, like the sky outside. And my mother rocks a little from the waist, and my father's eyes are closed. Everyone is looking at something a child can't see. For a minute they've forgotten the children. Maybe a kid is lying on the rug, half asleep. Maybe somebody's got a kid in his lap and is absent-mindedly stroking the kid's head. Maybe there's a kid, quiet and big-eyed, curled up in a big chair in the corner. The silence, the darkness coming, and the darkness in the faces frightens the child obscurely. He hopes that the hand which strokes his forehead will never stop—will never die. He hopes that there will never come a time when the old folks won't be sitting around the living room, talking about where they've come from, and what they've seen, and what's happened to them and their kinfolk.

But something deep and watchful in the child knows that this is bound to end, is already ending. In a moment someone will get up and turn on the light. Then the old folks will remember the children and they won't talk any more that day. And when light fills the room, the child is filled with darkness. He knows that every time this happens he's moved just a little closer to that darkness outside. The darkness outside is what the old folks have been talking about. It's what they've come from. It's what they endure. The child knows that they won't talk any more because if he knows too much about what's happened to *them,* he'll know too much too soon, about what's going to happen to *him.*

The last time I talked to my mother, I remember I was restless. I wanted to get out and see Isabel. We weren't married then and we had a lot to straighten out between us.

There Mama sat, in black, by the window. She was humming an old church song, *Lord, you brought me from a long ways off.* Sonny was out somewhere. Mama kept watching the streets.

"I don't know," she said. "if I'll ever see you again, after you go off from here. But I hope you'll remember the things I tried to teach you."

"Don't talk like that," I said, and smiled. "You'll be here a long time yet."

She smiled, too, but she said nothing. She was quiet for a long time. And I said, "Mama, don't you worry about nothing. I'll be writing all the time, and you be getting the checks. . . ."

"I want to talk to you about your brother," she said, suddenly. "If anything happens to me he ain't going to have nobody to look out for him."

"Mama," I said, "ain't nothing going to happen to you *or* Sonny. Sonny's all right. He's a good boy and he's got good sense."

"It ain't a question of his being a good boy," Mama said, "nor of his having good sense. It ain't only the bad ones, nor yet the dumb ones that gets sucked under." She stopped, looking at me. "Your Daddy once had a brother," she said, and she smiled in a way that made me feel she was in pain. "You didn't never know that, did you?"

"No," I said, "I never knew that," and I watched her face.

"Oh, yes," she said, "your Daddy had a brother." She looked out of the window again. "I know you never saw your Daddy cry. But *I* did—many a time, through all these years."

I asked her, "What happened to his brother? How come nobody's ever talked about him?"

This was the first time I ever saw my mother look old.

"His brother got killed," she said, "when he was just a little younger than you are now. I knew him. He was a fine boy. He was maybe a little full of the devil, but he didn't mean nobody no harm."

Then she stopped and the room was silent, exactly as it had sometimes been on those Sunday afternoons. Mama kept looking out into the streets.

"He used to have a job in the mill," she said, "and, like all young folks, he just liked to perform on Saturday nights. Saturday nights, him and your father would drift around to different places, go to dances and things like that, or just sit around with people they knew, and your father's brother would sing, he had a fine voice, and play along with himself on his guitar. Well, this particular Saturday night, him and your father was coming home from some place, and they were both a little drunk and there was a moon that night, it was bright like day. Your father's brother was feeling kind of good, and he was whistling to himself, and he had his guitar slung over his shoulder. They was coming down a hill and beneath them was a road that turned off from the highway. Well, your father's brother, being always kind of frisky, decided to run down this hill, and he did, with that guitar banging and clanging behind him, and he ran across the road, and he was making water behind a tree. And your father was sort of amused at him and he was still coming down the hill, kind of slow. Then he heard a car motor and that same minute his brother stepped from behind the tree, into the road, in the moonlight. And he started to cross the road. And your father started to run down the hill, he says he don't know why. This car was full of white men. They was all drunk, and when they seen your father's brother they let out a great whoop and holler and they aimed the car straight at him. They was having fun, they just wanted to scare him, the way they do sometimes, you know. But they was drunk. And I guess the boy, being drunk, too, and scared, kind of lost his head. By the time he jumped it was too late. Your father says he heard his brother scream when the car rolled over him, and he heard the wood of that guitar when it give, and he heard them strings go flying, and he heard them white men shouting, and the car kept on a-going and it ain't stopped till this day. And, time your father got down the hill, his brother weren't nothing but blood and pulp."

Tears were gleaming on my mother's face. There wasn't anything I could say.

"He never mentioned it," she said, "because I never let him mention it before you children. Your Daddy was like a crazy man that night and for many a night thereafter. He says he never in his life seen anything as dark as that road after the lights of that car had gone away. Weren't nothing, weren't nobody on that road, just your Daddy and his brother and that busted guitar. Oh, yes. Your Daddy never did really get right again. Till the day he died he weren't sure but that every white man he saw was the man that killed his brother."

She stopped and took out her handkerchief and dried her eyes and looked at me.

"I ain't telling you all this," she said, "to make you scared or bitter or to make you hate nobody. I'm telling you this because you got a brother. And the world ain't changed."

I guess I didn't want to believe this. I guess she saw this in my face. She turned away from me, toward the window again, searching those streets.

"But I praise my Redeemer," she said at last, "that He called your Daddy home before me. I ain't saying it to throw no flowers at myself, but, I declare, it keeps me from feeling too cast down to know I helped your father get safely through this world. Your father always acted like he was the roughest, strongest man on earth. And everybody took him to be like that. But if he hadn't had *me* there—to see his tears!"

She was crying again. Still, I couldn't move. I said, "Lord, Lord, Mama. I didn't know it was like that."

"Oh, honey," she said, "there's a lot that you don't know. But you are going to find it out." She stood up from the window and came over to me. "You got to hold on to your brother," she said, "and don't let him fall, no matter what it looks like is happening to him and no matter how evil you gets with him. You going to be evil with him many a time. But don't you forget what I told you, you hear?"

"I won't forget," I said. "Don't you worry, I won't forget. I won't let nothing happen to Sonny."

My mother smiled as though she were amused at something she saw in my face. Then, "You may not be able to stop nothing from happening. But you got to let him know you's *there.*"

Two days later I was married and then I was gone. And I had a lot of things on my mind and I pretty well forgot my promise to Mama until I got shipped home on a special furlough for her funeral.

And, after the funeral, with just Sonny and me alone in the empty kitchen, I tried to find out something about him.

"What do you want to do?" I asked him.

"I'm going to be a musician," he said.

For he had graduated, in the time I had been away, from dancing to the juke box to finding out who was playing what, and what they were doing with it, and he had bought himself a set of drums.

"You mean, you want to be a drummer?" I somehow had the feeling that being a drummer might be all right for other people but not for my brother Sonny.

"I don't think," he said, looking at me very gravely, "that I'll ever be a good drummer. But I think I can play a piano."

I frowned. I'd never played the role of the older brother quite so seriously before, had scarcely ever, in fact, *asked* Sonny a damn thing. I sensed myself in the presence of something I didn't really know how to handle, didn't understand. So I made my frown a little deeper as I asked: "What kind of musician do you want to be?"

He grinned. "How many kinds do you think there are?"

"Be *serious,*" I said.

He laughed, throwing his head back, and then looked at me. "I *am* serious."

"Well, then, for Christ's sake, stop kidding around and answer a serious question. I mean, do you want to be a concert pianist, you want to play classical music and all that, or—or what?" Long before I finished he was laughing again. "For Christ's *sake,* Sonny!"

He sobered, but with difficulty. "I'm sorry. But you sound so—*scared!*" and he was off again.

"Well, you may think it's funny now, baby, but it's not going to be so funny when you have to make your living at it, let me tell you *that.*" I was furious because I knew he was laughing at me and I didn't know why.

"No," he said, very sober now, and afraid, perhaps, that he'd hurt me, "I don't want to be a classical pianist. That isn't what interests me. I mean"—he paused, looking hard at me, as though his eyes would help me to understand, and then gestured helplessly, as though perhaps his hand would help—"I mean, I'll have a lot of studying to do, and I'll have to study *everything,* but, I mean, I want to play *with*—jazz musicians." He stopped. "I want to play jazz," he said.

Well, the word had never before sounded as heavy, as real, as it sounded that afternoon in Sonny's mouth. I just looked at him and I was probably frowning a real frown by this time. I simply couldn't see why on earth he'd want to spend his time hanging around nightclubs, clowning around on bandstands, while people pushed each other around a dance floor. It seemed—beneath him, somehow. I had never thought about it before, had never been forced to, but I suppose I had always put jazz musicians in a class with what Daddy called "good-time people."

"Are you *serious?*"

"Hell, *yes,* I'm serious."

He looked more helpless than ever, and annoyed, and deeply hurt.

I suggested, helpfully: "You mean—like Louis Armstrong?"

His face closed as though I'd struck him. "No. I'm not talking about none of that old-time, down home crap."

"Well, look, Sonny, I'm sorry, don't get mad. I just don't altogether get it, that's all. Name somebody—you know, a jazz musician you admire."

"Bird."

"Who?"

"Bird! Charlie Parker! Don't they teach you nothing in the goddamn army?"

I lit a cigarette. I was surprised and then a little amused to discover that I was trembling. "I've been out of touch," I said. "You'll have to be patient with me. Now. Who's this Parker character?"

"He's just one of the greatest jazz musicians alive," said Sonny, sullenly, his hands in his pockets, his back to me. "Maybe *the* greatest," he added, bitterly, "that's probably why *you* never heard of him."

"All right," I said, "I'm ignorant. I'm sorry. I'll go out and buy all the cat's records right away, all right?"

"It don't," said Sonny, with dignity, "make any difference to me. I don't care what you listen to. Don't do me no favors."

I was beginning to realize that I'd never seen him so upset before. With another part of my mind I was thinking that this would probably turn out to be one of those things kids go through and that I shouldn't make it seem important by pushing it too hard. Still, I didn't think it would do any harm to ask: "Doesn't all this take a lot of time? Can you make a living at it?"

He turned back to me and half leaned, half sat, on the kitchen table. "Everything takes time," he said, "and—well, yes, sure, I can make a living at it. But what I don't seem to be able to make you understand is that it's the only thing I want to do."

"Well, Sonny," I said, gently, "you know people can't always do exactly what they *want* to do—"

"*No,* I don't know that," said Sonny, surprising me. "I think people *ought* to do what they want to do, what else are they alive for?"

"You getting to be a big boy," I said desperately, "it's time you started thinking about your future."

"I'm thinking about my future," said Sonny, grimly. "I think about it all the time."

I gave up. I decided, if he didn't change his mind, that we could always talk about it later. "In the meantime," I said, "you got to finish school." We had already decided that he'd have to move in with Isabel and her folks. I knew this wasn't the ideal arrangement because Isabel's folks are inclined to be dicty and they hadn't especially wanted Isabel to marry me. But I didn't know what else to do. "And we have to get you fixed up at Isabel's."

There was a long silence. He moved from the kitchen table to the window. "That's a terrible idea. You know it yourself."

"Do you have a *better* idea?"

He just walked up and down the kitchen for a minute. He was as tall as I was. He had started to shave. I suddenly had the feeling that I didn't know him at all.

He stopped at the kitchen table and picked up my cigarettes. Looking at me with a kind of mocking, amused defiance, he put one between his lips. "You mind?"

"You smoking already?"

He lit the cigarette and nodded, watching me through the smoke. "I just wanted to see if I'd have the courage to smoke in front of you."He grinned and blew a great cloud of smoke to the ceiling. "It was easy." He looked at my face. "Come on, now. I bet you was smoking at my age, tell the truth."

I didn't say anything but the truth was on my face, and he laughed. But now there was something very strained in his laugh. "Sure. And I bet that ain't all you was doing."

He was frightening me a little. "Cut the crap," I said. "We already decided that you was going to go and live at Isabel's. Now what's got into you all of a sudden?"

"*You* decided it," he pointed out. "*I* didn't decide nothing." He stopped in front of me, leaning against the stove, arms loosely folded. "Look, brother. I don't want to stay in Harlem no more, I really don't." He was very earnest. He looked at me, then over toward the kitchen window. There was something in his eyes I'd never seen before, some thoughtfulness, some worry all his own. He rubbed the muscle of one arm. "It's time I was getting out of here."

"Where do you want to *go*, Sonny?"

"I want to join the army. Or the navy, I don't care. If I say I'm old enough, they'll believe me."

Then I got mad. It was because I was so scared. "You must be crazy. You goddamn fool, what the hell do you want to go and join the *army* for?"

"I just told you. To get out of Harlem."

"Sonny, you haven't even finished *school*. And if you really want to be a musician, how do you expect to study if you're in the *army?*"

He looked at me, trapped, and in anguish. "There's ways. I might be able to work out some kind of deal. Anyway, I'll have the G.I. Bill when I come out."

"*If* you come out." We stared at each other. "Sonny, please. Be reasonable. I know the setup is far from perfect. But we got to do the best we can."

"I ain't learning nothing in school," he said. "Even when I go." He turned away from me and opened the window and threw his cigarette out into the narrow alley. I watched his back. "At least, I ain't learning nothing you'd want me to learn." He slammed the window so hard I thought the glass would fly out, and turned back to me. "And I'm sick of the stink of these garbage cans!"

"Sonny," I said, "I know how you feel. But if you don't finish school now, you're going to be sorry later that you didn't." I grabbed him by the shoulders. "And you only got another year. It ain't so bad. And I'll come back and I swear I'll help you do *whatever* you want to do. Just try to put up with it till I come back. Will you please do that? For me?"

He didn't answer and he wouldn't look at me.

"Sonny. You hear me?"

He pulled away. "I hear you. But you never hear anything *I* say."

I didn't know what to say to that. He looked out of the window and then back at me. "OK," he said, and sighed. "I'll try."

Then I said, trying to cheer him up a little, "They got a piano at Isabel's. You can practice on it."

And as a matter of fact, it did cheer him up for a minute. "That's right," he said to himself. "I forgot that." His face relaxed a little. But the worry, the thoughtfulness, played on it still, the way shadows play on a face which is staring into the fire.

But I thought I'd never hear the end of that piano. At first, Isabel would write me, saying how nice it was that Sonny was so serious about his music and how, as soon as he came in from school, or wherever he had been when he was supposed to be at school, he went straight to that piano and stayed there until suppertime. And, after supper, he went back to that piano and stayed there until everybody went to bed. He was at the piano all day Saturday and all day Sunday. Then he bought a record player and started playing records. He'd play one record over and over again, all day long sometimes, and he'd improvise along with it on the piano. Or he'd play one section of the record, one chord, one change, one progression, then he'd do it on the piano. Then back to the record. Then back to the piano.

Well, I really don't know how they stood it. Isabel finally confessed that it wasn't like living with a person at all, it was like living with sound. And the sound didn't make any sense to her, didn't make any sense to any of them—naturally. They began, in a way, to be afflicted by this presence that was living in their home. It was as though Sonny were some sort of god, or monster. He moved in an atmosphere which wasn't like theirs at all. They fed him and he ate, he washed himself, he walked in and out of their door; he certainly wasn't nasty or unpleasant or rude, Sonny isn't any of those things; but it was as though he were all wrapped up in some cloud, some fire, some vision all his own; and there wasn't any way to reach him.

At the same time, he wasn't really a man yet, he was still a child, and they had to watch out for him in all kinds of ways. They certainly couldn't throw him out. Neither did they dare to make a great scene about that piano because even they dimly sensed, as I sensed, from so many thousands of miles away, that Sonny was at that piano playing for his life.

But he hadn't been going to school. One day a letter came from the school board and Isabel's mother got it—there had, apparently, been other letters but Sonny had torn them up. This day, when Sonny came in, Isabel's mother showed him the letter and asked where he'd been spending his time. And she finally got it out of him that he'd been down in Greenwich Village, with musicians and other characters, in a white girl's apartment. And this scared her and she started to scream at him and what came up, once she began—though she denies it to this day—was what sacrifices they were making to give Sonny a decent home and how little he appreciated it.

Sonny didn't play the piano that day. By evening, Isabel's mother had calmed down but then there was the old man to deal with, and Isabel herself. Isabel says she did her best to be calm but she broke down and started crying. She says she just watched Sonny's face. She could tell, by watching him, what was happening with him. And what was happening was that they penetrated his cloud, they had reached him. Even if their fingers had been a thousand times more gentle than human fingers ever are, he could hardly help feeling that they had stripped him naked and were spitting on that nakedness. For he also had to see that his presence, that music, which was life or death to him, had been torture for them and that they had endured it, not at all for his sake, but only for mine. And Sonny couldn't take that. He can take it a little better today than he could then but he's still not very good at it and, frankly, I don't know anybody who is.

The silence of the next few days must have been louder than the sound of all the music ever played since time began. One morning, before she went to work, Isabel was in his room for something and she suddenly realized that all of his records were gone. And she knew for certain that he was gone. And he was. He went as far as the navy would carry him. He finally sent me a postcard from some place in Greece and that was the first I knew that Sonny was still alive. I didn't see him any more until we were both back in New York and the war had long been over.

He was a man by then, of course, but I wasn't willing to see it. He came by the house from time to time, but we fought almost every time we met. I didn't like the way he carried himself, loose and dreamlike all the time, and I didn't like his friends, and his music seemed to be merely an excuse for the life he led. It sounded just that weird and disordered.

Then we had a fight, a pretty awful fight, and I didn't see him for months. By and by I looked him up, where he was living, in a furnished room in the Village, and I tried to make it up. But there were lots of other people in the room and Sonny just lay on his bed, and he wouldn't come downstairs with me, and he treated these other people as though they were his family and I weren't. So I got mad and then he got mad, and then I told him that he might just as well be dead as live the way he was living. Then he stood up and he told me not to worry about him any more in life, that he *was* dead as far as I was concerned. Then he pushed me to the door and the other people looked on as though nothing were happening, and he slammed the door behind me. I stood in the hallway, staring at the door. I heard somebody laugh in the room and then the tears came to my eyes. I started down the steps, whistling to keep from crying, I kept whistling to myself, *You going to need me, baby, one of these cold, rainy days.*

I read about Sonny's trouble in the spring. Little Grace died in the fall. She was a beautiful little girl. But she only lived a little over two years. She died of polio and she suffered. She had a slight fever for a couple of days, but it didn't seem like anything and we just kept her in bed. And we would certainly have called the doctor, but the fever dropped, she seemed to be all right. So we thought it had just been a cold. Then, one day, she was up, playing, Isabel was in the kitchen fixing lunch for the two boys when they'd come in from school, and she heard Grace fall down in the living room. When you have a lot of children you don't always start running when one of them falls, unless they start screaming or something. And, this time, Grace was quiet. Yet, Isabel says that when she heard that *thump* and then that silence, something happened in her to make her afraid. And she ran to the living room and there was little Grace on the floor, all twisted up, and the reason she hadn't screamed was that she couldn't get her breath. And when she did scream, it was the worst sound, Isabel says, that she'd ever heard in all her life, and she still hears it sometimes in her dreams. Isabel will sometimes wake me up with a low, moaning, strangled sound and I have to be quick to awaken her and hold her to me and where Isabel is weeping against me seems a mortal wound.

I think I may have written Sonny the very day that little Grace was buried. I was sitting in the living room in the dark, by myself, and I suddenly thought of Sonny. My trouble made his real.

One Saturday afternoon, when Sonny had been living with us, or, anyway, been in our house, for nearly two weeks, I found myself wandering aimlessly about the living room, drinking from a can of beer, and trying to work up the courage to search Sonny's room. He was out, he was usually out whenever I was home, and Isabel had taken the children to see their grandparents. Suddenly I was standing still in front of the living room window, watching Seventh Avenue. The idea of searching Sonny's room made me still. I scarcely dared to admit to myself what I'd be searching for. I didn't know what I'd do if I found it. Or if I didn't.

On the sidewalk across from me, near the entrance to a barbecue joint, some people were holding an old-fashioned revival meeting. The barbecue cook, wearing a dirty white apron, his conked hair reddish and metallic in the pale sun, and a cigarette between his lips, stood in the doorway, watching them. Kids and older people paused in their errands and stood there, along with some older men and a couple of very tough-looking women who watched everything that happened on the avenue, as though they owned it, or were maybe owned by it. Well, they were watching this, too. The revival was being carried on by three sisters in black, and a brother. All they had were their voices and their Bibles and a tambourine. The brother was testifying and while he testified two of the sisters stood together, seeming to say, amen, and the third sister walked around with the tambourine outstretched and a couple of people dropped coins into it. Then the brother's testimony ended and the sister who had been taking up the collection dumped the coins into her palm and transferred them to the pocket of her long black robe. Then she raised both hands, striking the tambourine against the air, and then against one hand, and she started to sing. And the two other sisters and the brother joined in.

It was strange, suddenly, to watch, though I had been seeing these street meetings all my life. So, of course, had everybody else down there. Yet, they paused and watched and listened and I stood still at the window. *"Tis the old ship of Zion,"* they sang, and the sister with the tambourine kept a steady, jangling beat, *"it has rescued many a thousand!"* Not a soul under the sound of their voices was hearing this song for the first time, not one of them had been rescued. Nor had they seen much in the way of rescue work being done around them. Neither did they especially believe in the holiness of the three sisters and the brother, they knew too much about them, knew where they lived, and how. The woman with the tambourine, whose voice dominated the air, whose face was bright with joy, was divided by very little from the woman who stood watching her, a cigarette between her heavy, chapped lips, her hair a cuckoo's nest, her face scarred and swollen from many beatings, and her black eyes glittering like coal. Perhaps they both knew this, which was why, when, as rarely, they addressed each other, they addressed each other as Sister. As the singing filled the air the watching, listening faces underwent a change, the eyes focusing on something within; the music seemed to soothe a poison out of them; and time seemed, nearly, to fall away from the sullen, belligerent, battered faces, as though they were fleeing back to their first condition, while dreaming of their last. The barbecue cook half shook his head and smiled, and dropped his cigarette and disappeared into his joint. A man fumbled in his pockets for change and stood holding it in his hand impatiently, as though he had just remembered a pressing appointment further up the avenue. He looked furious. Then I saw Sonny, standing on the edge of the crowd. He was carrying a wide, flat notebook with a green cover, and it made him look, from where I was standing, almost like a schoolboy. The coppery sun brought out the copper in his skin, he was very faintly smiling, standing very still. Then the singing stopped, the tambourine turned into a collection plate again. The furious man dropped in his coins and vanished, so did a couple of the women, and Sonny dropped some change in the plate, looking directly at the woman with a little smile. He started across the avenue, toward the house. He has a slow, loping walk, something like the way Harlem hipsters walk, only he's imposed on this his own half-beat. I had never really noticed it before.

I stayed at the window, both relieved and apprehensive. As Sonny disappeared from my sight, they began singing again. And they were still singing when his key turned in the lock.

"Hey," he said.

"Hey, yourself. You want some beer?"

"No. Well, maybe." But he came up to the window and stood beside me, looking out. "What a warm voice," he said.

They were singing *If I could only hear my mother pray again!*

"Yes," I said, "and she can sure beat that tambourine."

"But what a terrible song," he said, and laughed. He dropped his notebook on the sofa and disappeared into the kitchen. "Where's Isabel and the kids?"

"I think they went to see their grandparents. You hungry?"

"No." He came back into the living room with his can of beer. "You want to come some place with me tonight?"

I sensed, I don't know how, that I couldn't possibly say no. "Sure. Where?"

He sat down on the sofa and picked up his notebook and started leafing through it. "I'm going to sit in with some fellows in a joint in the Village."

"You mean, you're going to play, tonight?"

"That's right." He took a swallow of his beer and moved back to the window. He gave me a sidelong look. "If you can stand it."

"I'll try," I said.

He smiled to himself and we both watched as the meeting across the way broke up. The three sisters and the brother, heads bowed, were singing *God be with you till we meet again.* The faces around them were very quiet. Then the song ended. The small crowd dispersed. We watched the three women and the lone man walk slowly up the avenue.

"When she was singing before," said Sonny, abruptly, "her voice reminded me for a minute of what heroin feels like sometimes—when it's in your veins. It makes you feel sort of warm and cool at the same time. And distant. And—and sure." He sipped his beer, very deliberately not looking at me. I watched his face. "It makes you feel—in control. Sometimes you've got to have that feeling."

"Do you?" I sat down slowly in the easy chair.

"Sometimes." He went to the sofa and picked up his notebook again. "Some people do."

"In order," I asked, "to play?" And my voice was very ugly, full of contempt and anger.

"Well"—he looked at me with great, troubled eyes, as though, in fact, he hoped his eyes would tell me things he could never otherwise say—"they *think* so. And *if* they think so—!"

"And what do *you* think?" I asked.

He sat on the sofa and put his can of beer on the floor. "I don't know," he said, and I couldn't be sure if he were answering my question or pursuing his thoughts. His face didn't tell me. "It's not so much to *play.* It's to *stand* it, to be able to make it at all. On any level." He frowned and smiled: "In order to keep from shaking to pieces."

"But these friends of yours," I said, "they seem to shake themselves to pieces pretty goddamn fast."

"Maybe." He played with the notebook. And something told me that I should curb my tongue, that Sonny was doing his best to talk, that I should listen. "But of course you only know the ones that've gone to pieces. Some don't—or at least they haven't *yet* and that's just about all *any* of us can say." He paused. "And then there are some who just live, really, in hell, and they know it and they see what's happening and they go right on. I don't know." He sighed, dropped the notebook, folded his arms. "Some guys, you can tell from the way they play, they on something *all* the time. And you can see that, well, it makes something real for them. But of course," he picked up his beer from the floor and sipped it and put the can down again, "they *want* to, too, you've got to see that. Even some of them that say they don't—*some*, not all."

"And what about you?" I asked—I couldn't help it. "What about you? Do *you* want to?"

He stood up and walked to the window and remained silent for a long time. Then he sighed. "Me," he said. Then: "While I was downstairs before, on my way here, listening to that woman sing, it struck me all of a sudden how much suffering she must have had to go through—to sing like that. It's *repulsive* to think you have to suffer that much."

I said: "But there's no way not to suffer—is there, Sonny?"

"I believe not," he said and smiled, "but that's never stopped anyone from trying." He looked at me. "Has it?" I realized, with this mocking look, that there stood between us, forever, beyond the power of time or forgiveness, the fact that I had held silence—so long!—when he had needed human speech to help him. He turned back to the window. "No, there's no way not to suffer. But you try all kinds of ways to keep from drowning in it, to keep on top of it, and to make it seem—well, like *you*. Like you did something, all right, and now you're suffering for it. You know?" I said nothing. "Well you know," he said, impatiently, "why *do* people suffer? Maybe it's better to do something to give it a reason, *any* reason."

"But we just agreed," I said, "that there's no way not to suffer. Isn't it better, then, just to—take it?"

"But nobody just takes it," Sonny cried, "that's what I'm telling you! *Everybody* tries not to. You're just hung up on the *way* some people try—it's not *your* way!"

The hair on my face began to itch, my face felt wet. "That's not true," I said, "that's not true. I don't give a damn what other people do, I don't even care how they suffer. I just care how *you* suffer." And he looked at me. "Please believe me," I said, "I don't want to see you—die—trying not to suffer."

"I won't," he said, flatly, "die trying not to suffer. At least, not any faster than anybody else."

"But there's no need," I said, trying to laugh, "is there? in killing yourself."

I wanted to say more, but I couldn't. I wanted to talk about will power and how life could be—well, beautiful. I wanted to say that it was all within; but was it? or, rather, wasn't that exactly the trouble? And I wanted to promise that I would never fail him again. But it would all have sounded—empty words and lies.

So I made the promise to myself and prayed that I would keep it.

"It's terrible sometimes, inside," he said, "that's what's the trouble. You walk these streets, black and funky and cold, and there's not really a living ass to talk to, and there's nothing shaking, and there's no way of getting it out—that storm inside. You can't talk it and you can't make love with it, and when you finally try to get with it and play it, you realize *nobody's* listening. So *you've* got to listen. You got to find a way to listen."

And then he walked away from the window and sat on the sofa again, as though all the wind had suddenly been knocked out of him. "Sometimes you'll do *anything* to play, even cut your mother's throat." He laughed and looked at me. "Or your brother's." Then he sobered. "Or your own." Then: "Don't worry. I'm all right now and I think I'll *be* all right. But I can't forget—where I've been. I don't mean just the physical place I've been. I mean where I've *been*. And *what* I've been."

"What have you been, Sonny?" I asked.

He smiled—but sat sideways on the sofa, his elbow resting on the back, his fingers playing with his mouth and chin, not looking at me. "I've been something I didn't recognize, didn't know I could be. Didn't know anybody could be." He stopped, looking inward, looking helplessly young, looking old. "I'm not talking about it now because I feel *guilty* or anything like that—maybe it would be better if I did, I don't know. Anyway, I can't really talk about it. Not to you, not to anybody," and now he turned and faced me. "Sometimes, you know, and it was actually when I was most *out* of the world, I felt that I was in it, that I was *with* it, really, and I could play or I didn't really have to *play*, it just came out of me, it was there. And I don't know how I played, thinking about it now, but I know I did awful things, those times, sometimes, to people. Or it wasn't that I *did* anything to them—it was that they weren't real." He picked up the beer can; it was empty; he rolled it between his palms: "And other times—well, I needed a fix, I needed to find a place to lean, I needed to clear a space to *listen*—and I couldn't find it, and I—went crazy, I did terrible things to *me*, I was terrible *for* me." He began pressing the beer can between his hands, I watched the metal begin to give. It glittered, as he played with it, like a knife, and I was afraid he would cut himself, but I said nothing. "Oh well. I can never tell you. I was all by myself at the bottom of something, stinking and sweating and crying and shaking, and I smelled it, you know? *my* stink, and I thought I'd die if I couldn't get away from it and yet, all the same, I knew that everything I was doing was just locking me in with it. And I didn't know," he paused, still flattening the beer can, "I didn't know, I still *don't* know, something kept telling me that maybe it was good to smell your own stink, but I didn't think that *that* was what I'd been trying to do—and—who can stand it?" and he abruptly dropped the ruined beer can, looking at me with a small, still smile, and then rose, walking to the window as though it were the lodestone rock. I watched his face, he watched the avenue. "I couldn't tell you when Mama died—but the reason I wanted to leave Harlem so bad was to get away from drugs. And then, when I ran away, that's what I was running from—really. When I came back, nothing had changed, *I* hadn't changed, I was just—older." And he stopped, drumming with his fingers on the windowpane. The sun had vanished, soon darkness would fall. I watched his face. "It can come again," he said, almost as though speaking to himself. Then he turned to me. "It can come again," he repeated. "I just want you to know that."

"All right," I said, at last. "So it can come again. All right."

He smiled, but the smile was sorrowful. "I had to try to tell you," he said.

"Yes," I said. "I understand that."

"You're my brother," he said, looking straight at me, and not smiling at all.

"Yes," I repeated. "Yes. I understand that."

He turned back to the window, looking out. "All that hatred down there," he said, "all that hatred and misery and love. It's a wonder it doesn't blow the avenue apart."

We went to the only nightclub on a short, dark street, downtown. We squeezed through the narrow, chattering, jam-packed bar to the entrance of the big room, where the bandstand was. And we stood there for a moment, for the lights were very dim in this room and we couldn't see. Then, "Hello, boy," said a voice and an enormous black man, much older than Sonny or myself, erupted out of all that atmospheric lighting and put an arm around Sonny's shoulder. "I been sitting right here," he said, "waiting for you."

He had a big voice, too, and heads in the darkness turned toward us.

Sonny grinned and pulled a little away, and said, "Creole, this is my brother. I told you about him."

Creole shook my hand. "I'm glad to meet you, son," he said, and it was clear that he was glad to meet me *there,* for Sonny's sake. And he smiled, "You got a real musician in *your* family," and he took his arm from Sonny's shoulder and slapped him, lightly, affectionately, with the back of his hand.

"Well. Now I've heard it all," said a voice behind us. This was another musician, and a friend of Sonny's, a coal-black, cheerful-looking man, built close to the ground. He immediately began confiding to me, at the top of his lungs, the most terrible things about Sonny, his teeth gleaming like a lighthouse and his laugh coming up out of him like the beginning of an earthquake. And it turned out that everyone at the bar knew Sonny, or almost everyone; some were musicians, working there, or nearby, or not working, some were simply hangers-on, and some were there to hear Sonny play. I was introduced to all of them and they were all very polite to me. Yet, it was clear that, for them, I was only Sonny's brother. Here, I was in Sonny's world. Or, rather: his kingdom. Here, it was not even a question that his veins bore royal blood.

They were going to play soon and Creole installed me, by myself, at a table in a dark corner. Then I watched them, Creole, and the little black man, and Sonny, and the others, while they horsed around, standing just below the bandstand. The light from the bandstand spilled just a little short of them and, watching them laughing and gesturing and moving about, I had the feeling that they, nevertheless, were being most careful not to step into that circle of light too suddenly: that if they moved into the light too suddenly, without thinking, they would perish in flame. Then, while I watched, one of them, the small, black man, moved into the light and crossed the bandstand and started fooling around with his drums. Then—being funny and being, also, extremely ceremonious—

Creole took Sonny by the arm and led him to the piano. A woman's voice called Sonny's name and a few hands started clapping. And Sonny, also being funny and being ceremonious, and so touched, I think, that he could have cried, but neither hiding it nor showing it, riding it like a man, grinned, and put both hands to his heart and bowed from the waist.

Creole then went to the bass fiddle and a lean, very bright-skinned brown man jumped up on the bandstand and picked up his horn. So there they were, and the atmosphere on the bandstand and in the room began to change and tighten. Someone stepped up to the microphone and announced them. Then there were all kinds of murmurs. Some people at the bar shushed others. The waitress ran around, frantically getting in the last orders, guys and chicks got closer to each other, and the lights on the bandstand, on the quartet, turned to a kind of indigo. Then they all looked different there. Creole looked about him for the last time, as though he were making certain that all his chickens were in the coop, and then he—jumped and struck the fiddle. And there they were.

All I know about music is that not many people ever really hear it. And even then, on the rare occasions when something opens within, and the music enters, what we mainly hear, or hear corroborated, are personal, private, vanishing evocations. But the man who creates the music is hearing something else, is dealing with the roar rising from the void and imposing order on it as it hits the air. What is evoked in him, then, is of another order, more terrible because it has no words, and triumphant, too, for that same reason. And his triumph, when he triumphs, is ours. I just watched Sonny's face. His face was troubled, he was working hard, but he wasn't with it. And I had the feeling that, in a way, everyone on the bandstand was waiting for him, both waiting for him and pushing him along. But as I began to watch Creole, I realized that it was Creole who held them all back. He had them on a short rein. Up there, keeping the beat with his whole body, wailing on the fiddle, with his eyes half closed, he was listening to everything, but he was listening to Sonny. He was having a dialogue with Sonny. He wanted Sonny to leave the shoreline and strike out for the deep water. He was Sonny's witness that deep water and drowning were not the same thing—he had been there, and he knew. And he wanted Sonny to know. He was waiting for Sonny to do the things on the keys which would let Creole know that Sonny was in the water.

And while Creole listened, Sonny moved, deep within, exactly like someone in torment. I had never before thought of how awful the relationship must be between the musician and his instrument. He has to fill it, this instrument, with the breath of life, his own. He has to make it do what he wants it to do. And a piano is just a piano. It's made out of so much wood and wires and little hammers and big ones, and ivory. While there's only so much you can do with it, the only way to find this out is to try; to try and make it do everything.

And Sonny hadn't been near a piano for over a year. And he wasn't on much better terms with his life, not the life that stretched before him now. He and the piano stammered, started one way, got scared, stopped; started another way, panicked, marked time, started again; then seemed to have found a direction, panicked again, got stuck. And the face I saw on Sonny I'd never seen before. Everything had been burned out of it, and, at the same time, things usually hidden were being burned in, by the fire and fury of the battle which was occurring in him up there.

Yet, watching Creole's face as they neared the end of the first set, I had the feeling that something had happened, something I hadn't heard. Then they finished, there was scattered applause, and then, without an instant's warning, Creole started into something else, it was almost sardonic, it was *Am I Blue*. And, as though he commanded, Sonny began to play. Something began to happen. And Creole let out the reins. The dry, low, black man said something awful on the drums, Creole answered, and the drums talked back. Then the horn insisted, sweet and high, slightly detached perhaps, and Creole listened, commenting now and then, dry, and driving, beautiful and calm and old. Then they all came together again, and Sonny was part of the family again. I could tell this from his face. He seemed to have found, right there beneath his fingers, a damn brand-new piano. It seemed that he couldn't get over it. Then, for awhile, just being happy with Sonny, they seemed to be agreeing with him that brand-new pianos certainly were a gas.

Then Creole stepped forward to remind them that what they were playing was the blues. He hit something in all of them, he hit something in me, myself, and the music tightened and deepened, apprehension began to beat the air. Creole began to tell us what the blues were all about. They were not about anything very new. He and his boys up there were keeping it new, at the risk of ruin, destruction, madness, and death, in order to find new ways to make us listen. For, while the tale of how we suffer, and how we are delighted, and how we may triumph is never new, it always must be heard. There isn't any other tale to tell, it's the only light we've got in all this darkness.

And this tale, according to that face, that body, those strong hands on those strings, has another aspect in every country, and a new depth in every generation. Listen, Creole seemed to be saying, listen. Now these are Sonny's blues. He made the little black man on the drums know it, and the bright, brown man on the horn. Creole wasn't trying any longer to get Sonny in the water. He was wishing him Godspeed. Then he stepped back, very slowly, filling the air with the immense suggestion that Sonny speak for himself.

Then they all gathered around Sonny and Sonny played. Every now and again one of them seemed to say, amen. Sonny's fingers filled the air with life, his life. But that life contained so many others. And Sonny went all the way back, he really began with the spare, flat statement of the opening phrase of the song. Then he began to make it his. It was very beautiful because it wasn't hurried and it was no longer a lament. I seemed to hear with what burning he had made it his, with what burning we had yet to make it ours, how we could cease lamenting. Freedom lurked around us and I understood, at last, that he could help us to be free if we would listen, that he would never be free until we did. Yet, there was no battle in his face now. I heard what he had gone through, and would continue to go through until he came to rest in earth. He had made it his: that long line, of which we knew only Mama and Daddy. And he was giving it back, as everything must be given back, so that, passing through death, it can live forever. I saw my mother's face again, and felt, for the first time, how the stones of the road she had walked on must have bruised her feet. I saw the moonlit road where my father's brother died. And it brought something else back to me, and carried me past it. I saw my little girl again and felt Isabel's tears again, and I felt my own tears begin to rise. And I was yet aware that this was only a moment, that the world waited outside, as hungry as a tiger, and that trouble stretched above us, longer than the sky.

Then it was over. Creole and Sonny let out their breath, both soaking wet, and grinning. There was a lot of applause and some of it was real. In the dark, the girl came by and I asked her to take drinks to the bandstand. There was a long pause, while they talked up there in the indigo light and after awhile I saw the girl put a Scotch and milk on top of the piano for Sonny. He didn't seem to notice it, but just before they started playing again, he sipped from it and looked toward me, and nodded. Then he put it back on top of the piano. For me, then, as they began to play again, it glowed and shook above my brother's head like the very cup of trembling.

Robert A. Stone

WALK DON'T RUN

Early in the morning, before ten, Geraldine got up and went to shop at Schweggman's on the Frenchman Street bus. Rheinhardt lay in bed drifting in and out of dreams. Hot, disquieting sunlight came into his eyes through the colored oilcloth over the rear window; he would awaken for a moment, turn, and within seconds fall back into a throbbing coma that carried his mind out of waking focus. He had, in the last months, become quite aware of this morning process; it was a regular and formal state—it was what the committed juice heads meant when they talked about the "picture show." It complicated the business of mornings but there was no proper way out of it except to run the gauntlet of trips to whatever was on the other side. In the early stages at least, this was dependably the day at hand.

The last dream went on in some littered darkness, a dim loft-like place—he was pressed into a glass booth the size of a coffin from which he could see a floor of worn wooden planks that was strewn with burnt charcoal and wrapping paper. There were piles of coal and heaps of green sticks, rusted nails upright, and stretching into the darkness rows of dusty glass display cases where shapeless artifacts lay covered with mold. He was conscious of a noise in the place—not in the booth because, of course, the booth was soundproofed—but beyond, in the dimness, roared some terrible noise just out of hearing; he could feel the noise against the glass. He kept trying to rise on his toes to test the top of the booth but it was always higher than his head; he sank down bending his knees to look at the planks of the floor and saw small bright-eyed animals with furred parabolic ears rising from their heads who came forward in darts and rushes to peer in at him and press bared teeth and quivering nostrils against the glass walls. Cavies, he thought, they were called cavies.

While he watched them, in the dark place beyond, there appeared two, then three white lights like the glare of welders' torches; they flickered and burst to light the dim loft like a sheet of summer lightning. The place exploded into light and around the booth grew great stalks of bright green plants and the presence of hundreds of wings flapping together—the glass cracked like yielding ice and for a part of a second the outside noise howled in his ears like a radio turned by mistake to full volume. Then the vegetation boiled up around him and the fluttering of wings rose and died away. Wingdale, he thought. Wingdale. Then it was light, actually light with the light of day; he could see a long white plain stretching beneath him and hear chords—FCG, repeated at soft intervals—FCG. He was awake, jammed against the wall beside the bed; the ghost of the winged sound was fluttering with his eyelids. In one of the near apartments someone was playing chords on a guitar—FCG.

He got out of bed and went into the hot bright kitchen to look for the bourbon bottle. There was only a finger or two in the bottle; he poured it into a water glass and filled the drink with cold orange juice from the refrigerator. When he opened the shutters to the balcony the breeze he had expected was not there. The street below was empty and seemingly wet with rain but the sun was high at afternoon, there was no wind. He stood looking down at the street, listening to the drone of flies and the clip-clop of a horse-drawn wagon in the next block. His face was hot and flushed with the bourbon, his heartbeat alarmingly fast, his breathing quick and shallow. He was sweating. He could close his eyes and see the white light.

He went inside again, turned on the air-conditioner and sat down to finish the bourbon and orange juice. The way, he thought, has become lined with all manner of things. With a sudden chill, he remembered the place in the dream and took a long sip of his drink. Wingdale.

By God, he thought, they are running me off the map; there was just hardly any margin at all. He had practiced for so long at staying out of the bad places that he approached even nights with a kind of confidence. But now he was finding himself in places far worse than the ones he avoided with such skilled calculation.

"The way . . . is getting lined," he said aloud, and rubbed his sweating palm along the cool glass. In another apartment the man with the guitar played chords—FCG.

The way is getting lined and you can end up all sorts of places. Bad place the corners of the night, the roughest neighborhoods of all. Very shortly, he told himself, you will belong to pathology.

Nights betrayed him. He could get into bed with the girl, lose himself in the turns of her body, in the sweet gaming that was the only rest of his time in bed, in soothing and bringing her along (she was very tender—it seemed always at the threshold she would draw back thinking to be hurt and sigh with wonder when it went well), taking her once or twice, and then almost always for a while he would sleep. But in time, and he was never sure how much, he would be awake again and there would be nothing to do but lie back and hold on and let the show start. It had happened to him many times before, of course, on the road, or when he had not been able to get something to drink—but it came—no matter how drunk he was. They were not visions, or Shakespearean portents, or anything personal or particular to him; he knew quite well that there were names for them all—The Picture Show, the Whirlies, the White Light. It was not undiscovered country, it was—pathology.

First the pictures would come to the dark of his eyes, in quick flashes without continuity. Then they would begin to hang together and take direction; he followed streets that ended suddenly in empty white cities—skeletons of Rio or Montevideo or Beirut that he had seen. Or sometimes the color would be quite different; he would trip through the dark varnished wooden rooms of his grandparents' house. There would be sounds—passage practice repeated over and over or wind in his ears or the breathless soprano droning of children at their prayers. (At St. Walburga's Parochial School in Mountain Home he would drift off in class while from the separate girls' classrooms would come the interminable half-chant of the after-lunchtime rosary, the quick unmodulated chatter of the prayer leader picked up by the sing-song response, over and over—Blessed is the fruit of Thywombjesus; he would sit dreaming, count it out in stops, make notes of it.)

Often he might follow some quiet spectre of recollection to see it whirl suddenly, unmask itself, fix him with a cold kiss, and leave him betrayed in some unutterable place—the soft fibers of his mind to be keelhauled over the strange and wondrous, poison-spined creature on the underside of nights . . . (whatever scene there was suddenly bright with iridescence and the white lights, his jaw fighting to lock; his hands and fingers turning inward, uncontrollable; his legs struggling in fits to stretch themselves over folds of hot wet rubber . . . and the thing then would be to fight up out of bed and smoke a cigarette unless the rhythm of match and smoke and lip proved too complex and he would fall into a chair or back to the bed and drift out along another track to pass the night sleepwalking in a pyramid from one rotting chamber to the next).

Once, he had gotten up—he was yelling, Geraldine said—and he had gone all the way to the balcony to light that cigarette, had seen the ironwork across the way glow with white light and crowds of shimmering shadow people in the street below calling Now Watch Him Fall; he had stood shivering in night-cold sweat until the match burned his fingers and she came out to help him in.

I could be bound in a nutshell, Rheinhardt thought, carefully lighting a cigarette; but the way is getting lined. In small hotels near the bus station solitary men burnt themselves up in motheaten armchairs. Defend me friends, I am but hurt.

He finished the drink, showered and dressed. For a while he stood before the bathroom mirror and tried to see the tic in his eye where the lid was convulsing. In another month he would be thirty. Too soon, he thought. But too soon for what?

In the middle of the journey of our life, he recited silently, I found myself in a dark wood . . . for I had lost the straight path. He stretched his hand before him and saw the long yellowed fingers rise on invisible wires; his eyelid marked it in one-two time, faintly suggesting Angel Feathers. The forests of the night. Yes, indeed, Rheinhardt thought; he felt the wings again. The thought of which renews my fear. Wingdale.

He went out on the patio stairs, breathing without satisfaction the heavy plant-scented air. The Pastorale was on in Bogdanovich's apartment.

"What was it you think we did to you?" she had written him. She had sent him a picture of them with her address on it; he was supposed to carry it in case he dropped dead. The letter containing it was returned from Chicago. She thought she was pregnant by a married man, she was going to have an abortion. "You could have gone ahead and killed yourself and us and it would have been almost the same. I lived for you, I swear, that was the way it was with me."

(And at length we emerged to see again the stars.)

He started down, clenching one hand in his trouser pocket, the other tight on the stair rail.

One flight down, he came upon a bearded man in blue farmer's overalls who was lying across the landing, balanced on an elbow. The man looked up at him with bright madman's eyes.

"Man," he said as Rheinhardt started for the lower story, "how you makin' it, man?"

"Good," Rheinhardt said. "How you makin' it?"

The man laughed a mock negro laugh and ground his strangely white front teeth together. "Bad," he said, "bad news makin' it. You have a cigarette?"

The door of Bogdanovich's opened and a girl came out to them. She was about twenty-five, dark and slim with small black eyes and a pale long face; she reminded Rheinhardt for all the world of a homosexual yeoman who had once propositioned him at the Anacostia Naval Air Station.

"We have cigarettes in here, Marvin," she told the bearded man.

Rheinhardt looked at her. She was wearing a khaki officer's shirt and trousers with brown sandals.

"I've got some," Rheinhardt said. "Do you want one too?"

Marvin took a cigarette and laughed his negro laugh again, baring his teeth at the girl.

"You're upstairs, aren't you?" she asked Rheinhardt. "Next to him?" She raised the knuckle of her index finger to indicate the floor above.

"The guitar man?"

"No," the girl said, "that's Ringo. Across from him. The strange cat. Rainey."

"Yeah," Rheinhardt said. "We don't see him much."

"We see your wife in the laundry. Geraldine?"

"Yeah," Rheinhardt said.

"I used to know some beautiful people one time," the bearded man on the landing said. "Beautiful people, man."

"Where are they now?" Rheinhardt said, still looking at the girl.

"Yeah," Marvin the Madman said, "where are they?"

The storm in the Pastorale broke, and Bogdanovich strode out through the stylized lightning, smiling a monkish smile.

"Hey," he said to Rheinhardt, "are you comfortable?"

"We're fine," Rheinhardt said. "I was just talking to this gentleman."

"Yes," Bogdanovich said, "he used to know some beautiful people.

He did, too. I knew some of them."

"They were O.K.," the girl said. "They weren't subtle though. You could lose patience with them."

"Oh subtle," Marvin said. "Poppycock." He turned his madman's eyes on Rheinhardt. "Poppycock."

"Where was that?" Rheinhardt asked him. "Where did you know them?"

"In the mountains, man," the madman said. "In the groovy high mountains of the high west."

"In California," Bogdanovich said benignly. He looked at Rheinhardt and smiled. "Where else?"

"Where else indeed?" Rheinhardt said, lighting his own cigarette. He found himself beginning to return the limp beatific smile that everyone else was wearing when it occurred to him that his auditors must, of course, be high.

He looked at them and saw that all—Bogdanovich, the girl, Mad Marvin—were displaying what dear Natasha liked to call Philosopher's Eye; they were tea heads and they were quietly blasted. He felt a sudden rush of affection for them on Natasha's account.

"What was your scene?" Bogdanovich asked him softly.

"Oh, well . . ." Rheinhardt said. "New York."

"Of course," Bogdanovich said, with the manner of one who had graciously turned a compliment. Rheinhardt bowed.

"Tell me," he asked them, "did you know Natasha Kaplan?"

"Of course," Bogdanovich said.

"Of course," Marvin said. "I did."

"No, truly, man, did you know my Natasha?"

"Why not?" Marvin asked. Everyone looked thoughtful.

"She's in Wingdale," Rheinhardt told them.

"Ah," they said, and nodded approvingly.

"You were in Wingdale, Marvin," the dark girl asked. "Did you know her?"

"When I was in Wingdale," Marvin said, "listen—when I was in Wingdale . . ." he closed his eyes and moved his head from side to side, "there was nothing—there was *nothing*—that I knew!"

Everyone nodded again.

"But in the mountains—in the mountains, man—I knew all of it."

"Yes," Bogdanovich said.

"Truly," Marvin said. "Believe it."

"Of course," Bogdanovich said.

Marvin looked from face to face and stopped at Rheinhardt. "Man," he said, "that wasn't the California you know. No mufflers. No titty tatty. No ogla bee. No gasoline smell grease trap taco stand plastic supermarket shit. No fatwoman drive-ins. No polite killer cops. No oregano salesmen. No Northbeach. No Southbeach. No Beach Beach. It wasn't like that, man—you think it was?"

"No," Rheinhardt said. "It couldn't have been."

"It couldn't have been," Marvin said soberly. "It could not have been. And it was not."

"It was a California of the mind," the girl said.

"My God," Bogdanovich said, stepping forward in wide-eyed astonishment, "what a California that would be." As they watched, he raised his hands to describe a box and held them palm facing palm. "Look," he told them, "that's your mind, dig? And here it's all gray, it's all nowhere, it's just dry and barren and terrible trips. But here, dig—at the western end there's a curving beach and white surf rolling up on it. And there's blue and purple islands and high cold mountains and forests with a carpet of pine needles. And orange juice in the clear desert."

"And orange juice in the desert!" the dark girl sighed. She put a hand to her mouth and moaned with longing.

"At that place, man. At the end of that dry hairiness, on the other side of the skeletons and the windies and the terrible salt flats, at the further edge of the bad trips—that's the California of the mind. Suddenly you find it there!"

"Yeah!" Marvin said. "Tell more. Tell more!"

"Well, man, there's nothin' but miles of it—ocean and prairie and rangeland and all of San Francisco and fair L.A.—all in the mind. And canyon creeks with trout and Herefords and velvety green hills of the mind, green and sweet-smelling."

"Yeah," Marvin said.

"And fishing boats of the mind," the girl said.

"And abalones of the mind. And glider contests of the mind."

"Motorcycles of the mind. Chinatowns of the mind."

"And Chinamen of the mind."

"And wine of the mind," Rheinhardt said.

"Oh, shit yes, man!" Marvin said ecstatically, "and wine of the mind."

"Oaklands of the mind."

"And Watsonvilles of the mind."

"And cliffs and seals and sulfur baths of the mind. At the western end of your mind, man. All of it, man."

"And beautiful people," Marvin said.

"Beautiful people," the dark girl said, sighing again with longing.

"Yes," Bogdanovich said.

"We had raccoons," Marvin said. "At night—raccoons."

"Raccoons of the mind," Rheinhardt said idly.

"Fuck that," the girl said.

"Yeah," Marvin said. "Raccoons are groovy, but not so groovy are the raccoons of the mind."

"Oh," the girl said, shuddering now and moaning with revulsion, "the dirty raccoons of the mind."

"That's the worst kind of raccoons there are," Bogdanovich told them with a scholarly air. "The ravagey little raccoons of the mind."

"Are they in the mind's California?" the girl asked fearfully.

"No," Bogdanovich said, "the raccoons are actual raccoons."

"Thank God," the girl said.

Rheinhardt closed his eyes and saw the furry creatures of the night before—cavies of the mind. "How did you get down here?" he asked Bogdanovich.

"Who knows?" Bogdanovich said.

"How?" Marvin said. "Why does anyone come to California, man? The sea the sky the air, man!"

"This isn't California, Marv," the girl said gently. "This is Louisiana here."

Marvin started to his feet in alarm. "Louisiana," he cried. "Louisiana! Holy shit, man, that ain't no place to be! We gotta get out of here."

"Louisiana is where New Orleans is, man," the girl explained. "There's no way around it, actually. California was another time."

"That's right," Marvin agreed. "That's what we're talking about, right?"

"Right," the girl said.

"Say," Rheinhardt said after a moment, "where can a man score around here?"

"Score what?" Bogdanovich asked him.

"Score what," the girl said in a small voice.

"Yeah," Marvin said, "what is that—score?"

They looked at him angrily.

"Everything's cool," Rheinhardt said. "I'm not fuzz or anything. I'm just looking to score a lid."

"We don't know too much about that," Bogdanovich said. "Next to nothing."

"Hey Bogdan," Marvin said. "How come you always say that lately? Next to nothing—what kind of a groove is that?"

"Well, I don't know," Bogdanovich said, turning away from Rheinhardt, "it's something people say. It sort of makes a picture."

"It sure does," Marvin said. "Like there's her and there's you and there's me and there's nothing. So I'm next to nothing."

"That's what I'm trying to convey, man."

"I'm always next to nothing," Marvin said. "Nothing is with me, night and day."

"Marvin is an outsider," Bogdanovich explained.

"I see," Rheinhardt said. "Well I'll see you all later."

"Where are you off to?" Bogdanovich asked him.

"I thought I'd take a walk around."

"I'm going to the laundry. You want to walk me?"

"Sure," Rheinhardt said.

They left Marvin and the girl to listen to the Pastorale again and went out into the street. There were people out now, walking up from the bus stop at the French Market. The late afternoon fruit vendors pushed their carts before them, calling their buyers with cries that were part Sicilian patois and part field holler:

"Trawberries! . . . tutti cuam!"

They bought a bag each from an old man with dyed sideburns.

"Thanks, dad," Bogdanovich told him.

Chewing the huge sweet berries, wiping the rich juice from their mouths, they walked to Decatur Street.

"Oh, man," Bogdanovich said. "Strawberries."

Down at the Levee the longshoremen were changing shifts, the bars and winebarrel rooms were full. Passing the Harbor Bar bar, they saw a small fat Cuban bring his fist down on the glass topping of a pinball machine and look with triumphant malice at the shattered glass and the streaks of blood on his arm.

"*Chinga tu madre,*" he said. Groans and curses came from further inside. A jukebox in the barrelhouse at the corner of St. Philip was playing "Walk Don't Run."

Bogdanovich took a running step across the sidewalk, and whirled to face Rheinhardt—fierce-eyed and brandishing the strawberry bag. "*Chinga tu madre,*" he said, snarling. And he smiled. "I wish I could do that."

"Your mother?" Rheinhardt asked cautiously.

"Oh, no no no man," Bogdanovich said. "My mother! My poor old mother! No, I mean I wish I could take on the world and say—*Chingo su madre!*"

"I wish I could too," Rheinhardt said.

"But if I did, the world would say—what? The world would say, WHAT WAS THAT ABOUT MY MOTHER?"

"Then you would have had it," Rheinhardt agreed.

"The world would shake and crack and open up and down I'd go, man, and the world would say, THAT'S FOR WHAT YOU SAID ABOUT MY MOTHER."

"Thus conscience doth make cowards of us all," Rheinhardt said.

"Conscience don't make no coward of Marvin," Bogdanovich said as they turned on to Elysian Fields. "He never learned fear. But he pays, man, he pays all the time."

"He looks it."

"Yeah, they're always taking poor angel Marvin away. When they don't find him, he goes out looking for them."

They followed the dun squares of Elysian Fields for several blocks until they came to a line of wooden stores surrounded by the dry stalks of dead banana trees. Bogdanovich opened a door marked Laundrymatic Inc.

"My employers," he told Rheinhardt.

At the far end of a row of dryers a sad-faced young man with a crew haircut was waiting for them.

"Hey, there's some shit in this here number ten dryer," the young man declared.

"Shit?" Bogdanovich asked him.

"Some damn sneak put a rug in here or somethin'. I put a out-of-order sign on it. If Cruz don't get here with the service truck you gonna have to clean it out yourself."

"All right," Bogdanovich said. "I won't mind that."

"Who's this," the young man said, nodding toward Rheinhardt.

"He's my buddy," Bogdanovich said. "His name is Buddy. He's an efficiency expert."

"How do you do?" the young man asked.

"How do you do," Rheinhardt told him.

"O.K., then, " the young man said. "You could turn the coolers on later if you feel like it. I'll see you tomorrow."

When he was outside, Bogdanovich locked the street door behind him. "He's such a scene, that guy. I could talk to him for hours. As a launderer, he's one of the best in the business."

"What do you do?" Rheinhardt asked him.

"Well, the modern launderer doesn't wash clothes," Bogdanovich said. "The modern launderer has to have executive capability. And above all, he needs a sure insight into human nature—because laundry is a public service profession."

"Certainly," Rheinhardt said.

They left the machines and went into a bare room lined with shelves on which stood boxes of soap, bottles of bleach and disinfectant.

"You never have to buy soap in this business," Bogdanovich said, laying out a thin line of marijuana across a roll of Zig Zag paper. "That's another thing about it."

He lit the joint, breathed his toke, and passed it to Rheinhardt. Rheinhardt inhaled and held his breath.

"A service profession," Bogdanovich went on, "in many subtle ways. For example, laundry is always dirty. People laundry is always all dirty and shit-stained and foul—on a cumulative basis, man, it's just staggering. People always want to sort of sneak it into the machine, like they wrap their real organic laundry up in clean towels, you dig?"

"Sure," Rheinhardt said.

"So it's a little like being a maitre d'. Unobtrusiveness. You observe only what it is required to observe. You serve the public by assuming a very low visibility."

Rheinhardt found himself standing beside a mahogany desk in a lavishly appointed office, viewing a monstrous factory complex through the Observation Screen. "Jesus," he said. He went to the window and, putting his hand on the glass, discovered it to be a set of fuse boxes of extraordinarily satisfactory aspect. "How about that?"

"What?" Bogdanovich asked him.

"I was just adjusting the Big Picture," Rheinhardt said.

"Sure. Well, what we feature, man, is no dealings. Everything is perfectly cool. You go into any other laundry around here and you have dealings. You have to deal with a capitalist and his line of spades. It's like a bank, man, it's a bad groove. Like, where will the bad eye come from. It's all charged with humanity, dig, too much humanity for a laundry. There's the capitalist, he wears a sportshirt and a rubber glove—he says hello, you say hello—he gives your laundry the rubber glove. I mean, that's bizarre, man, nobody likes that. Then behind him those poor chicks are scrubbing for their daily bread—it's a tableau, dig, it's too much world for one small room."

The joint passed between them, glowing hotter. From outside, the washers and dryers purred at the ready.

"But here . . ."

"Just machines," Rheinhardt said.

"Here," Bogdanovich said, "no capitalist, no spades. No deals. Just the machines. The machines have slots, you put your money in them and they go click. You get a satisfying thrust of the wrist, and in the end you pull out your very own laundry, warm and wet."

"It's like birth," Rheinhardt said.

"Re-birth, man," Bogdanovich said. "That's what it's like. It's a link with the real nitty gritty, dig. It's a connection to the elemental stuff of life."

"Then too," Rheinhardt said, "there's the dryers."

"Oh, man, you know, man, I won't say no more. Just go out there and spread your arms out and put yourself up against one of those dryers and see what that's like. Warmth, man," he said in a deep hoarse whisper. "Warmth."

From his shirt pocket he took an alligator clip in which he bound the last fraction of the joint.

"And just in case you get lost in all the automation, there's me. For Love, man, the barest trace of a human hand."

Bogdanovich stuffed the remnants into the end of a Kool and went out to open the street door. Rheinhardt pressed his cold palms against one of the dryers, and then he began to laugh.

"Do they like to talk?" he asked Bogdanovich.

"A lot of them do. You know how these people are. A lot of them like to talk. I been able to turn a lot of them onto health foods—they come back sometimes and tell me about how they feel better. Y'see, they have a very unhealthy diet down here. They fry everything. Veal, they like. Veal." He made an unpleasant grimace and shrugged. "I tell them about eating dead animal flesh. A lot of them listen."

"Hmm," Rheinhardt said.

"I'm very gregarious, dig, and I like to turn people on to the good action. Sometimes I get carried away." He poured some soap in the number ten washer and turned it on with a key that was attached to his alligator clip. "Did you ever see a blue-eyed spade?"

"Sure."

"Blue-eyed spades are a scene. I was in here after midnight about three weeks ago, I was just going to close down and I locked the door and went back in there to blow up. I had just about cleared my head when I heard these little rattles on the door, and I heard it open and I looked out and here's this little blue-eyed spade working one of the machines. Like he's got a file and a plastic strip and all this stuff, and a straw hat with a groovy band, very dapper cat, very dapper. He's bending over givin' it hell singing souly music, dig, but he can't break that thing, man, because he ain't equipped. Pretty soon he starts blowin' his cool—he calls 'em down, he starts bangin' them. He knows he got to hit all the machines to make any bread and pretty soon the cops are coming by. Well, I was fascinated, man, I just stood fascinated and watched him wail. Then he straightened up and got this funny look on his face. What was happening, dig, is I got the door open and he's smelling the gage drift out. Before I could stop myself I was out there talking to him. I told him, be cool, don't worry man, there ain't no bread in there worth cutting cane for. If you're real short I'll loan you two bucks. And I start in tellin' him how it was. I couldn't stop myself, I was just out there doin' it. I was skulled, dig, I didn't know who I was.

"For a long time he just stood there lookin' at me with those baby blue eyes, he was sort of a little cat. And you know what his eyes say?"

"What?" Rheinhardt asked.

"Nothing. I don't mean they don't say anything, I mean they say nothing. Nothing. Not here. Nobody home. Forget it. Like it was a mistake. I had no business in the world out there. I should have stayed behind the door and blown my gage. But it's too late now. There's him, there's me, the existence principle is all turned on. He stands there tellin' me Nothing with those eyes and then he sort of giggles and his jaw shifts gears and I can see the face muscle going up and down. He giggles and he says, 'Hey, dad, you some kind of a fool?'"

"So," Rheinhardt said. "I see."

"I told him that's right, dad, you can look at it that way, I'm some kind of a fool. And I talked to him some more but I was just talking now, I was just marking it. All of a sudden his face lights up in a great big smile and the next thing I knew there was a whoosh by my ear and my man has a five-pound claw hammer and he just tried to drive me through the floor of my own laundry like he was John Henry and I was the Golden Rivet. I grab up a box of Tide and let him have it by the handful. You should have seen it, man, you should have been me to see it. I festooned the motherfucker. Saved my life, man. A box of Tide. But I think that's very sad. Why should he want to do me that way?"

"Maybe he didn't think you were the Golden Rivet," Rheinhardt said. "Maybe he thought you were the Captain."

"Ah, Captain," Bogdanovich said. "Captain Marvel. Captain Midnight. I think that's very sad, man."

"Well, you can't save the world that way, Bogdanovich," Rheinhardt said. "I don't have to tell you that."

"Shit," Bogdanovich said. "Save it! You can't even talk to it. You can't even hail the son of a bitch."

"You can't hail it," Rheinhardt said, "you can't tell it to *chingo* its *madre*."

"Maybe you can turn it on."

"It doesn't turn on," Rheinhardt said. "It's too busy. It has to concentrate all the time."

"Yeah, it's like some chicks. Well, maybe you can break its cool. You can tell it how it's flat." He took a short jump in the air and brought both feet down on the tiled floor. "Hey, butch, you're flat, man," he told the world. "I know what we can do, Rheinhardt, we can try to reach it on the radio."

He went to a counter near the window that was piled with back copies of *Life* and flicked on an old splintering Emerson. "What's the call sign for the World, man?"

"Try KNOW. Six Seven Oh."

"World," Bogdanovich said, "this is Hetman Bogdanovich of the Laundrymatic Corporation. I give you the Great Motherfinger. How do you read me? Over."

The room was suddenly filled with the voice of Farley the Sailor.

". . . that over the vast fields of the slumbering Republic," Farley was saying, "assisted by sinister cohorts of an inflamed and servile ignorance, by ill-sorted legions of the ill-fitted and the unfit, by the vile mouthings of rash youth educated beyond its intelligence, and by the omnipresent spectre of an inexorably devouring insatiably consuming hydra-like federal government the twin pterodactyls of atheistic communism and communistic atheism spread the winged shadow of Beelzebub . . ."

"Holy shit," Bogdanovich said, "this must be that Orson Welles jive."

"No, it's politics," Rheinhardt said.

"Man, those poor people asleep in those towns, man. He sounds like somebody, don't he? Somebody real."

"He sounds sort of like Churchill," Rheinhardt said. "He's doing that."

"Where then are the Paul Reveres of our imperiled age? Where indeed, when those ready to ride and spread the alarm over, as it were, every Middlesex village and farm are treacherously unhorsed by the deceitful grooms in the pay of foreign dynasties. Oh Lord, hear us that You let the scales fall from the eyes of Thy people, that they may arise, in the towns and the cities, in the farms and fields, as one, the mighty and the humble together, shoulder to shoulder, rank on rank, not to bend their steel into the ploughshares of serfdom, but rather to raise in the pure unsullied sunlight of Thy grace, the invincible Excalibur of States' Rights, Free Enterprise, and Individual Initiative."

"What a great cat!" Bogdanovich said. "Hooray, man! Let's wake up and glomm those fuckin' birds, man!"

"Yeah, he's a scene," Rheinhardt said. "He's one of the best in the business."

"And now," Farley said, "Let us ask together that a Great and Good God continue to endow us with the holy fire of living grace, until, if He will it, we meet again!"

"Amen, man," Bogdanovich said.

The announcer's voice came on: "You have heard the Living Grace Hour, another weekly address by the Very Reverend Pastor Heathcliffe Jensen of the Living Grace Missionary Society of New Orleans. The Society is a nonprofit religious enterprise, dedicated to the spiritual rehabilitation of the misguided. Your financial support helps this good work; send contributions to . . ."

"Hey," Bogdanovich said. "That's somebody too."

"That's me."

"You too," Bogdanovich said wonderingly. "You're out there too . . ."

"I'm always out there," Rheinhardt said. "I weave in and out of the stuff. I'm part of it."

Bogdanovich turned off the Emerson and looked out to the street. "Man," he said, "that's some radio. And those concepts—they're weird, man."

"Concepts?"

"They're weird. Like the darkling pterodactyls and the encroaching federal government. That's a very weird concept."

"It's all weird. It's the world, you remember."

"You think all that's going on?"

"That's his trip. That's the way he likes it. Something's going on out there."

"Yeah? The concepts, though—the pterodactyls, the deceitful grooms, all that shit, man. The Communist concept and the other people concept and all those concepts, you think that's really going on? Maybe it's all a put-on. How about that? Look," he said, pointing a finger at Rheinhardt, "you stand right here where I'm standing and it's very quiet. There's nothing to hear but the machines and us. From where I'm standing I can't see anything either, not a soul, just an empty street. Then I turn on that radio, dig, and people—you, man—start talking this rebop with grooms and pterodactyls and the United States of America. And the Russians and the Indians and the Cowboys and the Toronto Maple Leafs. All these . . . all these concepts, man? You say that's really going on out there?"

"What's going on out there," Rheinhardt said, "is there are like a few billion people walking around and every one of them has a head with a lot of stuff going on in it. And if you want to hear what that sounds like just turn on the radio. You don't need television to see it. You can just walk outside that door and put your hand in its goddam side."

"Not me," Bogdanovich said. "I'm not going out that door. I think it's a put-on, man. There isn't anything outside that door but Now. That's all, man. Just Now. If you kept on going past all those people and their trips, you know what it would all look like? Stars, man. Stars."

"Oh," Rheinhardt said. "Stars."

"Stars. And how about inside, man? That's just as big, the inside. Galaxies, man. These people with their concepts. They're tripping out, man. They're insane."

"Bogdanovich, between the galaxies out there—past where all the people are—and the galaxies in here, they got what they call civilization, and they never turn it off. That's the name of the trip. That's what you hear in the box."

"Man, that's not civilization," Bogdanovich said anxiously. "Civilization is music and the arts, man. Civilization is cultivated women like your Natasha and my Natasha. Civilization is proper diet. *Mens sana in corpore sano,* that's what civilization is."

"That's the civilization of the mind," Rheinhardt said. "That's your trip."

"I used to know this cat," Bogdanovich said, "every time you told him something he would say, 'Everything is relative.'"

"He was right. But he probably didn't know how relative everything was, or he wouldn't have said it."

"He didn't know anything, man. Nothing. All he knew was to say 'Everything is relative.' But the fact of the matter is that everything is so fucking relative that I'm going out of my mind. I'm going somewhere and flip. But until then, man, I'm staying right here in this laundry, because out there, man," he pointed to the twilight street, "it's too relative."

Rheinhardt went to the door and looked past the banana stalks at the frame houses opposite. The sun was not quite gone. But it happened so damn fast when the dark came on. So fast. He watched the line of reddening sunlight play on the green top shutters of the house opposite. God, he thought, the air. How sweet it is. "Listen," he asked Bogdanovich, "tell me about flipping. Tell me about that."

"Ah, man," Bogdanovich said sadly. "Why?" He unplugged the number ten machine and turned to look at Rheinhardt. "Marvin's the man to talk to about that. He could set you hip. Marvin could tell you about it. He's an authority. He says you have to work up to it for it to be worthwhile, like you have to blow a lot of pot to get the fantasy equipment going, and not sleep for a couple of days. You probably don't eat right anyway. He says you get to a scene where the stuff that the world is made of changes—like you can tell when you put your hand on it because it feels different. And the light's different. He says you get this taste in your mouth, and then you're set up. But that's him."

"Yes," Rheinhardt said.

"Why, do you feel like it?"

"I think about it."

"Nobody ought to do it unless they have to, man. But you know that."

"Sure," Rheinhardt said, laughing, "everything is relative."

"That's right, man," Bogdanovich said. "Hey listen, you want to blow some more? Clear your head?"

"No," Rheinhardt said. "I'm going to finish the walk."

He shook hands with Bogdanovich and went out into the street. Children were playing Red Light in muddy gardens rounded with iron fences; a covey of teenaged girls at a corner Sno-Ball stand saluted him in mock horror. Idly walking, he crossed the street to the last thin line of sunlight and found himself following a tall stone wall grown with honeysuckle; it brought him to a latticed gate over which a small iron Christ stared down in wide-eyed rusty death from the gibbet of a green-oxided cross. Great roses were growing all around it; the vines were making their way between the nails and feet, climbing the staff of the cross itself. Rheinhardt passed beneath it and down a gravel path between two straight rows of dark stone tombs. The sun had disappeared behind the distant uptown buildings, the day's last light hung round a cluster of live oaks at the end of the corridor of tombs. There was still no wind, the place was absolutely quiet except for the chattering sparrows that darted over the gravel.

Rheinhardt walked from crypt to crypt inspecting the carved urns and the black brass bolts over the seals. The gage, he thought, was funny stuff, it could make you so cold. And tired. He kept walking toward the trees, a great fatigue rising in him.

At the feet of a man named Prosper Thibault, he paused to lean against a stone bench and saw the inside of the wall that faced the street; it was itself set with more modest tombs, niches actually, like a shelf of drawers. The slabs stood four high, engraved neatly with the names and chronology of the occupants; there were several generations of families, a section of infants, a row of nuns from the last century. Rheinhardt kept on, breathing the sweet honeysuckle, wanting more and more to lie down across the path, to lay his head on the soft bright grass that grew by the foot of the wall. He touched a niche, fingering the stone; it was carved with the folds of a mantle and ring, and a heart from which ran stone drops of blood.

A shadow lengthened from the trees and he saw a figure weaving toward him. It was a boy riding his bicycle up the path. Thrust between the handlebars the boy had a bamboo pole from which a brace of wet catfish hung at either end. The boy came straight for him, the bike wobbling with its burden on the unsteady ground, and Rheinhardt moved against the entombments and saw the boy glance at him briefly and fearfully, a line of perspiration round his close-cropped hair, frowning, bending over the bars to pedal harder for the gate and home. Rheinhardt looked after him, then turned to see the live oaks grown dark and barely visible; it was nearly night.

He had stopped to rest at another bench when he became aware of footsteps in the place—other than his own. He became suddenly afraid; crouching in the friezework of one of the tombs, he saw a man's shadow darting in and out of the rows. He moved forward quickly to the next path and came upon a young man in a worn raincoat. The young man stepped back in surprise, squinting at him in the failing light—the young man's face was lusterless and drawn, his Adam's apple bobbed over an open collar button. It was Rainey, the strange cat—Rainey, their neighbor, the Morgue Attendant.

"Jesus," Rheinhardt said. He looked at Rainey, feeling a powerful and inexplicable anger suddenly fill him; he's a ghost, Rheinhardt thought, not a Morgue Attendant.

"Are you all right?" Morgan Rainey asked.

"I'm groovy," Rheinhardt said.

"I'm sorry," Morgan Rainey said. He made no move to pass. "I recognized you from the . . . house."

"Sure," Rheinhardt said. "I'm taking a walk, you dig, only at the moment I'm not walking because I happen to be standing here."

"I thought you might have been ill," Rainey said, and stepped round him to go on up the path.

Rheinhardt looked after him, gnawing his lip, thoroughly surprised with his own rage. In all this time, he thought, you have looked on every manner of thing without a stirring, and when you hate for the first time, your object is a fool who chances on you in a boneyard and asks after your health. Ah. But he was stricken, this Rainey, that was it, whoever he was, he dragged the feathers of a shaft behind him, that was reason enough. So we drive off the ones who bleed and pant before the following wolves— you are more stricken than I and I hate you for it. And fools are evil, someone said. All fools are evil.

He walked for blocks up Elysian Fields, stopping at last in a bar across from the City Park. The bartender was a small squat old man, an ex-lightweight from the 'twenties; he had the place fairly lined with pictures of himself—there was one with his arm around Ralph Dupas and one of him standing suited in the ring with Po' Boy Italo Pozzi. Rheinhardt watched him stand at the tap, nodding and weaving with the boys on the screen, laughing, turning with a gesture to his cronies at the end of the bar. After watching a few rounds, Rheinhardt went across the street to the park to catch the Claiborne Street bus uptown.

It was a hot close night; the street lights on Canal were ringed with mist, the foul exhumations from the riverfront breweries hung fetid on the air. At the action corner of Bourbon Street, Rheinhardt played the pinball machines for a quarter's worth and bought a paper container of beer to take to the studio. Walking down Iberville Street toward the freight entrance of Torneille's he heard the clear rounded report of a pistol from somewhere deeper in the Quarter; he stopped momentarily, walked on and ten paces later heard the first siren, then others, rising until they filled the night and died. The jukeboxes in the corner bars played "Walk Don't Run," farther away a weary clarinet gave the piccolo treatment to "That's A'Plenty" for the four-thousandth time. Rheinhardt went on toward Torneille's ramp.

He was just turning in when a woman's voice held him; he turned and saw someone crouched in a doorway beside the freight railing, a woman with a delicate, rodent-like face and straw-colored hair, just visible in the glass-reflected light. Her legs were stretched out before her, encased in metal braces, and her eyes stared straight ahead at some place beyond seeing.

"Go back to the one that loves ye," the woman crooned and laughed softly.

"What?" Rheinhardt said. "Philomene?"

Still staring she began to sing.

"Oh go back to the one that loves ye
Or the tides of life'll drag ye apart
And the black clouds that roll up above ye
Will close on the hopes of your heart."

Rheinhardt bent over her and moved his hand before her gaze. She never blinked. "Philomene," he said, "are you all right?"

This is a night for solicitude, Rheinhardt thought, we all want to know if we're all all right. Actually everybody is fine, everybody is just out for a walk tonight.

"Can you stand up, love?" he asked Philomene.

Philomene took his arm and pushed herself upright, still staring into the beyond.

"I'm teasing them," she said. "I'm hiding out on them one time." She took a rattling step forward and whistled in pain. "Ah, shit," she said. "Go back to the one that loves ye, friends."

"You sing very well," Rheinhardt told her. He put two dollars in her hand and watched her move toward Royal Street laughing and whistling to herself.

The elevators in Torneille's and KNOW's bright new reception room were staffed by young men in rayon suits who looked as though they might enjoy close-order drills; they wore lapel pins with the Eagle and Thunderbolt. The young man at the visitors' desk Rheinhardt remembered from the Bing Chemical Company.

"Good evening, Mr. Rheinhardt," he said, pressing the electronic door control.

Rheinhardt told him good evening and went into the studio corridor. Jack Noonan came out of the ticker room with a folder full of copy and salaamed to him.

"Bingamon wants to see you tomorrow, Rheinhardt old buddy. You continue to delight him."

"This is my home," Rheinhardt said, "and he's my daddy."

Irving the Engineer was sitting at his turntable in the booth reading the day's log. He turned to give Rheinhardt a look of profound sympathy.

"How's school, bubbala?"

"School is delightfully wonderful," Irving said. "How about you, bubbala? You drunk again?"

"Thirsty work, lad, thirsty work."

"Listen," Irving said, "tomorrow I'm coming in drunk." He held up a red transcription press. "I've listened to some stupid idiots around this place, but here," he waved the press, "is the most preposterous stupid idiot I have ever heard."

"That can only be one man," Rheinhardt said thoughtfully.

Irving stood up, opened the studio door, and stood listening silently. At length they heard the loud and reassuring laughter of Farley the Sailor. Irving closed the door.

"You hear? That's him. He's the champion *schmuck* of the earth. You have to hear him to believe him. Parson Heathcliffe or something, he's called."

"I caught his windup this afternoon. He does have a way with him."

"The windup was nothing. Jesus, let me play the first part for you." He glanced at his watch. "We got time."

"I'll listen to it when we close," Rheinhardt said. "I want to go dig him in the flesh. He's my old goodbuddy."

He went out and down the corridor to the employees' lounge, following the rich tones of Farley in full flower. "The natural law . . ." Farley was declaiming earnestly ". . . the perennial philosophy." He was standing beside a bonsai pine, dressed for a Papal audience; his customary suit of solemn black was the true silk, his shirt white on white, his necktie Cambridge. On a nearby chair a light homburg awaited his pensive brow. His listener was a freckled lady of about forty, richly dressed and with rather a pleasing build; her unashamed reverence was addressed to Farley's countenance.

Rheinhardt approached piously. "Excuse me, Eminence," he said to Farley. "Excuse me, Ma'am."

The lady burbled. Farley cleared his throat.

"Might we have a word about next week's lesson?"

"Of course, my boy," Farley said. "Mrs. MacAllister, this is Mr. Rheinhardt, an . . . official . . . of the station—Rheinhardt, Sister MacAllister, a steadfast receiver of the Good News."

"How do you do," Rheinhardt said.

They went through a set of double doors into the studio corridor, where Farley looked at Rheinhardt with displeasure.

"Where's your mucking cool, eh Rhein? I mean, stow that Eminence crap. The woman may be slow but she's not a cretin and moreover she's a bloody Baptist."

"Sorry, Pastor. What's the word?"

Farley smiled and leaned forward with a transcendental leer. "Well I'm all right, Jack." He fingered his somber lapels. "The word is Good . . . Fucking . . . News. Did you dig today's lesson?"

"I sure did," Rheinhardt said. "It wiped me out."

Farley chortled. "You don't think it was a bit . . . purple?"

"Not a bit of it."

"You have no idea, Rheinhardt, the number of letters that came in after only three broadcasts. Thanks for the help in writing it, by the way."

"I enjoy it," Rheinhardt said. "Anytime."

"Yes, by God, the gold flag is up and you put me on to it. I won't forget you, shipmate."

"It's nothing, Heathcliffe. What's working with the lady?"

"Widow," Farley said wolfishly, "rich as Croesus. They make pepper. She's helping with organization in the society."

"Bingamon won't like it if you branch too far in your own hustle. Isn't he the Living Grace Society now?"

"Oh, he's the Great White Father, mate, I don't question that. But I run the Society for him and I've got a free hand in a few directions at least." He glanced over his shoulder toward the lounge. "It's bigger than I'd dared to hope, Rheinhardt." He looked suddenly soulful. "There you came to my door, mate, wretched, diseased with drink. If my heart had been hardened I might have turned you away. But instead I took you in and you led me straight to a recompense greater than anything I'd ever known. I'd have to be the most hardened of atheists to overlook the pattern there."

"Listen, Heathcliffe," Rheinhardt said brightly. "If you ever feel like turning on for auld lang syne I can get us some grass. You want to?"

Farley recoiled in horror. "Get the bloody hell behind me, Satan," he said sternly. "Are you out of your mind? You're a sick man, Rheinhardt—you're fucking depraved, old boy. I clean you up from the juice and now you're a tea head. You'll end up like Natasha that way." He moved off down the corridor. "Anyway, that's not my high, what?" He gestured toward where Mrs. MacAllister sat. "I've got my toke in there." Smoothing his forelock he passed through the double doors. Rheinhardt went back to his turntable and broke out the log book. Irving was in the control booth watching the clock.

"Hey, Rhein," he called through the intercom, "why don't you use another Elvis?"

"Crazy," Rheinhardt said. "Drop the Paul Anka and we'll run 'Heartbreak Hotel.'"

"You want 'Who Wrote the Book of Love' twice?"

"Yeah," Rheinhardt said.

Irving threw the switches and ran a commercial press, the red lights went on overhead, the bulb beside Rheinhardt's microphone flashed. The commercial ended, Irving threw the cue, and Rheinhardt came in over his theme—"Walk Don't Run."

"Yeah," he said, "all you swingers in this great big wonderful Southland, all you guys and you pretty little girls, you folks on the Nightside—whether you're driving or having a groovy White Fortress Dixieburger or out there in the all-night laundries—Hello, you all!" He turned his volume switch down and took a quick sip of beer. "Let's have us some crazy sounds . . ."

DEATH

Yukio Mishima

PATRIOTISM

On the twenty-eighth of February, 1936 (on the third day, that is, of the February 26 Incident), Lieutenant Shinji Takeyama of the Konoe Transport Battalion—profoundly disturbed by the knowledge that his closest colleagues had been with the mutineers from the beginning, and indignant at the imminent prospect of Imperial troops attacking Imperial troops—took his officer's sword and ceremonially disemboweled himself in the eight-mat room of his private residence in the sixth block of Aoba-chō, in Yotsuya Ward. His wife, Reiko, followed him, stabbing herself to death. The lieutenant's farewell note consisted of one sentence: "Long live the Imperial Forces." His wife's, after apologies for her unfilial conduct in thus preceding her parents to the grave, concluded: "The day which, for a soldier's wife, had to come, has come. . . ." The last moments of this heroic and dedicated couple were such as to make the gods themselves weep. The lieutenant's age, it should be noted, was thirty-one, his wife's twenty-three; and it was not half a year since the celebration of their marriage.

2

Those who saw the bride and bridegroom in the commemorative photograph—perhaps no less than those actually present at the lieutenant's wedding—had exclaimed in wonder at the bearing of this handsome couple. The lieutenant, majestic in military uniform, stood protectively beside his bride, his right hand resting upon his sword, his officer's cap held at his left side. His expression was severe, and his dark brows and wide-gazing eyes well conveyed the clear integrity of youth. For the beauty of the bride in her white over-robe no comparisons were adequate. In the eyes, round beneath soft brows, in the slender, finely shaped nose, and in the full lips, there was both sensuousness and refinement. One hand, emerging shyly from a sleeve of the over-robe, held a fan, and the tips of the fingers, clustering delicately, were like the bud of a moonflower.

After the suicide, people would take out this photograph and examine it, and sadly reflect that too often there was a curse on these seemingly flawless unions. Perhaps it was no more than imagination, but looking at the picture after the tragedy it almost seemed as if the two young people before the gold-lacquered screen were gazing, each with equal clarity, at the deaths which lay before them.

Thanks to the good offices of their go-between, Lieutenant General Ozeki, they had been able to set themselves up in a new home at Aoba-chō in Yotsuya. "New home" is perhaps misleading. It was an old three-room rented house backing onto a small garden. As neither the six- nor the four-and-a-half-mat room downstairs was favored by the sun, they used the upstairs eight-mat room as both bedroom and guest room. There was no maid, so Reiko was left alone to guard the house in her husband's absence.

The honeymoon trip was dispensed with on the grounds that these were times of national emergency. The two of them had spent the first night of their marriage at this house. Before going to bed, Shinji, sitting erect on the floor with his sword laid before him, had bestowed upon his wife a soldierly lecture. A woman who had become the wife of a soldier should know and resolutely accept that her husband's death might come at any moment. It could be tomorrow. It could be the day after. But, no matter when it came—he asked—was she steadfast in her resolve to accept it? Reiko rose to her feet, pulled open a drawer of the cabinet, and took out what was the most prized of her new possessions, the dagger her mother had given her. Returning to her place, she laid the dagger without a word on the mat before her, just as her husband had laid his sword. A silent understanding was achieved at once, and the lieutenant never again sought to test his wife's resolve.

In the first few months of her marriage Reiko's beauty grew daily more radiant, shining serene like the moon after rain.

As both were possessed of young, vigorous bodies, their relationship was passionate. Nor was this merely a matter of the night. On more than one occasion, returning home straight from maneuvers, and begrudging even the time it took to remove his mud-splashed uniform, the lieutenant had pushed his wife to the floor almost as soon as he had entered the house. Reiko was equally ardent in her response. For a little more or a little less than a month, from the first night of their marriage Reiko knew happiness, and the lieutenant, seeing this, was happy too.

Reiko's body was white and pure, and her swelling breasts conveyed a firm and chaste refusal; but, upon consent, those breasts were lavish with their intimate, welcoming warmth. Even in bed these two were frighteningly and awesomely serious. In the very midst of wild, intoxicating passions, their hearts were sober and serious.

By day the lieutenant would think of his wife in the brief rest periods between training; and all day long, at home, Reiko would recall the image of her husband. Even when apart, however, they had only to look at the wedding photograph for their happiness to be once more confirmed.

Reiko felt not the slightest surprise that a man who had been a complete stranger until a few months ago should now have become the sun about which her whole world revolved.

All these things had a moral basis, and were in accordance with the Education Rescript's injunction that "husband and wife should be harmonious." Not once did Reiko contradict her husband, nor did the lieutenant ever find reason to scold his wife. On the god shelf below the stairway, alongside the tablet from the Great Ise Shrine, were set photographs of their Imperial Majesties, and regularly every morning, before leaving for duty, the lieutenant would stand with his wife at this hallowed place and together they would bow their heads low. The offering water was renewed each morning, and the sacred sprig of *sasaki* was always green and fresh. Their lives were lived beneath the solemn protection of the gods and were filled with an intense happiness which set every fiber in their bodies trembling.

3

Although Lord Privy Seal Saitō's house was in their neighborhood, neither of them heard any noise of gunfire on the morning of February 26. It was a bugle, sounding muster in the dim, snowy dawn, when the ten-minute tragedy had already ended, which first disrupted the lieutenant's slumbers. Leaping at once from his bed, and without speaking a word, the lieutenant donned his uniform, buckled on the sword held ready for him by his wife, and hurried swiftly out into the snow-covered streets of the still darkened morning. He did not return until the evening of the twenty-eighth.

Later, from the radio news, Reiko learned the full extent of this sudden eruption of violence. Her life throughout the subsequent two days was lived alone, in complete tranquillity, and behind locked doors.

In the lieutenant's face, as he hurried silently out into the snowy morning, Reiko had read the determination to die. If her husband did not return, her own decision was made: she too would die. Quietly she attended to the disposition of her personal possessions. She chose her sets of visiting kimonos as keepsakes for friends of her schooldays, and she wrote a name and address on the stiff paper wrapping in which each was folded. Constantly admonished by her husband never to think of the morrow, Reiko had not even kept a diary and was now denied the pleasure of assiduously rereading her record of the happiness of the past few months and consigning each page to the fire as she did so. Ranged across the top of the radio were a small china dog, a rabbit, a squirrel, a bear, and a fox. There were also a small vase and a water pitcher. These comprised Reiko's one and only collection. But it would hardly do, she imagined, to give such things as keepsakes. Nor again would it be quite proper to ask specifically for them to be included in the coffin. It seemed to Reiko, as these thoughts passed through her mind, that the expressions on the small animals' faces grew even more lost and forlorn.

Reiko took the squirrel in her hand and looked at it. And then, her thoughts turning to a realm far beyond these childlike affections, she gazed up into the distance at the great sunlike principle which her husband embodied. She was ready, and happy, to be hurtled along to her destruction in that gleaming sun chariot—but now, for these few moments of solitude, she allowed herself to luxuriate in this innocent attachment to trifles. The time when she had genuinely loved these things, however, was long past. Now she merely loved the memory of having once loved them, and their place in her heart had been filled by more intense passions, by a more frenzied happiness. . . . For Reiko had never, even to herself, thought of those soaring joys of the flesh as a mere pleasure. The February cold, and the icy touch of the china squirrel, had numbed Reiko's slender fingers; yet, even so, in her lower limbs, beneath the ordered repetition of the pattern which crossed the skirt of her trim *meisen* kimono, she could feel now, as she thought of the lieutenant's powerful arms reaching out toward her, a hot moistness of the flesh which defied the snows.

She was not in the least afraid of the death hovering in her mind. Waiting alone at home, Reiko firmly believed that everything her husband was feeling or thinking now, his anguish and distress, was leading her—just as surely as the power in his flesh—to a welcome death. She felt as if her body could melt away with ease and be transformed to the merest fraction of her husband's thought.

Listening to the frequent announcements on the radio, she heard the names of several of her husband's colleagues mentioned among those of the insurgents. This was news of death. She followed the developments closely, wondering anxiously, as the situation became daily more irrevocable, why no Imperial ordinance was sent down, and watching what had at first been taken as a movement to restore the nation's honor come gradually to be branded with the infamous name of mutiny. There was no communication from the regiment. At any moment, it seemed, fighting might commence in the city streets, where the remains of the snow still lay.

Toward sundown on the twenty-eighth Reiko was startled by a furious pounding on the front door. She hurried downstairs. As she pulled with fumbling fingers at the bolt, the shape dimly outlined beyond the frosted-glass panel made no sound, but she knew it was her husband. Reiko had never known the bolt on the sliding door to be so stiff. Still it resisted. The door just would not open.

In a moment, almost before she knew she had succeeded, the lieutenant was standing before her on the cement floor inside the porch, muffled in a khaki greatcoat, his top boots heavy with slush from the street. Closing the door behind him, he returned the bolt once more to its socket. With what significance, Reiko did not understand.

"Welcome home."

Reiko bowed deeply, but her husband made no response. As he had already unfastened his sword and was about to remove his greatcoat, Reiko moved around behind to assist. The coat, which was cold and damp and had lost the odor of horse dung it normally exuded when exposed to the sun, weighed heavily upon her arm. Draping it across a hanger, and cradling the sword and leather belt in her sleeves, she waited while her husband removed his top boots and then followed behind him into the "living room." This was the six-mat room downstairs.

Seen in the clear light from the lamp, her husband's face, covered with a heavy growth of bristle, was almost unrecognizably wasted and thin. The cheeks were hollow, their luster and resilience gone. In his normal good spirits he would have changed into old clothes as soon as he was home and have pressed her to get supper at once, but now he sat before the table still in his uniform, his head drooping dejectedly. Reiko refrained from asking whether she should prepare the supper.

After an interval the lieutenant spoke.

"I knew nothing. They hadn't asked me to join. Perhaps out of consideration, because I was newly married. Kano, and Homma too, and Yamaguchi."

Reiko recalled momentarily the faces of high-spirited young officers, friends of her husband, who had come to the house occasionally as guests.

"There may be an Imperial ordinance sent down tomorrow. They'll be posted as rebels, I imagine. I shall be in command of a unit with orders to attack them. . . . I can't do it. It's impossible to do a thing like that."

He spoke again.

"They've taken me off guard duty, and I have permission to return home for one night. Tomorrow morning, without question, I must leave to join the attack. I can't do it, Reiko."

Reiko sat erect with lowered eyes. She understood clearly that her husband had spoken of his death. The lieutenant was resolved. Each word, being rooted in death, emerged sharply and with powerful significance against this dark, unmovable background. Although the lieutenant was speaking of his dilemma, already there was no room in his mind for vacillation.

However, there was a clarity, like the clarity of a stream fed from melting snows, in the silence which rested between them. Sitting in his own home after the long two-day ordeal, and looking across at the face of his beautiful wife, the lieutenant was for the first time experiencing true peace of mind. For he had at once known, though she said nothing, that his wife divined the resolve which lay beneath his words.

"Well, then . . ." The lieutenant's eyes opened wide. Despite his exhaustion they were strong and clear, and now for the first time they looked straight into the eyes of his wife. "Tonight I shall cut my stomach."

Reiko did not flinch.

Her round eyes showed tension, as taut as the clang of a bell.

"I am ready," she said. "I ask permission to accompany you."

The lieutenant felt almost mesmerized by the strength in those eyes. His words flowed swiftly and easily, like the utterances of a man in delirium, and it was beyond his understanding how permission in a matter of such weight could be expressed so casually.

"Good. We'll go together. But I want you as a witness, first, for my own suicide. Agreed?"

When this was said a sudden release of abundant happiness welled up in both their hearts. Reiko was deeply affected by the greatness of her husband's trust in her. It was vital for the lieutenant, whatever else might happen, that there should be no irregularity in his death. For that reason there had to be a witness. The fact that he had chosen his wife for this was the first mark of his trust. The second, and even greater mark, was that though he had pledged that they should die together he did not intend to kill his wife first—he had deferred her death to a time when he would no longer be there to verify it. If the lieutenant had been a suspicious husband, he would doubtless, as in the usual suicide pact, have chosen to kill his wife first.

When Reiko said, "I ask permission to accompany you," the lieutenant felt these words to be the final fruit of the education which he had himself given his wife, starting on the first night of their marriage, and which had schooled her, when the moment came, to say what had to be said without a shadow of hesitation. This flattered the lieutenant's opinion of himself as a self-reliant man. He was not so romantic or conceited as to imagine that the words were spoken spontaneously, out of love for her husband.

With happiness welling almost too abundantly in their hearts, they could not help smiling at each other. Reiko felt as if she had returned to her wedding night.

Before her eyes was neither pain nor death. She seemed to see only a free and limitless expanse opening out into vast distances.

"The water is hot. Will you take your bath now?"

"Ah yes, of course."

"And supper . . . ?"

The words were delivered in such level, domestic tones that the lieutenant came near to thinking, for the fraction of a second, that everything had been a hallucination.

"I don't think we'll need supper. But perhaps you could warm some sake?"

"As you wish."

As Reiko rose and took a *tanzen* gown from the cabinet for after the bath, she purposely directed her husband's attention to the opened drawer. The lieutenant rose, crossed to the cabinet, and looked inside. From the ordered array of paper wrappings he read, one by one, the addresses of the keepsakes. There was no grief in the lieutenant's response to this demonstration of heroic resolve. His heart was filled with tenderness. Like a husband who is proudly shown the childish purchases of a young wife, the lieutenant, overwhelmed by affection, lovingly embraced his wife from behind and implanted a kiss upon her neck.

Reiko felt the roughness of the lieutenant's unshaven skin against her neck. This sensation, more than being just a thing of this world, was for Reiko almost the world itself, but now—with the feeling that it was soon to be lost forever—it had freshness beyond all her experience. Each moment had its own vital strength, and the senses in every corner of her body were reawakened. Accepting her husband's caresses from behind, Reiko raised herself on the tips of her toes, letting the vitality seep through her entire body.

"First the bath, and then, after some sake . . . lay out the bedding upstairs, will you?"

The lieutenant whispered the words into his wife's ear. Reiko silently nodded.

Flinging off his uniform, the lieutenant went to the bath. To faint background noises of slopping water Reiko tended the charcoal brazier in the living room and began the preparations for warming the sake.

Taking the *tanzen,* a sash, and some underclothes, she went to the bathroom to ask how the water was. In the midst of a coiling cloud of steam the lieutenant was sitting cross-legged on the floor, shaving, and she could dimly discern the rippling movements of the muscles on his damp, powerful back as they responded to the movement of his arms.

There was nothing to suggest a time of any special significance. Reiko, going busily about her tasks, was preparing side dishes from odds and ends in stock. Her hands did not tremble. If anything, she managed even more efficiently and smoothly than usual. From time to time, it is true, there was a strange throbbing deep within her breast. Like distant lightning, it had a moment of sharp intensity and then vanished without trace. Apart from that, nothing was in any way out of the ordinary.

The lieutenant, shaving in the bathroom, felt his warmed body miraculously healed at last of the desperate tiredness of the days of indecision and filled—in spite of the death which lay ahead—with pleasurable anticipation. The sound of his wife going about her work came to him faintly. A healthy physical craving, submerged for two days, reasserted itself. The lieutenant was confident there had been no impurity in that joy they had experienced when resolving upon death. They had both sensed at that moment—though not, of course, in any clear and conscious way—that those permissible pleasures which they shared in private were once more beneath the protection of Righteousness and Divine Power, and of a complete and unassailable morality. On looking into each other's eyes and discovering there an honorable death, they had felt themselves safe once more behind steel walls which none could destroy, encased in an impenetrable armor of Beauty and Truth. Thus, so far from seeing any inconsistency or conflict between the urges of his flesh and the sincerity of his patriotism, the lieutenant was even able to regard the two as parts of the same thing.

Thrusting his face close to the dark, cracked, misted wall mirror, the lieutenant shaved himself with great care. This would be his death face. There must be no unsightly blemishes. The clean-shaven face gleamed once more with a youthful luster, seeming to brighten the darkness of the mirror. There was a certain elegance, he even felt, in the association of death with this radiantly healthy face.

Just as it looked now, this would become his death face! Already, in fact, it had half departed from the lieutenant's personal possession and had become the bust above a dead soldier's memorial. As an experiment he closed his eyes tight. Everything was wrapped in blackness, and he was no longer a living, seeing creature.

Returning from the bath, the traces of the shave glowing faintly blue beneath his smooth cheeks, he seated himself beside the now well-kindled charcoal brazier. Busy though Reiko was, he noticed, she had found time lightly to touch up her face. Her cheeks were gay and her lips moist. There was no shadow of sadness to be seen. Truly, the lieutenant felt, as he saw this mark of his young wife's passionate nature, he had chosen the wife he ought to have chosen.

As soon as the lieutenant had drained his sake cup he offered it to Reiko. Reiko had never before tasted sake, but she accepted without hesitation and sipped timidly.

"Come here," the lieutenant said.

Reiko moved to her husband's side and was embraced as she leaned backward across his lap. Her breast was in violent commotion, as if sadness, joy, and the potent sake were mingling and reacting within her. The lieutenant looked down into his wife's face. It was the last face he would see in this world, the last face he would see of his wife. The lieutenant scrutinized the face minutely, with the eyes of a traveler bidding farewell to splendid vistas which he will never revisit. It was a face he could not tire of looking at—the features regular yet not cold, the lips lightly closed with a soft strength. The lieutenant kissed those lips, unthinkingly. And suddenly, though there was not the slightest distortion of the face into the unsightliness of sobbing, he noticed that tears were welling slowly from beneath the long lashes of the closed eyes and brimming over into a glistening stream.

When, a little later, the lieutenant urged that they should move to the upstairs bedroom, his wife replied that she would follow after taking a bath. Climbing the stairs alone to the bedroom, where the air was already warmed by the gas heater, the lieutenant lay down on the bedding with arms outstretched and legs apart. Even the time at which he lay waiting for his wife to join him was no later and no earlier than usual.

He folded his hands beneath his head and gazed at the dark boards of the ceiling in the dimness beyond the range of the standard lamp. Was it death he was now waiting for? Or a wild ecstasy of the senses? The two seemed to overlap, almost as if the object of this bodily desire was death itself. But, however that might be, it was certain that never before had the lieutenant tasted such total freedom.

There was the sound of a car outside the window. He could hear the screech of its tires skidding in the snow piled at the side of the street. The sound of its horn re-echoed from near-by walls. . . . Listening to these noises he had the feeling that this house rose like a solitary island in the ocean of a society going as restlessly about its business as ever. All around, vastly and untidily, stretched the country for which he grieved. He was to give his life for it. But would that great country, with which he was prepared to remonstrate to the extent of destroying himself, take the slightest heed of his death? He did not know; and it did not matter. His was a battlefield without glory, a battlefield where none could display deeds of valor: it was the front line of the spirit.

Reiko's footsteps sounded on the stairway. The steep stairs in this old house creaked badly. There were fond memories in that creaking, and many a time, while waiting in bed, the lieutenant had listened to its welcome sound. At the thought that he would hear it no more he listened with intense concentration, striving for every corner of every moment of this precious time to be filled with the sound of those soft footfalls on the creaking stairway. The moments seemed transformed to jewels, sparkling with inner light.

Reiko wore a Nagoya sash about the waist of her *yukata,* but as the lieutenant reached toward it, its redness sobered by the dimness of the light, Reiko's hand moved to his assistance and the sash fell away, slithering swiftly to the floor. As she stood before him, still in her *yukata,* the lieutenant inserted his hands through the side slits beneath each sleeve, intending to embrace her as she was; but at the touch of his finger tips upon the warm naked flesh, and as the armpits closed gently about his hands, his whole body was suddenly aflame.

In a few moments the two lay naked before the glowing gas heater.

Neither spoke the thought, but their hearts, their bodies, and their pounding breasts blazed with the knowledge that this was the very last time. It was as if the words "The Last Time" were spelled out, in invisible brushstrokes, across every inch of their bodies.

The lieutenant drew his wife close and kissed her vehemently. As their tongues explored each other's mouths, reaching out into the smooth, moist interior, they felt as if the still-unknown agonies of death had tempered their senses to the keenness of red-hot steel. The agonies they could not yet feel, the distant pains of death, had refined their awareness of pleasure.

"This is the last time I shall see your body," said the lieutenant. "Let me look at it closely." And, tilting the shade on the lampstand to one side, he directed the rays along the full length of Reiko's outstretched form.

Reiko lay still with her eyes closed. The light from the low lamp clearly revealed the majestic sweep of her white flesh. The lieutenant, not without a touch of egocentricity, rejoiced that he would never see this beauty crumble in death.

At his leisure, the lieutenant allowed the unforgettable spectacle to engrave itself upon his mind. With one hand he fondled the hair, with the other he softly stroked the magnificent face, implanting kisses here and there where his eyes lingered. The quiet coldness of the high, tapering forehead, the closed eyes with their long lashes beneath faintly etched brows, the set of the finely shaped nose, the gleam of teeth glimpsed between full, regular lips, the soft cheeks and the small, wise chin . . . these things conjured up in the lieutenant's mind the vision of a truly radiant death face, and again and again he pressed his lips tight against the white throat—where Reiko's own hand was soon to strike—and the throat reddened faintly beneath his kisses. Returning to the mouth he laid his lips against it with the gentlest of pressures, and moved them rhythmically over Reiko's with the light rolling motion of a small boat. If he closed his eyes, the world became a rocking cradle.

Wherever the lieutenant's eyes moved his lips faithfully followed. The high, swelling breasts, surmounted by nipples like the buds of a wild cherry, hardened as the lieutenant's lips closed about them. The arms flowed smoothly downward from each side of the breast, tapering toward the wrists, yet losing nothing of their roundness or symmetry, and at their tips were those delicate fingers which had held the fan at the wedding ceremony. One by one, as the lieutenant kissed them, the fingers withdrew behind their neighbor as if in shame. . . . The natural hollow curving between the bosom and the stomach carried in its lines a suggestion not only of softness but of resilient strength, and while it gave forewarning of the rich curves spreading outward from here to the hips it had, in itself, an appearance only of restraint and proper discipline. The whiteness and richness of the stomach and hips was like milk brimming in a great bowl, and the sharply shadowed dip of the navel could have been the fresh impress of a raindrop, fallen there that very moment. Where the shadows gathered more thickly, hair clustered, gentle and sensitive, and as the agitation mounted in the now no longer passive body there hung over this region a scent like the smoldering of fragrant blossoms, growing steadily more pervasive.

At length, in a tremulous voice, Reiko spoke.

"Show me. . . . Let me look too, for the last time."

Never before had he heard from his wife's lips so strong and unequivocal a request. It was as if something which her modesty had wished to keep hidden to the end had suddenly burst its bonds of constraint. The lieutenant obediently lay back and surrendered himself to his wife. Lithely she raised her white, trembling body, and—burning with an innocent desire to return to her husband what he had done for her—placed two white fingers on the lieutenant's eyes, which gazed fixedly up at her, and gently stroked them shut.

Suddenly overwhelmed by tenderness, her cheeks flushed by a dizzying uprush of emotion, Reiko threw her arms about the lieutenant's close-cropped head. The bristly hairs rubbed painfully against her breast, the prominent nose was cold as it dug into her flesh, and his breath was hot. Relaxing her embrace, she gazed down at her husband's masculine face. The severe brows, the closed eyes, the splendid bridge of the nose, the shapely lips drawn firmly together . . . the blue, clean-shaven cheeks reflecting the light and gleaming smoothly. Reiko kissed each of these. She kissed the broad nape of the neck, the strong, erect shoulders, the powerful chest with its twin circles like shields and its russet nipples. In the armpits, deeply shadowed by the ample flesh of the shoulders and chest, a sweet and melancholy odor emanated from the growth of hair, and in the sweetness of this odor was contained, somehow, the essence of young death. The lieutenant's naked skin glowed like a field of barley, and everywhere the muscles showed in sharp relief, converging on the lower abdomen about the small, unassuming navel. Gazing at the youthful, firm stomach, modestly covered by a vigorous growth of hair, Reiko thought of it as it was soon to be, cruelly cut by the sword, and she laid her head upon it, sobbing in pity, and bathed it with kisses.

At the touch of his wife's tears upon his stomach the lieutenant felt ready to endure with courage the cruelest agonies of his suicide.

What ecstasies they experienced after these tender exchanges may well be imagined. The lieutenant raised himself and enfolded his wife in a powerful embrace, her body now limp with exhaustion after her grief and tears. Passionately they held their faces close, rubbing cheek against cheek. Reiko's body was trembling. Their breasts, moist with sweat, were tightly joined, and every inch of the young and beautiful bodies had become so much one with the other that it seemed impossible there should ever again be a separation. Reiko cried out. From the heights they plunged into the abyss, and from the abyss they took wing and soared once more to dizzying heights. The lieutenant panted like the regimental standard-bearer on a route march. . . . As one cycle ended, almost immediately a new wave of passion would be generated, and together—with no trace of fatigue—they would climb again in a single breathless movement to the very summit.

4

When the lieutenant at last turned away, it was not from weariness. For one thing, he was anxious not to undermine the considerable strength he would need in carrying out his suicide. For another, he would have been sorry to mar the sweetness of these last memories by overindulgence.

Since the lieutenant had clearly desisted, Reiko too, with her usual compliance, followed his example. The two lay naked on their backs, with fingers interlaced, staring fixedly at the dark ceiling. The room was warm from the heater, and even when the sweat had ceased to pour from their bodies they felt no cold. Outside, in the hushed night, the sounds of passing traffic had ceased. Even the noises of the trains and streetcars around Yotsuya station did not penetrate this far. After echoing through the region bounded by the moat, they were lost in the heavily wooded park fronting the broad driveway before Akasaka Palace. It was hard to believe in the tension gripping this whole quarter, where the two factions of the bitterly divided Imperial Army now confronted each other, poised for battle.

Savoring the warmth glowing within themselves, they lay still and recalled the ecstasies they had just known. Each moment of the experience was relived. They remembered the taste of kisses which had never wearied, the touch of naked flesh, episode after episode of dizzying bliss. But already, from the dark boards of the ceiling, the face of death was peering down. These joys had been final, and their bodies would never know them again. Not that joy of this intensity—and the same thought had occurred to them both—was ever likely to be reexperienced, even if they should live on to old age.

The feel of their fingers intertwined—this too would soon be lost. Even the wood-grain patterns they now gazed at on the dark ceiling boards would be taken from them. They could feel death edging in, nearer and nearer. There could be no hesitation now. They must have the courage to reach out to death themselves, and to seize it.

"Well, let's make our preparations," said the lieutenant. The note of determination in the words was unmistakable, but at the same time Reiko had never heard her husband's voice so warm and tender.

After they had risen, a variety of tasks awaited them.

The lieutenant, who had never once before helped with the bedding, now cheerfully slid back the door of the closet, lifted the mattress across the room by himself, and stowed it away inside.

Reiko turned off the gas heater and put away the lamp standard. During the lieutenant's absence she had arranged this room carefully, sweeping and dusting it to a fresh cleanness, and now—if one overlooked the rosewood table drawn into one corner—the eight-mat room gave all the appearance of a reception room ready to welcome an important guest.

"We've seen some drinking here, haven't we? With Kanō and Homma and Noguchi . . ."

"Yes, they were great drinkers, all of them."

"We'll be meeting them before long, in the other world. They'll tease us, I imagine, when they find I've brought you with me."

Descending the stairs, the lieutenant turned to look back into this calm, clean room, now brightly illuminated by the ceiling lamp. There floated across his mind the faces of the young officers who had drunk there, and laughed, and innocently bragged. He had never dreamed then that he would one day cut open his stomach in this room.

In the two rooms downstairs husband and wife busied themselves smoothly and serenely with their respective preparations. The lieutenant went to the toilet, and then to the bathroom to wash. Meanwhile Reiko folded away her husband's padded robe, placed his uniform tunic, his trousers, and a newly cut bleached loincloth in the bathroom, and set out sheets of paper on the living-room table for the farewell notes. Then she removed the lid from the writing box and began rubbing ink from the ink tablet. She had already decided upon the wording of her own note.

Reiko's fingers pressed hard upon the cold gilt letters of the ink tablet, and the water in the shallow well at once darkened, as if a black cloud had spread across it. She stopped thinking that this repeated action, this pressure from her fingers, this rise and fall of faint sound, was all and solely for death. It was a routine domestic task, a simple paring away of time until death should finally stand before her. But somehow, in the increasingly smooth motion of the tablet rubbing on the stone, and in the scent from the thickening ink, there was unspeakable darkness.

Neat in his uniform, which he now wore next to his skin, the lieutenant emerged from the bathroom. Without a word he seated himself at the table, bolt upright, took a brush in his hand, and stared undecidedly at the paper before him.

Reiko took a white silk kimono with her and entered the bathroom. When she reappeared in the living room, clad in the white kimono and with her face lightly made up, the farewell note lay completed on the table beneath the lamp. The thick black brushstrokes said simply:

"Long Live the Imperial Forces—Army Lieutenant Takeyama Shinji."

While Reiko sat opposite him writing her own note, the lieutenant gazed in silence, intensely serious, at the controlled movement of his wife's pale fingers as they manipulated the brush.

With their respective notes in their hands—the lieutenant's sword strapped to his side, Reiko's small dagger thrust into the sash of her white kimono—the two of them stood before the god shelf and silently prayed. Then they put out all the downstairs lights. As he mounted the stairs the lieutenant turned his head and gazed back at the striking, white-clad figure of his wife, climbing behind him, with lowered eyes, from the darkness beneath.

The farewell notes were laid side by side in the alcove of the upstairs room. They wondered whether they ought not to remove the hanging scroll, but since it had been written by their go-between, Lieutenant General Ozeki, and consisted, moreover, of two Chinese characters signifying "Sincerity," they left it where it was. Even if it were to become stained with splashes of blood, they felt that the lieutenant general would understand.

The lieutenant, sitting erect with his back to the alcove, laid his sword on the floor before him.

Reiko sat facing him, a mat's width away. With the rest of her so severely white the touch of rouge on her lips seemed remarkably seductive.

Across the dividing mat they gazed intently into each other's eyes. The lieutenant's sword lay before his knees. Seeing it, Reiko recalled their first night and was overwhelmed with sadness. The lieutenant spoke, in a hoarse voice:

"As I have no second to help me I shall cut deep. It may look unpleasant, but please do not panic. Death of any sort is a fearful thing to watch. You must not be discouraged by what you see. Is that all right?"

"Yes."

Reiko nodded deeply.

Looking at the slender white figure of his wife the lieutenant experienced a bizarre excitement. What he was about to perform was an act in his public capacity as a soldier, something he had never previously shown his wife. It called for a resolution equal to the courage to enter battle; it was a death of no less degree and quality than death in the front line. It was his conduct on the battlefield that he was now to display.

Momentarily the thought led the lieutenant to a strange fantasy. A lonely death on the battlefield, a death beneath the eyes of his beautiful wife . . . in the sensation that he was now to die in these two dimensions, realizing an impossible union of them both, there was sweetness beyond words. This must be the very pinnacle of good fortune, he thought. To have every moment of his death observed by those beautiful eyes—it was like being borne to death on a gentle, fragrant breeze. There was some special favor here. He did not understand precisely what it was, but it was a domain unknown to others: a dispensation granted to no one else had been permitted to himself. In the radiant, bridelike figure of his white-robed wife the lieutenant seemed to see a vision of all those things he had loved and for which he was to lay down his life—the Imperial Household, the Nation, the Army Flag. All these, no less than the wife who sat before him, were presences observing him closely with clear and never-faltering eyes.

Reiko too was gazing intently at her husband, so soon to die, and she thought that never in this world had she seen anything so beautiful. The lieutenant always looked well in uniform, but now, as he contemplated death with severe brows and firmly closed lips, he revealed what was perhaps masculine beauty at its most superb.

"It's time to go," the lieutenant said at last.

Reiko bent her body low to the mat in a deep bow. She could not raise her face. She did not wish to spoil her make-up with tears, but the tears could not be held back.

When at length she looked up she saw hazily through the tears that her husband had wound a white bandage around the blade of his now unsheathed sword, leaving five or six inches of naked steel showing at the point.

Resting the sword in its cloth wrapping on the mat before him, the lieutenant rose from his knees, resettled himself cross-legged, and unfastened the hooks of his uniform collar. His eyes no longer saw his wife. Slowly, one by one, he undid the flat brass buttons. The dusky brown chest was revealed, and then the stomach. He unclasped his belt and undid the buttons of his trousers. The pure whiteness of the thickly coiled loincloth showed itself. The lieutenant pushed the cloth down with both hands, further to ease his stomach, and then reached for the white-bandaged blade of his sword. With his left hand he massaged his abdomen, glancing downward as he did so.

To reassure himself on the sharpness of his sword's cutting edge the lieutenant folded back the left trouser flap, exposing a little of his thigh, and lightly drew the blade across the skin. Blood welled up in the wound at once, and several streaks of red trickled downward, glistening in the strong light.

It was the first time Reiko had ever seen her husband's blood, and she felt a violent throbbing in her chest. She looked at her husband's face. The lieutenant was looking at the blood with calm appraisal. For a moment—though thinking at the same time that it was hollow comfort—Reiko experienced a sense of relief.

The lieutenant's eyes fixed his wife with an intense, hawklike stare. Moving the sword around to his front, he raised himself slightly on his hips and let the upper half of his body lean over the sword point. That he was mustering his whole strength was apparent from the angry tension of the uniform at his shoulders. The lieutenant aimed to strike deep into the left of his stomach. His sharp cry pierced the silence of the room.

Despite the effort he had himself put into the blow, the lieutenant had the impression that someone else had struck the side of his stomach agonizingly with a thick rod of iron. For a second or so his head reeled and he had no idea what had happened. The five or six inches of naked point had vanished completely into his flesh, and the white bandage, gripped in his clenched fist, pressed directly against his stomach.

He returned to consciousness. The blade had certainly pierced the wall of the stomach, he thought. His breathing was difficult, his chest thumped violently, and in some far deep region, which he could hardly believe was a part of himself, a fearful and excruciating pain came welling up as if the ground had split open to disgorge a boiling stream of molten rock. The pain came suddenly nearer, with terrifying speed. The lieutenant bit his lower lip and stifled an instinctive moan.

Was this *seppuku*?—he was thinking. It was a sensation of utter chaos, as if the sky had fallen on his head and the world was reeling drunkenly.

His will power and courage, which had seemed so robust before he made the incision, had now dwindled to something like a single hairlike thread of steel, and he was assailed by the uneasy feeling that he must advance along this thread, clinging to it with desperation. His clenched fist had grown moist. Looking down, he saw that both his hand and the cloth about the blade were drenched in blood. His loincloth too was dyed a deep red. It struck him as incredible that, amidst this terrible agony, things which could be seen could still be seen, and existing things existed still.

The moment the lieutenant thrust the sword into his left side and she saw the deathly pallor fall across his face, like an abruptly lowered curtain, Reiko had to struggle to prevent herself from rushing to his side. Whatever happened, she must watch. She must be a witness. That was the duty her husband had laid upon her. Opposite her, a mat's space away, she could clearly see her husband biting his lip to stifle the pain. The pain was there, with absolute certainty, before her eyes. And Reiko had no means of rescuing him from it.

The sweat glistened on her husband's forehead. The lieutenant closed his eyes, and then opened them again, as if experimenting. The eyes had lost their luster, and seemed innocent and empty like the eyes of a small animal.

The agony before Reiko's eyes burned as strong as the summer sun, utterly remote from the grief which seemed to be tearing herself apart within. The pain grew steadily in stature, stretching upward. Reiko felt that her husband had already become a man in a separate world, a man whose whole being had been resolved into pain, a prisoner in a cage of pain where no hand could reach out to him. But Reiko felt no pain at all. Her grief was not pain. As she thought about this, Reiko began to feel as if someone had raised a cruel wall of glass high between herself and her husband.

Ever since her marriage her husband's existence had been her own existence, and every breath of his had been a breath drawn by herself. But now, while her husband's existence in pain was a vivid reality, Reiko could find in this grief of hers no certain proof at all of her own existence.

With only his right hand on the sword the lieutenant began to cut sideways across his stomach. But as the blade became entangled with the entrails it was pushed constantly outward by their soft resilience; and the lieutenant realized that it would be necessary, as he cut, to use both hands to keep the point pressed deep into his stomach. He pulled the blade across. It did not cut as easily as he had expected. He directed the strength of his whole body into his right hand and pulled again. There was a cut of three or four inches.

The pain spread slowly outward from the inner depths until the whole stomach reverberated. It was like the wild clanging of a bell. Or like a thousand bells which jangled simultaneously at every breath he breathed and every throb of his pulse, rocking his whole being. The lieutenant could no longer stop himself from moaning. But by now the blade had cut its way through to below the navel, and when he noticed this he felt a sense of satisfaction, and a renewal of courage.

The volume of blood had steadily increased, and now it spurted from the wound as if propelled by the beat of the pulse. The mat before the lieutenant was drenched red with splattered blood, and more blood overflowed onto it from pools which gathered in the folds of the lieutenant's khaki trousers. A spot, like a bird, came flying across to Reiko and settled on the lap of her white silk kimono.

By the time the lieutenant had at last drawn the sword across to the right side of his stomach, the blade was already cutting shallow and had revealed its naked tip, slippery with blood and grease. But, suddenly stricken by a fit of vomiting, the lieutenant cried out hoarsely. The vomiting made the fierce pain fiercer still, and the stomach, which had thus far remained firm and compact, now abruptly heaved, opening wide its wound, and the entrails burst through, as if the wound too were vomiting. Seemingly ignorant of their master's suffering, the entrails gave an impression of robust health and almost disagreeable vitality as they slipped smoothly out and spilled over into the crotch. The lieutenant's head drooped, his shoulders heaved, his eyes opened to narrow slits, and a thin trickle of saliva dribbled from his mouth. The gold markings on his epaulettes caught the light and glinted.

Blood was scattered everywhere. The lieutenant was soaked in it to his knees, and he sat now in a crumpled and listless posture, one hand on the floor. A raw smell filled the room. The lieutenant, his head drooping, retched repeatedly, and the movement showed vividly in his shoulders. The blade of the sword, now pushed back by the entrails and exposed to its tip, was still in the lieutenant's right hand.

It would be difficult to imagine a more heroic sight than that of the lieutenant at this moment, as he mustered his strength and flung back his head. The movement was performed with sudden violence, and the back of his head struck with a sharp crack against the alcove pillar. Reiko had been sitting until now with her face lowered, gazing in fascination at the tide of blood advancing toward her knees, but the sound took her by surprise and she looked up.

The lieutenant's face was not the face of a living man. The eyes were hollow, the skin parched, the once so lustrous cheeks and lips the color of dried mud. The right hand alone was moving. Laboriously gripping the sword, it hovered shakily in the air like the hand of a marionette and strove to direct the point at the base of the lieutenant's throat. Reiko watched her husband make this last, most heart-rending, futile exertion. Glistening with blood and grease, the point was thrust at the throat again and again. And each time it missed its aim. The strength to guide it was no longer there. The straying point struck the collar and the collar badges. Although its hooks had been unfastened, the stiff military collar had closed together again and was protecting the throat.

Reiko could bear the sight no longer. She tried to go to her husband's help, but she could not stand. She moved through the blood on her knees, and her white skirts grew deep red. Moving to the rear of her husband, she helped no more than by loosening the collar. The quivering blade at last contacted the naked flesh of the throat. At that moment Reiko's impression was that she herself had propelled her husband forward; but that was not the case. It was a movement planned by the lieutenant himself, his last exertion of strength. Abruptly he threw his body at the blade, and the blade pierced his neck, emerging at the nape. There was a tremendous spurt of blood and the lieutenant lay still, cold blue-tinged steel protruding from his neck at the back.

5

Slowly, her socks slippery with blood, Reiko descended the stairway. The upstairs room was now completely still.

Switching on the ground-floor lights, she checked the gas jet and the main gas plug and poured water over the smoldering, half-buried charcoal in the brazier. She stood before the upright mirror in the four-and-a-half-mat room and held up her skirts. The bloodstains made it seem as if a bold, vivid pattern was printed across the lower half of her white kimono. When she sat down before the mirror, she was conscious of the dampness and coldness of her husband's blood in the region of her thighs, and she shivered. Then, for a long while, she lingered over her toilet preparations. She applied the rouge generously to her cheeks, and her lips too she painted heavily. This was no longer make-up to please her husband. It was make-up for the world which she would leave behind, and there was a touch of the magnificent and the spectacular in her brushwork. When she rose, the mat before the mirror was wet with blood. Reiko was not concerned about this.

Returning from the toilet, Reiko stood finally on the cement floor of the porchway. When her husband had bolted the door here last night it had been in preparation for death. For a while she stood immersed in the consideration of a simple problem. Should she now leave the bolt drawn? If she were to lock the door, it could be that the neighbors might not notice their suicide for several days. Reiko did not relish the thought of their two corpses putrifying before discovery. After all, it seemed, it would be best to leave it open. . . . She released the bolt, and also drew open the frosted-glass door a fraction. . . . At once a chill wind blew in. There was no sign of anyone in the midnight streets, and stars glittered ice-cold through the trees in the large house opposite.

Leaving the door as it was, Reiko mounted the stairs. She had walked here and there for some time and her socks were no longer slippery. About halfway up, her nostrils were already assailed by a peculiar smell.

The lieutenant was lying on his face in a sea of blood. The point protruding from his neck seemed to have grown even more prominent than before. Reiko walked heedlessly across the blood. Sitting beside the lieutenant's corpse, she stared intently at the face, which lay on one cheek on the mat. The eyes were opened wide, as if the lieutenant's attention had been attracted by something. She raised the head, folding it in her sleeve, wiped the blood from the lips, and bestowed a last kiss.

Then she rose and took from the closet a new white blanket and a waist cord. To prevent any derangement of her skirts, she wrapped the blanket about her waist and bound it there firmly with the cord.

Reiko sat herself on a spot about one foot distant from the lieutenant's body. Drawing the dagger from her sash, she examined its dully gleaming blade intently, and held it to her tongue. The taste of the polished steel was slightly sweet.

Reiko did not linger. When she thought how the pain which had previously opened such a gulf between herself and her dying husband was now to become a part of her own experience, she saw before her only the joy of herself entering a realm her husband had already made his own. In her husband's agonized face there had been something inexplicable which she was seeing for the first time. Now she would solve that riddle. Reiko sensed that at last she too would be able to taste the true bitterness and sweetness of that great moral principle in which her husband believed. What had until now been tasted only faintly through her husband's example she was about to savor directly with her own tongue.

Reiko rested the point of the blade against the base of her throat. She thrust hard. The wound was only shallow. Her head blazed, and her hands shook uncontrollably. She gave the blade a strong pull sideways. A warm substance flooded into her mouth, and everything before her eyes reddened, in a vision of spouting blood. She gathered her strength and plunged the point of the blade deep into her throat.

Translated by Geoffrey W. Sargent

ANALYSIS

"Patriotism" is intensely dramatic; it is the kind of work that makes even the most indifferent student of literature clutch his brow in anguish and read on in spite of his impulse to turn away from the spectacle he is watching. The ritualistic double suicide of two Japanese lovers is an experience in horror in which it is impossible to avoid becoming emotionally caught up. "Patriotism," whatever else it does, makes you *feel*.

Brutality of any kind, when badly presented and graphically described, can make a reader flinch. Mickey Spillane does it all the time. The difference between Spillane and Mishima is really in purpose more than in kind. Spillane bludgeons his victims simply to watch their blood flow; he is preoccupied with violence for its own sake and totally indifferent to its causes and effects. Mishima's purpose quite obviously bears no resemblance to Spillane's. It is the state of mind which enables the young lieutenant and his wife to take their lives without a qualm, and the ritual which is as much a part of their daily existence as it is of their ceremonial deaths, with which the story is primarily concerned. Indeed, four fifths of the action is devoted to establishing the ritual pattern of the characters' lives, and only one fifth to the actual suicide.

It is not accident that Mishima reveals his entire plot at the outset of the story.

On the twenty-eighth of February, 1936 (on the third day, that is, of the February 26 Incident), Lieutenant Shinji Takeyama of the Konoe Transport Battalion—profoundly disturbed by the knowledge that his closest colleagues had been with the mutineers from the beginning, and indignant at the imminent prospect of Imperial troops attacking

Imperial troops—took his officer's sword and ceremonially disemboweled himself in the eight-mat room of his private residence in the sixth block of Aoba-cho, in Yotsuya Ward. His wife, Reiko, followed him, stabbing herself to death.

The opening paragraph does two things. It establishes an impersonal, objective, narrative tone (a distance which is essential when we come to the horrible fact of the disembowelment), and it lets us know that our attention is to be focused on the psychological makeup of the characters *that leads to their deaths* rather than on the self-execution itself. The interest, in other words, is in the telling, since we already know what happens.

Mishima constructs his foundations carefully and subtly. We see the intense sobriety which lies behind even the most pleasurable acts of the lieutenant and his wife. They are young and newly married and their love-making is ardent, but "even in bed these two were frighteningly and awesomely serious. In the very midst of wild, intoxicating passions, their hearts were sober and serious." We see their passionate devotion to each other ("By day the lieutenant would think of his wife in the brief rest periods between training; and all day long, at home, Reiko would recall the image of her husband") and we understand their unyielding respect for honor and tradition ("On the god shelf below the stairway, alongside the tablet from the Great Ise Shrine, were set photographs of their Imperial Majesties, and regularly every morning, before leaving for duty, the lieutenant would stand with his wife at this hallowed place and together they would bow their heads low"). Their home is warm and happy, yet there is a real sense of rigidity in its order. The offering water before the god shelf is renewed each morning; ". . . the sacred spring of *sasaki* is always green and fresh."

And it is this same sense of seriousness and rigidity in the lieutenant's code of honor that dictates his final actions. He will be asked to turn on his mutinous comrades and "friendship" will not permit him to do this. "There may be an Imperial ordinance sent down tomorrow," he tells his wife. "They'll be posted as rebels, I imagine. I shall be in command of a unit with orders to attack them. . . . I can't do it. It's impossible to do a thing like that."

At the same time the lieutenant's loyalty to the Imperial service will not permit him to disobey a command. That too is impossible. There is only one honorable way to resolve the conflict, and his determination is immediate and unquestioned: "Tonight I shall cut my stomach."

The same code applies, of course, to the lieutenant's wife. Her duty, as well as her desire, is to remain united with her husband, spiritually if no longer physically, and she pursues her course without hesitation or doubt. "I ask permission to accompany you."

Had we not been prepared for this resolve, both by the opening statement and by our glimpse into the private life of the soldier and his bride, we might find it incredible. As our civil and religious sanctions imply, the concept of death as a legitimate means of escape is alien to the Western mind—so abhorrent, in fact, that we prefer to think of mercy killers and suicides as, at least temporarily, insane. To convince a reader that in the incredible event he is watching there is nothing really remarkable at all—that it is perfectly reasonable that two vital young lovers with a lifetime of happiness ahead should calmly destroy themselves over an incident in which they played no part whatever—takes skill and conviction. Certainly not the least remarkable thing about "Patriotism" is that Mishima makes it believable.

Into this story of self-inflicted death, Mishima introduces a subtle undercurrent of sexuality. The lieutenant and his wife are, as we have noted, young, beautiful, and recently married; their last act before taking their lives is to make love. It is not difficult to imagine how a less skillful writer might handle this, but in "Patriotism" the act, although it is performed with considerable joy and heat, becomes, like all of their final preparations, a ceremony—a ritual leave-taking of their bodies and a confirmation of their spiritual union. The lieutenant wonders, as he waits upstairs for his wife, "Was it death he was now waiting for? Or a wild ecstasy of the senses? The two seemed to overlap, almost as if the object of this bodily desire was death itself." The equation of the impulses toward sex and death is not insisted upon by the author, nor does he carry the speculation beyond the lieutenant's remark. But the physical union is clearly symbolic (for the lieutenant and his wife as well as for us) of the spiritual fusion they expect to enjoy in the hereafter, and their calm acceptance of death becomes all the more understandable for the inclusion of the sexual theme.

That Mishima is able to handle so delicate a subject as suicide by disembowelment without turning its final scenes into a mawkish spectacle is due in part to an unemotional, unembellished prose style, but even more to the way in which he prepares the reader for his brutal conclusion by convincing us that his characters' actions are neither cowardly nor unreasoned; that they are the result, in fact, of a courageous sense of honor. It is the fusion of form and content that makes "Patriotism" finally such a powerful and deeply moving story.

J. M. G. LeClezio

A DAY OF OLD AGE

In the cold morning, with the sun not giving a great deal of light, the country was very quiet. It was a kind of suburb, full of low houses, with poor streets where there were no shops, and the tarred surface had been ripped off in patches. If there had been a hill round there, from which one could have had a general view, one would have seen a grey, drab, insignificant place, scattered with dusty trees, gardens where the lawns had bare patches, and dirty houses. Brooks that might have been gutters ran in all directions across the plots of land. To the south, the town began, no doubt, with tall white buildings and straight streets like avenues. To the north was the open country. Between the two was here, this weeded, battered park, inhabited by people who were not to be seen.

Lanes ran between the properties, past the old stone walls, and met to form melancholy crossroads where one or two children played, or sometimes a dog. Species of mimosa with no flowers, pepper-trees and unrecognizable shrubs grew here and there in the gardens. One heard, coming from goodness knows where, a piercing, inhuman shriek, no doubt uttered by a chained-up parrot. Tiny creatures were making their difficult way over the dusty ground, where the cold of the night still held its place with little crystals. In hollows in the rocks and above garage doors, lizards were asleep. There were cocoons everywhere, and even the tiniest holes were occupied by snowy, opaque balls to which dewdrops still clung. The noise of a train was heard from some distance, on the far side of the suburb; it came slowly on, receded, came closer again, disappeared completely, and then re-emerged from the far end of the gaps between the houses. From time to time men went off to work, riding motorized bicycles.

Inside their houses, people were bustling about; wireless sets were bawling in front of the open windows. The steady wail of a vacuum cleaner dispersed into the air. Slipping behind the clouds, the sun was climbing higher in the sky. When it reached its zenith the midday siren would be heard; dishes of food would be laid on the kitchen tables, and the men would come back from their work, to eat. The tree-trunks would crackle with gentle heat, the spiders would walk about in their lairs. Lean cats would come and slink round the gardens, searching for a bone or a cabbage stump. Life was simple in those days. Very quiet and discreet. There were no warlike cries, no tumult or murder. One could stay motionless for hours, among the streets and houses, watching a blade of grass grow. The earth looked quite like a park, and the weather was a miniature. Squares of dust and pale warmth, the imperceptible forward motion of a snail. Sweetish smells, fires everywhere, and the marvellously distant expanse of layers of mauve colour.

Nothing to be afraid of, the earth didn't belong to the tigers or the wolves; it belonged to the mice, to the mosquitoes, to the lizards; they were walking about on it all the time, leaping from one hiding-place to another; at night, they nibbled. The little race of rodents; sand-coloured, with rapid gestures, their tiny hearts beating fit to burst.

In a kitchen with plastic curtains, a boy was sitting on the edge of a stool. Opposite him, at the other end of the white wooden table, an old woman was sitting likewise, in a big wicker armchair. She was not moving, and under her faded pinafore-dress her breast rose and fell slowly, painfully. The skin of her face was white, framed in locks of grey hair, and a little blood had trickled down a deep wrinkle at the corner of her mouth. Her dim eyes, motionless between half-open lids were looking at nothing. On her long, dry hands, warped by the years, the veins stood out, winding between the bones like roots. No one who saw her like this could have had any doubt that the old woman was dying. Gently, for hours already, life had been ebbing from her; it was moving out of one cell after another, leaving only emptiness in its place.

When Joseph, the boy, had come into the house an hour before, bringing her a bag of provisions, he had found her lying on the kitchen floor, half-unconscious. With difficulty, he had hoisted the heavy, inert weight into the armchair, and had spoken to her. She had recovered consciousness; and it was a strange thing, but fear had assailed her at once. She had begun to talk, trembling all the time, believing in her bewilderment that it was Joseph who had hit her, so as to steal her money. She had threatened to call for help if he didn't go away at once. Then she had implored him to go and fetch a doctor, a nurse, a priest, a neighbour, anybody, because she thought she had fractured her skull. She had talked and trembled like that for a good half-hour and then, tired, she had fallen silent. Her movements had grown rarer, her eyes had been drowned in a sort of mist of tears, and her slightly open mouth, from which a little blood was trickling, uttered only incoherent words.

Joseph had stood motionless for a long time, looking at the old woman. He had fixed his eyes on the frightened, suffering face as though he were trying to capture it in an imperishable, photographic pose beneath which he could one day have written a fine surname, fitting, majestic, the living soul of this vanished body.

Mademoiselle Maria VANONI

Then he had sat down facing her, on this kitchen stool; he had put questions to her, in a halting voice. He had spoken gently to her, asking where it hurt, if she were thirsty, if she would like a glass of water, or something. She had nodded, and Joseph had brought her a big glass of water, holding it carefully to her mouth while she drank. After that he had taken the provisions out of the bag and laid them out on the table in front of her. There were: a tin of medium-large peas; three eggs; half a litre of milk; a stick of fine white bread; 200 grammes of gruyère; three tomatoes and some other vegetables; a box of matches; a roll of toilet paper; a cardboard packet of clothes-pegs.

Now Joseph was sitting on the stool again, facing the old woman; he was watching her with all his strength, as time went by. He was staring hungrily at the pale eyes lost in the distance, the half-smiling mouth, the cheeks, criss-crossed with wrinkles so fine that it would certainly have taken months to count them. The heavy, motionless body, almost like a piece of furniture beneath the blackened stuff of the overall. The legs like pillars, the feet buried in incomprehensible masses of elastic stockings, socks and woollen slippers. The face, perhaps beautiful perhaps ugly, with the head leaning back in the armchair, as though offered to the impavid surface of the ceiling. An insinuating smell of phosphorus came softly out of the woman's body, enfolding it like a protection, settling into the atmosphere. Through the kitchen window, other smells came in from the garden, drifted into the room and fought against the old woman's smell: the smell of earth and grass, the smell of burnt leaves, of wind, of trees. They tried to get under the skin, they were seeking the weak point, unhurriedly. If they found it, everything would be finished, once and for all; they would settle into the body, they would fill it, crush it; when they emerged from the woman again she would no longer be a woman, but a sort of abandoned heap of earth and dry branches.

Joseph bent forward on his stool. In a low, almost inaudible voice, he said:

'Are you—Are you afraid of dying, Mademoiselle Marie?'

The glaucous eyes moved in the slit between the eyelids. Joseph said again:

'Are you afraid of dying?'

The old woman uttered a groan.

'Yes, yes—I'm dying—I—'

She began to tremble again. Joseph went on very fast, to reassure her.

'No, you'll see, you're going to get better. I'll fetch the doctor. You'll get better, you'll see. I'll nurse you. Does it hurt? Would you like another drink?'

She shook her head.

'I expect you must have a lot of memories?' said Joseph.

Her eyes brightened a little.

'What's your oldest memory?' asked Joseph. 'If you try to remember as far back as you can, what do you see?'

Maria raised her head slightly.

'I remember everything,' she whispered; 'everything. And it's not so long ago as all that.'

'How old were you?'

'I don't know,' said Maria, 'four or five, perhaps. Perhaps less than that. I was with my sister . . . in our garden . . . There was a terrible thunderstorm, with lightning everywhere. Father came, he said to us, come indoors,—Come indoors, or the lightning will hit you . . . And the lightning did hit the garden . . . It struck a big eucalyptus at the far end. I saw a white light. And I was knocked down on the ground. A cannon shot, there was a cannon shot . . . I was frightened . . .'

She moved her hand.

'It was raining so hard . . .' she whispered.

'That must have been terrifying,' said Joseph.

For a moment neither of them said anything. Then she began talking again.

'My sister's dead too . . . Ten years ago . . . Already . . .'

'She was older than you?'

'No . . . I was the elder . . .'

'What was her name?'

'My sister's? Ida . . . Her name was Ida . . . She went to live in Italy, later on . . . At Verona . . .'

She sighed.

'And now, it's my turn.'

Joseph again tried to reassure her.

'No, no, you'll get better, you'll see, you—'

But she interrupted him with a sort of violence.

'No, that's not true—It's not true, I know I'm going to die now. It can't be helped, my time's come, I know it has.'

She raised her head a little further, dirty grey locks fell over her forehead and the blood ran out of her mouth.

'I'm frightened,' she said; 'I'm frightened . . . And I'm cold . . .'

'What are you thinking about?' asked Joseph.

'Nothing . . . It's there . . . In front of me . . . I know it has to come . . .'

'Does it hurt you?'

'Yes, yes, it hurts. Here, in my head . . . Like an animal biting me . . . And in—in my back—In my legs—Ah.'

'Try to remember some more. Something about when you were little . . .'

'No—No, I can't . . .'

'Your first picture-book, your toys. Try to remember.'

'My toys—Yes . . .'

'What were they like?'

'What . . .'

'Yes, your toys. What kind of toys did you have? Dolls?'

'Yes . . . Dolls.'

'What were they like? Try to remember.'

'There was—A fair-haired one—I called her Nani—And a dark-haired one, too—I called her Sarah . . .'

'And then? What else?'

'There was—A cat . . . He was my cat, I remember . . . I was very fond of him . . . And then, when he died—They buried him—I remember, it's remained there, carved in my head. I've never been able to forget it . . . It's stayed in my head . . . Carved for ever . . .'

Story of the Black-and-White Cat

When the black-and-white cat began to die, the little girl picked him up in her arms and carried him away to the bottom of the garden. He had been a fine cat in his day, big and fat, with a glossy coat, soft paws, a broad head with shining green eyes, long, stiff whiskers, and a black spot just above his nose. When he walked through the tall grass in the garden he seemed like a lion or something of the kind—powerful, muscular, lithe, really formidable. He would creep silently up to a lizard, and suddenly his paw would dart like greased lightning, claws widespread, and the little creature would roll over, its spine broken. Or he would lie asleep on the terrace, in the sunshine, both arms outstretched in front of him and his head high, stately and handsome as a sphinx. In rutting periods he would go long distances to hunt out other cats and fight them. Sometimes he came home with deep wounds over his ears, and the little girl would bandage him. He spent most of the day lying on the stones, not moving. Except, perhaps, from time to time, the tip of his black and white tail would wriggle nervously on the ground. He had funny pads under his feet, and his eye-teeth were so long they pushed up the corners of his mouth like a fixed grin. Sometimes he was angry, and then his fur would slowly bristle up all over, hair by hair. His green eyes would flash lightning, he would keep sheathing and unsheathing his claws, and he would prowl round, breathing hoarsely, his tail lashing against his flanks. At night he used to go out of the house and roam about the garden, aimlessly, for hours on end. Then his eyes would shine in the shadows with a strange, uneasy glint, as though things rose up in him during the darkness, feverish instincts, millions of years old, all the fear and all the cruelty of the wild beasts alone amid nature, their proffered victim. On that particular night, before he died, he had uttered two piercing cries. The little girl carried him away in her arms to the bottom of the garden; she hid in the old, unused hen-house and watched the cat. She listened to his gasps, she felt the long painful shudders running up through his fur. The cat's mouth was open, he was trying to bite the child's hands. But it was too late already; the great green, phosphorescent eyes could see nothing any more, the nose was no longer sniffing up smells. A sticky, dirty emptiness had come in everywhere. It had blurred the pupils of the eyes, and the animal's defeated gaze was turned to pulp. Inside the loose sack of the body the organs—muscles, heart, lungs—were all mixed up as well. The little girl watched the cat without crying, then she stroked him where he liked to be stroked, behind his head, at the back of his neck, in the small of his back. She blew into his ears. Then she laid him on a silk scarf in a big wooden box. To one side of the box, touching the tiny head, she placed an ivory crucifix which must have been a present from one of her godmothers. She didn't put the lid on at once, but stayed gazing at the heap of shabby fur, with its dirty white and dirty black patches. She looked at it hard, so as not to forget it. Then she went back to the house and said nothing about it. And every day, in secret, she returned to the hen-house and took the lid off the box. It was the frightful smell that warned her parents, after a fortnight. They said nothing, but they poured petrol over the box and threw a match on it.

'How old was he?'
'Fifteen—That's old for a cat.'
'He must have been a fine cat.'
'Yes—Oh yes. He was a fine cat . . .'
The old woman rested her head on the back of the chair.
'I've been thinking for a long time that I should have to die, you know . . .' she said.
'Me too . . .' said Joseph.

'Oh no, it's not the same with you . . . You're too young . . . You don't really think about it.'

'I—'

'It surely doesn't frighten you . . . Whereas I . . .'

'Why be afraid?'

'Because it's there, so close . . . There's nothing to be done, you understand? Nothing—Because it's inside me, and I can feel it coming softly, softly, without seeming to.'

She closed her eyes.

'Because I see it everywhere, everywhere, everywhere. Everything I see is old, worn out . . . Old like me.'

'Try to forget.'

'Try to forget—Impossible. I can't do it.'

'Why not?'

'When I shut my eyes, I see things—Strange things. Terrifying things. Skulls, I see skulls . . . And devils coming up to me and saying . . . It's your turn . . . It's your turn . . .'

'But you—You believe in God?'

'Why . . . Why do you ask that?'

'You believe in eternal life, don't you?'

The old woman lifted her head with difficulty. She murmured:

'Yes, yes—I believe in God—But sometimes, when I'm frightened, I think . . . I think, suppose it's not true? Suppose there's nothing? Nothing at all? All this life, all that . . . For nothing . . . I'm frightened . . .'

'You haven't got confidence?'

She looked at Joseph with a sort of anger:

'No! No! I haven't got confidence! I haven't got confidence!'

She began trembling again.

'If I had confidence—If I really had confidence, I shouldn't be frightened. But I feel—It seems to me, I—I feel there's nothing there, where I'm going. There's nothing waiting for me. I feel that. I'm so cold. That's because there's nothing . . .'

She tried to smile, but only succeeded in pulling an ugly face.

'I'm not very brave, am I?'

Joseph looked at her, deeply touched.

'But you are—You're very brave,' he said.

She struggled to speak.

'In the old days—I thought dying was easy. But it's difficult. I don't want . . . I don't want to feel myself slipping away. I don't want to find I can't breathe any more. To fight against death . . . Against it . . . I want to stay here, to stay here. I'm afraid it will hurt. That I shan't be able to . . .'

She looked at Joseph with clouded eyes.

'Like the cat . . . He tried to bite me . . . To bite me, me . . . Why— Why are you staying here—Watching me . . . Help me. No, go away! Go away!'

She began to breathe more heavily. Her head fell back and her eyes stared up at the ceiling; a kind of sweat was moistening her forehead, near the grey locks, and her dress, round the shoulders.

'I can hear my heart . . .' she said; 'it's beating. It's beating hard. I don't want it to stop. It's beating so hard. I want to remain myself . . . Not to disappear, no, not to disappear . . . It mustn't . . .'

Joseph got up and went to fetch a glass of water; then he came back to the woman, who was breathing with difficulty, and poured a little water between her lips. She drank thirstily.

'That's good . . . Thank you . . .' she whispered.

'Just keep quiet,' said Joseph.

She looked at him weakly.

'Why are you staying?' she faltered.

'You—You'd rather I went away?' asked Joseph.

'No, no—Stay here,' she said; 'I think it's over. It'll be better now.'

'Just rest. Don't think about anything,' said Joseph.

'Yes . . . I'm very tired now . . . I'm done up.'

'Just rest.'

'Yes, I'll rest.'

'Go to sleep, try to go to sleep.'

'Yes, perhaps . . . I'll try.'

She closed her eyes; her breathing was almost regular again, and her withered face, so distorted a little time ago, seemed to be reconstructing itself. Joseph walked about the kitchen for a moment, making no noise. He looked out of the window, between the plastic curtains, and saw the great expanse of clear blue sky, with big white and grey clouds scurrying across it. In the garden a bird was calling intermittently. The trees stood straight, and their leaves were twirling round in the wind like little metal weathercocks.

The boy went out on to the terrace and walked a little way along its mosaic-pebbled floor. In a corner a full dustbin had been taken by storm by the ants. A broom was propped against the wall, head in air; the bristles were full of some sort of downy fluff mixed with hair. Joseph picked up some dates that had fallen from the date-palm, and threw them one by one into the garden.

When he returned to the kitchen he saw that the old woman's eyes were still closed. He went up to her and said:

'Are you asleep?'

'No,' she replied, without raising her eyelids.

The plaster was peeling off the cream-washed walls of the room and there were stains everywhere; on the floor, near the furniture, on the door, on the ceiling. Funny whitish patches, with big, colourless rings round them. The smell of death pervaded the whole place. To begin with, it was quiet, with an absolute stillness that brought a lump into your throat; repressed scents, too, subtle shapes which had ceased to pry about in the air, had all turned towards the woman's body and were overwhelming it.

Thus, everything was going on there, inside; there was nothing outside, nothing arriving unexpectedly to surprise you. It was a continual flight, the retreat of the organs and bones, a gradual, furtive obliteration. Joseph stood in front of the old woman lying back in the armchair; and from her closed eyes, her dry, compressed lips which stirred with a weak sucking movement, from her whole forlorn, overall-clad body, he received, as it were, deep, cruel blows in his own face. Her broad face, full of cartilage and flesh, with its livid skin, closed down in the centre like a sea-anemone. Her hands, her legs, her sunken bust, all seemed to be drawn in by a savage mouth, by a star-shaped wound whose wrinkled edges were clinging together, making ghastly efforts to skin over. In fact there was nothing left but this mouth, or this anus, which was retracting, folding back, an old snake-skin, smothering itself, swallowing itself, swallowing itself without disgust. One should do the same, no doubt—live inside oneself, push one's head down into one's body, feed on one's own flesh, consume oneself completely, criminally, to the point of oblivion. Then, if time were emptied of its drugs, one would perceive the dark expanse, a veritable hall with shining holes in it, where words and suffering have no more hold, where everything is bare, swallowed up, suffocated. In the depths of this glasshouse one would sometimes hear the crystal footfalls of eternity, a trembling music which licks at sleep. Like that. Lasciviously. Indolently. For its own satisfaction.

Joseph touched the old woman's hand.

'Are you asleep now?' he said softly.

As before, she answered, without opening her eyes:

'No . . .'

'Don't you want to sleep a little?'

'No . . . I'm quite all right now.'

'You're not frightened any longer?'

'No . . . I'm all right.'

'Would you—like me to go for the doctor, now?'

'No, no—There's no more need, now. I'm all right . . . Quite all right . . .'

'You're not afraid of dying, any more?'

'I'm going to die, yes . . .'

'And you're not afraid, any longer?'

'No . . . I'm all right . . .'

'It doesn't hurt any more?'

'. . . No . . . I'm cold, but it doesn't matter . . .'

'Would you like a blanket?'

'No, no, it's—The cold is inside me.'

'Are you thirsty? Shall I bring you a glass of water?'

'No, no . . .'

'What are you thinking about?'

'I'm all right—Really.'

'What makes you feel so comfortable?'

'I don't know—It seems to me—I see such lovely things . . .'

'You see things? What do you see?'

'It's beautiful . . .'

'But what does it look like? Tell me.'

'I don't know . . . Clouds, perhaps . . . Horses . . .'

'What else? What else?'

'. . . Yes, horses . . . Men in armour . . . Gilded . . . In a golden rain . . . And tall, so tall that their heads are in the clouds . . . It's strange . . .

White mountains, too. Snow everywhere . . . They have helmets on their heads . . .'

'What else is there?'

'Fire. I see fire. It doesn't move . . . Burning all the time . . . In all directions . . . The flames are coming towards me . . . They're shooting up . . . It's beautiful . . .'

'What's it burning? Houses?'

'Yes . . . It seems—It seems as though it were burning down in the water . . . With big bubbles. Big black bubbles. And smoke.'

'What else do you see, Mademoiselle Maria?'

'There's a very tall man, too . . . He's coming nearer . . . All white, he's hovering in the air . . . He's smiling . . . He's stretching out his arms like a cross . . . And he's speaking . . . Jesus . . . It's Jesus . . .'

'What's he like?'

'. . . He's praying . . . No—He's laughing . . . He's laughing loudly. I feel like laughing too . . . I don't understand—I don't understand why Jesus is laughing . . . In front of me . . . It's funny . . . With such a white face . . . Like my father . . . And his arms stretched out . . . Sweat pouring down his forehead . . . Drops of blood pouring down his forehead . . . He's still laughing . . . There are people round him . . . Women . . .'

'Women?'

'Yes, Martha, Mary . . . I can see them . . . They're laughing too . . . And Jesus . . . Is wearing a helmet . . . He has armour that shines like gold . . . His teeth are shining like gold . . . Like gold . . .'

'What's he doing now?'

'I don't know . . . He's disappeared . . . No, he's coming back . . . With pillars, there, round him . . . The women are touching his robe . . . I can hear his heart beating . . . Everything is rising into the air . . . It's smoke . . . There are balconies . . . Children—Doors . . . And windows . . . With light . . .'

'And Jesus? What's he doing?'

'He's singing . . . I'm singing with him . . . With him . . .'

'You can hear him?'

'Yes, yes . . . I can hear him . . . For me . . . He's singing . . . With my voice . . .'

'What else is there?'

'His hands are bleeding . . . And the blood is falling down as precious stones . . . rubies . . . They're glittering everywhere . . . I can pick them up in my hands . . . They're warm . . . The red . . . Is . . . Warm . . . Rubies . . . Topazes . . . There, in the water . . . And the flowers, and— The gold, the gold, pouring out . . . Through the windows . . . With the army . . . of the knights . . . In white . . . The crosses, the crosses . . . The pillars in the grass . . . Gold everywhere, everywhere . . . It's mounting up . . . It's burning me . . . I want . . . To laugh . . . With Jesus . . . Again . . . Ah . . . Ah . . .'

The old woman's voice died away in a sort of moan; the soft, sad murmur entered into Joseph's head and paralysed him. With throbbing heart and hands damp with sweat, he could only hear it, hear it without pause, without defence. The sound nailed him to the spot like this for another few seconds. Then it stopped, silence leapt into the kitchen and separated everything.

Hours had gone by, and Joseph was walking in the town. To begin with he had hung about the streets near the shabby house where the old woman was alone, asleep in her wicker armchair. He had not met anybody, except perhaps some groups of children playing, and two or three Arab workmen who were employed in a builder's yard. For a moment he had thought hesitantly of going home, to be with his parents. Then he had gone on along the streets, strolling with his hands in his pockets, his mind a blank. A sort of small anguish was occupying his spirit; it made him see things clearly, the minutest details of the scenery, the unevenness of the ground, the twisted shapes of the houses with their open windows. He looked at it all with burning, empty eyes, and it was as though he were walking inside himself, with no noise, no colour, no hatred, along a road enclosed in a glass box, down endless paths where his feet sank in deep and were held fast.

Perhaps he was no longer himself, now; perhaps it had really become meaningless to refer to himself by his name, Joseph Charon, son of Frédéric Charon, house-agent, and Mme Gertrude Charon, née Ciabarelli. What matter if he were tall or short, thin, fat, blue-eyed or brown-eyed? Bound to the moving features of one single old woman, impotent as she was—linked to her glassy, melancholy gaze, stripped of all strength by the memory of her sagging muscles and flaccid skin, treacherously invaded by the whole of that derelict body, in cold and dizziness and silence, Joseph was, so to speak, being lived by her. He was living like a picture, something in the nature of a damp reflection, exposed every second to annihilation and evaporation. That was the real danger. Somewhere beyond the plots of ground and the low houses, in a kitchen, an old woman might depart from the world almost without noticing it.

She would pass easily, in the midst of a shudder, and with her would go all the secrets, all the hopes, all the odious mysteries of life. Those one had to know. Those that were of great value.

Joseph reached the main road, turned left and began to walk along by the grass bank. Cars rushed past in groups of three or four. As they went over a slight rise, their wheels shivered and clanked. When they reached the bend they changed gears, because after that there was a short, steep hill. Joseph watched them as he went along; he saw red ones, blue ones, black ones, grey ones; all makes; all shapes; some of them had bumps on their coachwork, usually along the mudguards. Inside these hermetic shells people sat huddled together, their heads poking forward slightly. For a split second one saw their pale faces, their dark glasses, their hands clutching the wheel. Some of them threw a quick sideways glance in Joseph's direction; then they went on, straight ahead, as though drawn along rails. The sound of their engines rapidly diminished, and stopped before they reached the bend, far down the road. There was something hard and malevolent while these cars rushed straight along the flat road;

an obstinacy, a stiff, almost painful force. Uninterruptedly they streamed by, in groups of three or four, like that, and with noises that didn't remain. Their rounded metal rumps drew away, shining, side-slipping all the time, like heavy, clumsy insects. The hard meteors flashed across the scene, brushing past Joseph, and turned the corner. Leaving no trace, not digging the slightest furrow. An independent phenomenon, sliding past, full of malice and chaos. Each self-contained, each taking the bend towards its own domain, with its own time and space, and these stretches of road swallowed up and paid out under its belly. Inside the little prisons with their open windows, the scenery marched past together with the wind. Each of them carried death in it, the brutal pylon that would split open the metal crust and search down to the man's heart, to the depths of his shattered breast, quickly, very quickly, no longer than was needed for him to open his mouth with a cry cut short at once. That was certain. As cruel and sharp as fear. For these people, these fat men in their cloth suits, nothing mattered except the leakage of minutes and of money, like this, down to the last second of their paltry lives, without cohesion, irrationally.

A small stone got into Joseph's right shoe and slid under the sole of his foot. As he walked, the boy could feel it working through his sock and scratching his skin. He went on for a few yards, limping slightly, trying unsuccessfully to wriggle the stone down to the tip of his sock by curling his toes and shaking his foot. Then, when he realized that the scrap of gravel would stay where it was and, if he didn't care, would grow huge, a suppurating wound, and soon fill all his thoughts, he stopped on the edge of a kind of pavement and took off his shoe; he turned it upside down, and with a brief tinkle the stone fell into the gutter and vanished among a sea of other little stones, all looking alike. Joseph put on his shoe again and walked away.

He came to the beginning of the bend. There was a grocer's shop there, with a queue of people; along the pavement outside the shop there was a row of big earthenware vases with geraniums in them. Joseph stopped and stood leaning against the wall of the grocery. It was shady here; the pavement, the road, the opposite houses, were full of a queer melancholy that hovered over the whitewashed walls, the rough concrete surfaces, the windowless curtains where there was a single, black, quite motionless gleam. One didn't know what to do. There was dust everywhere, and the sound of the cars changing gears was interspersed with bursts of twanging music, an accordion or perhaps a mouth-organ. The telegraph poles rose up stiffly towards the cloudy sky, planes often flew above the roofs. There was no means of guessing the time, nothing caught or arrested one's attention. It was all bare, rapid, poverty-stricken. Concrete; cubes of concrete jumped together, with here and there some kind of earthy fissures where shrubs were trying to grow. Joseph watched all this without moving. Suddenly, with no warning, the air began to stir. The wind began to blow from the far end of the road; a very cold, continuous wind that blew down towards the town and broke on the objects it met. It whistled in the boy's ears, rushing straight in his stubborn direction, flattening his clothes against his body and making his flesh quiver. It ruffled his hair, raised the dust and threw it in his eyes, causing hot tears which evaporated at once. Its invisible presence covered the flat surfaces of the earth, constantly filling up all hollows and uneven places. Noiselessly, or almost, except for this long-drawn-out whistle that seemed to penetrate the very substance of things, to mingle with it until nothing certain, dissociable remained, between that emptiness and that fullness, the wind blew, advanced yet remained, slid like a sheet of water, undecided at times and then flapping in sharp gusts, searching down into the depths of the flesh for everything cold and stupid so as to bring it back to the surface and score a victory.

Joseph, still leaning against the wall outside the grocery, saw the landscape slowly changing into a desert; he felt the continual movement of the air entering his lungs, edging into the most secret depths of his organs. Icy breezes began to blow inside his body; his bones grew weak, his muscles ceased to obey him. His clothes hung loosely on him like tattered rags, as though upon a scarecrow, and his hands, their fingers mottled, opened and closed several times, meeting only emptiness. The wind was blowing in his head as well; it had tightened into a sort of icy, restless, tumultuous ball, which had scattered all his ideas. The whole landscape had got into his skull, a great scene of nakedness and cold, where the street lay motionless, lined with white houses, where the pavements were taken up by earthenware pitchers in which geraniums shivered with tiny vibrations, where every object, moving, calm and ferocious—the cars, the black-glinting window-panes, the translucid sky, the concrete telegraph poles, the road—was set there as though to all eternity, immovable, disorderly, crushing in its weight and silence, stable and savage in the corridor through which the wind was rushing.

Vacancy had taken complete possession of Joseph's mind; the boy could stay there, leaning against the shop-wall, staring straight ahead of him, for a whole year, no doubt. Indistinguishable from the grey wall, spread out right in the middle of the daubs of paint, more invisible than a stain, he could have gazed and gazed to his heart's content. Nothing would have moved, for his gaze would have somehow paralysed the scene; in this place, covered with dust or perhaps with snow, abominable time would have gained no hold. For the boy's gaze would have gone beyond, to the very heart, it would have sought in the midst of things for what is called the picture, the imperishable, serene photograph, nature in person, neither living nor dead, where the world makes only one single, majestic movement of birth, of fulfilment, and there the gaze would have stopped, have ceased to be a gaze, have become in its turn an act of complete enjoyment, the delectable fusion of two beings without purpose.

But the time had not yet come, for Joseph. For him, life was still to be long; a burden with no future and no joy, which he would probably have to bear for at least another fifty years. The moment of infinity was not yet due; time would be long, his body would be eager for food and movement. The trivialities were awaiting him, men's jobs, exchanges of idle words, money, women, all that, all that, all this hideous fatigue piling up ahead of him. He must pull himself together, tear his eyes away from the fascination of the empty scene, close his whole body to the wind that had begun to enter into it.

Joseph left the support of the wall and walked on again. He went down the road towards the town. He began to pass people. The earth was decidedly a populous place; in all directions there were moving figures, faces, legs in action. Nothing was at rest. At the street-crossings the traffic lights blinked away with an electrical purr. The houses were all different, some tall, twelve or thirteen storeys, others squat, painted beige, others ancient, with colonnades of a sort. There were a lot of shops, and people were crowding round their windows. Noise was rising from all sides, confused, jerky, and smells were wafting out of all the doors, tiny living particles which had broken away from the hot objects spread out for sale: sausages, brioches, textiles, flowers, oranges, chickens, coffee, books, fish, cars. The colours were harassing, too; they glowed on walls, on clothes, in the backs of shops. Blues, yellows, golds, milky whites. The light falling from the sky was reflected back from their varnished surfaces, it got into your eyes, thrust itself into your head; phrases took birth under its familiar impulses, sterile, half-formed phrases. Their echoes had magic power, which disturbed everything, made you a man once and for all. No escape from them: there they were, mixed up with every passing second, they were subjugating you to time and space. Words stamped on the memory, engraved on it, prisoners of the same form, indelible, indecipherable. They sang. Or they lit up, one letter after another, without fatigue, O.L.I.V.E.T.T.I. Feverishly they jotted down on pieces of cardboard their little breathless, aggressive, unhesitating signs. One was their property, one listened as they talked, one never denied them anything. KODAK. Aspro banishes pain.

If you want to
Give
Your friends
A treat
Remember
Offer them
A Martini
I like Shell!

Philips is more reliable.

HERTZ

Coca-Cola
Dubo, Dubon, Dubonnet.

Végétaline for fried potatoes.

Esso Motor Oil Anti-Sludge
TERGAL Polyester Fibre and Wool
Gillette Razors
Have you Macleaned your teeth?
TELEFUNKEN
Adelshoffen
Honda
State Express Filter Kings
Eterna-matic

The Astorians
Persil washes Whiter

Triumph of pain—Treachery of the eyes, the ears, the skin. One has to trudge through this desert all one's life. To see and hear. To hear and see. To eat. To laugh. To talk, smoke, drink. To feel. To procreate. To write. To breathe. To be in pain. To bleed, to tremble. To be angry. To suffer. To cry out, to sleep, to wait. Fatigue is everywhere. There is no way, really no way of avoiding it. One has to toil, to feel hot, to feel cold. To caress. To enjoy. To understand, to understand without pause. Every day. Like that, every day, without exception. To urinate. To taste. To let oneself be carried away by useless words, to adopt paces and habits. To seek for phrases, to stretch one's ears and eyes, to stretch one's skin. To pretend to love, to love really, perhaps. All that, not even for nothing; for it's not even possible to resort to nothingness so as to determine one's life; man is not alone; vulgar, garish things inhabit him, shape him. There's no way of judging. There is no absurdity, for there is not even any separation between what is and what ought to be. God, if he exists, must be left in full control: never, no, never, shall we really know what a little worm man is.

The road, as it crossed the town, had become a boulevard. In a gentle slope, it led Joseph down to the sea; at this point there was no beach, only a sort of overhanging cliff. Joseph leant on the iron railing and looked at the precipice. And then, all of a sudden, another fascination loomed up to take possession of his mind. The abyss became a narrow, deep, absolutely empty well. Right at the bottom the water gleamed in the sun, like a tiny puddle; an almost imperceptible movement ruffled its surface, troubling the reflection of the sky; little waves were going and coming in all directions, crossing one another, mingling like the waves of the wind over an expanse of grass. At the edge of the abyss, thick black rocks lay side by side; from time to time an exceptionally large wave heaved up the surface of the water and covered their rumps; the transparent water spread over the rounded masses, filled up hollow places, cascaded down furrows, swam where it lay, like smoke. Then the wave withdrew, and strange dark mouths opened out and closed up, seething with bubbles; soon, where they had been, along the shiny rocks, nothing was left except a fringe of foam, a patch of tattered, dirty froth, drifting away over the sea like spittle.

Joseph stared down into the abyss for a long time. With his head bent forward, over the balustrade, he felt himself gradually invaded by dangerous vertigo; the precipitous fall of rock, the ebb and flow of the water, flat like a manhole cover, the noise of the surf, were all calling to him. He let his body curve forward, as though drawn by an invisible air-pocket. He saw himself falling, rising in reverse, towards the centre of the earth. His fixed, wide-open eyes were already staring at the point of impact; they were already feeling the hard, undulating surface of the sea, they were melting into the whirlpools like great, indolent pieces of seaweed.

Just as he was perhaps really about to fall, to shoot over the iron railing and be turned to stone, someone touched his arm. Joseph looked round and saw a man staring at him. He heard a voice asking him a question, tearing him out of his dream. The voice said again:

'Don't you feel well?'

The man was watching him with a sort of cruel gleam in his eyes; Joseph saw him very distinctly; a tweed jacket, gold-rimmed spectacles, bald head, lines round the mouth and on the forehead. The man's hand was still on his arm, and Joseph saw a metal ring with two entwined initials: X.C.

He freed himself with a jerk. The man, who was about fifty, said hesitantly:

'Don't you feel well?'

Joseph muttered:

'Yes—Yes, I'm all right . . .'

And he walked quickly away.

Further on he went past a school and saw the time by its clock: 2.30.

He looked at a kind of war memorial as well, a great slab of white marble with names carved on it. The ground really belonged to these dead. The rocks, the olive-trees, the beaches, the rows of vines, were all their property. One could pretend not to know it, but they, with their names carved there, with their tranquil names spreading over the slabs, they owned everything, they were the masters. They were vigilant, hidden underground, they were watching everything through the port-holes of their tombs; they were the secret judges, and nothing escaped them.

Joseph went on his way. He wasn't hungry, and didn't know what to do. So he went into a non-stop cinema and sat through the film two or three times. It was *Quand la Marabunta gronde, Sept heures avant la frontière*, or something of the sort.

When Joseph came out of the cinema it wasn't so very light any more. The sky was covered with grey clouds, and the people in the streets were hurrying to get home. In front of the cinema the boy hesitated for a moment. Then he turned left and walked up the road towards the suburb again. He walked for quite a long time like that, while the shadows deepened and the first strips of neon began to light up in the shop windows. Men and women were always the same, everywhere; in their pale faces the features didn't move, their noses remained fixed and their wrinkles grew no more numerous. And yet they were in movement, constantly, they were living uninterruptedly. Their footfalls rapped out along the pavements, counting the seconds, the minutes, the hours. Even if you saw nothing pass, you should be under no illusion; their skin was crumpling, their hearts were wearing out, then and there, gently, with every gesture, at every opportunity. Sometimes their children were scampering round them, those little morsels of flesh and blood which had come out of themselves and would be old one day. Men and women might escape all massacres and all wars, they might emerge unscathed from poliomyelitis and railway accidents, but they wouldn't escape from their children. That was the truth, which must be known once and for all. In forty years, or perhaps sooner, these will be words written by a dead man. And in two hundred years, in any case, nothing that exists today, nothing of this second, will still be alive. When you've read this line, you must turn your eyes away from the mean little scrawl. Breathe, take a strong, deep breath, be alive to the point of ecstasy. Because soon, truly, there won't be much left of you.

Joseph halted on the kerb, near a bus-stop. To the left of the metal post, which bore the notice IA, several people were waiting. Two women in raincoats, a man in a brown suit, a student, a workman, and three other women carrying bags. Joseph studied them at his leisure, one by one. They had undistinguished, rather ugly faces, marked by the fatigue of the day's work. The man in the brown suit was finishing a cigarette; the student was carrying books and kept tapping on the ground with the toe of his right shoe; the two women in the front row watched the cars go by in silence; the workman's hands were thrust into the pockets of his overalls; the three women at the back were chatting, two of them animatedly, the third putting in a word now and then. When the bus arrived they would go off in it, without looking back. They would get off the bus further along, on the edge of the town, and go home to cook supper. Their houses would be hot and noisy, with a wireless or television set talking to itself against the dining-room wall.

Joseph ran over every detail of their faces, as though he meant to caricature them. Long noses, straight or too-curled hair, dark-ringed eyes, faint moustaches, crows' feet, dry lips. Why should all this have to change? Weren't things all right as they were? A mawkish sadness emanated from these creatures; wreaths of memories rose up from every angle of their faces. That precise instant, that meeting of nose and lip, of a lock of hair and the line of a cheek, had no existence. So that was reality! A passage, a fall, a burial. For the days of childhood had gone by right enough, as well. The childish bodies, the bright laughter, the clean eyes. And the time of their mothers' childhood had succumbed too, with its long dresses and pigtails. Everything was buried one within the other, under layers and layers of filth, excrement, oblivion. These women's faces, so clear-cut in appearance, so firm that they seemed to be moulded in bronze, did not really exist; they were only gelatine, trails of mud, rottenness, abscess, gangrene!

A tanker-waggon came slowly along the boulevard; Joseph saw it from a long way off; it was snorting like a pig, the iron plates on its flanks were rattling, the glass panes of the driver's cab were flashing with dark glints. Overloaded, no doubt, it crawled painfully along the kerb, its effort so visible that it seemed to be tearing off scraps of asphalt. On the front of the roof there was printed, as though in letters of fire, a magic word:

TOTAL

Joseph watched the approach of the word, of the ridiculous yet haughty sign. He felt something stir inside him—fear, or perhaps obedience. Then he looked at the wheels of the lorry, and his recent vertigo swept over him again. The bulging surfaces were revolving, advancing ponderously alongside the pavement, and the sort of pattern that was stamped on the rubber seemed to zigzag as it went down towards the ground. There, everything vanished under the weight of the tanker-waggon; the elastic mass crushed down on the sanded surface and the wheel went on turning, advancing, without a jerk, without a pause, like the gigantic mouth of some devouring beast. A smell of vulcanite hung in the air, mixed with the clouds of petrol fumes; in front, behind and to either side there must surely be silence. For all violence seemed to have concentrated in the belly of the machine, of the quivering, steel-plated monster on whose brow the magic word was written, while from each open wing, as though from a mouth, there poured the uninterrupted cascade of the wheels, the torrents of black rubber stamped with Z's which tore this weight from the motionless ground and hauled it forward, toilsomely, majestically, advancing so slowly that they seemed hardly to move from the spot.

For a moment Joseph was seized by a desire to throw himself under the enormous wheels, to make himself into a road, and to feel the pattern of the rubber being stamped into his skin. It was a temptation resembling the one he had felt two or three years before, when he was thirteen. One evening he had unhooked the native dagger from a trophy on the drawing-room wall, taken it away to his bedroom and there, alone, had pressed the point against his chest. Anxiously, he had heard the dull vibrations of his heart climbing up the blade of the knife to his hand, clenched round the hilt. He'd tried to press a little harder, so as to pierce the skin. But he had jerked the dagger away, not so much because it hurt as because he was terrified by those vibrant heart-beats. Never would he forget it: the disgusting intoxication of feeling that life and soul can be deflated by a single prick, like a bladder full of air.

The tanker-waggon went past, close to the kerb, a few inches from the boy, who didn't move; then, blowing its horn, it drove on, out of the town. Joseph, with a last glance at the women and the men, who were still waiting, walked away too.

Among the thickening shadows of the kitchen, the old woman was still seated in her wicker armchair. Nothing had moved. The plastic curtains were hanging at the window, the walls and ceiling had the same pale marks, and on the table the provisions were still spread out, just as they had rolled out of the bag. Joseph advanced a few steps into the room, trying to see through the dusk. His eyes fell on the body lying back in the chair, shapeless under its dress. The old woman's feet were flat on the ground, both pointing in his direction. Her head lay against the chair-back, her face was expressionless. With closed eyes, pinched nostrils and tight lips, it was attached to the rest of her body like a block of grey stone, almost without need. One had the impression that one could just as well have taken it off and put it somewhere else, like a cushion.

The approach of darkness had covered everything, as it were, with whitish, dusty cobwebs, which floated on the surface of things and gathered in corners. The vague glow from the sky was still coming in through the window, but it was not lighting up the room: on the contrary, it was removing colour and outline from the contents of the kitchen. Like water, water dirty from having done thousands and thousands of washes, the shadow was muddying the living shapes and picking out, in the old woman's face, everything that was decrepit and lacklustre. For a few seconds, even, Joseph had the impression she was really dead. He tiptoed up to the armchair and whispered:

'Mademoiselle Maria? Mademoiselle Maria?'

Bending over the ashen face, he saw the faint signs of life: a palpitation of the nostrils, a wheezing slightly gurgling respiration, movements of the eyes beneath the closed lids. He touched the old woman's shoulder with his hand and said again:

'Mademoiselle Maria?'

'Mademoiselle Maria?'

She seemed to hear; her lids quivered, her lips parted. A strange sound emerged from the yellow, dried-up mouth where the blood had clotted:

'Ah. Ah. Ah. Ah. Ah.'

'Does it hurt you?' asked Joseph.

Her eyes appeared, between the swollen lids; two glassy, transparent eyes, without a tear. The voice struggled to speak:

'Ah. Ah. I can't see any more. Ah. Ah. I can't see anything any more. Ah. Ah. Ah.'

But these words wouldn't come. Somewhere in the brain they had got stuck, hidden with the tons of pictures and memories, and they could not escape from their prison any more. Soon, in a few hours at most, they would be rotting underground, the words, they would be obliterated like the pages of a dictionary. The songs and poems were finished. Words were only reflections, fleeting reflections easily covered by the darkness. The ideas, the fine phrases, the monuments, those are the vain imaginings. Not one of them will beget life, not one will escape the order they are trying to battle with. And if it must be said, there is not one temple, with its marble arcades, not one tool, not one book that is worth the tiniest gnat lost in the world.

Joseph listened for a moment to the murmurs which were trying to cross the barrier of her mouth. Then he began to speak:

'Do you hear me, Mademoiselle Maria? You hear me, don't you?'

The dark face assented.

'I want—I want you not to die. I don't know how to put it—You understand? Try to speak to me. Try to tell me something. Like just now. What you're seeing. For you are seeing things, aren't you? You're seeing things? I'd so much like—Tell me what you see. Like just now, like just now, you remember?'

The lips quivered, but no sound could get out. Everything in her throat was dry, no doubt. With a sort of desperation, Joseph sensed that everything was going to escape him. The moment he had so much longed for, the ineffable instant when mind topples and rejoins matter, was going to be lost in the distance. A whole life, seventy-five years of fatigue and enjoyment, peace and unhappiness, would dissolve into smoke, useless, abandoned. Joseph bent close to the old woman's face and looked at her with implacable resolution. But nothing came. Suddenly he had a brilliant idea; if she couldn't speak any longer, perhaps she could write? With feverish gestures, Joseph tore off a piece of paper from the wrapping round the string beans; with great care he placed a ball-point pencil between the limp fingers and holding the paper steady, he said rapidly:

'Mademoiselle Maria? You hear me, don't you? Write. Write what you're feeling. I want you to. Write. I'll help you to write. Will you do it? Do you hear me? Write. Please Write.'

The old hand began to move, falteringly; slowly, awkwardly, the ball-point wrote letters, one after another, capital letters. Then, when it was finished, the hand fell down and dangled for a moment, with open fingers. Across the piece of greyish paper sprawled a line of funny-looking black letters. They read:

I'M CO
L
D

Leonid Andreyev

THE SEVEN WHO WERE HANGED

I At one p.m. your Excellency

As the minister was a very stout man, inclined to apoplexy, all possible precautions were taken so that he should not be dangerously excited by the news that a serious attempt on his life was about to be made. On seeing, however, that the minister took the information calmly, and even smiled, he was given the details. The assassination was planned for the following morning, when he would be due to leave the house with his official report. A number of terrorists had been denounced by an informer and were being kept under vigilant watch by detectives. Armed with bombs and revolvers, they were to meet at one p.m. in front of the house to await his coming out. There they were to be trapped.

"Wait a minute," said the minister in surprise. "How do they know that I am to go with my report at one p.m., when I myself only knew it the day before yesterday?"

The chief of the secret service made a vague gesture with his hands.

"Exactly at one p.m., your Excellency," he said.

The minister shook his head, half in surprise, half in approval of the measures taken by the police, who had managed things so well; and a gloomy smile appeared on his thick, dark lips. Then, obediently and still with the same smile on his face, he got ready quickly, so as not to hamper the police, and drove off to spend the night in the hospitable mansion put at his disposal. His wife and two children were also removed from the dangerous house round which the bomb throwers were to gather next day.

While lights were on in the friend's mansion and polite, familiar faces bowed to him and smilingly expressed their indignation, the dignitary felt a kind of pleasant excitement—as if he had been given or was about to be given some great and unexpected prize. But people went away, the lights were put out and through the plate-glass windows a ghastly, lace-like light from the electric street lamps lay upon the ceiling and walls. Alien to the house, with its statues, and silence, the light entering from the street, quiet and undefined, evoked the agonising thought of the futility of bolts and guards and walls. It was then, in the stillness and solitude of the night in a strange bedroom, that the dignitary was overcome with unbearable fear.

He had been suffering from kidney trouble and any great agitation caused his face, feet and hands to swell, making him still heavier, fatter and more massive. Now, lying, a huge mass of bloated flesh on top of the pressed down bedsprings, he was aware, with a sick man's agony, of the swollen face, which seemed not his own, and could not stop thinking of the cruel fate that had been prepared for him. He recollected, one after the other, all the recent terrible cases when bombs had been thrown at people of his, or even of higher rank. He imagined the bombs tearing the bodies to pieces, spattering the brains against filthy brick walls and knocking out teeth from their roots. These imaginings made him feel as if his own fat, sick body, stretched out on the bed, belonged to someone else and had already undergone the fiery might of the explosion. He fancied that his arms had become detached from his shoulders, his teeth were knocked out, his brain scattered, and his feet numb and motionless, toes upward, like those of a dead man. He made a violent movement, breathed loudly and coughed, so that he should not have the remotest likeness to a corpse. He tried to surround himself with the live noise of grating springs and rustling blankets; and in order to prove that he was very much alive, not a bit dead and indeed far removed from death—just like anyone else, in fact—he spoke out in a loud, deep, abrupt voice in the quietness and loneliness of the bedroom.

"Brave fellows! Brave fellows! Brave fellows!"

He was praising the detectives, the police, the soldiers and all those who were guarding his life and had managed so skilfully and in such good time to avert his assassination. But even whilst he moved in bed, praised his preservers, and smiled with a forced, wry smile, indicating his contempt for those stupid, unsuccessful terrorists, he did not believe in his rescue and knew that life would be torn from him suddenly and at once. Death, which had been planned for him and which yet only existed in the thoughts and intentions of his would-be assassins, seemed to be already standing there in the room. It would remain there and not go away till those people had been caught, the bombs taken away from them and they themselves locked up behind strong bars. There, in that corner, stood Death, and would not go, could not go, like an obedient soldier placed on guard at the will and order of a superior.

"At one p.m., your Excellency." The phrase, modulated in a variety of tones, kept on sounding—now gaily mocking, now angry, now blunt and stubborn. As if there were hundreds of wound-up gramophones in the bedroom and they were all shouting, one after the other, with idiotic, mechanical persistence, the words commanded them:

"At one p.m., your Excellency."

And that one p.m. tomorrow, which only recently was no different from any other hour, but was only a steady movement of the hand across the dial of his golden watch, suddenly acquired an ominous importance. It jumped off the dial and began to live independently, stretching out till it was like a great black pillar cutting the whole of life in two; as if there were no other hours before or after, and this insolent, conceited hour alone had a right to some special existence.

"Well, what do you want?" asked the minister angrily, through his teeth.

The gramophones roared: "At one p.m., your Excellency!" and the black pillar grinned and bowed. Grinding his teeth, the minister raised himself in bed, sat up and leaned his face on the palm of his hand; it was quite impossible for him to find sleep on that hideous night.

Pressing his face with his swollen perfumed palms, he pictured to himself with terrifying clearness how on the next day he would have got up in the morning, knowing nothing, would have taken his coffee, knowing nothing, and then put on his things in the hall. Neither he, nor the butler, who would have helped him on with his fur coat, nor the footman, who would have brought him his coffee, would have known that it was quite futile to drink coffee or put on the fur coat, since in the next few minutes everything, the fur coat, his body and the coffee inside him, would have been annihilated, caught up by death. Then the butler would open the glass door . . . Yes, with his own hands, the nice, good, polite butler with the blue, soldierly eyes and medals across his chest, would open the terrible door, because he knew nothing. Everybody would smile, because they knew nothing.

"Oh," came suddenly and loudly from the minister and he slowly removed his hands from his face. Looking far into the darkness with a fixed strained glance, he stretched out his arm with the same slow movement, felt for the switch and turned on the light. Then he rose, and, without putting on his slippers, walked barefoot over the carpet of the unfamiliar, strange bedroom, found the switch of a wall lamp and turned it on. The room became light and pleasant and only the disordered bed with the blanket dropped on the floor witnessed to a terror not yet completely passed.

In his night attire, with beard ruffled by his restless movements, and angry eyes, the dignitary looked just like any other angry old man suffering from insomnia and asthma. It was as if the death which people were planning for him had laid him bare, tearing away the magnificence and imposing splendour by which he was surrounded. It was difficult to believe that he possessed great power and that his body, such an ordinary human body, was to perish terribly in the flame and crash of a monstrous explosion. He did not dress himself and, without feeling the cold, sat down on the nearest chair, propped his dishevelled beard on his hand, and fixed his eyes with the concentration of deep and calm reflexion upon the unfamiliar plaster ceiling.

So that was it! That was why he had trembled with fear and agitation! That was why Death stood in the corner and would not, could not, disappear!

"Fools!" he said with weighty contempt.

"Fools!" he repeated louder and turned his head slightly towards the door, so that those of whom he was speaking could hear him. He was speaking of those whom he had just now called brave fellows, but who in an excess of zeal had given him a detailed account of the forthcoming plot.

"Of course," he pondered deeply with sudden force and clearness of thought, "now, since they told me, I know and am terrified, but had I not known I should have drunk my coffee peacefully. Later, of course, this death . . . but am I really so much afraid of death? Here have I been suffering from kidney trouble and no doubt shall die of it one day, but I do not feel terrified, because I know nothing. But those idiots told me: 'At one p.m., your Excellency.' They thought, the fools, that I should be glad, instead of which *It* appeared in the corner and would not go. *It* will not go, because *It* is my thought. It is not death, but the knowledge of death, which is terrifying. Life would be impossible if man knew positively and precisely the day and hour of his death. Yet those idiots warned me: 'At one p.m., your Excellency.'"

He began to feel cheerful and relieved as if someone had told him that he was immortal and would never die. With a renewed sense of his own strength and cleverness amidst that bunch of idiots, who were so absurdly and imprudently invading the mystery of the future, he began to ponder the blissfulness of the unknown, arranging his thoughts with difficulty like an old, sick and greatly tried man. No living creature, neither man nor beast, was given to know the day and hour of its death. He, for instance, had been ill recently and his doctors told him that he was dying and ought to make his final arrangements. He had not believed them and actually he had lived. Something similar had happened in his youth. He had come to grief in life and decided to commit suicide. He got ready the revolver, wrote the last letters, even fixed the time for his suicide, and then, just before the end, he had suddenly changed his mind. Something may always change at the very last minute, an unforeseen accident may occur, and therefore nobody can tell when he will die.

"At one p.m., your Excellency," those amiable asses had told him, and, though they did so only because death had been averted, the very knowledge of the possible hour filled him with terror. It was quite likely that some day he would be assassinated, but it was not to happen tomorrow, and he might sleep confidently like an immortal. Fools, they did not realise what a great law they had tampered with, what an abyss they had opened, when they said with that idiotic amiability, "At one p.m., your Excellency."

"No, not at one p.m., your Excellency. It is not known when. Not known when. What?"

"Nothing," was the reply of the stillness, "nothing."

"No, you are saying something."

"No, nothing much. I am saying—tomorrow at one p.m."

With a sharp agony at his heart, he suddenly realised that there would be no sleep or peace or joy for him till that black, cursed hour, torn out of the clock-face, should have passed. It was only the shadow of the knowledge of what should be unknown to every living creature that stood there in the corner, and yet its presence sufficed to eclipse the light and cast on man an impenetrable darkness of horror. The terror of death, once aroused, spread throughout the body, penetrated the bones and looked palely out of each pore.

It was no longer the assassins of tomorrow that he feared; they had disappeared, were forgotten, swallowed up in a crowd of persons and happenings hostile to his everyday life. What he now feared was something sudden and inevitable—an apoplectic fit, heart failure or the weakness of some silly, thin artery, which might suddenly fail to bear the pressure of blood and burst like a lightly stretched glove on plump fingers.

His short, thick neck filled him with terror. It was unbearable to look at his short, swollen fingers and to feel how short they were and filled with the moisture of death.

If before, in the darkness, he had had to move so as not to feel like a dead man, now, in that bright, coldly-hostile, horrible light, it was terrifying, almost impossible to stir, even to get a cigarette or to ring for somebody. His nerves were on edge. And each nerve seemed like a rearing, bent-up wire, crowned by a small head, with eyes staring madly from fear and convulsively open, gasping, speechless mouth. He could not breathe.

Suddenly, in the darkness amidst dust and cobwebs, an electric bell came to life somewhere on the ceiling. The little metallic tongue struck convulsively in terror the edge of the tinkling cup. It stopped for a while, then again went on, moving in an unceasing, frightened ringing. It was his Excellency ringing from his room.

People began to run. Single little lamps flashed here and there in chandeliers and on walls. They did not give much light, but enough to create shadows. These appeared everywhere. They stood in corners, stretched across the ceiling, clung tremulously to every elevation, lay upon walls. It was really difficult to understand where they had been before—those numberless, ugly, silent shadows, the voiceless souls of voiceless objects.

A deep, trembling voice said something loudly. Then the doctor was summoned on the 'phone—the dignitary was in a bad way. His Excellency's wife was also summoned.

II Condemned to death by hanging

Everything happened as the police had foretold. Four terrorists, three men and a woman, armed with bombs, infernal machines and revolvers, were caught near the entrance of the house; the fifth was found and arrested in her own flat, where the conspiracy had been hatched. A great deal of dynamite, half-finished bombs and other weapons, were seized on the occasion. All the arrested persons were very young; the eldest of the men was twenty-eight, the younger of the women was only nineteen. They were sentenced in the same fortress in which they had been imprisoned after their arrest, and were tried quickly and secretly, as was the custom in those merciless days.

At their trial all five were calm, but very grave and thoughtful. Their contempt for the judges was so boundless that none of them felt like stressing their hardihood even by an unnecessary smile or any pretended expression of gaiety. They were calm in proportion to the need to screen their souls, caught up in the great agony of coming death, from the evil, hostile glances of strangers. Sometimes they refused, sometimes they consented, to answer questions; if the latter, they answered briefly, simply and precisely, as if addressing not judges, but statisticians, concerned in filling up some special forms. Three of them, one woman and two men, gave their real names. The other two refused to do so and remained unknown to the court. To all happenings in the court they showed that kind of mild, hazy curiosity, characteristic either of very sick people or of those who are absorbed in some all-engrossing idea. They would look up quickly, catch some specially interesting stray word and lapse again into their own thoughts at the point at which they had been diverted from them.

Nearest to the judges sat the prisoner who called himself Sergey Golovin. He was the son of a retired colonel and had himself been an officer. He was very young and broad-shouldered, with fair hair and such good health that neither prison nor the prospect of inevitable death had been able to take the vivid colour from his cheeks, nor the expression of youthful, happy naïvety from his blue eyes. He kept pulling energetically at his fair ruffled beard, to which he had not yet got accustomed. Screwing up his eyes and blinking incessantly, he looked out of the window.

All this took place at the end of winter when, in the midst of snowstorms and dim, frozen days, the approaching spring sent as forerunner a bright sunny day or single hour, which was so spring-like, so vividly young and glittering, that the sparrows in the street went mad with joy and people felt almost intoxicated. And now, through the dusty top window, uncleaned since last summer, a very strange, lovely sky could be seen. At first glance it seemed milky grey and dim, but, when you looked longer, blue began to appear and grew in depth, becoming ever brighter and more boundless. And the fact that it did not disclose itself at once, but hid chastely behind the dimness of transparent clouds, made it sweet as a young girl one loves. Sergey Golovin looked at the sky, pulled his little beard, screwed up first one eye and then the other behind their long silken lashes, and pondered something intensely. At one moment he even moved his fingers quickly, whilst an expression of naïve joy appeared on his face, but he looked round and his smile was extinguished like a trodden-out spark. And almost instantly, through the red of his cheeks, which had scarcely grown pale, showed an earthy, deathly grey; and the downy hair, painfully plucked out by the roots, was pressed in his white-tipped fingers, as in a vice. But the joy of life and the spring were stronger—and in a few minutes the same young ingenuous face was turned again towards the spring sky.

A young pale unknown girl, with the nickname of Mousia, also looked out in the same direction at the sky. She was younger than Golovin, but she seemed older because of her severity and the darkness of her direct proud eyes. Only her very thin and slender neck and her delicate, girlish arms revealed her age. Besides there was that something intangible which is youth itself and which sounded so clearly in her pure harmonious voice, tuned to perfection like a precious instrument, disclosing its musical richness in every simple word and exclamation. She was very pale, but her pallor was not deathly but of that special burning whiteness characteristic of persons who are consumed by a powerful inward flame, when the body seems transparently illuminated like fine Sèvres porcelain. She sat almost motionless, only occasionally touching, with a scarcely visible movement, the circular mark on the third finger of her right hand left by a ring recently removed. The glance she turned to the sky was without tenderness or joyful recollections, and she only looked at it because, in that dirty official hall, the strip of blue sky was the one lovely, pure, true thing in sight—and did not try to learn secrets from her eyes.

The judges pitied Sergey Golovin, but they hated her.

Her neighbour, unknown, but nicknamed Werner, also sat motionless in a somewhat affected posture, with hands folded between his knees. If a face can be bolted, as one bolts a heavy door, the unknown prisoner had bolted his face like an iron door and hung an iron lock on it. He stared down motionless at the dirty wooden floor, and it was impossible to tell whether he was calm or intensely excited, whether pondering something or listening to the informers giving evidence before the court. He was not tall; his features were subtle and noble. His beauty was so delicate that he reminded one of a moonlight night in the South, where cypresses throw their dark shadows on the seashore; whilst at the same time he inspired a feeling of great calm force, unconquerable determination and cold and daring courage. The very politeness of his brief and precise answers seemed somehow dangerous on his lips and given with his slight bow. Whilst on all the others the prisoners' dress looked like an awkward joke, one failed to notice it on him—so alien was the attire to the man. And though bombs and infernal machines had been found on the other terrorists and only a black revolver on Werner, the judges for some reason considered him the leader and addressed him with some respect as well as briefly and to the point.

The next prisoner to him, Vassily Kashirin, was absorbed in a great unbearable terror of death as well as in a desperate effort to suppress that terror and hide it from the judges. Since early morning, when they had brought him before the court, he had begun to choke from palpitation of the heart. Drops of sweat continually appeared on his forehead, his hands were moist and cold and his cold sweaty shirt clung to his body, hampering his movements. By the exercise of superhuman will-power he kept his fingers from trembling, his voice firm and clear and his eyes steady. He saw nothing around him and voices came to him as through a mist, into which he strained desperately—to answer firmly, to answer loudly. But having once answered, he immediately forgot both question and reply and resumed the silent desperate struggle with himself. Death was so apparent in him that the judges avoided looking at him, and it was almost as impossible to tell his age as that of a corpse which has begun to decompose. According to his papers he was only twenty-three. Once or twice Werner gently touched his knee with his hand and each time Vassily answered in the same phrase, "All right."

The most awful moments for him were when he was suddenly seized with the longing to shout aloud, without words, with the desperate yell of a beast. Then he would touch Werner gently and the latter, without raising his eyes, would answer softly, "It's all right, Vasia, it will soon be over."

Tanya Kovalchuk, the fifth terrorist, embraced them all with a motherly, solicitous glance and appeared devoured with anxiety. She had never had children; she was still very young and red-cheeked, like Sergey Golovin, but somehow seemed the mother of them all. The expression of her face, with its smiles and fears, was full of solicitude and boundless love. She paid no attention to the Court, as if it were something extraneous, but only listened to the way the others answered questions and tried to make out whether their voices trembled, whether they were afraid or needed water.

She could not look at Vasia without anguish and wrung her plump fingers silently; but Mousia and Werner she watched with pride and admiration, a grave and serious expression on her face, whilst with Sergey Golovin she tried to exchange smiles.

"The dear boy is looking at the sky. Look, look, my dear one," she said to herself whilst watching him.

"And Vasia? What is it? My God, my God. . . . What am I to do with him? To say something might make things still worse—supposing he burst into tears."

Like a quiet pool at dawn, reflecting every passing cloud, she reflected on her plump, dear, kind face every transient feeling and thought of each of those four. To the fact that she herself was also on trial and that she, too, would be hanged, she did not give a thought and was completely indifferent to the matter. It was in her flat that a store of bombs and dynamite had been discovered, and strangely enough it was she who had fired on the police and wounded one detective in the head.

The trial ended at eight p.m., when it was beginning to get dark. Gradually the blue sky faded away before the eyes of Mousia and Sergey Golovin; it did not flush and smile quietly, as on summer evenings, but thickened, grew grey, and suddenly became cold and wintry. Golovin heaved a sigh, stretched himself and looked once again out of the window but already there was only cold wintry gloom. Still pulling at his little beard, he began, with childlike curiosity, to observe the judges, the soldiers with their rifles, and to smile at Tanya Kovalchuk. But Mousia, after the sky had faded away, steadily, without lowering her eyes to the ground, directed them to a corner where a spider's web rocked slightly under the invisible current from the steam heating, and remained thus till the sentence was pronounced.

After the verdict, the condemned took leave of the frock-coated barristers, avoiding their disconcertingly pitying and guilty eyes, and crowded together in the doorway for a minute, exchanging short remarks.

"All right, Vasia, soon all will be over," said Werner.

"I am all right, brother," Kashirin replied loudly, calmly and even almost cheerfully. And indeed his face had a slight tinge of red and no longer resembled a decomposing corpse.

"The devil take them, they have hanged us all," naïvely cursed Golovin.

"That was only to be expected," retorted Werner calmly.

"Tomorrow the sentence will be formally pronounced and we shall all be placed together," said Kovalchuk reassuringly. "We shall remain together until the execution."

Mousia was silent. Then she resolutely moved forward.

III   I must not be hanged

A fortnight before the terrorists were tried, other judges of the same regional military court had tried and condemned to death by hanging, Ivan Yanson, a peasant.

This Ivan Yanson was a farm labourer, who worked for a well-to-do farmer and differed in no way from other such workmen. He was a native of Vesenberg in Estonia and as, in the course of a few years, he moved from one farm to another, he gradually drew nearer the capital. He spoke Russian very badly, and as his master was a Russian called Lazarev and there were no Estonians in the neighbourhood, Yanson scarcely spoke at all for nearly two years. Apparently he was not in general given to talkativeness and was silent with men as well as with beasts. He watered and harnessed a horse in silence, sauntering round it with slow uncertain steps; and when the horse, annoyed by his silence, began to rear and prance, he would beat it in silence with a huge whip. He beat it cruelly with cold wicked persistence, and if this happened when he had been drinking heavily, he worked himself up into a frenzy. On such occasions the hissing of the whip and the frightened broken anguished tapping of the hooves on the wooden floor of the barn could be heard in the house. When Yanson beat the horse in this way the master would beat him, but he could not change him, so he gave it up.

Once or twice a month Yanson got drunk. This happened on the occasions when he drove his master to the big railway station, where there was a bar. After having dropped his master at the station, he would drive off about half a mile, park his sledge and horse deep in the snow at the side of the road and wait there till the train had left. The sledge would lie on its side, almost upside down, and the horse, up to his belly in a snow-drift, would stand with legs astraddle and put down his nose every now and then to lick the soft friable snow. Yanson, meanwhile, half lay on the sledge in an awkward posture and seemed to slumber. The untied ear-flaps of his much-worn fur cap would hang down helplessly, like the ears of a spaniel, and his small red nose would run.

Then Yanson would go back to the station and quickly get drunk.

On the return journey he would gallop the whole ten versts to the farm. The mercilessly beaten little horse, mad with terror, would jump with all four legs at once, like a frenzied creature. The sledge rolled about, almost turned over, knocked into posts; and Yanson, dropping the reins and each moment in danger of being flung out, would yell something in jerky Estonian, which sounded half song, half shout. But usually he would not even sing. Silently, his teeth set firmly in an access of incomprehensible fury, suffering and delight, he would drive on like a blind man.

Passers-by went unnoticed and unwarned, and he did not slow down his mad race round turnings or down hills. How he had failed not to kill someone or do himself an injury on one of these wild drives was a miracle.

He ought to have been sacked long ago, as he had been from other places, but he was cheap and other workmen were not much better, so he stayed there two years. There were no events in Yanson's life. One day he received a letter written in Estonian, but as he was illiterate and the others did not know Estonian, the letter remained unread; and, with a kind of savage, fanatical indifference, as if unaware of the fact that the letter might bring news from home, Yanson threw it on the manure heap. At one time, evidently longing for a woman, he tried to woo the cook, but he was unsuccessful and was repulsed and scorned. He was short and sickly, with a pitted freckled face, and his sleepy eyes were of a dirty greenish colour. Yanson took the rebuff with indifference and did not molest the cook again.

Though he spoke little, Yanson seemed always to be listening to something. He listened to the dismal plain with its hillocks of frozen manure, looking like rows of little snow-covered graves; he listened to the delicate blue distances, to the buzzing of telegraph poles and to people's talk. What the plain and the telegraph poles said to him, he alone knew, but people's talk was disquieting, full of rumours of murders, robberies and arson. And one night from the neighbouring village was heard the thin, helpless tinkling of the tiny church bell and the crackling of flames. Strangers from no one knew where had robbed a rich farm, murdered the farmer and his wife and set the house on fire.

On Yanson's farm, too, there was an uneasy feeling; the dogs were kept unchained by day as well as by night and the master slept with a gun by his side. He wanted to give Yanson a similar gun, though one-barrelled and old, but the latter turned it round in his hands, shook his head over it, and for some reason refused it. The master could not understand why Yanson would not have it and scolded him, but the servant had more faith in his Finnish knife than in the old rusty gun.

"It would be the death of me," he said, looking sleepily at his master with his glassy eyes. The master threw up his hands in despair.

"What a fool you are, Ivan! How is one to get anything done with such workmen?"

One winter evening, when the other workmen had been sent to the station, that same Ivan Yanson, who had refused to trust the gun, made an extremely complicated attempt at robbery, murder and rape. He did it in an amazingly simple way. He locked the cook in the kitchen, then, lazily, pretending to be almost dead with sleep, he approached his master from behind and stabbed him several times quickly in the back. The master fell unconscious to the ground, his wife began to run screaming round the room, and Yanson, grinning and brandishing his knife, started to ransack the trunks and chests of drawers. He found the money and then, as if noticing his mistress for the first time, and seemingly to his own surprise, rushed upon her to violate her. But as he happened to drop his knife at this moment, the mistress proved to be the stronger, and not only did not allow herself to be violated, but almost succeeded in strangling him. At this point the farmer on the floor began to show signs of life, whilst the cook thundered with the oven-fork in an effort to force the kitchen door, and Yanson ran off into the fields. He was caught an hour later squatting behind a corner of the barn, striking one dead match after the other in an attempt to set the farm on fire.

A few days later the farmer died from blood poisoning, and Yanson's turn having come, amongst the other robbers and murderers, he was tried and sentenced to death. In the court he looked as he always did; a small sickly man with a freckled face and sleepy, glassy little eyes. He did not quite seem to realise what was going on around him and appeared to be completely indifferent. He blinked his white eyelashes dully, gazed, without any curiosity at the unfamiliar, imposing court room and picked his nose with his rough, horny, stiff finger. Only those who had seen him on Sundays at church could have guessed that he had smartened himself up; he wore round his neck a knitted, dirty red scarf and had damped down his hair in places. Where the hair was moist it looked darker and lay smoothly, but where it was not it stuck up in fair thin tufts, like wisps of straw on a meadow laid waste by hail.

When the sentence was pronounced—death by hanging—Yanson suddenly became agitated. He turned deep red and began to tie and untie the scarf as though it were strangling him. Then he started to wave his arms about aimlessly and said, addressing the judge who had not read the sentence, whilst pointing to the one who had, "*She* said that I was to be hanged."

"Who is *she?*" asked, in a deep bass voice, the presiding judge who had pronounced the sentence. Everyone smiled, trying to conceal their smiles in their moustaches or papers, but Yanson, pointing with his finger at the presiding judge, answered frowningly and angrily, "You."

"Well?"

Yanson again turned his eyes to the silent, reticently smiling judge, in whom he sensed a friend and a person quite unconcerned in the sentence, and repeated, "She has said that I am to be hanged. I must not be hanged."

"Take the prisoner away."

But Yanson managed to repeat once more, weightily and with conviction, "I must not be hanged."

His little angry face and his attempt to be imposing with outstretched finger were so absurd that even the escorting soldier broke the rules by saying half aloud as he led him from the court, "What a fool you are, lad!"

"I must not be hanged," repeated Yanson stubbornly.

"They will hitch you up quickly, you won't have time to jerk."

"Keep quiet now," shouted another guard angrily. But he could not refrain from adding, "Another robber! Why did you take a human life, you fool? Now you will hang."

"They might pardon him," said the first soldier, who felt sorry for Yanson.

"What! Pardon the likes of him. . . . Now that's enough talking."

But Yanson was already silent. He was taken again to the same cell where he had spent more than a month and to which he had grown accustomed, as he had become accustomed to everything, to blows, to vodka, and to the gloomy snow-covered fields strewn with hillocks like a graveyard. Now he felt almost cheerful at the sight of his bed, and his window with the iron bars, and he was given something to eat, for he had had nothing since the morning. The only unpleasant thing was the occurrence in court, but he could not think, was incapable of thinking about it. And death by hanging he could not picture to himself at all.

Though Yanson was under sentence of death, there were many other prisoners of this kind, and the prison warders did not regard him as a dangerous criminal. They talked to him, therefore, without fear or respect, as they talked to the other prisoners who were not condemned to death. Actually, they did not consider his death as death. On hearing the sentence, his jailor said to him admonishingly, "Well, brother, so they are going to hang you?"

"When will they hang me?" asked Yanson incredulously.

"Well, you will have to wait, brother," was the reply, "till there are a number of you. They will not put themselves out for one man, especially a man like you. They want something bigger."

"So when?" asked Yanson insistently. He was not offended that he was not considered worth hanging alone, nor did he believe it. He thought it was only an excuse for postponing his execution in order to grant him a reprieve later on. He became cheerful; the dim terrible moment, about which he could not think, had moved far into the distance and become fantastic and impossible, as death always seems.

"When, when?" growled the jailor, a stupid old man. "It isn't like hanging a dog, which you take behind the barn and finish off in the twinkling of an eye. Or would you like it to be done that way, you fool?"

"I don't want to be hanged," said Yanson with a cheerful grimace. "It was she who said I was to be hanged, but I don't want to be."

And that was perhaps the first time in his life that he had laughed. It was a grating, foolish, but extremely cheerful merry laugh, like the cackling of a goose—ga-ga-ga. The jailor looked at him with surprise and frowned sternly. The silly cheerfulness of a man condemned to death was an insult to the prison and the execution itself and made them appear in a strange light. Suddenly for a second, or rather the fraction of a second, that old jailor, who had spent all his life in prison and to whom its laws were laws of nature, saw the prison and all its life as something like a lunatic asylum, in which he, the jailor, was the chief madman.

"The devil take it," he said spitting. "Why are you grinning? This is not a public house!"

"I don't want to be hanged, ga-ga-ga," laughed Yanson.

"Satan!" cried the jailor, feeling he must make the sign of the cross.

Nothing could have been more unlike Satan, however, than this little man with the small, flabby face, but something in his goose cackle was destructive of the sanctity and might of the prison. If he went on laughing, the rotten walls might collapse and the rusty gratings fall to pieces and he, the jailor himself, might find himself bringing the prisoners to the gates and saying: "Please, gentlemen, take a walk in the town, or perhaps you would prefer the country?" Satan!

But Yanson had already stopped laughing and only screwed up his eyes cunningly.

"Well, take care," said the jailor in a vaguely threatening tone and went away with a backward glance.

All that evening Yanson was calm and even cheerful. He kept repeating to himself the phrase, "I must not be hanged," and it seemed to him so convincing, so wise and so irrefutable that there was nothing to worry about. He had long ago forgotten about his crime and only sometimes felt sorry that he had not succeeded in violating the farmer's wife. But even that he soon forgot.

Every morning Yanson would ask when he was to be hanged and every morning the jailor would answer angrily, "There is plenty of time, Satan. Wait." And he would hastily retreat before Yanson had time to burst out laughing.

Because of these monotonously reiterated words and because every day began, passed and ended in the most ordinary manner, Yanson became irretrievably convinced that there would be no execution. He began very quickly to forget about the trial and would loll all day long on his bunk day-dreaming vaguely and happily. His dreams were of the dismal snow-covered fields with their hillocks, the station bar and other still brighter and more distant things. He was well fed in prison, so that in a few days he became stouter and began to put on airs a little.

"She would have loved me now," he said to himself once, thinking of the master's wife. "Now I look fat, just like the master."

His only great longing was for vodka; to drink it and to drive a little horse, swiftly, swiftly, at a gallop.

When the news of the arrest of the terrorists reached the prison and Yanson asked the routine question, the jailor answered unexpectedly and roughly, "Now it won't be long."

Then he looked at Yanson calmly and pompously and repeated, "Now it won't be long. I should say in a week."

Yanson grew pale and so dim was the glance of his glassy eyes that he might have been falling asleep as he asked, "Are you joking?"

"First you could not wait, and now you say I am joking. We don't joke here. It is you who like to joke, but for us jokes are not fitting," said the jailor with dignity and walked out.

That very evening Yanson grew thinner. His skin, which had temporarily stretched and grown smooth, suddenly contracted into a number of tiny wrinkles and even seemed to hang down in places. His eyes became sleepy and all his movements were as slow and sluggish as if every turn of his head or movement of his fingers or feet had become a complicated and cumbersome undertaking, requiring great previous consideration. At night he lay down on his bed but did not close his eyes; though sleepy, they remained open till morning.

"Oho," said the jailor delightedly, on seeing him the next day. "This is no public house, you see, my fine fellow."

With great satisfaction, like a scientist whose experiment has been proved correct again, he surveyed the condemned man attentively and in detail from head to foot. Now all would go as it should. Satan was disgraced and the sanctity of prison and executions restored once more. Condescendingly, even with sincere sympathy, the old man enquired, "Do you want to see anyone or not?"

"Why should I?"

"Well, to say good-bye. Your mother or your brother?"

"I must not be hanged," said Yanson in a low voice and gave a sidelong glance at the jailor. "I don't want to be."

The jailor looked at him and silently made a gesture with his hand.

Towards evening Yanson had calmed down somewhat. The day had been as usual; the cloudy winter sky looked as it always did, footsteps and some business conversation in the corridor sounded just as usual, and the cabbage soup smelt so natural and ordinary that he began to disbelieve in the execution. But at night he was overcome by fear. Formerly night to him had been simply darkness, that special dark period when one had to sleep, but now he felt in it something mysterious and ominous. In order not to believe in death, one must be surrounded by customary sights and sounds—steps, voices, light, cabbage soup. But now everything had become strange and the very stillness and darkness were something like death.

And the longer the night dragged on, the more terrible it became. With the simplicity of a savage or a child, who thinks everything is possible, Yanson felt like shouting out to the sun—"Shine." He begged and implored the sun to shine, but the night drew its dark hours steadfastly over the earth and there was no power which could stop its course. This impossibility, which for the first time was clearly visualised by Yanson's weak brain, filled him with terror. Still without daring to face it clearly, he realised the inevitability of approaching death, and placed his benumbed foot on the first step of the gallows.

Day soothed him again and night frightened him again, and this went on until one night when he knew and felt that death was unavoidable and that it would take place in three days' time at dawn, with the sunrise.

He had never considered what death was and death had no form for him, but now he felt distinctly, saw and knew that it had entered the cell and was looking for him, groping with its hands. To save himself he began running round the cell.

But the cell was so small that the corners seemed to be all round instead of angular and they were all thrusting him into the centre. And there was nothing behind which he could hide. And the door was locked and it was light. His body struck several times against the wall and bounced once against the door—there was a hollow, empty sound. He stumbled over something and fell face downwards and then he felt that it was catching him. He lay on his stomach, clinging to the floor, hiding his face in the dirty dark asphalt, and began to yell in terror. He lay there and shouted at the top of his voice till someone came. Even after he had been lifted from the floor, placed on his bed and cold water poured over his head, Yanson could not bring himself to open his tightly closed eyes. He opened one eye, saw the light, empty corner and someone's boot in the emptiness and began to cry out again.

But the cold water began to have its effect. And several blows on the head, administered as medicine by the jailor on duty, that same old man, were also helpful. The sensation of life they produced really drove death away and Yanson opened his eyes and, his brain thoroughly muddled, slept soundly the rest of the night. He lay on his back, his mouth open, and snored loudly and furiously. The flat dead white of the eye without pupil was visible between his half-closed eyelids.

Later everything in the world, day, night, steps, voices and cabbage soup, became one continual nightmare and put him into a state of wild and indescribably confused bewilderment. His feeble mind could not combine two ideas which so fantastically contradicted each other—the usual bright day and the taste and smell of cabbage soup with the fact that in two days, or a day, he must die. He did not think at all, he did not even count the hours, he simply stood there, numb with terror, faced with a contradiction that split his brain in two. His face became evenly pale, with no patches of white or red, and he appeared calm. But he took no food and stopped sleeping altogether. He either sat all night on a little stool, cross-legged and terrified, or walked about the cell with quiet, stealthy, sleepy glances. He kept his mouth half open all the time, as if he were in a state of continual amazement, and he scrutinised the most trivial thing before taking it up, and handled it distrustfully.

When he had reached this stage, the warders and the soldier, who had been watching him through the small grating, paid no more attention to him. That was the normal state of the condemned. It was, in the jailor's opinion, though he had never experienced it, similar to the state of cattle led to the slaughter, after they have been stunned by a blow on the forehead from the butt end of an axe.

"Now he is stunned, now he will feel nothing till death itself," said the jailor, looking at him with his experienced eyes. "Ivan, do you hear? Hallo, Ivan!"

"I must not be hanged," answered Yanson gloomily and his lower jaw dropped again.

"If you had not murdered someone, you would not be hanged," said the senior jailor in an admonitory tone. He was still young, but pompous, with medals on his breast. "But you have committed murder and yet don't want to be hanged."

"You wanted to kill a man without paying for it. He's stupid, stupid but cunning."

"I don't want . . ." began Yanson.

"Well, friend, you may want it or not, that's your business," said the senior jailor indifferently. "Instead of talking nonsense, however, you had better make arrangements about your belongings."

"He hasn't got any. One shirt and pants. Yes, and a fur cap, the dandy!"

So the time passed till Thursday. On Thursday at midnight a number of persons entered Yanson's cell and a gentleman with epaulettes said, "Well, get ready, we must be off."

Moving in the same slow way, Yanson put on all he had and tied his dirty red scarf about his neck. Watching him while he dressed, the man with the epaulettes smoked cigarettes and said to someone, "What a warm morning. Just like spring."

Yanson's little eyes were stuck together and he seemed to be falling asleep. He moved so slowly and stiffly that the jailor shouted at him, "Hurry up, are you dreaming?"

Yanson suddenly stood still.

"I don't want . . ." he said feebly.

They took him by the arms and led him away and he marched obediently, shrugging his shoulders. Outside he was fanned by a moist spring air and his small nose began to run. Although it was night, the thaw was increasing and from somewhere came the merry sound of quick drops falling on stone. As he waited while the police, clanking their sabres and bending their heads, got into the black, unlighted carriage, Yanson idly moved his finger under his running nose and adjusted his badly tied scarf.

IV   We of Oryol

The same judges of the regional military court, who had tried Yanson, sentenced to execution by hanging a peasant from Eletz in the province of Oryol. This was Michael Golubetz, nicknamed Mishka Tziganok, a Tartar. His last crime, for which there was indubitable evidence, had been robbery with violence and included the murder of three people. Before that the trail of his dark past was shrouded in deep mystery. There were vague rumours of his having been implicated in a whole series of other robberies and murders; blood and fire and dark, drunken debauchery seemed to have accompanied his steps. With complete frankness and outspokenness he called himself a robber, and regarded with scorn those who adopted the modern title of "expropriators." Seeing that denial was of no avail, he voluntarily confessed his last crime down to the last detail. When questioned further about his past, however, he only grinned and whistled, saying, "Ask the wind that blows in the field."

When hard pressed with questions, Tziganok would assume a serious and dignified air.

"We of Oryol are all hot-heads," he remarked gravely and with deliberation. "The first-class thieves live in Oryol and Kromy. Karatshev and Livny are the best places for thieves; but Eletz is the head and front of all thieves. What more is there to say!"

He was nicknamed Tziganok, the Gipsy, because of his appearance and thievish ways. His hair was of most extraordinary blackness, he was lean and had spots from yellow fever on his sharp, Tartar-like cheek-bones. He rolled the whites of his eyes as horses do and was in a perpetual hurry. His glance was short and quick but terrifyingly direct and full of curiosity. When he looked quickly at an object, it was as if it lost something, gave him part of itself and became different. One did not easily or without an unpleasant feeling pick up a cigarette at which he had looked, for it was as if it had been in his mouth. He was possessed by a perpetual restlessness, which sometimes twisted him like a rope and sometimes sent him flying like a broad shower of scattering sparks. He drank water almost by the bucketful, like a horse.

When questioned in court, he jumped quickly to his feet and answered briefly, firmly and even with some satisfaction, "Right."

Sometimes he would stress the word, as, "R-r-right."

Once, suddenly, when some quite different point was under discussion, he jumped to his feet and asked the presiding judge, "Do you give me leave to whistle?"

"What for?" said the judge in surprise.

"Evidence has been given that I signalled to my comrades and I will show you how I did it. It is very interesting."

Though rather disconcerted, the judge agreed to the request. Tziganok quickly put four fingers in his mouth, two from each hand, and rolled his eyes savagely. A real wild robber's whistle rent the dead atmosphere of the court, a whistle which made the deafened horses leap and rear and people's faces involuntarily turn white. The mortal anguish of the victim, the wild joy of the murderer, the ominous warning, the summons, the darkness and loneliness of a stormy autumn night—all were heard in that piercing sound, which was neither quite human nor quite bestial.

The presiding judge shouted something and waved his hand at Tziganok, who stopped obediently. And like an artist, who has triumphantly performed a difficult but always successful aria, he sat down wiping his wet fingers on his prison dress, and looked round at the audience with a self-satisfied air.

"A real brigand!" said one of the judges, rubbing his ear. And another judge, who had a broad Russian beard and the eyes of a Tartar, like those of Tziganok, looked dreamily into space above the prisoner's head, smiled and remarked, "This is really interesting."

Light-heartedly, without the slightest pity or compunction, the judge pronounced the death sentence.

"Right," said Tziganok, when the verdict was given. "In the open field on a cross-beam. Right."

And turning to the guard, he said with bravado, "Well, let's go, sour-face. Keep a good hold of your gun or I'll have it from you!"

The soldier looked at him sternly and with fear, exchanging glances with the other guard and feeling the lock of his gun. The other did the same. All the way to the prison they seemed to fly rather than walk. So absorbed were they in the criminal, that they were unconscious of the ground they trod on, and forgot time and themselves.

Like Yanson, Mishka Tziganok had to spend seventeen days in prison before the execution. The whole seventeen days passed for him as quickly as if it were one, and was filled with a continuous inextinguishable dream of escape, liberty and life. The restlessness, which possessed him, and was now kept under by walls and gratings and the dead window through which nothing could be seen, turned all its rage inwards and burned Tziganok's mind like scattered coals. As in drunken dreams, bright unfinished pictures swarmed upon him, jostled each other and became confused, and were then borne along in an irresistible dazzling whirl. They all tended towards one end—escape, liberty and life. Sometimes, expanding his nostrils like a horse, Tziganok would inhale the air for hours on end. It seemed to him that he could smell hemp, the smoke of a fire and the faintly acrid odour of burning. Sometimes he would circle the cell like a wolf, quickly touching the walls, tapping, measuring, piercing the ceiling with his glance, sawing through the gratings. His restlessness wearied out the soldier, who watched him through the peephole, so that the fellow sometimes threatened to shoot him. Tziganok retorted rudely and with mockery, and if everything ended peacefully, it was because the quarrel soon took on the character of an ordinary inoffensive peasants' brawl, where shooting seemed quite out of place.

At night Tziganok slept soundly, almost without stirring, in the unchanging but living immobility of a spring temporarily out of action. But once on his feet he immediately resumed his circling, planning and touching. His hands were continually dry and hot, but his heart often turned suddenly cold, as if in his breast had been placed a piece of unmelting ice which sent a small dry shiver all over his body. Always swarthy, at such moments Tziganok would turn still darker and take on a bluish cast-iron colour. He developed a strange habit. He kept licking and smacking his lips, as if he had eaten something excessively and nauseatingly sweet, and spat out on the floor, hissing as he did so, the saliva which kept accumulating in his mouth. When speaking he left his words unfinished, for so quickly did his thoughts run that his tongue could not catch up with them.

One day the chief warder, accompanied by a guard, entered his cell. He looked askance at the bespattered floor and said gloomily, "Look how he has filthied the place!"

Tziganok retorted quickly, "You, fat face, have filthied the whole world and have I reproached you? What have you come here for?"

In the same gloomy way the warder offered him the job of executioner. Tziganok bared his teeth in a grin and then burst out laughing.

"So you cannot find anybody? I like that! Go ahead and do the hanging yourself, ha-ha. You have got the necks and the rope and nobody to do the job. By God, I like that!"

"Your life would be spared in return."

"I should say so! As a corpse I could scarcely do the hanging for you! What a fool!"

"Well, what do you say? Is it the same to you either way?"

"How do you do the hanging? I expect you strangle people secretly."

"No, to music," snarled the warder.

"What a fool he is! Of course it should be done to music—this way," and he began to sing something with bravado.

"You seem to have gone quite crazy, my friend," said the warder. "Well, what is your answer? Talk sense."

Tziganok grinned: "You're in too much of a hurry. You must come again, then I'll tell you."

And now, into the whirl of bright, unfinished pictures, which rushed past Tziganok, torturing him by their rapidity, came a new one. How splendid to become an executioner in a red shirt! He pictured vividly to himself a square with a big crowd, a high scaffold and himself, Tziganok, pacing up and down with an axe in his hand. The sun shone upon the heads of the people, and was gaily reflected in the axe, and everything was so cheerful and bright that even the victim whose head was to be chopped off smiled too. Carts and horses' heads were visible behind the crowd—the peasants had come in from the village. Beyond he could see the open fields.

"Tz-ah," exclaimed Tziganok, smacking and licking his lips, and spat out the accumulated saliva. Suddenly he felt as if a fur cap had been pulled over his head right down to his mouth; it was dark and stifling and his heart turned into a lump of unmelting ice, sending a slight shiver all over him.

The warder came twice again, but Tziganok grinned and said, "You seem to be in a hurry. It won't hurt you to come once more."

At last, however, the warder shouted casually through the peep-hole, "You have lost your chance, you crow! They have found someone else."

"The devil take you, go and hang them yourself," snapped Tziganok. And he dropped day-dreaming about the executioner's job.

But when, finally, the time of the execution drew near the rush of broken images became unbearable. Tziganok wanted to stop, to set his feet wide in order to come to a standstill, but the whirling current carried him away and there was nothing to hold on to—everything swam around him. His sleep now became restless too. He was visited by new dreams, heavy as coloured wooden blocks and even more violent than his thoughts. They no longer came in a stream, but in an endless fall from an endless mountain, in a whirling flight through the whole visible world of colours. Tziganok had had a rather dashing moustache, but in prison he grew a short black bristling beard, which gave him a terrifying, almost insane appearance. At times he was really out of his mind and senselessly circled the cell, still tapping the rough plastered walls. And he drank water like a horse.

One evening, when the lights were put on, Tziganok went on all fours in the middle of the cell and began to utter a trembling wolf-like howl. He did it with great seriousness, howling as if he were performing a most important and necessary rite. He breathed in deeply and out slowly in a prolonged and trembling howl, then, blinking his eyes, he listened attentively to the effect. The very tremor in his voice seemed somehow artificial. He did not howl at random but carefully produced each note in that animal cry full of terror and grief.

Suddenly he broke off the howling and remained silently on all fours for a few minutes. Then he whispered to the ground, "Dear good people, dear good people, have mercy. . . . Dear good people!"

And here, too, he seemed to listen to the effect of his words. After each word—he stopped and listened. Then he jumped to his feet and for an hour on end gave vent to the most terrible curses.

"You so-and-so," he shouted, rolling his blood-shot eyes, "if you hang me, you hang me, but for you there will be . . ."

Meanwhile the soldier on guard, white as chalk and weeping with anguish and terror, pounded on the door with the butt end of his rifle and shouted helplessly, "I'll shoot you, by God, I'll shoot you. Do you hear?"

But he dared not shoot; if there were no open mutiny, those sentenced to death were never shot. Tziganok ground his teeth, swore and spat. His human brain, placed on that marvellously narrow verge between life and death, was falling to pieces like a lump of dry weather-beaten clay.

On the night when they came into the cell to take Tziganok to execution, he bestirred himself and seemed to revive. The sweet taste in his mouth became still sweeter and the saliva was not to be held back, but his cheeks took on a little colour and some of his former savage cunning sparkled in his eyes. Whilst dressing he asked an official, "Who is going to do the hanging? The new man? He won't have got his hand in yet."

"You need not worry about that," said the official dryly.

"How can I help worrying, your Honour? They are going to hang me, not you. At least do not be sparing of the Government's soap on the loop."

"All right, all right, please keep quiet."

"This man has eaten up all your soap," said Tziganok, pointing at the warder. "Look how his face shines."

"Silence!"

"Do not be stingy!"

Tziganok burst out laughing, but the taste of sweetness in his mouth was increasing and his legs suddenly became strangely numb. When he came out into the yard, however, he managed to shout, "The carriage for the Count of Bengal!"

V   Kiss him and be silent

The sentence on the five terrorists was pronounced in its final form and ratified the same day. The condemned were not told when they were to be executed, but, judging by what had been done on other occasions, they knew they would be hanged the same night or, at latest, the following. When they were offered an opportunity of seeing their relatives the next day, Thursday, they understood that the execution would take place on Friday at dawn.

Tanya Kovalchuk possessed no near relations, and those she had lived somewhere in a remote spot in Little Russia and probably knew nothing of the trial and imminent execution. Mousia and Werner, the unidentified prisoners, were presumed to have no relatives, and only two of them, Sergey Golovin and Vassily Kashirin, were to see their parents. They were both filled with anguish and terror at the thought of this meeting, but somehow could not bring themselves to refuse the old folks a last talk and embrace.

Sergey Golovin, especially, was perturbed by the forthcoming meeting. He was extremely fond of his father and mother, had seen them not long before and was now terrified as to what was going to happen. The execution itself, defeating thought by its monstrous strangeness and madness, was easier to imagine, and seemed less terrifying than these few short incomprehensible minutes, which were as if outside time, outside life itself. His human brain refused to contemplate how he was to look, or what he was to think and say. The simplest and most ordinary behaviour—to take his father's hand, to kiss him and say, "How are you, Father?"—seemed incredibly horrible, because of the monstrous, in-human, insane lie concealed in it.

After the sentence the condemned were not placed together in one cell, as assumed by Kovalchuk. Each went back to solitary confinement. All the morning till eleven o'clock, when his parents came, Sergey Golovin paced furiously up and down the cell, plucking his little beard, frowning piteously and muttering. From time to time he stopped in full course to take breath and gasped like a man who has been too long under water. He was of such excellent physique, however, his youthful vitality was so great, that even in these moments of cruel suffering the blood pulsated vividly under his skin, giving colour to his cheeks, and his blue eyes shone brightly and innocently.

However, everything went off better than Sergey had anticipated.

Sergey's father, Nikolay Sergeevich Golovin, a retired colonel, was the first to enter the room. He was of an even white all over—face, beard, hair and hands—as if a white marble statue had been dressed in men's clothes. He wore the same old coat as ever, well cleaned and smelling of benzine, with new cross epaulettes. He entered with a firm military steady step and, stretching out his dry white hand, said in a loud voice, "How do you do, Sergey?"

The mother followed him with short steps, smiling strangely. She, too, shook his hand and repeated loudly, "How do you do, Seryoshenka?"

She kissed his lips and sat down in silence. She did not fall upon his neck, did not burst into tears, in short did none of those terrible things which Sergey had feared so much; she kissed him and sat down in silence. She even straightened her black silk frock with her trembling hands.

Sergey did not know that the whole of the preceding night the colonel, having locked himself in his little study, had given himself up entirely to working out the details of this meeting. We must strive not to make harder, but to ease, our son's last minutes, was the colonel's firm decision, and he weighed carefully every sentence and every movement of the next day's meeting. Now and then he became confused, forgot the sentence he had just prepared and wept bitterly, sitting on a corner of his oil-cloth-covered divan. Next morning he explained to his wife how to behave at the meeting.

"The main thing is to kiss him and be silent," he instructed her. "Later on you may speak, a little later, but when you kiss him, be silent. Do not speak soon after the kiss, do you understand? For you may say something better left unsaid."

"I understand, Nikolay Sergeevich," the mother answered, crying.

"And do not cry. For Heaven's sake, don't weep! You will kill him if you do that, old woman."

"And why do you weep yourself?"

"How can one help weeping with you! You must not weep, do you hear?"

"Very well, Nikolay Sergeevich."

Riding in the cab, he wanted to repeat his admonitions once more, but forgot them. So they both rode in silence, both of them bent, old and grey and lost in thought, while the city was full of gay sounds. It was Shrovetide and the streets were crowded and noisy.

They sat down. The colonel placed himself in his prepared pose with right hand in the lapel of his coat. Sergey sat down for a minute, looked close at his mother's wrinkled face and jumped up.

"Sit down, Seryoshenka," begged his mother.

"Sit down, Sergey," repeated his father.

There was silence. The mother smiled oddly.

"We have done everything in our power for you, Seryoshenka. Father . . ."

"It was no good, Mamma dear . . ."

The colonel said firmly, "We had to do it, Sergey, so that you should not think your parents had deserted you."

There was silence again. It was terrible to utter a word, for every spoken word seemed to have lost its real significance and meant only one thing—death. Sergey looked at his father's clean little overcoat, which smelt of benzine, and thought, "They have no servant now, so he has to clean it himself. How is it that I have never noticed when he cleans his coat? Probably in the mornings." And he asked suddenly, "How is my sister? Is she well?"

"Ninochka knows nothing," said his mother quickly.

But the colonel stopped her sternly. "Why tell a lie? The girl read it in the papers. Let Sergey know that everybody, that all his dearest . . . have been thinking of him at this time and . . ."

He could not go on and stopped. Suddenly the mother's face crumpled up all at once, ran down with tears, shook and became wet and wild. Her faded eyes stared frenziedly and her breathing became quicker, shorter and louder.

"Se . . . Ser . . . Se . . . Se . . ." she repeated without moving her lips.

"Mamma dear!"

The colonel stepped forward. He was trembling all over, in every fold of his coat and every wrinkle of his face, and, without realising how terrifying he looked in his deathly whiteness, in his heroic and desperate firmness, he said to his wife, "Be silent. Do not torment him. Do not torment him. He has to die. Do not torment him!"

She had already stopped in terror, but he still shook his clenched fist in front of his chest and repeated, "Do not torment him."

Then he stepped back and, putting his trembling arm behind his back, asked loudly with white lips and an expression of forced calm, "When?"

"Tomorrow morning," answered Sergey, whose lips were white also.

The mother looked at the ground, chewing her lips, as though she heard nothing. Still chewing her lips, she uttered, as if casually, the simple strange words, "Ninochka asked us to kiss you for her, Seryoshenka."

"Kiss her for me," said Sergey.

"We will. The Khvostovs also sent you their love."

"Which Khvostovs? Oh, yes."

The colonel interrupted, "Well, we must go. Get up, Mother, we must go."

They both helped the enfeebled mother to rise.

"Bid him farewell," ordered the colonel. "Make the sign of the cross."

She did everything she was told. But while making the sign of the cross and kissing her son with a brief kiss, she shook her head and repeated meaninglessly, "No, it's not so, no, not so. No, no. And afterwards, what shall I do, what shall I say? No, not so."

"Good-bye, Sergey," said his father. They shook hands and embraced each other firmly but briefly.

"You . . ." began Sergey.

"Well," asked his father abruptly.

"No, it is not so. No, no. What shall I say?" murmured his mother, shaking her head. Meanwhile she had sat down again and was rocking herself backwards and forwards.

"You . . ." began Sergey again. Suddenly his face crumpled up pathetically like a child's and his eyes all at once filled with tears. Through their shining gleams he saw his father's white face near him, with eyes also full of tears.

"You, Father, are a noble man."

"Don't, don't," said his father in terror, and suddenly, as if he had broken in two, his head fell upon his son's shoulder. He used to be taller than Sergey, but now he had shrunk and his dry downy head rested like a little white ball on his son's shoulder. They kissed each other eagerly and silently. Sergey kissed the fluffy white hair and his father the prisoner's dress.

"And what about me?" said a loud voice suddenly.

They turned round. Sergey's mother stood there, her head thrown back, and looked at them angrily, almost with hate.

"What is it, Mother?" asked the colonel.

"What about me?" said she, shaking her head, with extravagant emphasis. "You kiss each other, and what about me? You men kiss, and I? And I?"

"Mamma dear," and Sergey rushed to her.

What followed cannot and should not be described.

The colonel's last words were, "I bless you in your death, Seryosha. Die bravely as befits an officer."

And they left. Somehow they left. They had been there, stood there and spoken, and suddenly they were gone. It was here Mother sat, there stood Father—and suddenly, somehow, they were gone. On coming back to his cell Sergey lay down on his bed, his face turned to the wall to hide it from the soldiers, and he wept for a long time. Then, exhausted by his tears, he slept soundly.

Only his mother came to see Vassily Kashirin. His father, a well-to-do merchant, refused to visit him. When the old woman entered, Vassily was pacing up and down the cell, shivering all over with cold, though the day was warm, almost hot. And their conversation was brief and painful.

"You should not have come, Mamma. You are only giving pain to yourself and me."

"Why all this, Vasia? Why did you do it? Oh, Lord!" and the old woman began to weep, wiping her tears with the corner of her black woollen kerchief. As it had been his and his brothers' habit to shout at their mother, because she did not understand anything, Vassily stopped and, shivering with cold, said angrily, "There it is! I knew it! You do not understand a thing, Mamma. Not a thing!"

"All right, all right. What is the matter with you? Are you cold?"

"Cold!" Vassily cut her short and continued to pace the room, looking at her askance and angrily.

"Perhaps you have caught cold?"

"Ah, Mamma, what is a cold, when . . ." and he waved his hand hopelessly.

The old woman was about to say, "And our old man has ordered pancakes* to be served from Monday on," but she was frightened and began to wail, "I said to him—'Isn't he your son? Go and give him absolution.' But he was as obstinate as an old goat."

"To hell with him. What kind of a father has he been to me? He has been a scoundrel all his life and such he has remained."

"Vasenka, you are speaking of your father," said the old woman, drawing herself up disapprovingly.

"Certainly, of my father."

"Your own father."

"What kind of a father has he been to me?"

It was all absurd and dreadful. He was almost face to face with death, and here was this small, futile, unwanted something, which sprang up and made words sound like empty nut-shells cracking under one's feet. He almost wept for sorrow of that eternal misunderstanding which all his life had stood like a big wall between him and his family, and even now, in these last hours before death, peered at him with its small stupid eyes. Vassily shouted out, "Do take it in. I am going to be hanged! Hanged! Do you understand or not? Hanged!"

"You should have left people alone, then you would not . . ." cried the old woman.

"God above! How can this be! Even the beasts are better! Am I your son or not?"

He began to cry and sat down in a corner. Sitting in her corner, the old woman burst into tears. Unable even for an instant to unite in a feeling of love, and so confront the horror of approaching death, they both shed cold tears of loneliness, which gave no solace to the heart. The mother said, "You asked whether I was your mother or not, you reproach me. And I have gone quite white these last days. I have become an old woman. And yet you talk and reproach me."

"All right, all right, Mamma. Forgive me. You must go now. Kiss my brothers for me."

"Am I not your mother? Do you think I do not pity you?"

At last she went away. She cried bitterly, wiping her eyes with the corner of her kerchief, and did not see the road. The farther she went from the prison, the more scalding her tears became. She turned back towards the prison, but somehow got hopelessly lost in the city in which she had been born, bred and grown old. She finally found herself in a little deserted garden with some old lopped trees and sat down upon a bench

*Translator's Note: Pancakes are served in Russia after funerals.

wet with thaw. Suddenly it flashed upon her—he was going to be hanged tomorrow.

The old woman jumped up and tried to run, but her head suddenly began to turn round and she fell to the ground. The little icy path was wet and slippery and the old woman could not get up. She turned around, tried to raise herself on her elbows, then on her knees, but she fell on her side. The black kerchief had slipped from her head, showing a bald patch on the back amidst dirty grey hair. She fancied for some reason that she was at a wedding feast, that her son was getting married and that she had drunk a great deal and was thoroughly intoxicated.

"No more, I cannot, really I cannot," she kept saying, shaking her head as she crawled over the wet icy snow crust and imagining they were pouring out more and more wine for her.

She felt sick at heart amidst the drunken laughter and the wild dancing and feasting. But they went on pouring out wine, ever more and more wine.

VI The hours fly

There was a bell tower with an old-fashioned clock in the fortress where the condemned prisoners were kept. Every hour, every half hour and every quarter of an hour the clock rang out, in a long-drawn sorrowful peal, which slowly faded away in the sky, like the distant mournful call of birds of passage. During the day that strange sorrowful music was lost in the bustle of the large and crowded city street which ran past the fortress. Trams clanged, the pavement rang with horse hooves, and swaying cars hooted in the distance. Special carnival peasant drivers had come up to town from the outskirts for the Shrovetide season, and the little bells on the necks of their stunted horses filled the air with tinkling. There was chatter, rather intoxicated, merry Shrovetide chatter; and the fresh spring thaw with its dirty pools on the pavement, and the trees grown suddenly dark in the square, seemed to go well with the discordant bustle. A warm wind blew from the sea in strong damp gusts. One could almost see with the naked eye the tiny fresh particles of air frolicking as they were borne along into boundless space.

At night the street became silent in the solitary light of its large electric suns. And then the big fortress with its flat walls, in which was no single light, disappeared into the darkness and stillness. Thus a deep dividing line of silence, immobility and obscurity was drawn between it and the ever living, bustling city. Then the striking of the clock became audible. The strange melody, alien to the earth, was slowly born and faded out high up. It was born again, deceiving the ear, and rang out mournfully and quietly. It stopped and rang again. The hours and minutes fell into a metallic, softly ringing bowl, like big transparent glass drops falling from an unknown height. Or as if birds of passage were flying by.

That was the only sound that was carried day and night into the cells where the condemned prisoners sat each alone. It penetrated the roof and the thickness of the stone walls, stirring the stillness. It disappeared unnoticed and returned just as unnoticed. Sometimes they would forget and not hear it; sometimes they waited for it in despair, living from one hour to the next, distrustful of the stillness. Only important criminals were kept in this fortress, and its regulations were especially stern and harsh, hard as a corner of the fortress wall. And if there be any nobility in cruelty, then this dull, dead, mutely majestic stillness, stifling the smallest rustle, the slightest breath, was noble.

In this majestic stillness, broken only by the sorrowful peal of the flying minutes, five people, two women and three men, separated from every living thing, awaited nightfall, dawn and the execution; and each of them prepared for it in his or her own way.

VII   There is no death

Just as Tanya Kovalchuk had thought all her life of others and not of herself, so now she suffered and grieved deeply for her friends. She thought of death as something imminent and agonising for Seryosha Golovin, for Mousia and the others, but for her personally it seemed to have no concern.

And to make up for her enforced firmness in court, she now wept for hours on end—as old women weep, who have known great sorrow, or as those who are very pitiful and kind-hearted weep in youth. The thought that Seryosha might be short of tobacco and Werner deprived of his customary strong tea, when they were now to die, tormented her perhaps as much as the thought of the execution itself. The execution was something unavoidable and extraneous, and was not worth considering; but it was terrible that a prisoner on the eve of his execution should be deprived of tobacco. She recalled and relived in her memory pleasant details of their life together, and then grew numb with terror at the thought of Sergey's meeting with his parents.

She grieved especially over Mousia. For some time she had been under the impression that Mousia was in love with Werner, and although this was not so, she none the less longed ardently for something good and bright for both of them. When she was free Mousia used to wear a little silver ring engraved with a skull and bones, with a wreath of thorns around them. Tanya Kovalchuk regarded that ring as a symbol of doom and used to beg Mousia, sometimes seriously, sometimes in joke, to give it to her.

"Let me have it," she begged.

"No, Tanechka, I will not give it you. You will soon wear another ring on your finger."

They in their turn, for some reason, thought she would soon get married, which vexed her, for she did not want a husband. And as she remembered those half jesting conversations with Mousia, and knew that Mousia was now doomed, she choked with tears of motherly pity. Each time the clock struck she lifted her tear-stained face and listened—how did those others in their cells take this wearisome, obdurate summons of death?

But Mousia was happy.

Her hands folded behind her back, her prison dress, several sizes too large, making her look like a man or rather an adolescent boy, who had put on someone else's clothes, she paced the cell steadily and indefatigably. The sleeves of the dress were too long for her, so she tucked them up, and her thin arms, so emaciated that they were scarcely bigger than a child's, stuck out of its wide openings like flower stems appearing from a coarse dirty earthen pot. The rough material had rubbed and irritated her delicate white neck; and now and then, with a movement of both hands, Mousia freed her throat and carefully touched with her finger the spot where the skin was red and sore.

Mousia paced the cell and, reddening with excitement, thought out her exculpation before the world. She needed exculpation because she, so young and insignificant, who had achieved so little and was nothing of a heroine, was to be granted the same honourable and glorious death as real heroes and martyrs before her. Believing firmly in human kindness, pity and love, she pictured the sufferings of others on her account, their agony and distress, and blushed with shame. It was as if, in attaining the scaffold, she had committed some great blunder.

At her last meeting with her lawyer, she begged him to get her poison, but suddenly changed her mind. For what if he or others should think she was putting on airs, or was afraid; and, instead of dying modestly and unobtrusively, she made more fuss than was necessary. So she added hastily, "No, I don't think I want it after all."

Now she desired one thing only—to prove to people beyond a doubt that she was no heroine, and that death was not terrible, so that they should not worry or trouble about her. She wanted to explain that it was not her fault that she, so young and insignificant, should die such a death and have so much fuss made about her.

Like a person trying to clear himself from some real accusation, Mousia sought to exonerate herself by searching for something which would enhance her sacrifice and give it real value. She deliberated: "It is true that I am very young, that I might have lived for a long time, but . . ."

And as a candle fades in the glare of the rising sun, so her youth and life appeared dull and dark confronted by that great radiance which was about to shine around her modest head. There was no exoneration.

But perhaps that special gift she carried in her soul—boundless love, boundless readiness for danger, boundless disregard of herself? For indeed it was not her fault that she was not allowed to do all that she might and longed to have done. They had killed her on the threshold of the temple, at the foot of the altar.

But if a person's value is measured not only by what he has done, but by what he wishes to do, then . . . then she was worthy of the martyr's crown.

"Is it possible?" thought Mousia bashfully. "Am I really worthy of it? Worthy that people should weep and grieve over such a little, insignificant girl?"

An indescribable joy overcame her. There were no doubts or hesitations, she was accepted in their midst, she entered as an equal the ranks of those noble souls, who from time immemorial have attained high heaven by way of the stake, tortures and execution. She knew bright peace and rest and boundless, tranquil, radiant happiness. She felt as if she had already left life and soared bodiless in its light.

"And this is death? Can one call this death?" thought Mousia blissfully.

If scientists, philosophers and executioners from all over the world had assembled in her cell and spread out before her books, scalpels, axes and nooses in the effort to prove that death exists, that man dies and is killed and that there is no immortality—they would only have astonished her. How could there be no immortality, since she was already immortal? How could one speak of immortality and death, when she was already dead and immortal, as alive in death as she had been alive in life?

And if they were to bring a coffin containing her own decomposing body, filling the cell with stench, and say, "Look, that is you!"

She would have looked and answered, "No, that is not I."

And if they should try to convince her, through fear, that this ominous decaying body was she, she—Mousia—would have answered with a smile, "No, you think that *this* is I, but *this* is not I. I am she to whom you speak, how then could I be *this*?"

"But you will die and become like this."

"No, I shall not die."

"You will be executed. There's the noose."

"I shall be executed, but I shall not die. How can I die, since I am already immortal?"

And the scientists, philosophers and executioners would step back and say in trembling voices, "Do not touch this place. It is holy ground."

Of what else did Mousia think? Of many other things, for to her the thread of life was not broken by death, but ran on smoothly and evenly. She thought of her comrades; both of those far away, to whom her execution would cause grief and pain, and those near her, together with whom she would walk to the scaffold. She was astonished at Vassily's fear, for he had always been very brave and could even jest with death. On that Tuesday morning, for instance, when he with the rest of them were placing in their belts the explosives, which were to cause their ruin a few hours later, Tanya Kovalchuk's hand shook so that she had to be sent away; but Vassily joked, played the buffoon, whirled round and was so careless that Werner said sternly, "There is no need to take liberties with death."

Why was he afraid now? But this incomprehensible fear was so foreign to Mousia's soul that she soon ceased to think or try to find the cause of it. She suddenly had a desperate longing to see Seryosha Golovin and have a good laugh with him. After a few moments' thought, she longed still more desperately to see Werner and have a good argument with him. She imagined Werner to be pacing by her side with his even measured steps, digging his heels into the ground, and said, "No, Werner dear, that is all nonsense, it is of no importance whether you killed NN. or not. You are clever, but you reason as though you were playing chess—you make one move and then another, and then you have won. The important thing is, Werner, that we ourselves are ready to die. Do you understand? What do those people think? That there is nothing more terrible than death. Having invented death themselves, they are afraid of it and try to frighten us with it. But this is what I should like to do—step out all alone in front of a whole regiment of soldiers and fire at them with my Browning. I am alone, it is true, and there are thousands of them and I might kill no one. What matters is that they are thousands. When thousands kill one, it means that that one has conquered. It's true, Werner, my dear."

But this was so obvious that she did not feel like continuing the argument. No doubt Werner now realised it for himself. Perhaps, however, it was just that her mind refused to stay fixed on any one thing—like a lightly hovering bird that sees boundless horizons and is free of all the space and depth of the lovely tender blue sky. The clock rang out continually, stirring the mute stillness; and her thoughts mingled with the harmonious sound, made beautiful by distance, and also began to chime; as if the smoothly gliding images had turned into music. She seemed to herself to be riding along a broad smooth road; the night was quiet and dark and the springs of the carriage swayed whilst the little bells tinkled. All care and emotion had vanished; the tired body relaxed in the darkness, whilst the mind, weary but happy, created bright images and revelled in their colours and quiet peace. Mousia recalled the three comrades who had been hanged a short time ago, and their faces were bright and joyful and near, nearer than the faces of those who still lived. So does a man think with joy in the morning of his friends' home, which he will visit in the evening with greetings on his smiling lips.

Mousia had worn herself out with pacing. She lay down carefully on her plank bed and went on day-dreaming with her eyes lightly closed. The hours rang out continually, stirring the mute stillness, and bright singing images floated calmly in the wake of their chimes. Mousia thought, "Is this really death? My God, how glorious it is! Or is it life? I don't know. I don't know. I will look and listen."

For quite a time, since the first days of her imprisonment, she had begun to imagine sounds. Possessed of a very musical ear, rendered still more sensitive by the stillness, she invented whole musical patterns from a background of meagre grains of reality—the guards' footsteps in the corridor, the chimes of the clock, the rustling of the wind on the iron roof or the creaking of the lantern. At first this phenomenon frightened Mousia and she repelled it as an insane hallucination; later, when she realised that she was not crazy and that these sounds did not indicate any mental deterioration, she yielded to them tranquilly.

And now, suddenly, she seemed to hear quite distinctly the sound of military music. Bewildered, she opened her eyes and raised her head— there was night outside the window and the clock was striking. There it is again, she thought calmly, and shut her eyes. No sooner had she closed them than she heard the sound of music again. Soldiers, a whole regiment of them, were coming from the right of the building and passing by her window. Their feet beat time rhythmically upon the frozen ground, one—two, one—two. She could even hear the creaking of a leather boot, now and then, or a foot slip and regain the step. And the music came nearer; it was an unfamiliar, but very loud and cheerful festival march. They must be celebrating some special occasion in the fortress.

Now the band was just outside the window and the whole cell was filled with gay, rhythmic, harmonious sounds. One big brass trumpet was very much out of tune, now it was behind, now ran comically ahead. Mousia seemed to see the little soldier with that trumpet, his earnest face, and she laughed.

Then it all moved into the distance. The footsteps, one—two, one—two, died away. From afar the music sounded even gayer and more beautiful. Once or twice again the high-pitched brass voice of the trumpet was heard cheerfully out of tune, then everything was silent. Again the clock on the tower struck the hour, slowly, mournfully, scarcely stirring the stillness.

"They've gone," thought Mousia with faint regret. She missed the vanished sounds, so gay and amusing, she even missed the departed soldier boys, because they had brass trumpets and creaking boots and were quite different from those she wanted to shoot with her Browning.

"Please, once more," she begged gently. And they came again. They bent over her, enveloped her in a transparent cloud, lifted her high up, where birds of passage float and cry like heralds. To the right, to the left, up and down, they cry like heralds. They call, they proclaim, they announce their flight from afar. They spread their wings wide and the darkness supports them as does the light; and on their swelling breasts, cutting the air, is reflected from below the city shining blue. Mousia's heart beat more and more regularly, her breathing became more and more tranquil and low. She was falling asleep. Her face was tired and pale; there were circles under her eyes and her girlish arms were thin to emaciation, but there was a smile on her lips. Tomorrow, when the sun rose, this human face would be distorted in an inhuman grimace, the brain would be covered with thick blood and the glassy eyes bulge from their sockets; but today she sleeps quietly and smiles in her great immortality.

Mousia was asleep.

But the life of the prison continued its accustomed way, deaf and quick of hearing, blind and vigilant, like eternal fear itself. Somewhere people walked, somewhere people whispered, somewhere a gun clanked. Someone shrieked, it seemed; or perhaps no one shrieked, and it was only the stillness which made one think so.

The shutter in the door fell noiselessly, and in the black opening appeared a dark whiskered face, which stared at Mousia for a long time in astonishment, then disappeared noiselessly as it had come. The bells rang and chimed, slowly, poignantly; as if the wearied hours were climbing a high mountain to midnight, and the ascent was becoming ever more difficult. They slipped, they slid, they rushed down with a moan, and again began climbing painfully to their black summit.

Somewhere people talked. Somewhere people whispered. And already the horses were being harnessed in the black carriage without lights.

VIII   There is death and life also

Sergey Golovin had never thought of death, which seemed so alien as not to concern him at all. He was a cheerful youth of excellent physique, endowed with a bright, even temper and a capacity for enjoying life; and this quality caused every thought and feeling detrimental to life to be absorbed in his organism quickly and without trace. Just as all his cuts, wounds and bites healed rapidly, so everything painfully affecting his soul was immediately ejected and disappeared. He applied himself to everything with the same even temper and zest, whether business or pleasure, whether photography, cycling or the preparation of a terrorist attempt. He found everything in life pleasant and important and was under an equal necessity to do everything well.

And he did do everything well. He was a splendid sailor, an excellent shot, faithful in friendship as in love, and was a fanatical believer in the "word of honour." His friends laughed at him, saying that if a notorious informer, scoundrel or spy, should give him his word of honour that he was not an informer, Sergey would believe him and give him a friendly handshake. He had one failing, however. He was convinced that he sang well—though he had not the slightest ear for music, and sang abominably out of tune even in revolutionary songs; yet he took it amiss when his friends laughed at him.

"Either you are all asses or I am an ass," he would say seriously in an offended voice. After some thought, they would all agree, equally seriously, "It is you who are the ass. That is plain from your voice."

But, as often happens with charming people, his friends loved him more, perhaps, for this failing than for his virtues.

He was so fearless of death and regarded it so little, that on the fatal morning, before leaving Tanya Kovalchuk's flat, he was the only one who ate a good breakfast. He drank two glasses of tea and milk and ate a large white roll. Then, looking sadly at Werner's untouched bread, he said, "Why don't you eat anything? Eat and keep up your strength."

"I don't feel like it," was the answer.

"Well then, I'll have it. May I?"

"You certainly have a good appetite, Seryosha!"

Instead of replying, Sergey began, with his mouth full, to sing raucously and out of tune, "Terrible whirlwinds howl above us."

After the arrest, the thought that they had made a mess of it and done for themselves depressed him; but he went on to consider—"There is still one more thing to do well—to die"—and cheered up again. Strange as it may seem, he had not been in the fortress two days before he began to practice gymnastics according to the remarkably rational system of a certain German called Müller, about which he was an enthusiast. He stripped himself naked and, to the alarmed surprise of the watching warder, went conscientiously through all the prescribed eighteen exercises. As an enthusiast for Müller's system, it pleased him that the guard was looking on with astonishment; and, although he knew that there would be no reply, he remarked to the eye glued to the peep-hole, "It does you good, brother, makes you strong. This is what you need in your regiment." His tone was persuasive and kind, so as not to frighten the warder, and he had no idea that the soldier simply thought him a lunatic.

The terror of death came on him gradually, in spasms as it were. It was as though someone gripped him and thrust a fist violently into his heart from below. The feeling was rather painful than terrible. It would pass off only to recur a few hours later, and each time the attack was longer and more violent. And it began to reveal itself as the dim shadow of a great, well-nigh unbearable fear.

"Is it possible I am afraid?" thought Sergey with astonishment. "What nonsense!"

But it was not he who was afraid, it was his young strong healthy body, which could not be deceived by the exercises of the German Müller or by rubbings with a wet towel. And the stronger and fresher it felt after the cold water, the sharper and more unbearable was the sensation of sudden fear. It was just at that time in the morning when, in freedom, he felt happiest and most vigorous, after a sound night's sleep and physical exercises, that he now experienced the onset of an acute and, as it were, alien fear. He realised this and thought to himself, "You're a fool, brother Sergey. To make it easier for the body to die, you should weaken it, not strengthen it. Fool!"

So he gave up physical exercises and cold rubs. And he shouted to the guard in explanation of the change, "No matter that I've given it up. It's a fine thing, brother, only no good for those who are to hang. For everybody else it's excellent."

And actually things became somehow easier. He also tried to eat less, so as to grow still weaker; but, in spite of the lack of fresh air and exercise, his appetite was still very good. It was difficult to check it and he ate everything that was brought to him. Then he began to try another way; before ever beginning to eat, he would pour out half the hot meal into the pail. This seemed to help—a dull sleepiness and weariness set in as a result.

"I'll teach you!" he exclaimed threateningly to his body, passing his hand sadly and tenderly over the flabby softened muscles.

The body soon, however, adapted itself to the new order of things, and the terror of death appeared once again. True, the acute burning pain had turned to a dull nauseating one. "That's because there is so long to wait," thought Sergey. "It would be a good idea to sleep through till the day of execution," and he tried to sleep as much as possible. At first he succeeded in this, but later, either because he slept too much or for some other reason, insomnia set in. And with it came poignant far-sighted thoughts and a longing for life.

"Do I really fear that bugbear?" he thought to himself about death. "I regret my life. Life is a glorious thing, no matter what the pessimists say. And what if they hanged a pessimist? Ah, I regret life, I regret it very much. And why has my beard grown? For long it would not grow and now suddenly it has become long. Why?"

He shook his head sadly and heaved long-drawn painful sighs. He was silent, and then another long, deep sigh. Again a short silence followed by a still longer and heavier sigh.

And so it went on till the day of the trial and the last meeting with the old people. He awoke in his cell with the full consciousness that he had finished with life forever and that there were only a few hours left in that emptiness preceding death, and was overcome by a feeling of strangeness. It seemed as though he had been stripped of everything, stripped in a quite extraordinary way; not only had his clothes been taken from him, but he was bereft of the sun, noise and light, acts and speech. Death was not yet but life had already passed; and instead there was something new, something quite incomprehensible, which seemed now devoid of meaning, now full of meaning, but was so deep, mysterious and inhuman that it was impossible to understand.

"Damn it all," wondered Sergey painfully. "What is this? And where is this I? What is this I?"

He examined himself attentively and with interest, beginning with his large prison slippers and ending with his stomach, which stuck out beneath his prison dress. He walked across the cell with arms outspread, continuing to examine himself, like a woman in a new dress too long for her. He moved his head experimentally—it turned. And this thing, which was rather terrible for some reason, was he, Sergey Golovin, and it would cease to be.

He was overcome by a sense of the strangeness of everything. He tried to walk across the cell—walking seemed strange. He tried to sit down—sitting down seemed strange. He tried to drink some water—it seemed strange to drink or swallow or hold a cup in his fingers and strange that those fingers trembled. He choked and began to cough, and while coughing he thought—how strange to cough.

"What is the matter with me? Am I going mad?" thought Sergey shuddering. "That would be the last straw, the devil take it!"

He rubbed his forehead with his hand, but this action, too, seemed strange. Then, scarcely breathing, he remained perfectly motionless for hours on end, as it seemed to him, suppressing every thought, holding his breath, avoiding every movement; for every thought and movement was madness. Time had disappeared, as if it had turned into space, transparent, airless space, or a huge square on which was everything, earth, life and people. And all was visible at a glance, everything to the very end, to the mysterious abyss—death. And the agony was not in that death was visible, but that life and death were visible together. A sacrilegious hand had drawn aside the curtain which for countless ages had hidden the mystery of life and the mystery of death, and now they ceased to be mysteries, and yet they were not intelligible; like a truth engraved in an unknown language. There were no thoughts in his human brain, no words in his human speech, which could encompass what he saw. And the words "I am frightened" came into his mind only because there were no other words, because there did not and could not exist any other conception corresponding to this new set of conditions, so outside human experience. Thus might a human being feel if, while remaining within the bounds of human understanding, feeling and experience, he should suddenly see God himself. He would see and not understand, even though he knew that the name of this being was God, and he would shudderingly suffer the terrible torment of utter incomprehension.

"There's Müller for you!" he suddenly said loudly with extraordinary conviction, tossing up his head. And, with one of those unexpected emotional transitions so characteristic of the human soul, he burst into merry hearty laughter.

"Oh Müller, my dear Müller, my wonderful German! And yet you are right, Müller, and I am an ass, brother Müller."

He paced the cell quickly once or twice and then, once more greatly astonishing the soldier who watched him through the peep-hole, stripped himself naked and went through all the eighteen exercises gaily and most conscientiously. He stretched and expanded his young, rather thin body, squatted on his heels, stood on tiptoe and breathed in and breathed out, and flung out his legs and arms. And after each exercise he said with satisfaction, "That's right! That's something real, brother Müller!"

His cheeks glowed, drops of hot sweat came pleasantly from his pores, and his heart beat strongly and regularly.

"It's like this, Müller," reasoned Sergey, throwing out his chest so that his ribs were plainly visible beneath the thin stretched skin:—"It's like this, Muller; there is a nineteenth exercise—to be hanged by the neck in a motionless position. And that is called execution. Do you understand, Müller? They take a live man, say Sergey Golovin, bundle him up, as if he were a doll, and hang him by the neck till he is dead. It's a stupid business, Müller, but it cannot be helped, there is no way out."

He bent his body to the right and repeated, "There is no way out, brother Müller."

IX   The terror of loneliness

Separated from Sergey and Mousia only by a few empty cells, but feeling as desperately lonely as if he were alone in the universe, the unhappy Vassily Kashirin was ending his life in terror and grief, to the same sound of the chimes of the clock.

Covered with sweat, his moist shirt clinging to his body, his naturally curly hair matted and tangled, he raced convulsively and hopelessly up and down the cell, like a man with unbearable toothache. He would sit for a while, then rush about once more, then stop and press his forehead against the wall or search for something with his eyes, as if he were looking for medicine. He had changed so much that he almost seemed to have two faces, the young one which was his formerly and had disappeared somewhere, and a new terrible one which had come out of darkness in place of it.

For him the terror of death had come all at once and taken complete and overwhelming possession. During the morning he had accustomed himself to the idea of going to certain death, but as evening came on and he remained still locked in his solitary cell, he was enveloped and swamped in a mad wave of terror. So long as by his own free will he exposed himself to danger and death, so long as he held in his own hands the choice of a fate, however terrible, he felt at ease and almost cheerful. His terror, which belonged to the mean, shrivelled, old-womanish side of him, was swamped in a feeling of complete freedom, of delight in the bold, firm and fearless assertion of his will power. With an infernal machine at his belt, he himself seemed to have turned into an infernal machine, absorbed into himself the cruel force of dynamite and acquired its fiery death-dealing powers. And whilst walking in the street amidst ordinary bustling folk, immersed in their own affairs and in getting out of the way of cab-horses and trams, he had seemed to himself an emissary from another secret world, where death and fear were unknown.

Then suddenly came this abrupt, cruel and stupefying change. He could no longer move according to his own will, but must go where others took him. He could no longer choose his position, but was put into a stone cage and locked up like an inanimate object. He could no longer freely decide between life and death, like others, but was going to sure and inevitable extinction. He who had been the incarnation of will power, life and strength, had become in a moment an image of utter helplessness, a beast led to the slaughter, or a deaf and dumb object, which could be picked up and thrown into the fire or broken. No matter what he might say, no one would listen to him; if he attempted to shout, they would stop his mouth with a gag; wherever he might try to move on his own volition, they would take him away and hang him. If he resisted, struggled or lay down on the ground, they would overpower him, lift him up and bind him, and carry him bound to the scaffold. And the fact that this mechanical outrage would be carried through by people just like himself put them in a new, strange and evil light. Sometimes they seemed like phantoms, feigning to be people and appearing to him only for a special purpose; and sometimes like mechanical puppets on wires. They would seize hold of him, take him away, hang him, and jerk his legs. Then they would cut the rope, take him down, carry him away and bury him.

From the first day of his imprisonment people and life had been transformed for him into an incomprehensible and terrible world of apparitions and mechanical puppets. Almost frantic with fear he tried to bring to mind that people have tongues and speak, but he could not, for they seemed mute. He tried to remember their speech, the meaning of the words they used in intercourse, but he could not. Their mouths opened, sounds came, then they went away, moving their feet, and nothing was left.

Thus might a person feel if one night, when he was alone in the house, all the things came to life, moved and acquired unlimited power over him, the man; if the cupboard, the chair, the writing-table and the sofa should all suddenly sit in judgement on him. He would cry out and rush about, beseech them and shout for help, and they would speak to each other in their own language and then—the cupboard, the chair, the desk and the sofa—take him away to be hanged. And the rest of the furniture would look on.

And all things began to seem unreal, like so many toys, to Vassily Kashirin, the man who was sentenced to death by hanging; his cell, the door with the peep-hole, the strokes of the wound-up clock, the neatly moulded fortress, and especially that mechanical doll with the gun who stamped with his feet in the corridor, and the others who frightened him by peeping through the hole in the door and silently brought him food. What he felt was not the fear of death; rather did he wish for death. For with all its eternal, mysterious incomprehensibility, it was more accessible to his reason than this wildly and fantastically changed world. Moreover, death seemed to be completely annihilated in this mad world of ghosts and puppets; it had been deprived of its hugeness and mystery, becoming also a piece of mechanism, and terrible only for that reason. They would seize hold of him, take him away, hang him and jerk his legs. Then they would cut the rope, take him down, carry him away and bury him.

Human beings had disappeared from the world.

At the trial the proximity of his friends had brought Kashirin to himself, and once more, for an instant, he was capable of seeing people. They sat and passed judgement, said something in human speech, listened and seemed to understand. But already at the meeting with his mother, he felt clearly, with the terror of a man who is going out of his mind and realises it, that this old woman in the little black kerchief was just a well-contrived mechanical doll like those which say "pa-pa, ma-ma," only better constructed. As he tried to talk to her, he thought, shuddering.

"Oh, Lord, this is a doll. A mother doll. And out there is a soldier doll and at home there is a father doll and I am the doll Vassily Kashirin."

It seemed to him that in a moment he would hear somewhere the working of machinery, the creaking of unoiled wheels. When his mother began to cry, something human again flashed up for an instant, but no sooner did she begin to speak than it disappeared and his feeling became one of curiosity and terror at seeing tears flowing from the doll's eyes.

Later on, in his cell, when his terror became unbearable, Vassily Kashirin made an attempt to pray. Of all that, under the guise of religion, had surrounded his youthful years in the house of his father, a shop-keeper, there remained only the bitter dregs, which repelled and annoyed him. He had no faith. Once, however, perhaps in early childhood, he had heard a few words, which made him tremble with emotion and all his life sounded in his memory like quiet poetry. These words were, "The joy of all that mourn."

At difficult moments he would whisper to himself, not in prayer and without being definitely conscious of what he said, "The joy of all that mourn"—and suddenly he would feel better and long to complain in a low voice to someone he loved, "Our life . . . is it life at all? Oh, my dearest, is this really life?"

And suddenly life would become amusing and he would feel like ruffling his hair, kicking out his limbs, and crying: "Strike me," as he offered his chest to the world's blows.

He told no one, not even his closest friends, of his "joy of all that mourn," and so deep was it buried in his soul, that he himself was scarcely conscious of it. It was only on rare occasions and with caution that he brought it to mind.

And now, when the terror of the insoluble mystery was before him, covering him completely, as water at springtide submerges the willow twigs on the bank, he wanted to pray. He would have liked to go down on his knees, but he was ashamed to do so before the soldier, so, folding his arms across his chest, he whispered low, "Oh, joy of all that mourn."

He repeated imploringly and with anguish, "Oh, joy of all that mourn, come to me, help Vaska Kashirin!"

A long time ago, whilst he was in his first year at the university and still led a dissipated life, and before he met Werner and joined the revolutionary organisation, he used to call himself pathetically and in bravado, "Vaska Kashirin." Now, for some reason, he felt like calling himself that again. But the words of his prayer came out sounding dead, as if unable to arouse response, "Oh, joy of all that mourn."

Something stirred. Far away a silent and sorrowful image seemed to float and quietly disappear without irradiating the gloom of death. The wound-up clock on the tower struck the hour. The soldier in the corridor knocked with his sabre, or was it a gun? Then he began to yawn lengthily with pauses between the yawns.

"Oh, joy of all that mourn! And are you silent? You will not say a word to Vaska Kashirin?"

He smiled imploringly and waited. But in his soul and around him there was emptiness. The gentle sorrowful image did not reappear. Unwanted and painful memories came back to him. He remembered the burning wax candles, the priest in his cassock, the ikon painted on the wall, his father bending and straightening himself as he bowed to the ground in prayer, whilst throwing a glance sideways at Vaska to see whether he was praying or up to mischief. And his terror became even greater than before the prayer.

Everything became a blank.

Madness crept on him painfully. Consciousness was going out like the cooling ashes of a scattered and dying bonfire, or like the corpse of a man just dead, whose heart is still warm whilst his feet and hands are already stiff. Once again a spark of his dying reason flared up redly and told him that he, Vassily Kashirin, might go mad here, experience agony for which there is no name, reach such limits of pain and suffering as no earthly being had ever before felt; he knew that he might beat his head against the wall, put out his eyes with his own fingers, talk and shout as much as he liked, or declare weeping that he could bear no more, and all would be of no good. Nothing would happen.

And nothing did happen. The feet, which have their own life and consciousness, continued to walk and carry the damp, trembling body. The arms, which have their own consciousness, tried in vain to wrap closer the cloak across his chest, and to warm the trembling moist body. The body shook and shivered; the eyes stared. And that was almost calmness.

But there was still one more moment of wild terror. That was when people entered the cell. His mind did not even take in what that meant—that it was time to go to execution; he simply saw people and was frightened with an almost child-like terror.

"I will not, I will not," he whispered inaudibly with livid lips, and retreated silently into the cell, as in childhood when his father had lifted his hand to strike him.

"You must come," they said.

They talked and walked about and handed over something. He shut his eyes, swayed and started to get ready slowly. Apparently he began to come to himself, for suddenly he asked an official for a cigarette. The latter obligingly opened his cigarette case on which was engraved a decadent figure.

X   The walls fall down

The unknown prisoner, nicknamed Werner, was a man who was tired of life and of struggle. There was a time when he had felt a great love for life and enjoyed the theatre, literature and intercourse with his fellows. Endowed with a splendid memory and a strong will, he had mastered to perfection several European languages and could easily pass as a German, Frenchman, or Englishman. He spoke German as a rule with a Bavarian accent, but could when he wished talk like a real Berliner born. He liked to dress well, had beautiful manners, and was the only one of his confederates who could, without risk of detection, make an appearance at fashionable balls.

But for a long time now, unknown to his comrades, a grim disdain for people had grown up in his soul; he was filled with despair and a heavy, almost mortal weariness. By nature more of a mathematician than a poet, he had up till now known no moments of inspiration or ecstasy, and sometimes felt like a madman who tries to square the circle in pools of human blood. The enemy with whom he carried on a daily warfare could not inspire him with any respect. He found a closely woven net of stupidity, treachery, lies, filth and rotten deceit. The final thing, which, it seemed, had for ever destroyed in him the will to live, was the murder of an informer, carried out by him at the bidding of the Organisation. He did the killing calmly, but when he saw the dead face, false but all the same pitiful and now so peaceful, all respect for himself and his cause left him. Not that he felt remorse, but suddenly his own personality simply ceased to have any value for him, became a thoroughly insignificant, uninteresting, boring stranger. Being a man of single and integrated will, he did not leave the Organisation and outwardly remained the same; only deep down in his eyes was something cold and terrible. But he said nothing to anyone.

He possessed still another rare characteristic. As there are people who have never had a headache, so he did not know what fear was. And his attitude to the fear of others, though not censorious, was not specially sympathetic—as to a fairly widespread disease from which he, himself, had never suffered. He pitied his comrades, especially Vassily Kashirin; but it was a chilly, almost official pity, such as some of the judges might probably have felt.

Werner realised that execution is not only death but something else. But in any case he had determined to meet it calmly, as something purely extraneous; to live to the end as if nothing had happened or would happen. Only in this way could he express his complete disdain for the execution and preserve intact his inalienable freedom of soul. At the trial (although this, perhaps, even his own comrades, who well knew his cold indifference and disdain, would not have believed) he thought neither of life nor death. With concentration, with the closest and most tranquil attention, he was playing a difficult game of chess. An excellent player, he had begun this game on the first day of his imprisonment, and continued it without interruption. Nor did the verdict which sentenced him to death by hanging displace one figure on the unseen board.

Even the fact that he would not, apparently, be able to finish the game did not stop him; and he began the morning of the last day left to him on earth by correcting a not altogether successful move made the day before. He sat for a long time motionless with his hands pressed between his knees; then got up and began to walk about, considering. He had an individual gait; he bent the upper part of his body slightly forward and struck the ground with his heels firmly and decidedly, so that even on dry ground his feet left a deep, perceptible track. Quietly, on one breath, he whistled a simple Italian aria; it helped him to think.

But this time, for some reason, the game went badly. With the unpleasant feeling that he was making some big and even obvious mistake, he turned back more than once and checked the game almost from the beginning. He did not find any mistakes, but the feeling that he had made one not only did not disappear but became stronger and more unpleasant. And suddenly an unexpected and vexing thought came into his mind: did not his mistake consist in the fact that he was trying to distract his mind from the execution and shield it from that fear of death which was unavoidable for the condemned?

"No, why?" he answered coldly, and quietly closed the unseen board. And with the same concentrated attention with which he had played, and as if answering a stiff examination, he tried to realise the terror and hopelessness of his situation. Looking round the cell, and trying to leave nothing out of account, he calculated the hours that remained before the execution, and drew for himself an approximate and fairly accurate picture of the execution itself. He shrugged his shoulders.

"Well?" he remarked to someone half enquiringly—"That's all. What is there to be afraid of?"

He was certainly not afraid. And not only had he no fear, but, as if in opposition to fear, he found within himself a feeling of vague but great and daring joy. And the still undiscovered mistake no longer bothered or irritated him, but also seemed clearly to indicate something good and unexpected; as if a near and dear friend, whom he had thought dead, appeared alive and unhurt and laughed.

Werner once more shrugged his shoulders and felt his pulse; his heart was beating fast, but strongly and regularly with a certain resonant strength. Again, like a novice imprisoned for the first time, he looked attentively at the walls, the bolts, the chair screwed to the floor, and thought, "Why do I feel so easy, happy and free? Yes, free. I think of the execution tomorrow, and it is as if it did not exist. I look at the walls, and there seem to be no walls. And I feel as free as if I were not only not in prison, but had just come out of a prison in which I had been all my life. What is the meaning of this?"

His hands began to tremble, which was an unheard-of phenomenon for Werner. His mind beat about more and more furiously. Tongues of flame seemed to flare up in his head; the fire was trying to force its way out and illumine a wide distance, which was still under the darkness of night. And then it forced its way out and the light flashed over a wide prospect.

The dull weariness, which had exhausted Werner for the last two years, fell from his heart like a dead, cold and heavy serpent with closed eyes and ghastly shut mouth. Before the face of death his gay, splendid youth had returned. But this was more than splendid youthfulness. With that astonishing illumination of the soul, which at rare moments flashes on a person and raises him to the highest peaks of consciousness, Werner suddenly saw both life and death and was amazed by the vastness of the unknown spectacle. It was as if he had come by a path, narrow as a knife-blade, to the highest point of a mountain range, and on one side saw life and on the other death, like two gleaming, deep, beautiful seas mingling on the horizon in one limitless broad expanse.

"What is this? What a divine sight!" he said slowly, involuntarily half-rising and straightening himself, as if in the presence of a higher being. His eager and piercing glance annihilated walls, space and time, and he looked deeply and widely into his past life.

And he saw life afresh. He did not try as before to express what he saw in words, nor are such words to be found in human speech, which is after all poor and meagre. All that was mean, dirty and evil and had aroused in him disdain for his fellows, at times even making the sight of a human face distasteful to him, had completely disappeared. So, for a person who mounts in a balloon, disappear the rubbish and dirt of the crowded streets of the town he has left, and ugliness becomes beauty.

With an unconscious movement, Werner stepped to the table and leaned on it with his right hand. By nature proud and forceful, he had never yet assumed such a proud, free and forceful pose, never turned his neck with such dignity, never looked thus; for never yet had he felt so free and full of power as here in prison, separated by a few hours only from execution and death.

He saw people afresh and they seemed to his illuminated sight dear and delightful and not as of old. Soaring above time, he saw clearly how young humanity is, only yesterday howling like a beast in the woods. And what had seemed horrible in people, unforgivable and disgusting, suddenly became lovable; as a child's inability to walk like a grown-up is lovable, or his disconnected prattle sparkling with gems of genius, or his amusing blunders and faults, or his cruel bruises.

"My dear ones," suddenly and unexpectedly came from Werner with a smile; and at once he lost all the dignity of his pose and became once more a convict, who feels the closeness and discomfort of being under lock and key and is rather bored by the annoying, searching eye glued to the panel of the door. Strange to say, he almost immediately forgot what he had just seen so vividly and clearly, and, still more strangely, he did not even try to remember it. He simply sat down as comfortably as possible without his customary stiffness of posture, and looked round at the walls and gratings with a strangely weak and tender smile, quite unlike himself. And something else took place, which had never before happened to Werner; he suddenly began to cry.

"My dear comrades," he whispered and wept bitterly. "My dear comrades."

By what secret paths had he journeyed from a feeling of proud and boundless freedom to that tender and passionate pity? He did not know and did not think about it. And whether his pity was for his dear comrades, or whether his tears concealed something in him still loftier and more passionate—this, too, his suddenly resurrected and youthful heart did not know. He wept and whispered, "My dear comrades! Oh, my dear comrades!"

In this man, who wept so bitterly and smiled through his tears, no one would have recognised the cold, haughty, weary and arrogant Werner—neither the judges, nor his comrades, nor he himself.

XI   They are taken away

Before putting the condemned prisoners in carriages, all five of them were assembled in a big, cold room with a vaulted ceiling, which looked like a disused office or empty waiting-room. Here they were allowed to talk to each other.

But Tanya Kovalchuk was the only one who at once availed herself of that permission. The others silently and closely pressed each other's hands, some of which were cold as ice, others hot as fire, and in silence, trying not to look at each other, crowded together in an awkward distracted bunch. Now, when they were together, they were somehow ashamed of what each had felt when alone; and they were afraid to look at each other, not wishing to see or show that each had passed through or suspected in himself, a certain new rather shameful experience.

But after having glanced at each other once or twice and smiled, they suddenly felt natural and at ease with one another as before. No change seemed to have taken place, or if there was one, it had been so evenly distributed among all that it was not noticeable in each individual. They all moved and spoke strangely; abruptly and in spurts, and either too slowly or too quickly. Sometimes they swallowed their words and repeated them several times, and sometimes they did not finish the sentence they had begun or thought they had finished it. But all this they did not notice. They all blinked and looked at ordinary objects with curiosity, as if they did not recognise them, like people who usually wore eye-glasses and had suddenly taken them off. They all kept turning round suddenly, as though someone from behind were calling and wished to show them something. But this, too, they did not realise. Mousia's and Tanya Kovalchuk's cheeks and ears were burning. Sergey looked rather pale at first, but quickly got better and seemed as usual.

Only Vassily attracted everyone's attention. Even amongst them he looked different and ghastly. Werner was roused to tender anxiety and said to Mousia in a low voice, "What is it, Mousechka? Is it possible that he . . . What? Let's go to him."

Vassily looked at Werner from far away, as if he did not recognise him, and dropped his eyes.

"Vasia, what's wrong with your hair? What's the matter with you? All right, brother, it's all right, it will soon be over. You must bear up, you know."

Vassily was silent. But when it almost seemed that he would say nothing, there came a dull, belated, terribly distant reply—so might the grave itself answer after many calls.

"I'm all right. I'm bearing up."

And he repeated, "I'm bearing up."

Werner was delighted.

"That's right. That's a brave fellow. Good, good!"

But he met a dark, leaden glance, which seemed to come from remote depths, and thought with momentary anguish—"Where is he speaking from?" And with deep tenderness, as to one already in the grave, he said, "Vasia, do you hear me? I love you very much."

"And I love you, too," came from the tongue which moved with difficulty.

Mousia suddenly took Werner's arm and, with an expression of astonishment, said intensely, like an actress on the stage, "Werner, what's the matter with you? You said—'I love you.' Never before did you say to anybody 'I love you.' Why are you altogether so . . . bright and gentle? Why?"

"Why?"

And expressing his feelings, like an actor, with similar intensity, Werner pressed Mousia's hand close and said, "Yes, now I love people very much. Don't tell the others, I'm ashamed, but I feel great love."

Their glances met and burst into flame, whilst everything around seemed to go dark; so in a sudden flash of lightning all other lights are extinguished and the intensely yellow, brilliant flame casts its shadow upon the earth.

"Yes," said Mousia. "Yes, Werner."

"Yes," he answered. "Yes, Mousia."

Something had been made clear and irrevocably settled between them. And Werner, his glance bright, roused himself again and quickly stepped up to Sergey.

"Seryosha!"

But it was Tanya Kovalchuk who answered. Full of delight, almost weeping with maternal pride, she pulled Sergey violently by the sleeve and said, "Werner, listen! I have been crying my eyes out about him, grieving for him, and he—does gymnastics."

"According to Müller?" smiled Werner.

Sergey frowned in some confusion.

"You should not laugh, Werner. I have become thoroughly convinced . . ."

They all burst out laughing. They had drawn strength and courage from being together and had gradually become as they used to be; but this, too, they had not noticed and thought they had not changed. Werner suddenly stopped laughing and said to Sergey with great seriousness, "You are right, Seryosha. You are quite right."

"But you should understand . . ." began Golovin delightedly. "Of course we . . ."

But at that moment they were requested to set off. The guards were so obliging as to allow them to seat themselves in pairs according to their own choice. They were on the whole extraordinarily kind; they tried, on the one hand, to express their human attitude to them, and on the other, to efface themselves as much as possible as if the whole proceeding was automatic. But they were pale.

"You, Mousia, go with him," said Werner pointing at Vassily, who stood motionless.

"I understand," nodded Mousia. "And you?"

"I? Tanya with Sergey, you with Vasia . . . I alone. It's all right, I can do it, you know."

When they went outside, the damp darkness struck with soft but warm force against their faces and eyes; it took their breath away and immediately refreshed and tenderly enveloped their trembling bodies. It was difficult to believe that this astonishing thing was just a spring wind, a warm moist wind. It was a real spring night, astonishing in its loveliness, and smelling of melted snow and the purity of boundless space; one heard the tinkle of falling drops. The drops fell rapidly, chasing each other busily and quickly, uniting to beat out a harmonious song. Then one drop would suddenly get out of time and all the rest would entangle themselves in a merry splash and hasty confusion. Then a big stern drop would fall firmly and again the rapid spring song would strike up clearly and sonorously. A pale glow from the electric lights lay over the city and the fortress roofs.

"A-ah," came in a deep sigh from Sergey Golovin, and he held his breath for a while, as if unwilling to exhale from his lungs the fresh and lovely air.

"Has this weather been going on for long?" enquired Werner. "It is real spring."

"This is only the second day of it," was the obliging reply, made with politeness. "Before that we had nothing but frosts."

One after the other, the dark carriages rolled softly along. Each took up two people and disappeared in the darkness towards a small lantern which swung at the gates. Each carriage was surrounded by the dark silhouettes of the guards, and the hooves of their horses struck the ground rhythmically or floundered in the wet snow.

When Werner, bending, was about to enter the carriage, the guard said rather vaguely, "There is someone else riding with you."

Werner was astonished.

"Where to? Where is he going? Oh yes. Another one? Who is he?"

The soldier was silent. Indeed, something small and motionless, but alive, was pressed against the dark corner of the carriage, and an oblique ray from the lamp fell upon an open eye. In sitting down, Werner jolted the man's knee with his leg and said, "Excuse me, comrade."

There was no reply. Only after the carriage had begun to move, a stammering voice asked suddenly in broken Russian, "Who are you?"

"I am Werner," was the answer, "condemned to be hanged for an attempt on the life of NN. And who are you?"

"I am Yanson. I must not be hanged."

They were travelling to where they would stand, two hours later, before the face of the great insoluble mystery, to pass from life into death; and they made friends. Life and death were moving simultaneously on two planes and life, in all its stupid, funny trivialities, remained life until the very end.

"What have you done, Yanson?"

"I cut my master's throat with a knife. I stole money."

Judging by his voice, Yanson seemed to be falling asleep. In the darkness, Werner found his limp hand and pressed it. Yanson took away his hand with an equally limp movement.

"Are you frightened?" asked Werner.

"I don't want to be hanged."

They lapsed into silence. Werner again found the Estonian's hand and pressed it closely between his dry hot palms. It lay there as motionless as a piece of wood, but Yanson did not attempt to remove it again.

It was close and stuffy in the carriage. There was a smell of soldiers' clothes, fustiness, manure and the leather of wet boots. The young guard who sat opposite Werner breathed heavily upon him with a mixed odour of onions and cheap tobacco. The keen fresh air, however, penetrated through crevices and filled that stuffy moving box with a sensation of spring, still stronger than was to be felt outside. The carriage turned now right, now left, and sometimes appeared to have turned right round and be going back. At times they seemed, for some reason, to be circling for hours on end in the same spot. At first a bluish electric light pierced the thick curtains at the windows; then, after they had turned a corner, it suddenly grew dark, and only by this could they guess that they had reached the deserted streets in the outskirts and were approaching the Northern railway station. Sometimes, when the carriage turned sharply, Werner's live bent knee jolted in a friendly way against the similar live bent knee of the guard and it was difficult to believe in the approaching execution.

"Where are we going?" asked Yanson suddenly. His head swam slightly from constant turning in the dark box and he felt rather sick.

Werner answered, pressing the Estonian's hand still closer. He wanted to say something specially friendly and caressing to this sleepy little man, whom he already loved as he had never loved anyone before.

"My dear, you don't seem to be comfortable. Move this way, towards me."

After a pause, Yanson answered, "Thank you. I am all right. Are they going to hang you, too?"

"Yes," answered Werner with unexpected cheerfulness, almost laughingly, and waved his hand in a particularly free and light-hearted manner. It almost seemed as if the subject under discussion were an absurd, nonsensical joke, which some nice but extremely funny people were trying to play on him.

"Have you a wife?" asked Yanson.

"No. What should I do with a wife?" was the reply. "I am alone."

"I also am alone. Singly," corrected Yanson after a pause.

Werner's head also began to swim. It seemed at times as if they were riding to a festival; for it is a strange fact that almost everyone taken to execution has had this feeling, and experienced, together with anguish and terror, a vague rejoicing at the unusual event about to take place.

Reality becomes intoxicated with fantasy, and death, hand in hand with life, brings forth visions. It seemed quite possible that flags would wave from the houses.

"We've arrived!" said Werner merrily and with interest, as the carriage stopped, and he sprang out lightly. But with Yanson the business took longer; resisting silently and very limply, he tried not to get out. He clung to the handle, and the guard opened the helpless fingers and tore the hand away. Then he clung to the corner, the door, and the high wheel, but loosened his hold at once at the slightest effort on the part of the guard. Or, rather, the taciturn Yanson did not cling but sleepily stuck to every object, and was taken off easily and without effort. At last he stood on the ground.

There were no flags. As always at night, the station was dark, deserted and lifeless. There were no more passenger trains, and as for the train which awaited these passengers silently outside the station, there was no need for bright lights or bustle.

Werner was suddenly seized by boredom; not by fear or anguish, but by a feeling of enormously wearisome, tedious boredom, from which he longed to escape by going off somewhere, lying down, or closing his eyes tightly. He stretched himself and gave a prolonged yawn. Yanson also stretched himself and yawned quickly several times.

"I wish they would get it over quickly," said Werner wearily. Yanson said nothing and shrank into himself.

When the condemned prisoners were moving along the deserted platform, ringed round by the guard, to the dimly lit carriages, Werner found himself next Sergey Golovin. The latter pointed sideways and began to say something, but only the word "lamp" was clearly audible, the rest was drowned in his slow and weary yawns.

"What do you say?" asked Werner with an answering yawn.

"The lamp. The flame in the lamp is smoking," said Sergey.

Werner looked round. Indeed, the flame in the lamp was smoking thickly and the top of the glass had already turned black.

"Yes, it is smoking," he said. And then came the sudden thought, "What does it matter to me that the lamp is smoking, when . . ." The same thought, apparently, came to Sergey, for he threw a quick glance at Werner and turned away. But they stopped yawning, both of them.

They all walked unaided to the carriages, except Yanson, who had to be taken by the arms. First he resisted with his feet, as if gluing his soles to the boards of the platform, then bent his knees and hung on the arms of the guards, whilst his legs dragged like those of a drunkard and his toes scratched the boards. The business of pushing him through the door took some time, but was done in silence.

Vassily Kashirin, too, walked unaided, dimly imitating the movements of his comrades; he did everything they did. But as he mounted the platform of the carriage he stumbled and a guard took him by the elbows to support him. Vassily shuddered and gave a piercing shriek, tearing his arm away, "Ai!"

"Vasia, what's the matter?" asked Werner, dashing towards him. Vasia was silent and shook all over. The bewildered guard seemed rather hurt and explained, "I wanted to help him, but he . . ."

"Let's come along, Vasia, I'll help you," said Werner, and tried to take his arm. But Vassily again withdrew it and cried out even louder than before.

"Ai!"

"Vasia, it is I, Werner."

"I know. Do not touch me. By myself."

Still shaking, he entered the carriage by himself and sat down in a corner. Bending towards Mousia, Werner asked in a low voice, indicating Vassily with his eyes, "How goes it?"

"Badly," answered Mousia just as low. "He is already dead. Werner, tell me, is there such a thing as death?"

"I don't know, Mousia, but I think not," answered Werner, seriously and thoughtfully.

"So I thought. But he? I feel worn out after being with him in the carriage. It was like travelling with a corpse."

"I don't know, Mousia. Perhaps for some people there is death. For a time, and afterwards it will vanish. For me, too, there was death, but now it has gone."

Mousia's somewhat pale cheeks flushed, "For you, too, there was death, Werner? Truly?"

"There was, but now it has gone. As happened with you."

A noise was heard at the door of the carriage. Stamping loudly with his heels, breathing heavily and spitting with disgust, in came Mishka Tziganok. He threw a glance around him and stood still obstinately. "There's no room here, guard!" he shouted to the tired angry-looking soldier.

"Give me a place or I won't go, you can hang me here on the lamp-post. What a carriage they have given us, those scoundrels! Is this a carriage? It's the devil's belly, not a carriage!"

Suddenly, however, he bent his head, stretched out his neck, and in that posture went forward to the others. Framed in his dishevelled hair and beard, his black eyes looked out wildly and piercingly with a rather insane expression.

"Ah, gentlemen," he drawled. "So that's how it is! How do you do, sir?"

He gave Werner a poke with his hand and sat down opposite him. Bending close to him, he winked one eye and made a quick movement of his hand over his throat.

"You, too? Ah?"

"Yes," smiled Werner.

"Are all of them to be hanged?"

"All of them."

"Oho!" Tziganok grinned and quickly probed all of them with his glance, which rested a little longer on Mousia and Yanson. Then he winked at Werner again, "Was it a minister?"

"Yes, a minister. And you?"

"I, sir, am here for something else. A minister is too big game for me. I am a brigand, sir, that's what I am. A murderer. No matter, sir, press closer, it's not of my own free will that I'm crowding you. There will be plenty of room for everybody in the other world."

He looked round at everyone wildly, from under his ruffled hair, with a swift, distrustful glance. But they all regarded him silently, seriously and even with obvious sympathy. He grinned, struck Werner several times on the knee, and said, "That's it, sir! As in the song—'Don't rustle, Mother oak grove so green.'"

"Why do you call me sir, when we all . . ."

"That's true," agreed Tziganok with satisfaction. "A queer sort of gentleman when you are going to be hanged by my side! There's a gentleman for you," he added, prodding with his fingers at the silent guard. "But that one of yours is no worse than the likes of us," indicating Vassily with his eyes. "Sir, I say, sir, are you afraid?"

"It's all right," came from the stiffly moving tongue.

"Why say all right? Do not be ashamed, there's nothing to be ashamed of. Only a dog wags its tail and grins when it is taken to be hanged, but you are a human being. And who is that lop-eared fellow? He is not one of you?"

His eyes skipped about rapidly and he kept hissing and spitting out the sweet saliva which collected in his mouth.

The flaps of Yanson's worn-out fur cap stirred slightly as he sat pressed against the corner in a small motionless lump, but he did not answer. Werner replied for him, "He cut his master's throat."

"Oh, Lord," said Tziganok in astonishment, "why do they let the likes of him commit murder?"

For some time Tziganok had been casting sidelong glances at Mousia, and now, turning round quickly, he fixed her with his straight, rough glance.

"Miss, I say, miss! How is this? Her little cheeks are rosy and she laughs. Look, she is really laughing!" And he caught Werner's knee with fingers that clutched like iron. "Look, look!"

Blushing and with a rather embarrassed smile, Mousia gave him a look as straight as his own and caught the sad wild appeal in his piercing half-frenzied eyes.

Everybody was silent.

The wheels went on rattling fast and busily, the little carriages leapt along the narrow rails and ran forward persistently. When the little engine came to a bend or crossing, it gave a shrill eager whistle, for the driver was anxious not to run over anybody. And it was preposterous to think that human beings were expending so much of their customary care, effort and capability in order to hang people; that such simple sensible means were being applied to accomplish the maddest act on earth. The carriages ran and people sat in them as they always sat, and travelled as they usually travel; there would be the customary halt when "the train stops for a few minutes."

Then follows death, eternity, the great mystery.

XII The arrival

The little carriages ran on persistently.

Several years running Sergey Golovin had lived with his relatives in a country house on this same line. He used often to travel on it both by day and night and knew the line well. When he shut his eyes he could fancy that now, too, he was going home, having stayed in town late with friends and taken the last train back.

"It won't be long now," he said, opening his eyes, and looked at the dark mute window covered by a grating.

Nobody stirred or answered and only Tziganok quickly and repeatedly spat out sweet saliva. His eyes began to run over the carriage, probing the windows and doors, scanning the soldiers.

"Cold," said Vassily Kashirin with lips as stiff as if they were frozen, and he pronounced it co-o-d.

Tanya bestirred herself, "Here is a scarf, tie it round your neck. It is a very warm one."

"Round his neck?" asked Sergey unexpectedly, and was frightened at his own question. But, as the same thought had occurred to all of them, nobody heard him. It was as though no one had said anything or as if all of them had said the same thing at the same time.

"Never mind, Vasia, tie it on, tie it on, you will be much warmer," advised Werner. Then he turned to Yanson and asked him in a tender voice, "My dear, aren't you cold?"

"Werner, perhaps he would like to smoke? Comrade, wouldn't you like to smoke?" asked Mousia. "We have some cigarettes."

"Yes, I would," was the answer.

"Seryosha, give him a cigarette," said Werner delightedly, but Sergey had already got one out. All watched with affection as Yanson's fingers took the cigarette, the match burned up and blue smoke came from Yanson's lips.

"Thank you," said Yanson. "It's good."

"How extraordinary!" said Sergey.

"What is extraordinary?" said Werner, turning round. "What is extraordinary?"

"Just that—the cigarette."

He held a cigarette, an ordinary cigarette, between his two live fingers and, pale with astonishment, regarded it almost with terror. They all stared at the thin little tube, out of which curled a blue ribbon of smoke, blown to one side by the draught, whilst the gathering ash at the tip grew dark. It went out.

"It has gone out," said Tanya.

"Yes, it has gone out."

"The devil take it," said Werner frowning, and looked uneasily at Yanson, whose hand with the cigarette hung down as if dead. Suddenly Tziganok turned round quickly and bent close above Werner till their faces almost touched; rolling the whites of his eyes like a horse, he whispered, "Sir, what about doing the escort in . . . Well? Shall I try?"

"You must not," replied Werner, also in a whisper. "Drink the cup to the dregs."

"But why not? A fight is much jollier. I go for him and he goes for me, and you yourself don't notice that you've been killed. As though you hadn't died."

"No, it won't do," said Werner and turned to Yanson. "My dear, why aren't you smoking?"

Yanson's flabby face suddenly crumpled up pathetically, as if someone had suddenly pulled a string setting all his wrinkles in motion and they had all gone criss-cross. As though in a dream, Yanson began to whimper without tears, in a dry almost affected voice, "I don't want to smoke. Ak-ha. Ak-ha. Ak-ha. I must not be hanged. Ak-ha. Ak-ha. Ak-ha."

They fussed around him. Tanya Kovalchuk, weeping profusely, stroked his arm and adjusted the hanging flaps of his worn-out cap, as she said, "My own dear! Do not cry, my poor one! My poor unhappy fellow!"

Mousia looked sideways. Tziganok caught her glance and grinned, baring his teeth. "His Honour is a queer fellow! He drinks tea and yet has a cold belly," he said with a short laugh. But his own face had turned blue-black, like cast iron, and his big yellow teeth were chattering.

Suddenly the little carriages shook and the pace perceptibly slackened. All, except Yanson and Kashirin, half rose and sat down again as quickly.

"The station!" said Sergey.

All the air seemed suddenly to have been pumped out of the carriages, so difficult had it become to breathe. Their expanded hearts seemed to be bursting through their breasts, beating in their throats, tossing madly about, as if crying aloud in terror with blood-filled voices. But their eyes looked down at the shaking floor and their ears heard the wheels turn ever more slowly, slide, then turn again, and suddenly stop.

The train had halted.

Here the dream began. It was not very terrifying but rather unreal, unfamiliar, and somehow strange. The dreamer himself seemed to stand aside, and only his phantom moved about fleshlessly, walked noiselessly, spoke soundlessly and suffered without suffering. As in a dream they alighted from the carriage and grouped themselves in twos, inhaling the peculiar, fresh, wood-smelling spring air. As in a dream, Yanson resisted dully and feebly and was dragged out of the carriage in silence.

They went down steps.

"Are we going to walk?" asked someone almost cheerfully.

"It is not far," answered someone just as cheerfully.

Then, in a big black silent bunch, they walked through the forest on a rough, wet and soft spring road. A fresh, keen air blew from the snow in the forest. Their feet slipped and sometimes sank deep in the snow, and hands would involuntarily clutch a friend. Breathing heavily and loudly, the guards moved forward on both sides over the untouched snow. Someone's voice said angrily, "Why couldn't they clear the road? Fancy having to tumble about in the snow!"

Someone apologised guiltily, "They did clear it, your Honour. Only there's nothing to be done about the thaw."

Consciousness returned, but not fully, in strange scraps and fragments. Now the mind suddenly confirmed the fact in a business-like manner, "Of course they could not clear the road."

At times everything became a blank again and only the sense of smell remained: the unbearably fragrant smell of the air, of the forest and of melting snow. At times, everything became abnormally clear: the forest, the night, the road, and the fact that this very minute they were going to be hanged. Snatches of restrained conversation flashed out in whispers.

"It is almost four."

"I said we left early."

"It is dawn at five."

"Yes, of course, at five. So that's why it had to be . . ."

They halted in darkness in a little meadow. At some distance, behind the sparse trees, transparent in their wintriness, two small lanterns moved silently. There stood the gallows.

"I have lost a galosh," said Sergey Golovin.

"What's that?" said Werner, not understanding.

"I have lost a galosh. It's cold."

"But where's Vassily?"

"I don't know. There he is!"

Vassily stood dark and motionless.

"And where is Mousia?"

"I am here. Is that you, Werner?"

They began to look round, avoiding the direction of the two little lanterns, which continued to move silently and with terrible significance. On the left the denuded forest was thinner and through it could be seen something large, pale and flat; a damp wind blew from thence.

"The sea," said Sergey Golovin, inhaling the air through his nose and mouth. "There's the sea."

Mousia responded in deep tones, "My love, which is as boundless as the sea."

"What are you saying, Mousia?"

"The shores of life cannot contain my love, which is as boundless as the sea."

"My love, which is as boundless as the sea," repeated Sergey thoughtfully, carried away by the sound of her voice and the words.

"My love, which is as boundless as the sea," repeated Werner, and then cried in joyful astonishment: "Muska, what a girl you are still!"

Suddenly, at his very ear, Werner heard Tziganok's hot, suffocated whisper, "Sir, I say, sir! The forest! Oh, Lord, what's that? And there, where the little lanterns are, that's the peg for hanging us on, isn't it? What is it, I say?"

Werner looked up. Tziganok was in the throes of approaching death.

"We must say good-bye," said Tanya Kovalchuk.

"Wait, they have still to read out the sentence," replied Werner. "And where is Yanson?"

Yanson lay on the snow and people were busied about something around him. Suddenly came a pungent smell of ammonia.

"What is it, doctor? Will you be long?" asked someone impatiently.

"Nothing much, just an ordinary faint. Rub his ears with snow. He is already coming round. You may read the sentence."

The light from the dark lantern fell upon the paper and the white hands without gloves. Both trembled a little and so did the voice, "Gentlemen, perhaps there is no need to read the sentence. You know it? What do you think?"

"No need," answered Werner for all of them and the dark lantern was soon extinguished.

The services of the priest were also refused.

The dark broad silhouette moved back quickly into the darkness and disappeared. Apparently dawn was approaching; the snow grew whiter, the figures of people became darker and the forest looked sparser, sadder and less mysterious.

"Gentlemen, you must go in twos. Stand in pairs according to your choice, but please be quick."

Werner pointed to Yanson, who was now standing up, supported by two guards. "I'll go with him. And you, Seryosha, take Vassily. Go ahead."

"Good!"

"Shall we go together, Mousechka?" asked Kovalchuk. "Come, let us kiss each other good-bye."

They kissed each other quickly. Tziganok's kiss was firm and one could feel his teeth; Yanson kissed softly and flabbily with his mouth half open, scarcely realising what he was doing. When Sergey Golovin and Kashirin had already gone a few steps, the latter stopped suddenly and said loudly and distinctly in a completely strange and unfamiliar voice, "Good-bye, comrades!"

"Good-bye, comrade!" they answered.

They went off. Everything grew quiet. The little lanterns behind the trees became motionless. They expected to hear a scream, voices, a noise of some sort; but it was as silent there as with them and the little yellow lanterns remained motionless.

"Oh, Lord!" someone cried out hoarsely and wildly. They looked round; it was Tziganok in the throes of approaching death. "They are hanging them," he cried.

They turned away from him and again all became quiet. Tziganok writhed, clutching the air with his hands.

"How is it possible? Gentlemen, I say! Am I to go alone? It is livelier to go in company, gentlemen! What do you say?"

He grasped Werner's arm with his fingers, tightening and then relaxing them as if in play, "Sir, dear, cannot you go with me? Eh? Be so kind, don't say no!"

It hurt Werner to refuse, but he answered, "I cannot, my friend. I am going with him."

"Oh Lord! That means I have to go alone. How am I to do it? Oh, Lord!"

Mousia stepped forward and said in a low voice, "Come with me."

Tziganok recoiled and rolled the whites of his eyes at her wildly, "With you?"

"Yes."

"Look at her! Such a little girl! And you are not afraid? I'd better go alone. Never mind."

"No, I am not afraid."

Tziganok grinned, "Look at her! But I am a murderer. Don't you despise me? Better not come with me. I won't be angry with you."

Mousia was silent. In the dim light of dawn her face looked pale and mysterious. She suddenly stepped quickly up to Tziganok and, throwing her arms round his neck, kissed him firmly on the lips. He took her by the shoulders with his fingers, pushed her away, shook her, and then kissed her on the lips, nose and eyes, smacking his lips loudly.

"Come along, then!"

Suddenly the soldier standing nearest seemed to sway, opened his hands and let his gun drop. He did not bend to pick it up, however, but remained motionless for a while, then turned sharply and walked like a blind man over the untouched snow towards the forest.

"Where are you going?" whispered another soldier in a frightened voice. "Stop!"

But the other went on silently, trudging painfully through the deep snow. He stumbled over something, apparently, for he waved his arms and fell face downwards. There he remained lying.

"Pick up your gun, grey coat, or I'll do it for you!" said Tziganok threateningly. "You don't know your duty!"

The little lanterns began to move busily again. The turn of Werner and Yanson had come.

"Good-bye, sir!" said Tziganok loudly. "We shall meet in the other world; when you see me, don't turn away! And bring me some water to drink. I'll be having a hot time!"

"Good-bye!"

"I don't want to be hanged!" said Yanson weakly. But Werner took him by the arm and the Estonian made a few steps forward on his own. Then they saw him stop and fall down on the snow. Someone bent over him, lifted him up and carried him away; he struggled feebly in their arms. Why didn't he shout? He had probably forgotten he had a voice.

And the little yellow lanterns stood motionless again.

"And I, Mousechka, must I go alone?" said Tanya Kovalchuk sadly. "We have lived together, and now . . ."

"Tanechka, dear . . ."

But here Tziganok intervened excitedly. He held Mousia by the hand, as if afraid she might be taken from him, and spoke in a rapid, business-like tone, "Oh miss! You can go alone, you are a pure soul and can go anywhere alone. Do you understand? But I can't. As a murderer . . . you understand? It's impossible for me to go alone. 'Where are you going, you murderer?' they will ask. I have even stolen horses, by God! But with her I am as if . . . as if with an infant, do you see? Don't you understand?"

"I understand. Well, go together. Let me kiss you once more, Mousechka!"

"Go on, kiss each other," said Tziganok approvingly to the women. "You are made that way; it is right to bid each other a hearty farewell."

Mousia went forward with Tziganok. The woman walked carefully, slipping now and then, and, from habit, held her skirt off the ground. The man led her to death, holding her arm firmly, uttering cautions and feeling the ground with his foot.

The lights stopped moving. Around Tanya Kovalchuk was quietness and emptiness. The soldiers were silent, all grey in the colourless quiet light of the rising day.

"I am all alone," said Tanya suddenly and sighed. "Seryosha is dead, Werner is dead and Vasia. I am all alone, soldier boys; soldier boys, I say, I am all alone. Alone . . ."

The sun was rising over the sea.

The bodies were put into boxes. Then they were carried away. The necks were elongated, eyes bulged madly, and a swollen, blue tongue, like some unknown terrible flower, stuck out from the lips, flecked with bloody foam. The bodies were taken back by the same road along which they had travelled when alive. And the spring snow was just as soft and fragrant, and the spring air was just as fresh and keen. And the galosh which Sergey had lost lay wet and trampled, a black spot in the snow.

Thus did men greet the rising sun.

Translated by Herman Bernstein.

ESCAPE

Vladimir Nabokov

from PNIN

I

From the top platform of an old, seldom used lookout tower—a "prospect tower" as it was formerly termed—that stood on a wooded hill eight hundred feet high, called Mount Ettrick, in one of the fairest of New England's fair states, the adventurous summer tourist (Miranda or Mary, Tom or Jim, whose penciled names were almost obliterated on the balustrade) might observe a vast sea of greenery, composed mainly of maple, beech, tacamahac, and pine. Some five miles west, a slender white church steeple marked the spot where nestled the small town of Onkwedo, once famous for its springs. Three miles north, in a riverside clearing at the foot of a grassy knoll, one could distinguish the gables of an ornate house (variously known as Cook's, Cook's Place, Cook's Castle, or The Pines—its initial appellation). Along the south side of Mount Ettrick, a state highway continued east after passing through Onkwedo. Numerous dirt roads and foot trails crisscrossed the timbered plain within the triangle of land limited by the somewhat tortuous hypotenuse of a rural paved road that weaved northeast from Onkwedo to The Pines, the long cathetus of the state highway just mentioned, and the short cathetus of a river spanned by a steel bridge near Mount Ettrick and a wooden one near Cook's.

On a dull warm day in the summer of 1954, Mary or Almira, or, for that matter Wolfgang von Goethe, whose name had been carved in the balustrade by some old-fashioned wag, might have noticed an automobile that had turned off the highway just before reaching the bridge and was now nosing and poking this way and that in a maze of doubtful roads. It moved warily and unsteadily, and whenever it changed its mind, it would slow down and raise dust behind like a back-kicking dog. At times it might seem, to a less sympathetic soul than our imagined observer, that this pale blue, egg-shaped two-door sedan, of uncertain age and in mediocre condition, was manned by an idiot. Actually its driver was Professor Timofey Pnin, of Waindell College.

Pnin had started taking lessons at the Waindell Driving School early in the year, but "true understanding," as he put it, had come to him only when, a couple of months later, he had been laid up with a sore back and had done nothing but study with deep enjoyment the forty-page *Driver's Manual,* issued by the State Governor in collaboration with another expert, and the article on "Automobile" in the *Encyclopedia Americana,* with illustrations of Transmissions, and Carburetors, and Brakes, and a Member of the Glidden Tour, *circa* 1905, stuck in the mud of a country road among depressing surroundings. Then and only then was the dual nature of his initial inklings transcended at last as he lay on his sickbed, wiggling his toes and shifting phantom gears. During actual lessons with a harsh instructor who cramped his style, issued unnecessary directives in yelps of technical slang, tried to wrestle the wheel from him at corners, and kept irritating a calm, intelligent pupil with expressions of vulgar detraction, Pnin had been totally unable to combine perceptually the car he was driving in his mind and the car he was driving on the road. Now the two fused at last. If he failed the first time he took his driver's-license test, it was mainly because he started an argument with the examiner in an ill-timed effort to prove that nothing could be more humiliating to a rational creature than being required to encourage the development of a base conditional reflex by stopping at a red light when there was not an earthly soul around, heeled or wheeled. He was more circumspect the next time, and passed. An irresistible senior, enrolled in his Russian Language course, Marilyn Hohn, sold him for a hundred dollars her humble old car: she was getting married to the owner of a far grander machine. The trip from Waindell to Onkwedo, with an overnight stop at a tourist home, had been slow and difficult but uneventful. Just before entering Onkwedo, he had pulled up at a gas station and had got out for a breath of country air. An inscrutable white sky hung over a clover field, and from a pile of firewood near a shack came a rooster's cry, jagged and gaudy—a vocal coxcomb. Some chance intonation on the part of this slightly hoarse bird, combined with the warm wind pressing itself against Pnin in search of attention, recognition, anything, briefly reminded him of a dim dead day when he, a Petrograd University freshman, had arrived at the small station of a Baltic summer resort, and the sounds, and the smells, and the sadness——

"Kind of muggy," said the hairy-armed attendant, as he started to wipe the windshield.

Pnin took a letter out of his wallet, unfolded the tiny mimeographed-sketch map attached to it, and asked the attendant how far was the church at which one was supposed to turn left to reach Cook's Place. It was really striking how the man resembled Pnin's colleague at Waindell College, Dr. Hagen—one of those random likenesses as pointless as a bad pun.

"Well, there is a better way to get there," said the false Hagen. "The trucks have messed up that road, and besides you won't like the way it winds. Now you just drive on. Drive through the town. Five miles out of Onkwedo, just after you have passed the trail to Mount Ettrick on your left, and just before reaching the bridge, take the first left turn. It's a good gravel road."

He stepped briskly around the hood and lunged with his rag at the windshield from the other side.

"You turn north and go on bearing north at each crossing—there are quite a few logging trails in those woods but you just bear north and you'll get to Cook's in twelve minutes flat. You can't miss it."

Pnin had now been in that maze of forest roads for about an hour and had come to the conclusion that "bear north," and in fact the word "north" itself, meant nothing to him. He also could not explain what had compelled him, a rational being, to listen to a chance busybody instead of firmly following the pedantically precise instructions that his friend, Alexandr Petrovich Kukolnikov (known locally as Al Cook) had sent him when inviting him to spend the summer at his large and hospitable country house. Our luckless car operator had by now lost himself too thoroughly to be able to go back to the highway, and since he had little experience in maneuvering on rutty narrow roads, with ditches and even ravines gaping on either side, his various indecisions and gropings took those bizarre visual forms that an observer on the lookout tower might have followed with a compassionate eye; but there was no living creature in that forlorn and listless upper region except for an ant who had his own troubles, having, after hours of inept perseverance, somehow reached the upper platform and the balustrade (his *autostrada*) and was getting all bothered and baffled much in the same way as that preposterous toy car progressing below. The wind had subsided. Under the pale sky the sea of tree tops seemed to harbor no life. Presently, however, a gun shot popped, and a twig leaped into the sky. The dense upper boughs in that part of the otherwise stirless forest started to move in a receding sequence of shakes or jumps, with a swinging lilt from tree to tree, after which all was still again. Another minute passed, and then everything happened at once: the ant found an upright beam leading to the roof of the tower and started to ascend it with renewed zest; the sun appeared; and Pnin at the height of hopelessness, found himself on a paved road with a rusty but still glistening sign directing wayfarers "To The Pines."

II

Al Cook was a son of Piotr Kukolnikov, wealthy Moscow merchant of Old-Believers antecedents, self-made man, Maecenas and philanthropist—the famous Kukolnikov who under the last Tsar had been twice imprisoned in a fairly comfortable fortress for giving financial assistance to Social-Revolutionary groups (terrorists, mainly), and under Lenin had been put to death as an "Imperialistic spy" after almost a week of medieval tortures in a Soviet jail. His family reached America via Harbin, around 1925, and young Cook by dint of quiet perseverance, practical acumen, and some scientific training, rose to a high and secure position in a great chemical concern. A kindly, very reserved man of stocky build, with a large immobile face that was tied up in the middle by a neat little pince-nez, he looked what he was—a Business Executive, a Mason, a Golfer, a prosperous and cautious man. He spoke beautifully correct, neutral English, with only the softest shadow of a Slavic accent, and was a delightful host, of the silent variety, with a twinkling eye, and a highball in each hand; and only when some very old and beloved Russian friend was his midnight guest would Alexandr Petrovich suddenly start to discuss God, Lermontov, Liberty, and divulge a hereditary streak of rash idealism that would have greatly confused a Marxist eavesdropper.

He married Susan Marshall, the attractive, voluble, blond daughter of Charles G. Marshall, the inventor, and because one could not imagine Alexandr and Susan otherwise than raising a huge healthy family, it came as a shock to me and other well-wishers to learn that as the result of an operation Susan would remain childless all her life. They were still young, loved each other with a sort of old-world simplicity and integrity very soothing to observe, and instead of populating their country place with children and grandchildren, they collected, every even-year summer, elderly Russians (Cook's fathers or uncles, as it were); on odd-year summers they would have *amerikantsï* (Americans), Alexandr's business acquaintances or Susan's relatives and friends.

This was the first time Pnin was coming to The Pines but I had been there before. Émigré Russians—liberals and intellectuals who had left Russia around 1920—could be found swarming all over the place. You would find them in every patch of speckled shade, sitting on rustic benches and discussing émigré writers—Bunin, Aldanov, Sirin; lying suspended in hammocks, with the Sunday issue of a Russian-language newspaper over their faces in traditional defense against flies; sipping tea with jam on the veranda; walking in the woods and wondering about the edibility of local toadstools.

Samuil Lvovich Shpolyanski, a large majestically calm old gentleman, and small, excitable, stuttering Count Fyodor Nikitich Poroshin, both of whom, around 1920, had been members of one of those heroic Regional Governments that were formed in the Russian provinces by democratic groups to withstand Bolshevik dictatorship, would pace the avenue of pines and discuss the tactics to be adopted at the next joint meeting of the Free Russia Committee (which they had founded in New York) with another, younger, anti-Communist organization. From a pavilion half smothered by locust trees came fragments of a heated exchange between Professor Bolotov, who taught the History of Philosophy, and Professor Chateau, who taught the Philosophy of History: "Reality is Duration," one voice, Bolotov's, would boom. "It is not!" the other would cry. "A soap bubble is as real as a fossil tooth!"

Pnin and Chateau, both born in the late nineties of the nineteenth century, were comparative youngsters. Most of the other men had seen sixty and had trudged on. On the other hand, a few of the ladies, such as Countess Poroshin and Madam Bolotov, were still in their late forties and, thanks to the hygienic atmosphere of the New World, had not only preserved, but improved, their good looks. Some parents brought their offspring with them—healthy, tall, indolent, difficult American children of college age, with no sense of nature, and no Russian, and no interest whatsoever in the niceties of their parents' backgrounds and pasts. They seemed to live at The Pines on a physical and mental plane entirely different from that of their parents: now and then passing from their own level to ours through a kind of interdimensional shimmer; responding curtly to a well-meaning Russian joke or anxious piece of advice, and then fading away again; keeping always aloof (so that one felt one had engendered a brood of elves), and preferring any Onkwedo store product, any sort of canned goods to the marvelous Russian foods provided by the Kukolnikov household at loud, long dinners on the screened porch. With great distress Poroshin would say of his children (Igor and Olga, college sophomores), "My twins are exasperating. When I see them at home during breakfast or dinner and try to tell them most interesting, most exciting things—for instance, about local elective self-government in the Russian Far North in the seventeenth century or, say, something about the history of the first medical schools in Russia—there is, by the way, an excellent monograph by Chistovich on the subject, published in 1883— they simply wander off and turn on the radio in their rooms." Both young people were around the summer Pnin was invited to The Pines. But they stayed invisible; they would have been hideously bored in this out-of-the-way place, had not Olga's admirer, a college boy whose surname nobody seemed to know, arrived from Boston for the weekend in a spectacular car, and had not Igor found a congenial companion in Nina, the Bolotov girl, a handsome slattern with Egyptian eyes and brown limbs, who went to a dancing school in New York.

The household was looked after by Praskovia, a sturdy, sixty-year-old woman of the people with the vivacity of one a score of years younger. It was an exhilarating sight to watch her as she stood on the back porch surveying the chickens, knuckles on hips, dressed in baggy homemade shorts and a matronly blouse with rhinestones. She had nursed Alexandr and his brother when both were children in Harbin and now she was helped in her household duties by her husband, a gloomy and stolid old Cossack whose main passions in life were amateur bookbinding—a self-taught and almost pathological process that he was impelled to inflict upon any old catalogue or pulp magazine that came his way; the making of fruit liqueurs; and the killing of small forest animals.

Of that season's guests, Pnin knew well Professor Chateau, a friend of his youth, with whom he had attended the University of Prague in the early twenties, and he was also well acquainted with the Bolotovs, whom he had last seen in 1949 when he welcomed them with a speech at a formal dinner given them by the Association of Russian Émigré Scholars at the Barbizon-Plaza, upon the occasion of Bolotov's arrival from France. Personally, I never cared much for Bolotov and his philosophical works, which so oddly combine the obscure and the trite; the man's achievement is perhaps a mountain—but a mountain of platitudes; I have always liked, nowever, Varvara, the seedy philosopher's exuberant, buxom wife. When she first visited The Pines, in 1951, she had never seen the New England countryside before. Its birches and bilberries deceived her into placing mentally Lake Onkwedo, not on the parallel of, say, Lake Ohrida in the Balkans, where it belonged, but on that of Lake Onega in northern Russia, where she had spent her first fifteen summers, before fleeing from the Bolsheviks to western Europe, with her aunt Lidia Vinogradov, the well-known feminist and social worker. Consequently the sight of a hummingbird in probing flight, or a catalpa in ample bloom, produced upon Varvara the effect of some unnatural or exotic vision. More fabulous than pictures in a bestiary were to her the tremendous porcupines that came to gnaw at the delicious, gamy old wood of the house, or the elegant, eerie little skunks that sampled the cat's milk in the backyard. She was nonplused and enchanted by the number of plants and creatures she could not identify, mistook Yellow Warblers for stray canaries, and on the occasion of Susan's birthday was known to have brought, with pride and panting enthusiasm, for the ornamentation of the dinner table, a profusion of beautiful poison-ivy leaves, hugged to her pink, freckled breast.

III

The Bolotovs and Madam Shpolyanski, a little lean woman in slacks, were the first people to see Pnin as he cautiously turned into a sandy avenue, bordered with wild lupines, and, sitting very straight, stiffly clutching the steering wheel as if he were a farmer more used to his tractor than to his car, entered, at ten miles an hour and in first gear, the grove of old, disheveled, curiously authentic-looking pines that separated the paved road from Cook's Castle.

Varvara buoyantly rose from the seat of the pavilion—where she and Roza Shpolyanski had just discovered Bolotov reading a battered book and smoking a forbidden cigarette. She greeted Pnin with a clapping of hands, while her husband showed as much geniality as he was capable of by slowly waving the book he had closed on his thumb to mark the place. Pnin killed the motor and sat beaming at his friends. The collar of his green sport shirt was undone; his partly unzipped windbreaker seemed too tight for his impressive torso; his bronzed bald head, with the puckered brow and conspicuous vermicular vein on the temple, bent low as he wrestled with the door handle and finally dived out of the car.

"*Avtomobil', kostyum—nu pryamo amerikanets* (a veritable American), *pryamo Ayzenhauer!*" said Varvara, and introduced Pnin to Roza Abramovna Shpolyanski.

"We had some mutual friends forty years ago," remarked that lady, peering at Pnin with curiosity.

"Oh, let us not mention such astronomical figures," said Bolotov, approaching and replacing with a grass blade the thumb he had been using as a bookmarker. "You know," he continued, shaking Pnin's hand, "I am rereading *Anna Karenin* for the seventh time and I derive as much rapture as I did, not forty, but sixty, years ago, when I was a lad of seven. And, every time one discovers new things—for instance I notice now that Lyov Nikolaich does not know on what day his novel starts: it seems to be Friday because that is the day the clockman comes to wind up the clocks in the Oblonski house, but it is also Thursday as mentioned in the conversation at the skating rink between Lyovin and Kitty's mother."

"What on earth does it matter," cried Varvara. "Who on earth wants to know the exact day?"

"I can tell you the exact day," said Pnin, blinking in the broken sunlight and inhaling the remembered tang of northern pines. "The action of the novel starts in the beginning of 1872, namely on Friday,

February the twenty-third by the New Style. In his morning paper Oblonski reads that Beust is rumored to have proceeded to Wiesbaden. This is of course Count Friedrich Ferdinand von Beust, who had just been appointed Austrian Ambassador to the Court of St. James's. After presenting his credentials, Beust had gone to the continent for a rather protracted Christmas vacation—had spent there two months with his family, and was now returning to London, where, according to his own memoirs in two volumes, preparations were under way for the thanksgiving service to be held in St. Paul's on February the twenty-seventh for the recovering from typhoid fever of the Prince of Wales. However *(odnako)*, it really is hot here *(i zharko zhe u vas)!* I think I shall now present myself before the most luminous orbs *(presvetlïe ochi,* jocular) of Alexandr Petrovich and then go for a dip *(okupnutsya,* also jocular) in the river he so vividly describes in his letter."

"Alexandr Petrovich is away till Monday, on business or pleasure," said Varvara Bolotov, "but I think you will find Susanna Karlovna sun-bathing on her favorite lawn behind the house. Shout before you approach too near."

IV

Cook's Castle was a three-story brick-and-timber mansion built around 1860 and partly rebuilt half a century later, when Susan's father purchased it from the Dudley-Greene family in order to make of it a select resort hotel for the richer patrons of the curative Onkwedo Springs. It was an elaborate and ugly building in a mongrel style, with the Gothic bristling through remnants of French and Florentine, and when originally designed might have belonged to the variety which Samuel Sloan, an architect of the time, classified as An Irregular Northern Villa "well adapted to the highest requirements of social life" and called "Northern" because of "the aspiring tendency of its roof and towers." The piquancy of these pinnacles and the merry, somewhat even inebriated air the mansion had of having been composed of several smaller Northern Villas, hoisted into mid-air and knocked together anyhow, with parts of unassimilated roofs, half-hearted gables, cornices, rustic quoins, and other projections sticking out on all sides, had, alas, but briefly attracted tourists. By 1920, the Onkwedo waters had mysteriously lost whatever magic they had contained, and after her father's death Susan had vainly tried to sell The Pines, since they had another more comfortable house in the residential quarter of the industrial city where her husband worked. However, now that they had got accustomed to use the Castle for entertaining their numerous friends, Susan was glad that the meek, beloved monster had found no purchaser.

Within, the diversity was as great as without. Four spacious rooms opened from the large hall that retained something of its hostelic stage in the generous dimensions of the grate. The hand rail of the stairs, and at least one of its spindles, dated from 1720, having been transferred to the house, while it was being built, from a far older one, whose very site was no longer exactly known. Very ancient, too, were the beautiful sideboard panels of game and fish in the dining room. In the half dozen rooms of which each of the upper floors consisted, and in the two wings in the rear, one could discover, among disparate pieces of furniture, some charming satinwood bureau, some romantic rosewood sofa, but also all kinds of bulky and miserable articles, broken chairs, dusty marble-topped tables, morose *étagerès* with bits of dark-looking glass in the back as mournful as the eyes of old apes. The chamber Pnin got was a pleasant southeast one on the upper floor: it had remnants of gilt paper on the walls, an army cot, a plain washstand, and all kinds of shelves, brackets, and scrollwork moldings. Pnin shook open the casement, smiled at the smiling forest, again remembered a distant first day in the country, and presently walked down, clad in a new navy-blue bathrobe and wearing on his bare feet a pair of ordinary rubber overshoes, a sensible precaution if one intends to walk through damp and, perhaps, snake-infested grass. On the garden terrace he found Chateau.

Konstantin Ivanich Chateau, a subtle and charming scholar of pure Russian lineage despite his surname (derived, I am told, from that of a Russianized Frenchman who adopted orphaned Ivan), taught at a large New York university and had not seen his very dear Pnin for at least five years. They embraced with a warm rumble of joy. I confess to have been myself, at one time, under the spell of angelic Konstantin Ivanich, namely, when we used to meet every day in the winter of 1935 or 1936 for a morning stroll under the laurels and nettle trees of Grasse, southern France, where he then shared a villa with several other Russian expatriates. His soft voice, the gentlemanly St. Petersburgan burr of his *r*'s, his mild, melancholy caribou eyes, the auburn goatee he continuously twiddled, with a shredding motion of his long, frail fingers—everything about Chateau (to use a literary formula as old-fashioned as he) produced a rare sense of well-being in his friends. Pnin and he talked for a while, comparing notes. As not unusual with firm-principled exiles, every time they met after a separation they not only endeavored to catch up with a personal past, but also to sum up by means of a few rapid passwords— allusions, intonations impossible to render in a foreign language—the course of recent Russian history, thirty-five years of hopeless injustice following a century of struggling justice and glimmering hope. Next, they switched to the usual shop talk of European teachers abroad, sighing and shaking heads over the "typical American college student" who does not know geography, is immune to noise, and thinks education is but a means to get eventually a remunerative job. Then they inquired about each other's work in progress, and both were extremely modest and reticent about their respective researches. Finally, as they walked along a meadow path, brushing against the goldenrod, toward the wood where a rocky river ran, they spoke of their healths: Chateau, who looked so jaunty, with one hand in the pocket of his white flannel trousers and his lustring coat rather rakishly opened on the flannel waistcoat, cheerfully said that in the near future he would have to undergo an exploratory operation of the abdomen, and Pnin said, laughing, that every time *he* was X-rayed, doctors vainly tried to puzzle out what they termed "a shadow behind the heart."

"Good title for a bad novel," remarked Chateau.

As they were passing a grassy knoll just before entering the wood, a pink-faced venerable man in a seersucker suit, with a shock of white hair and a tumefied purple nose resembling a huge raspberry, came striding toward them down the sloping field, a look of disgust contorting his features.

"I have to go back for my hat," he cried dramatically as he drew near.

"Are you acquainted?" murmured Chateau, fluttering his hands introductively. "Timofey Pavlich Pnin, Ivan Ilyich Gramineev."

"*Moyo pochtenie* (My respects)," said both men, bowing to each other over a powerful handshake.

"I thought," resumed Gramineev, a circumstantial narrator, "that the day would continue as overcast as it had begun. By stupidity *(po gluposti)* I came out with an unprotected head. Now the sun is roasting my brains. I have to interrupt my work."

He gestured toward the top of the knoll. There his easel stood in delicate silhouette against the blue sky. From that crest he had been painting a view of the valley beyond, complete with quaint old barn, gnarled apple tree, and kine.

"I can offer you my panama," said kind Chateau, but Pnin had already produced from his bathrobe pocket a large red handkerchief: he expertly twisted each of its corners into a knot.

"Admirable. . . . Most grateful," said Gramineev, adjusting this headgear.

"One moment," said Pnin. "You must tuck in the knots."

This done, Gramineev started walking up the field toward his easel. He was a well-known, frankly academic painter, whose soulful oils— "Mother Volga," "Three Old Friends" (lad, nag, dog), "April Glade," and so forth—still graced a museum in Moscow.

"Somebody told me," said Chateau, as he and Pnin continued to progress riverward, "that Liza's boy has an extraordinary talent for painting. Is that correct?"

"Yes," answered Pnin. "All the more vexing *(tem bolee obidno)* that his mother, who I think is about to marry a third time, took Victor suddenly to California for the rest of the summer, whereas if he had accompanied me here, as had been planned, he would have had the splendid opportunity of being coached by Gramineev."

"You exaggerate the splendor," softly rejoined Chateau.

They reached the bubbling and glistening stream. A concave ledge between higher and lower diminutive cascades formed a natural swimming pool under the alders and pines. Chateau, a non-bather, made himself comfortable on a boulder. Throughout the academic year Pnin had regularly exposed his body to the radiation of a sun lamp; hence, when he stripped down to his bathing trunks, he glowed in the dappled sunlight of the riverside grove with a rich mahogany tint. He removed his cross and his rubbers.

"Look, how pretty," said observant Chateau.

A score of small butterflies, all of one kind, were settled on a damp patch of sand, their wings erect and closed, showing their pale undersides with dark dots and tiny orange-rimmed peacock spots along the hind-wing margins; one of Pnin's shed rubbers disturbed some of them and, revealing the celestial hue of their upper surface, they fluttered around like blue snowflakes before settling again.

"Pity Vladimir Vladimirovich is not here," remarked Chateau. "He would have told us all about these enchanting insects."

"I have always had the impression that his entomology was merely a pose."

"Oh no," said Chateau. "You will lose it some day," he added, pointing to the Greek Catholic cross on a golden chainlet that Pnin had removed from his neck and hung on a twig. Its glint perplexed a cruising dragonfly.

"Perhaps I would not mind losing it," said Pnin. "As you well know, I wear it merely from sentimental reasons. And the sentiment is becoming burdensome. After all, there is too much of the physical about this attempt to keep a particle of one's childhood in contact with one's breastbone."

"You are not the first to reduce faith to a sense of touch," said Chateau, who was a practicing Greek Catholic and deplored his friend's agnostic attitude.

A horsefly applied itself, blind fool, to Pnin's bald head, and was stunned by a smack of his meaty palm.

From a smaller boulder than the one upon which Chateau was perched, Pnin gingerly stepped down into the brown and blue water. He noticed he still had his wrist watch—removed it and left it inside one of his rubbers. Slowly swinging his tanned shoulders, Pnin waded forth, the loopy shadows of leaves shivering and slipping down his broad back. He stopped and breaking the glitter and shade around him, moistened his inclined head, rubbed his nape with wet hands, soused in turn each armpit, and then, joining both palms, glided into the water, his dignified breast stroke sending off ripples on either side. Around the natural basin, Pnin swam in state. He swam with a rhythmical splutter—half gurgle, half puff. Rhythmically he opened his legs and widened them out at the knees while flexing and straightening out his arms like a giant frog. After two minutes of this, he waded out and sat on the boulder to dry. Then he put on his cross, his wrist watch, his rubbers, and his bathrobe.

V

Dinner was served on the screened porch. As he sat down next to Bolotov and began to stir the sour cream in his red *botvinia* (chilled beet soup), wherein pink ice cubes tinkled, Pnin automatically resumed an earlier conversation.

"You will notice," he said, "that there is a significant difference between Lyovin's spiritual time and Vronski's physical one. In mid-book, Lyovin and Kitty lag behind Vronski and Anna by a whole year. When, on a Sunday evening in May 1876, Anna throws herself under that freight train, she has existed more than four years since the beginning of the novel, but in the case of the Lyovins, during the same period, 1872 to 1876, hardly three years have elapsed. It is the best example of relativity in literature that is known to me."

After dinner, a game of croquet was suggested. These people favored the time-honored but technically illegal setting of hoops, where two of the ten are crossed at the center of the ground to form the so-called Cage or Mousetrap. It became immediately clear that Pnin, who teamed with Madam Bolotov against Shpolyanski and Countess Poroshin, was by far the best player of the lot. As soon as the pegs were driven in and the game started, the man was transfigured. From his habitual, slow, ponderous, rather rigid self, he changed into a terrifically mobile, scampering, mute, sly-visaged hunchback. It seemed to be always his turn to play. Holding his mallet very low and daintily swinging it between his parted spindly legs (he had created a minor sensation by changing into Bermuda shorts expressly for the game), Pnin foreshadowed every stroke with nimble aim-taking oscillations of the mallet head, then gave the ball an accurate tap, and forthwith, still hunched, and with the ball still rolling, walked rapidly to the spot where he had planned for it to stop. With geometrical gusto, he ran it through hoops, evoking cries of admiration from the onlookers. Even Igor Poroshin, who was passing by like a shadow with two cans of beer he was carrying to some private banquet, stopped for a second and shook his head appreciatively before vanishing in the shrubbery. Plaints and protests, however, would mingle with the applause when Pnin, with brutal indifference, croqueted, or rather rocketed, an adversary's ball. Placing in contact with it his own ball, and firmly putting his curiously small foot upon the latter, he would bang at his ball so as to drive the other up the country by the shock of the stroke. When appealed to, Susan said it was completely against the rules, but Madam Shpolyanski insisted it was perfectly acceptable and said that when she was a child her English governess used to call it a Hong Kong.

After Pnin had tolled the stake and all was over, and Varvara accompanied Susan to get the evening tea ready, Pnin quietly retired to a bench under the pines. A certain extremely unpleasant and frightening cardiac sensation, which he had experienced several times throughout his adult life, had come upon him again. It was not pain or palpitation, but rather an awful feeling of sinking and melting into one's physical surroundings—sunset, red boles of trees, sand, still air. Meanwhile Roza Shpolyanski, noticing Pnin sitting alone, and taking advantage of this, walked over to him (*"sidite, sidite!"* don't get up) and sat down next to him on the bench.

"In 1916 or 1917," she said, "you may have had occasion to hear my maiden name—Geller—from some great friends of yours."

"No, I don't recollect," said Pnin.

"It is of no importance, anyway. I don't think we ever met. But you knew well my cousins, Grisha and Mira Belochkin. They constantly spoke of you. He is living in Sweden, I think—and, of course, you have heard of his poor sister's terrible end. . . ."

"Indeed, I have," said Pnin.

"Her husband," said Madam Shpolyanski, "was a most charming man. Samuil Lvovich and I knew him and his first wife, Svetlana Chertok, the pianist, very intimately. He was interned by the Nazis separately from Mira, and died in the same concentration camp as did my elder brother

Misha. You did not know Misha, did you? He was also in love with Mira once upon a time."

"*Tshay gotoff* (tea's ready)," called Susan from the porch in her funny functional Russian. "Timofey, Rozochka! *Tshay!*"

Pnin told Madam Shpolyanski he would follow her in a minute, and after she had gone he continued to sit in the first dusk of the arbor, his hands clasped on the croquet mallet he still held.

Two kerosene lamps cozily illuminated the porch of the country house. Dr. Pavel Antonovich Pnin, Timofey's father, an eye specialist, and Dr. Yakov Grigorievich Belochkin, Mira's father, a pediatrician, could not be torn away from their chess game in a corner of the veranda, so Madam Belochkin had the maid serve them there—on a special, small Japanese table, near the one they were playing at—their glasses of tea in silver holders, the curd and whey with black bread, the Garden Strawberries, *zemlyanika,* and the other cultivated species, *klubnika* (Hautbois or Green Strawberries), and the radiant golden jams, and the various biscuits, wafers, pretzels, zwiebacks—instead of calling the two engrossed doctors to the main table at the other end of the porch, where sat the rest of the family and guests, some clear, some grading into a luminous mist.

Dr. Belochkin's blind hand took a pretzel; Dr. Pnin's seeing hand took a rook. Dr. Belochkin munched and stared at the hole in his ranks; Dr. Pnin dipped an abstract zwieback into the hole of his tea.

The country house that the Belochkins rented that summer was in the same Baltic resort near which the widow of General N—— let a summer cottage to the Pnins on the confines of her vast estate, marshy and rugged, with dark woods hemming in a desolate manor. Timofey Pnin was again the clumsy, shy, obstinate, eighteen-year-old boy, waiting in the dark for Mira—and despite the fact that logical thought put electric bulbs into the kerosene lamps and reshuffled the people, turning them into aging émigrés and securely, hopelessly, forever wire-netting the lighted porch, my poor Pnin, with hallucinatory sharpness, imagined Mira slipping out of there into the garden and coming toward him among tall tobacco flowers whose dull white mingled in the dark with that of her frock. This feeling coincided somehow with the sense of diffusion and dilation within his chest. Gently he laid his mallet aside and, to dissipate the anguish, started walking away from the house, through the silent pine grove. From a car which was parked near the garden tool house and which contained presumably at least two of his fellow guests' children, there issued a steady trickle of radio music.

"Jazz, jazz, they always must have their jazz, those youngsters," muttered Pnin to himself, and turned into the path that led to the forest and river. He remembered the fads of his and Mira's youth, the amateur theatricals, the gypsy ballads, the passion she had for photography. Where were they now, those artistic snapshots she used to take—pets, clouds, flowers, an April glade with shadows of birches on wet-sugar snow, soldiers posturing on the roof of a boxcar, a sunset skyline, a hand holding a book? He remembered the last day they had met, on the Neva embankment in Petrograd, and the tears, and the stars, and the warm rose-red silk lining of her karakul muff. The Civil War of 1918-22 separated them; history broke their engagement. Timofey wandered southward, to join briefly the ranks of Denikin's army, while Mira's family escaped from the Bolsheviks to Sweden and then settled down in Germany, where eventually she married a fur dealer of Russian extraction. Sometime in the early thirties, Pnin, by then married too, accompanied his wife to Berlin, where she wished to attend a congress of psychotherapists, and one night, at a Russian restaurant on the Kurfürstendamm, he saw Mira again. They exchanged a few words, she smiled at him in the remembered fashion, from under her dark brows, with that bashful slyness of hers; and the contour of her prominent cheekbones, and the elongated eyes, and the slenderness of arm and ankle were unchanged, were immortal, and then she joined her husband who was getting his overcoat at the cloakroom, and that was all—but the pang of tenderness remained, akin to the vibrating outline of verses you know you know but cannot recall.

What chatty Madam Shpolyanski mentioned had conjured up Mira's image with unusual force. This was disturbing. Only in the detachment of an incurable complaint, in the sanity of near death, could one cope with this for a moment. In order to exist rationally, Pnin had taught himself, during the last ten years, never to remember Mira Belochkin—not because, in itself, the evocation of a youthful love affair, banal and brief, threatened his peace of mind (alas, recollections of his marriage to Liza were imperious enough to crowd out any former romance), but because, if one were quite sincere with oneself, no conscience, and hence no consciousness, could be expected to subsist in a world where such things as Mira's death were possible. One had to forget—because one could not live with the thought that this graceful, fragile, tender young woman with those eyes, that smile, those gardens and snows in the background, had been brought in a cattle car to an extermination camp and killed by an injection of phenol into the heart, into the gentle heart one had heard beating under one's lips in the dusk of the past. And since the exact form of her death had not been recorded, Mira kept dying a great number of deaths in one's mind, and undergoing a great number of resurrections, only to die again and again, led away by a trained nurse, inoculated with filth, tetanus bacilli, broken glass, gassed in a sham shower bath with prussic acid, burned alive in a pit on a gasoline-soaked pile of beechwood. According to the investigator Pnin had happened to talk to in Washington, the only certain thing was that being too weak to work (though still smiling, still able to help other Jewish women), she was selected to die and was cremated only a few days after her arrival in Buchenwald, in the beautifully wooded Grosser Ettersberg, as the region is resoundingly called. It is an hour's stroll from Weimar, where walked Goethe, Herder, Schiller, Wieland, the inimitable Kotzebue and others. "*Aber warum*—but why—" Dr. Hagen, the gentlest of souls alive, would wail, "why had one to put that horrid camp so near!" for indeed, it was near—only five miles from the cultural heart of Germany—"that nation of universities," as the President of Waindell College, renowned for his use of the *mot juste,* had so elegantly phrased it when reviewing the

European situation in a recent Commencement speech, along with the compliment he paid another torture house, "Russia—the country of Tolstoy, Stanislavski, Raskolnikov, and other great and good men."

Pnin slowly walked under the solemn pines. The sky was dying. He did not believe in an autocratic God. He did believe, dimly, in a democracy of ghosts. The souls of the dead, perhaps, formed committees, and these, in continuous session, attended to the destinies of the quick.

The mosquitoes were getting bothersome. Time for tea. Time for a game of chess with Chateau. That strange spasm was over, one could breathe again. On the distant crest of the knoll, at the exact spot where Gramineev's easel had stood a few hours before, two dark figures in profile were silhouetted against the ember-red sky. They stood there closely, facing each other. One could not make out from the road whether it was the Poroshin girl and her beau, or Nina Bolotov and young Poroshin, or merely an emblematic couple placed with easy art on the last page of Pnin's fading day.

ANALYSIS

Vladimir Nabokov's *Pnin* is a book that combines the deep pathos of suffering with hilarious comedy. It is an imaginative, heartbreaking comic novel about a transplanted misfit, sacrificed on the altar of academic snobbery and phony intellectualism. But its author is not content with portraying a chaotic, unregenerate world populated by the small, the mean, and the absurd. His hero, unlike so many heroes of contemporary fiction, is not one who wallows in a self-pitying condemnation of humanity. In the community of the afflicted to which Pnin belongs, the causes of anguish, for a change, matter.

Chapter Five is a complete episode which stands, even out of context, as a unified story. It is, moreover, in its form and content, a reflection of the larger structure from which it is excerpted. In this one chapter, all of the intentions of the novel are contained in miniature. We see that Pnin, as a real exile, suffers for a complete loss of home and direct cultural ties, for a total absence of love; the monsters that inhabit his dreams are not projections of self but very real Bolshevik and Nazi torturers. Pnin's hell, the one he strives to avoid, is not private. A perpetual wanderer, always ridiculed for his peculiarities, always depending for his very existence on the benevolence of other, and generally lesser, men, he never lapses into self-pity, never gives in to the despair that pushes rather frequently at the threshold of his consciousness, never postures and poses. His response to suffering is not a self-destructive howl at past horrors but a legitimate and admirable refuge in the antithesis of nightmare—the beauty of Russian lore and literature, the esthetics of art.

The movement of Chapter Five, like the movement of the book, is from comic to serious. In the first part of the chapter we see Pnin as a humorous victim of his automobile, his road map, his gas-station attendant, his inadequate English. We are told something about his pedantic nature in a brief aside on Pnin's learning to drive: He studied

with deep enjoyment the forty-page *Driver's Manual,* issued by the State Governor in collaboration with another expert, and the article on "Automobile" in the *Encyclopedia Americana*, with illustrations of Transmissions, and Carburetors, and Brakes, and a Member of the Glidden Tour, *circa* 1905, stuck in the mud of a country road among depressing surroundings.

In spite of Pnin's research, he fails the driving test because he argues with the examiner about the logicality of stopping at red lights when there is no one in sight "heeled or wheeled." We watch him as he bungles down the road, getting hopelessly lost and eventually arriving at his destination—the summer home of his friend, Al Cook—by pure chance.

At the outset, then, Pnin is a comic figure and we laugh at him. He is also a man out of his time and place—like Hank in Mark Twain's *A Connecticut Yankee in King Arthur's Court,* though in reverse order. Here a man from the past is projected into the present, and the contrast between the new world and the old is continued in the second part of the chapter. The guests at Al Cook's (Alexandr Petrovich Kukolnikov) are mostly Russian émigrés and their talk is quite naturally of the land and culture which they left behind and from which they are cut off. Their children, who have been brought up in America, have "no interest whatsoever in the niceties of their parents' backgrounds and pasts."

In the third part the focus is again on Pnin as he drives up the sandy road in front of the house, kills the engine, and sits "beaming" at his friends who come out to greet him. He is still a clownish figure:

The collar of his green sport shirt was undone; his partly unzipped windbreaker seemed too tight for his impressive torso; his bronzed bald head, with the puckered brow and conspicuous vermicular vein on the temple, bent low as he wrestled with the door handle and finally dived out of the car.

And it is not surprising, in view of the established contrast between the old world and the new, that Pnin's first conversation should concern the exact day on which Tolstoy's *Anna Karenin* begins. Pnin, ever the pedant, explains precisely its confusing chronology.

In the fourth part of the chapter, however, our attitude toward Pnin begins to alter. On his way to the river for a swim, he appears, characteristically, in a blue bathrobe and a pair of rubbers, "a sensible precaution if one intends to walk through damp and, perhaps, snake-infested grass." He meets his old friend Konstantin Ivanich Chateau and they walk together through the fields, but their conversation has none of the comic overtones that we have encountered heretofore. For one thing Chateau is of the same past, and although the contrast between past and present is very much in evidence as these two exiles talk, the tone has shifted away from the wry humor of the first three parts. There are comic lines, to be sure, but they are no longer directed at the actors. We see nothing amusing or absurd in the situation in which Pnin and his countrymen find themselves. When Chateau points to a Greek Catholic cross that Pnin wears and remarks, "You will lose it one day," we get the first real evidence in the chapter of a sensitive soul beneath that "impressive torso":

"Perhaps I would not mind losing it," said Pnin. "As you well know, I wear it merely from sentimental reasons. And the sentiment is becoming burdensome. After all, there is too much of the physical about this attempt to keep a particle of one's childhood in contact with one's breastbone."

By the last section of the chapter we have moved completely away from the comic depiction of Pnin, and the real depth of his suffering becomes apparent. Pnin is reminded by one of the guests, Roza Shpolyanski, of a girl named Mira whom he had loved before the Bolshevik revolution overturned their lives. Later they married other people and went different ways, but the pain of a politically interrupted love and the horror of Mira's eventual extermination in a Nazi concentration camp have affected Pnin's whole response to life. "Only in the detachment of an incurable complaint in the sanity of near death," Pnin thinks, would it be possible to cope with the image of Mira even for a moment:

In order to exist rationally, Pnin had taught himself, during the last ten years, never to remember Mira Belochkin—not because, in itself, the evocation of a youthful love affair, banal and brief, threatened his peace of mind . . . but because, if one were quite sincere with oneself, no conscience, and hence no consciousness, could be expected to subsist in a world where such things as Mira's death were possible.

Pnin simply is unable to live with the thought of the "graceful, fragile, tender young woman with those eyes, that smile, those gardens and snows in the background," being transported "in a cattle car to an extermination camp and killed by an injection of phenol into the heart. . . ." The peculiarities which make the bumbling, pedantic Pnin an object of laughter are the result in part of a necessary removal from reality. In order to continue to live, he has consciously trained himself to ignore the unbearable cruelty and horror of the world. That he refuses to allow the extremities of inhumanity to overwhelm his reason becomes, in the light of his past, more admirable than ridiculous to the reader.

And so we have come full round, in our view of misplaced, anachronistic Pnin, from detachment to sympathy, from amusement to compassion.

Chapter Five of *Pnin,* like most of Nabokov's work, exhibits a prose style that is as eloquent as one is likely to find in modern English literature, and style, to quote Proust, "is in no way an embellishment. . . ." It is like a painter's colors; it expresses the quality of the artist's perception and reveals a personal world that others do not see.

For example, at the opening of the chapter Pnin is approaching the summer house of his friend, Al Cook, and he is lost in the maze of roads that cut through the New England woods. Nabokov might simply have told us about Pnin's dilemma in flat narrative terms. The incident is not of great importance to the rest of the chapter and a lesser writer might have dispensed with it in a few sentences. Nabokov gives it a full, imaginative treatment:

On a dull warm day in the summer of 1954, Mary or Almira, or, for that matter, Wolfgang von Goethe, whose name had been carved in the balustrade by some old-fashioned wag, might have noticed an automobile that had turned off the highway just before reaching the bridge and was now nosing and poking this way and that in a maze of doubtful roads. It moved warily and unsteadily, and whenever it changed its mind, it would slow down and raise dust behind like a back-kicking dog. At times it might seem, to a less sympathetic soul than our imagined observer, that this pale blue, egg-shaped two-door sedan, of uncertain age and in mediocre condition, was manned by an idiot. Actually its driver was Professor Timofey Pnin, of Waindell College.

One is reminded of Anton Chekhov's advice to his brother Alex that commonplace imagery should be avoided, that "you will get the full effect of a moonlight night if you write that on the mill-dam a little glowing starpoint flashed from the neck of a broken bottle, and the round, black shadow of a dog, or a wolf, emerged and ran, etc. Nature becomes animated if you are not squeamish about employing comparisons of her phenomena with ordinary human activities, etc." Ordinary human activities become animated, one might add, if you are not squeamish about employing metaphorical and personified imagery to coalesce disparate objects. Pnin's car becomes animated because it appears to have a life of its own—even if it is a dog's life.

One comes away from Nabokov's prose awed by many things, but chiefly this: the dazzling display of verbal skill (often used to create simply pictorial meaning) that combines disparate objects and experiences in an entirely original use of metaphor. Consider, for example, the last lines of the chapter:

On the distant crest of the knoll, at the exact spot where Gramineev's easel had stood a few hours before, two dark figures in profile were silhouetted against the ember-red sky. They stood there closely, facing each other. One could not make out from the road whether it was the Poroshin girl and her beau, or Nina Bolotov and young Poroshin, or merely an emblematic couple placed with easy art on the last page of Pnin's fading day.

Nabokov's work reminds us that literature, like all other art forms, appeals to the senses as well as the intellect.

W. Somerset Maugham

THE LOTUS EATER

Most people, the vast majority in fact, lead the lives that circumstances have thrust upon them, and though some repine, looking upon themselves as round pegs in square holes, and think that if things had been different they might have made a much better showing, the greater part accept their lot, if not with serenity, at all events with resignation. They are like tramcars travelling for ever on the selfsame rails. They go backwards and forwards, backwards and forwards, inevitably, till they can go no longer and then are sold as scrap iron. It is not often that you find a man who has boldly taken the course of his life into his own hands. When you do, it is worth while having a good look at him.

That was why I was curious to meet Thomas Wilson. It was an interesting and a bold thing he had done. Of course the end was not yet, and until the experiment was concluded it was impossible to call it successful. But from what I had heard it seemed he must be an odd sort of fellow, and I thought I should like to know him. I had been told he was reserved, but I had a notion that with patience and tact I could persuade him to confide in me. I wanted to hear the facts from his own lips. People exaggerate, they love to romanticize, and I was quite prepared to discover that his story was not nearly so singular as I had been led to believe.

And this impression was confirmed when at last I made his acquaintance. It was on the Piazza in Capri, where I was spending the month of August at a friend's villa, and a little before sunset, when most of the inhabitants, native and foreign, gather together to chat with their friends in the cool of the evening. There is a terrace that overlooks the Bay of Naples, and when the sun sinks slowly into the sea the island of Ischia is silhouetted against a blaze of splendour. It is one of the most lovely sights in the world. I was standing there with my friend and host watching it, when suddenly he said:

"Look, there's Wilson."

"Where?"

"The man sitting on the parapet, with his back to us. He's got a blue shirt on."

I saw an undistinguished back and a small head of grey hair short and rather thin.

"I wish he'd turn round," I said.

"He will presently."

"Ask him to come and have a drink with us at Morgano's."

"All right."

The instant of overwhelming beauty had passed and the sun, like the top of an orange, was dipping into a wine-red sea. We turned round and, leaning our backs against the parapet, looked at the people who were sauntering to and fro. They were all talking their heads off, and the cheerful noise was exhilarating. Then the church bell, rather cracked, but with a fine resonant note, began to ring. The Piazza at Capri, with its clock tower over the footpath that leads up from the harbour, with the church up a flight of steps, is a perfect setting for an opera by Donizetti, and you felt that the voluble crowd might at any moment break out into a rattling chorus. It was charming and unreal.

I was so intent on the scene that I had not noticed Wilson get off the parapet and come towards us. As he passed us, my friend stopped him.

"Hulloa, Wilson, I haven't seen you bathing the last few days."

"I've been bathing on the other side for a change."

My friend then introduced me. Wilson shook hands with me politely, but with indifference; a great many strangers come to Capri for a few days, or a few weeks, and I had no doubt he was constantly meeting people who came and went; and then my friend asked him to come along and have a drink with us.

"I was just going back to supper," he said.

"Can't it wait?" I asked.

"I suppose it can," he smiled.

Though his teeth were not very good, his smile was attractive. It was gentle and kindly. He was dressed in a blue cotton shirt and a pair of grey trousers, much creased and none too clean, of a thin canvas, and on his feet he wore a pair of very old espadrilles. The get-up was picturesque, and very suitable to the place and the weather, but it did not at all go with his face. It was a lined, long face, deeply sunburned, thin-lipped, with small grey eyes rather close together and tight, neat features. The grey hair was carefully brushed. It was not a plain face—indeed in his youth Wilson might have been good looking—but a prim one. He wore the blue shirt open at the neck, and the grey canvas trousers, not as though they belonged to him, but as though, shipwrecked in his pyjamas, he had been fitted out with odd garments by compassionate strangers. Notwithstanding this careless attire he looked like the manager of a branch office in an insurance company, who should by rights be wearing a black coat with pepper and salt trousers, a white collar and an unobjectionable tie. I could very well see myself going to him to claim the insurance money when I had lost a watch, and being rather disconcerted, while I answered the questions he put to me, by his obvious impression, for all his politeness, that people who made such claims were either fools or knaves.

Moving off, we strolled across the Piazza and down the street till we came to Morgano's. We sat in the garden. Around us people were talking in Russian, German, Italian and English. We ordered drinks. Donna Lucia, the host's wife, waddled up and in her low, sweet voice passed the time of day with us. Though middle-aged now and portly, she had still traces of the wonderful beauty that, thirty years before, had driven artists to paint so many bad portraits of her. Her eyes, large and liquid, were the eyes of Hera, and her smile was affectionate and gracious. We three gossiped for a while, for there is always a scandal of one sort or another in Capri to make a topic of conversation, but nothing was said of particular interest, and in a little while Wilson got up and left us. Soon afterwards we strolled up to my friend's villa to dine. On the way he asked me what I had thought of Wilson.

"Nothing," I said. "I don't believe there's a word of truth in your story."

"Why not?"

"He isn't the sort of man to do that sort of thing."

"How does anyone know what anyone is capable of?"

"I should put him down as an absolutely normal man of business who's retired on a comfortable income from gilt-edged securities. I think your story's just the ordinary Capri tittle-tattle."

"Have it your own way," said my friend.

We were in the habit of bathing at a beach called the Baths of Tiberius. We took a fly down the road to a certain point and then wandered through lemon groves and vineyards, noisy with cicadas and heavy with the hot smell of the sun, till we came to the top of the cliff down which a steep winding path led to the sea. A day or two later, just before we got down, my friend said:

"Oh, there's Wilson back again."

We scrunched over the beach, the only drawback to the bathing-place being that it was shingle and not sand, and as we came along Wilson saw us and waved. He was standing up, a pipe in his mouth, and he wore nothing but a pair of trunks. His body was dark brown, thin but not emaciated, and, considering his wrinkled face and grey hair, youthful. Hot from our walk, we undressed quickly and plunged at once into the water. Six feet from the shore it was thirty feet deep, but so clear that you could see the bottom. It was warm, yet invigorating.

When I got out, Wilson was lying on his belly, with a towel under him, reading a book. I lit a cigarette and sat down beside him.

"Had a nice swim?" he asked.

He put his pipe inside his book to mark the place and, closing it, put it down on the pebbles beside him. He was evidently willing to talk.

"Lovely," I said. "It's the best bathing in the world."

"Of course people think those were the baths of Tiberius." He waved his hand towards a shapeless mass of masonry that stood half in the water and half out. "But that's all rot. It was just one of his villas, you know."

I did. But it is just as well to let people tell you things when they want to. It disposes them kindly towards you if you suffer them to impart information. Wilson gave a chuckle.

"Funny old fellow, Tiberius. Pity they're saying now there's not a word of truth in all those stories about him."

He began to tell me all about Tiberius. Well, I had read my Suetonius too, and I had read histories of the Early Roman Empire, so there was nothing very new to me in what he said. But I observed that he was not ill-read. I remarked on it.

"Oh, well, when I settled down here I was naturally interested, and I have plenty of time for reading. When you live in a place like this, with all its associations, it seems to make history so actual. You might almost be living in historical times yourself."

I should remark here that this was in 1913. The world was an easy, comfortable place, and no one could have imagined that anything might happen seriously to disturb the serenity of existence.

"How long have you been here?" I asked.

"Fifteen years." He gave the blue and placid sea a glance, and a strangely tender smile hovered on his thin lips. "I fell in love with the place at first sight. You've heard, I daresay, of the mythical German who came here on the Naples boat just for lunch and a look at the Blue Grotto and stayed forty years; well, I can't say I exactly did that, but it's come to the same thing in the end. Only it won't be forty years in my case. Twenty-five. Still, that's better than a poke in the eye with a sharp stick."

I waited for him to go on. For what he had just said looked indeed as though there might be something after all in the singular story I had heard. But at that moment my friend came dripping out of the water very proud of himself because he had swum a mile, and the conversation turned to other things.

After that I met Wilson several times, either in the Piazza or on the beach. He was amiable and polite. He was always pleased to have a talk and I found out that he knew not only every inch of the island but also the adjacent mainland. He had read a great deal on all sorts of subjects, but his speciality was the history of Rome, and on this he was very well informed. He seemed to have little imagination and to be of no more than average intelligence. He laughed a good deal, but with restraint, and his sense of humour was tickled by simple jokes. A commonplace man. I did not forget the odd remark he had made during the first short chat we had had by ourselves, but he never so much as approached the topic again. One day on our return from the beach, dismissing the cab at the Piazza, my friend and I told the driver to be ready to take us up to Anacapri at five. We were going to climb Monte Solaro, dine at a tavern we favoured, and walk down in the moonlight. For it was full moon, and the views by night were lovely. Wilson was standing by while we gave the cabman instructions, for we had given him a lift to save him the hot dusty walk, and more from politeness than for any other reason I asked him if he would care to join us.

"It's my party," I said.

"I'll come with pleasure," he answered.

But when the time came to set out, my friend was not feeling well, he thought he had stayed too long in the water, and would not face the long and tiring walk. So I went alone with Wilson. We climbed the mountain, admired the spacious view, and got back to the inn as night was falling, hot, hungry and thirsty. We had ordered our dinner beforehand. The food was good, for Antonio was an excellent cook, and the wine came from his own vineyard. It was so light that you felt you could drink it like water, and we finished the first bottle with our macaroni. By the time we had finished the second we felt that there was nothing much wrong with life. We sat in a little garden under a great vine laden with grapes. The air was exquisitely soft. The night was still, and we were alone. The maid brought us *bel paese* cheese and a plate of figs. I ordered coffee and strega, which is the best liqueur they make in Italy. Wilson would not have a cigar, but lit his pipe.

"We've got plenty of time before we need start," he said. "The moon won't be over the hill for another hour."

"Moon or no moon," I said briskly, "of course we've got plenty of time. That's one of the delights of Capri, that there's never any hurry."

"Leisure," he said. "If people only knew! It's the most priceless thing a man can have and they're such fools they don't even know it's something to aim at. Work? They work for work's sake. They haven't got the brains to realize that the only object of work is to obtain leisure."

Wine has the effect on some people of making them indulge in general reflections. These remarks were true, but no one could have claimed that they were original. I did not say anything, but struck a match to light my cigar.

"It was full moon the first time I came to Capri," he went on reflectively. "It might be the same moon as tonight."

"It was, you know," I smiled.

He grinned. The only light in the garden was what came from an oil lamp that hung over our heads. It had been scanty to eat by, but it was good now for confidences.

"I didn't mean that. I mean, it might be yesterday. Fifteen years it is, and when I look back it seems like a month. I'd never been to Italy before. I came for my summer holiday. I went to Naples by boat from Marseilles, and I had a look round—Pompeii, you know, and Paestum and one or two places like that; then I came here for a week. I liked the look of the place right away, from the sea, I mean, as I watched it come closer and closer; and then when we got into the little boats from the steamer and landed at the quay, with all that crowd of jabbering people who wanted to take your luggage, and the hotel touts, and the tumble-down houses on the Marina and the walk up to the hotel, and dining on the terrace—well, it just got me. That's the truth. I didn't know if I was standing on my head or my heels. I'd never drunk Capri wine before, but I'd heard of it; I think I must have got a bit tight. I sat on that terrace after they'd all gone to bed and watched the moon over the sea, and there was Vesuvius with a great red plume of smoke rising up from it. Of course I know now that wine I drank was ink, Capri wine my eye, but I thought it all right then. But it wasn't the wine that made me drunk, it was the shape of the island and those jabbering people, the moon and the sea and the oleander in the hotel garden. I'd never seen an oleander before."

It was a long speech, and it had made him thirsty. He took up his glass, but it was empty. I asked him if he would have another strega.

"It's sickly stuff. Let's have a bottle of wine. That's sound, that is, pure juice of the grape and can't hurt anyone."

I ordered more wine, and when it came filled the glasses. He took a long drink and after a sigh of pleasure went on.

"Next day I found my way to the bathing place we go to. Not bad bathing, I thought. Then I wandered about the island. As luck would have it, there was a *festa* up at the Punta di Timberio, and I ran straight into the middle of it. An image of the Virgin and priests, acolytes swinging censers, and a whole crowd of jolly, laughing, excited people, a lot of them all dressed up. I ran across an Englishman there and asked him what it was all about. 'Oh, it's the feast of the Assumption,' he said. 'At least that's what the Catholic Church says it is, but that's just their hanky-panky. It's the festival of Venus. Pagan, you know. Aphrodite rising from the sea and all that.' It gave me quite a funny feeling to hear him. It seemed to take one a long way back, if you know what I mean. After that I went down one night to have a look at the Faraglioni by moonlight. If the fates had wanted me to go on being a bank manager they oughtn't to have let me take that walk."

"You were a bank manager, were you?" I asked.

I had been wrong about him, but not far wrong.

"Yes. I was manager of the Crawford Street branch of the York and City. It was convenient for me because I lived up Hendon way. I could get from door to door in thirty-seven minutes."

He puffed at his pipe and relit it.

"That was my last night, that was. I'd got to be back at the bank on Monday morning. When I looked at those two great rocks sticking out of the water, with the moon above them, and all the little lights of the fishermen in their boats catching cuttlefish, all so peaceful and beautiful, I said to myself, well, after all, why should I go back? It wasn't as if I had anyone dependent on me. My wife had died of bronchial pneumonia four years before, and the kid went to live with her grandmother, my wife's mother. She was an old fool, she didn't look after the kid properly and she got blood poisoning, they amputated her leg, but they couldn't save her and she died, poor little thing."

"How terrible," I said.

"Yes, I was cut up at the time, though of course not so much as if the kid had been living with me, but I daresay it was a mercy. Not much chance for a girl with only one leg. I was sorry about my wife, too. We got on very well together. Though I don't know if it would have continued. She was the sort of woman who was always bothering about what other people'd think. She didn't like travelling. Eastbourne was her idea of a holiday. D'you know, I'd never crossed the channel till after her death."

"But I suppose you've got other relations, haven't you?"

"None. I was an only child. My father had a brother, but he went to Australia before I was born. I don't think anyone could easily be more alone in the world than I am. There wasn't any reason I could see why I shouldn't do exactly what I wanted. I was thirty-four at that time."

He had told me he had been on the island for fifteen years. That would make him forty-nine. Just about the age I should have given him.

"I'd been working since I was seventeen. All I had to look forward to was doing the same old thing day after day till I retired on my pension. I said to myself, 'Is it worth it? What's wrong with chucking it all up and spending the rest of my life down here?' It was the most beautiful place I'd ever seen. But I'd had a business training, I was cautious by nature. 'No,' I said, 'I won't be carried away like this, I'll go tomorrow like I said I would and think it over. Perhaps when I get back to London I'll think quite differently.' Damned fool, wasn't I? I lost a whole year that way."

"You didn't change your mind, then?"

"You bet I didn't. All the time I was working I kept thinking of the bathing here and the vineyards and the walks over the hills and the moon and the sea, and the Piazza in the evening when everyone walks about for a bit of a chat after the day's work is over. There was only one thing that bothered me; I wasn't sure if I was justified in not working like everybody else did. Then I read a sort of history book, by a man called Marion Crawford it was, and there was a story about Sybaris and Crotona. There were two cities; and in Sybaris they just enjoyed life and had a good time, and in Crotona they were hardy and industrious and all that. And one day the men of Crotona came over and wiped Sybaris out, and then after a while a lot of other fellows came over from somewhere else and wiped Crotona out. Nothing remains of Sybaris, not a stone, and all that's left of Crotona is just one column. That settled the matter for me."

"Oh?"

"It came to the same in the end, didn't it? And when you look back now, who were the mugs?"

I did not reply, and he went on.

"The money was rather a bother. The bank didn't pension one off till after thirty years' service, but if you retired before that they gave you a gratuity. With that and what I'd got for the sale of my house and the little I'd managed to save, I just hadn't enough to buy an annuity to last the rest of my life. It would have been silly to sacrifice everything so as to lead a pleasant life and not have a sufficient income to make it pleasant. I wanted to have a little place of my own, a servant to look after me, enough to buy tobacco, decent food, books now and then, and something over for emergencies. I knew pretty well how much I needed. I found I had just enough to buy an annuity for twenty-five years."

"You were thirty-five at the time?"

"Yes. It would carry me on till I was sixty. After all, no one can be certain of living longer than that; a lot of men die in their fifties, and by the time a man's sixty he's had the best of life."

"On the other hand no one can be sure of dying at sixty," I said.

"Well, I don't know. It depends on himself, doesn't it?"

"In your place I should have stayed on at the bank till I was entitled to my pension."

"I should have been forty-seven then. I shouldn't have been too old to enjoy my life here, I'm older than that now and I enjoy it as much as I ever did, but I should have been too old to experience the particular pleasure of a young man. You know, you can have just as good a time at fifty as you can at thirty, but it's not the same sort of good time. I wanted to live the perfect life while I still had the energy and the spirit to make the most of it. Twenty-five years seemed a long time to me, and twenty-five years of happiness seemed worth paying something pretty substantial for. I'd made up my mind to wait a year, and I waited a year. Then I sent in my resignation, and as soon as they paid me my gratuity I bought the annuity and came on here."

"An annuity for twenty-five years?"

"That's right."

"Have you never regretted?"

"Never. I've had my money's worth already. And I've got ten years more. Don't you think after twenty-five years of perfect happiness one ought to be satisfied to call it a day?"

"Perhaps."

He did not say in so many words what he would do then, but his intention was clear. It was pretty much the story my friend had told me, but it sounded different when I heard it from his own lips. I stole a glance at him. There was nothing about him that was not ordinary. No one, looking at that neat, prim face, could have thought him capable of an unconventional action. I did not blame him. It was his own life that he had arranged in this strange manner, and I did not see why he should not do what he liked with it. Still, I could not prevent the little shiver that ran down my spine.

"Getting chilly?" he smiled. "We might as well start walking down. The moon'll be up by now."

Before we parted, Wilson asked me if I would like to go and see his house one day; and two or three days later, finding out where he lived, I strolled up to see him. It was a peasant's cottage, well away from the town, in a vineyard, with a view of the sea. By the side of the door grew a great oleander in full flower. There were only two small rooms, a tiny kitchen and a lean-to in which firewood could be kept. The bedroom was furnished like a monk's cell, but the sitting room, smelling agreeably of tobacco, was comfortable enough, with two large armchairs that he had brought from England, a large roll-top desk, a cottage piano and crowded bookshelves. On the walls were framed engravings of pictures by G. F. Watts and Lord Leighton. Wilson told me that the house belonged to the owner of the vineyard who lived in another cottage higher up the hill, and his wife came in every day to do the rooms and the cooking. He had found the place on his first visit to Capri, and taking it on his return for good had been there ever since. Seeing the piano and music open on it, I asked him if he would play.

"I'm no good, you know, but I've always been fond of music, and I get a lot of fun out of strumming."

He sat down at the piano and played one of the movements from a Beethoven sonata. He did not play very well. I looked at his music, Schumann and Schubert, Beethoven, Bach and Chopin. On the table on which he had his meals was a greasy pack of cards. I asked him if he played patience.

"A lot."

From what I saw of him then and from what I heard from other people I made for myself what I think must have been a fairly accurate picture of the life he had led for the last fifteen years. It was certainly a very harmless one. He bathed; he walked a great deal, and he seemed never to lose his sense of the beauty of the island which he knew so intimately; he played the piano and he played patience; he read. When he was asked to a party he went and, though a trifle dull, was agreeable. He was not affronted if he was neglected. He liked people, but with an aloofness that prevented intimacy. He lived thriftily, but with sufficient comfort. He never owed a penny. I imagine he had never been a man whom sex had greatly troubled, and if in his younger days he had had now and then a passing affair with a visitor to the island whose head was turned by the atmosphere, his emotion, while it lasted, remained, I am pretty sure, well under his control. I think he was determined that nothing should interfere with his independence of spirit. His only passion was for the beauty of nature, and he sought felicity in the simple and natural things that life offers to everyone. You may say that it was a grossly selfish existence. It was. He was of no use to anybody, but on the other hand he did nobody any harm. His only object was his own happiness, and it looked as though he had attained it. Very few people know where to look for happiness; fewer still find it. I don't know whether he was a fool or a wise man. He was certainly a man who knew his own mind. The odd thing about him to me was that he was so immensely commonplace. I should never have given him a second thought but for what I knew, that on a certain day, ten years from then, unless a chance illness cut the thread before, he must deliberately take leave of the world he loved so well. I wondered whether it was the thought of this, never quite absent from his mind, that gave him the peculiar zest with which he enjoyed every moment of the day.

I should do him an injustice if I omitted to state that he was not at all in the habit of talking about himself. I think the friend I was staying with was the only person in whom he had confided. I believe he told me the story only because he suspected I already knew it, and on the evening on which he told it me he had drunk a good deal of wine.

My visit drew to a close, and I left the island. The year after, war broke out. A number of things happened to me, so that the course of my life was greatly altered, and it was thirteen years before I went to Capri again. My friend had been back some time, but he was no longer so well off, and had moved into a house that had no room for me; so I was putting up at the hotel. He came to meet me at the boat, and we dined together. During dinner I asked him where exactly his house was.

"You know it," he answered. "It's the little place Wilson had. I've built on a room and made it quite nice."

With so many other things to occupy my mind, I had not given Wilson a thought for years; but now, with a little shock, I remembered. The ten years he had before him when I made his acquaintance must have elapsed long ago.

"Did he commit suicide as he said he would?"

"It's rather a grim story."

Wilson's plan was all right. There was only one flaw in it, and this, I suppose, he could not have foreseen. It had never occurred to him that after twenty-five years of complete happiness, in this quiet backwater, with nothing in the world to disturb his serenity, his character would gradually lose its strength. The will needs obstacles in order to exercise its power; when it is never thwarted, when no effort is needed to achieve one's desires, because one has placed one's desires only in the things that can be obtained by stretching out one's hand, the will grows impotent. If you walk on a level all the time, the muscles you need to climb a mountain will atrophy. These observations are trite, but there they are. When Wilson's annuity expired he had no longer the resolution to make the end which was the price he had agreed to pay for that long period of happy tranquillity. I do not think, as far as I could gather, both from what my friend told me and afterwards from others, that he wanted courage. It was just that he couldn't make up his mind. He put it off from day to day.

He had lived on the island for so long and had always settled his accounts so punctually, that it was easy for him to get credit; never having borrowed money before, he found a number of people who were willing to lend him small sums when now he asked for them. He had paid his rent regularly for so many years that his landlord, whose wife Assunta still acted as his servant, was content to let things slide for several months. Everyone believed him when he said that a relative had died and that he was temporarily embarrassed because, owing to legal formalities, he could not for some time get the money that was due to him. He managed to hang on after this fashion for something over a year. Then he could get no more credit from the local tradesmen, and there was no one to lend him any more money. His landlord gave him notice to leave the house unless he paid up the arrears of rent before a certain date.

The day before this he went into his tiny bedroom, closed the door and the window, drew the curtain and lit a brazier of charcoal. Next morning when Assunta came to make his breakfast she found him insensible but still alive. The room was draughty, and though he had done this and that to keep out the fresh air he had not done it very thoroughly. It almost looked as though at the last moment, and desperate though his situation was, he had suffered from a certain infirmity of purpose. Wilson was taken to the hospital, and though very ill for some time he at last recovered. But as a result either of the charcoal poisoning or of the shock, he was no longer in complete possession of his faculties. He was not insane, at all events not insane enough to be put in an asylum, but he was quite obviously no longer in his right mind.

"I went to see him," said my friend. "I tried to get him to talk, but he kept looking at me in a funny sort of way, as though he couldn't quite make out where he'd seen me before. He looked rather awful lying there in bed, with a week's growth of grey beard on his chin; but except for that funny look in his eyes he seemed quite normal."

"I don't know exactly how to describe it. Puzzled. It's an absurd comparison, but suppose you threw a stone up into the air and it didn't come down but just stayed there . . ."

"It would be rather bewildering," I smiled.

"Well, that's the sort of look he had."

It was difficult to know what to do with him. He had no money and no means of getting any. His effects were sold, but for too little to pay what he owed. He was English, and the Italian authorities did not wish to make themselves responsible for him. The British consul in Naples had no funds to deal with the case. He could of course be sent back to England, but no one seemed to know what could be done with him when he got there. Then Assunta, the servant, said that he had been a good master and a good tenant, and as long as he had the money had paid his way; he could sleep in the woodshed in the cottage in which she and her husband lived, and he could share their meals. This was suggested to him. It was difficult to know whether he understood or not. When Assunta came to take him from the hospital, he went with her without remark. He seemed to have no longer a will of his own.

She had been keeping him now for two years.

"It's not very comfortable, you know," said my friend. "They've rigged him up a ramshackle bed and given him a couple of blankets, but there's no window, and it's icy cold in winter and like an oven in summer. And the food's pretty rough. You know how these peasants eat: macaroni on Sundays and meat once in a blue moon."

"What does he do with himself all the time?"

"He wanders about the hills. I've tried to see him two or three times, but it's no good; when he sees you coming he runs like a hare. Assunta comes down to have a chat with me now and then, and I give her a bit of money so that she can buy him tobacco, but God knows if he ever gets it."

"Do they treat him all right?" I asked.

"I'm sure Assunta's kind enough. She treats him like a child. I'm afraid her husband's not very nice to him. He grudges the cost of his keep. I don't believe he's cruel or anything like that, but I think he's a bit sharp with him. He makes him fetch water and clean the cowshed and that sort of thing."

"It sounds pretty rotten," I said.

"He brought it on himself. After all, he's only got what he deserved."

"I think on the whole we all get what we deserve," I said. "But that doesn't prevent its being rather horrible."

Two or three days later my friend and I were taking a walk. We were strolling along a narrow path through an olive grove.

"There's Wilson," said my friend suddenly. "Don't look, you'll only frighten him. Go straight on."

I walked with my eyes on the path, but out of the corners of them I saw a man hiding behind an olive tree. He did not move as we approached, but I felt that he was watching us. As soon as we had passed I heard a scamper. Wilson, like a hunted animal, had made for safety. That was the last I ever saw of him.

He died last year. He had endured that life for six years. He was found one morning on the mountainside lying quite peacefully as though he had died in his sleep. From where he lay he had been able to see those two great rocks called the Faraglioni which stand out of the sea. It was full moon, and he must have gone to see them by moonlight. Perhaps he died of the beauty of that sight.

Anton Chekhov

Gusev

It is already dark, it will soon be night.

Gusev, a discharged private, half rises in his bunk and says in a low voice:

"Do you hear me, Pavel Ivanych? A soldier in Suchan was telling me: while they were sailing, their ship bumped into a big fish and smashed a hole in its bottom."

The individual of uncertain social status whom he is addressing, and whom everyone in the ship infirmary calls Pavel Ivanych, is silent as though he hasn't heard.

And again all is still. The wind is flirting with the rigging, the screw is throbbing, the waves are lashing, the bunks creak, but the ear has long since become used to these sounds, and everything around seems to slumber in silence. It is dull. The three invalids—two soldiers and a sailor—who were playing cards all day are dozing and talking deliriously.

The ship is apparently beginning to roll. The bunk slowly rises and falls under Gusev as though it were breathing, and this occurs once, twice, three times . . . Something hits the floor with a clang: a jug must have dropped.

"The wind has broken loose from its chain," says Gusev, straining his ears.

This time Pavel Ivanych coughs and says irritably:

"One minute a vessel bumps into a fish, the next the wind breaks loose from its chain . . . Is the wind a beast that it breaks loose from its chain?"

"That's what Christian folks say."

"They are as ignorant as you . . . They say all sorts of things. One must have one's head on one's shoulders and reason it out. You have no sense."

Pavel Ivanych is subject to seasickness. When the sea is rough he is usually out of sorts, and the merest trifle irritates him. In Gusev's opinion there is absolutely nothing to be irritated about. What is there that is strange or out of the way about that fish, for instance, or about the wind breaking loose from its chain? Suppose the fish were as big as the mountain and its back as hard as a sturgeon's, and supposing, too, that over yonder at the end of the world stood great stone walls and the fierce winds were chained up to the walls. If they haven't broken loose, why then do they rush all over the sea like madmen and strain like hounds tugging at their leash? If they are not chained up what becomes of them when it is calm?

Gusev ponders for a long time about fishes as big as a mountain and about stout, rusty chains. Then he begins to feel bored and falls to thinking about his home, to which he is returning after five years' service in the Far East. He pictures an immense pond covered with drifts. On one side of the pond is the brick-colored building of the pottery with a tall chimney and clouds of black smoke; on the other side is a village. His brother Alexey drives out of the fifth yard from the end in a sleigh; behind him sits his little son Vanka in big felt boots, and his little girl Akulka also wearing felt boots. Alexey has had a drop, Vanka is laughing, Akulka's face cannot be seen, she is muffled up.

"If he doesn't look out, he will have the children frostbitten," Gusev reflects. "Lord send them sense that they may honor their parents and not be any wiser than their father and mother."

"They need new soles," a delirious sailor says in a bass voice. "Yes, yes!"

Gusev's thoughts abruptly break off and suddenly without rhyme or reason the pond is replaced by a huge bull's head without eyes, and the horse and sleigh are no longer going straight ahead but are whirling round and round, wrapped in black smoke. But still he is glad he has had a glimpse of his people. In fact, he is breathless with joy, and his whole body, down to his fingertips, tingles with it. "Thanks be to God we have seen each other again," he mutters deliriously, but at once opens his eyes and looks for water in the dark.

He drinks and lies down, and again the sleigh is gliding along, then again there is the bull's head without eyes, smoke, clouds . . . And so it goes till daybreak.

II

A blue circle is the first thing to become visible in the darkness—it is the porthole; then, little by little, Gusev makes out the man in the next bunk, Pavel Ivanych. The man sleeps sitting up, as he cannot breathe lying down. His face is gray, his nose long and sharp, his eyes look huge because he is terribly emaciated, his temples are sunken, his beard skimpy, his hair long. His face does not reveal his social status: you cannot tell whether he is a gentleman, a merchant, or a peasant. Judging from his expression and his long hair, he may be an assiduous churchgoer or a lay brother, but his manner of speaking does not seem to be that of a monk. He is utterly worn out by his cough, by the stifling heat, his illness, and he breathes with difficulty, moving his parched lips. Noticing that Gusev is looking at him he turns his face toward him and says:

"I begin to guess . . . Yes, I understand it all perfectly now."

"What do you understand, Pavel Ivanych?"

"Here's how it is . . . It has always seemed strange to me that terribly ill as you fellows are, you should be on a steamer where the stifling air, the heavy seas, in fact everything, threatens you with death; but now it is all clear to me . . . Yes . . . The doctors put you on the steamer to get rid of you. They got tired of bothering with you, cattle . . . You don't pay them any money, you are a nuisance, and you spoil their statistics with your deaths . . . So, of course, you are just cattle. And it's not hard to get rid of you . . . All that's necessary is, in the first place, to have no conscience or humanity, and secondly, to deceive the ship authorities. The first requirement need hardly be given a thought—in that respect we are virtuosos, and as for the second condition, it can always be fulfilled with a little practice. In a crowd of four hundred healthy soldiers and sailors, five sick ones are not conspicuous; well, they got you all onto the steamer, mixed you with the healthy ones, hurriedly counted you over, and in the confusion nothing untoward was noticed, and when the steamer was on the way, people discovered that there were paralytics and consumptives on their last legs lying about the deck . . ."

Gusev does not understand Pavel Ivanych; thinking that he is being reprimanded, he says in self-justification:

"I lay on the deck because I was so sick; when we were being unloaded from the barge onto the steamer, I caught a bad chill."

"It's revolting," Pavel Ivanych continues. "The main thing is, they know perfectly well that you can't stand the long journey and yet they put you here. Suppose you last as far as the Indian Ocean, and then what? It's horrible to think of . . . And that's the gratitude for your faithful, irreproachable service!"

Pavel Ivanych's eyes flash with anger. He frowns fastidiously and says, gasping for breath, "Those are the people who ought to be given a drubbing in the newspapers till the feathers fly in all directions."

The two sick soldiers and the sailor have waked up and are already playing cards. The sailor is half reclining in his bunk, the soldiers are sitting near by on the floor in most uncomfortable positions. One of the soldiers has his right arm bandaged and his wrist is heavily swathed in wrappings that look like a cap, so that he holds his cards under his right arm or in the crook of his elbow while he plays with his left. The ship is rolling heavily. It is impossible to stand up, or have tea, or take medicine.

"Were you an orderly?" Pavel Ivanych asks Gusev.

"Yes, sir, an orderly."

"My God, my God!" says Pavel Ivanych and shakes his head sadly. "To tear a man from his home, drag him a distance of ten thousand miles, then wear him out till he gets consumption and . . . and what is it all for, one asks? To turn him into an orderly for some Captain Kopeykin or Midshipman Dyrka! How reasonable!"

"It's not hard work, Pavel Ivanych. You get up in the morning and polish the boots, start the samovars going, tidy the rooms, and then you have nothing more to do. The lieutenant drafts plans all day, and if you like, you can say your prayers, or read a book or go out on the street. God grant everyone such a life."

"Yes, very good! The lieutenant drafts plans all day long, and you sit in the kitchen and long for home . . . Plans, indeed! . . . It's not plans that matter but human life. You have only one life to live and it mustn't be wronged."

"Of course, Pavel Ivanych, a bad man gets no break anywhere, either at home or in the service, but if you live as you ought and obey orders, who will want to wrong you? The officers are educated gentlemen, they understand . . . In five years I have never once been in the guard house, and I was struck, if I remember right, only once."

"What for?"

"For fighting. I have a heavy hand, Pavel Ivanych. Four Chinks came into our yard; they were bringing firewood or something, I forget. Well, I was bored and I knocked them about a bit, the nose of one of them, damn him, began bleeding . . . The lieutenant saw it all through the window, got angry, and boxed me on the ear."

"You are a poor, foolish fellow . . ." whispers Pavel Ivanych. "You don't understand anything."

He is utterly exhausted by the rolling of the ship and shuts his eyes; now his head drops back, now it sinks forward on his chest. Several times he tries to lie down but nothing comes of it: he finds it difficult to breathe.

"And what did you beat up the four Chinks for?" he asks after a while.

"Oh, just like that. They came into the yard and I hit them."

There is silence . . . The card-players play for two hours, eagerly, swearing sometimes, but the rolling and pitching of the ship overcomes them, too; they throw aside the cards and lie down. Again Gusev has a vision: the big pond, the pottery, the village . . . Once more the sleigh is gliding along, once more Vanka is laughing and Akulka, the silly thing, throws open her fur coat and thrusts out her feet, as much as to say: "Look, good people, my felt boots are not like Vanka's, they're new ones."

"Going on six, and she has no sense yet," Gusev mutters in his delirium. "Instead of showing off your boots you had better come and get your soldier uncle a drink. I'll give you a present."

And here is Andron with a flintlock on his shoulder, carrying a hare he has killed, and behind him is the decrepit old Jew Isaychik, who offers him a piece of soap in exchange for the hare; and here is the black calf in the entry, and Domna sewing a shirt and crying about something, and then again the bull's head without eyes, black smoke . . .

Someone shouts overhead, several sailors run by; it seems that something bulky is being dragged over the deck, something falls with a crash. Again some people run by. . . . Has there been an accident? Gusev raises his head, listens, and sees that the two soldiers and the sailor are playing cards again; Pavel Ivanych is sitting up and moving his lips. It is stifling, you haven't the strength to breathe, you are thirsty, the water is warm, disgusting. The ship is still rolling and pitching.

Suddenly something strange happens to one of the soldiers playing cards. He calls hearts diamonds, gets muddled over his score, and drops his cards, then with a frightened, foolish smile looks round at all of them.

"I shan't be a minute, fellows . . ." he says, and lies down on the floor.

Everybody is nonplussed. They call to him, he does not answer.

"Stepan, maybe you are feeling bad, eh?" the soldier with the bandaged arm asks him. "Perhaps we had better call the priest, eh?"

"Have a drink of water, Stepan . . ." says the sailor. "Here, brother, drink."

"Why are you knocking the jug against his teeth?" says Gusev angrily. "Don't you see, you cabbage-head?"

"What?"

"What?" Gusev mimics him. "There is no breath in him, he's dead! That's what! Such stupid people, Lord God!"

III

The ship has stopped rolling and Pavel Ivanych is cheerful. He is no longer cross. His face wears a boastful, challenging, mocking expression. It is as though he wants to say: "Yes, right away I'll tell you something that will make you burst with laughter." The round porthole is open and a soft breeze is blowing on Pavel Ivanych. There is a sound of voices, the splash of oars in the water . . . Just under the porthole someone is droning in a thin, disgusting voice; must be a Chinaman singing.

"Here we are in the harbor," says Pavel Ivanych with a mocking smile. "Only another month or so and we shall be in Russia. M'yes, messieurs of the armed forces! I'll arrive in Odessa and from there go straight to Kharkov. In Kharkov I have a friend, a man of letters. I'll go to him and say, 'Come, brother, put aside your vile subjects, women's amours and the beauties of Nature, and show up the two-legged vermin . . . There's a subject for you.'"

For a while he reflects, then says:

"Gusev, do you know how I tricked them?"

"Tricked who, Pavel Ivanych?"

"Why, these people . . . You understand, on this steamer there is only a first class and a third class, and they only allow peasants, that is, the common herd, to go in the third. If you have got a jacket on and even at a distance look like a gentleman or a bourgeois, you have to go first class, if you please. You must fork out five hundred rubles if it kills you. 'Why do you have such a regulation?' I ask them. 'Do you mean to raise the prestige of the Russian intelligentsia thereby?' 'Not a bit of it. We don't let you simply because a decent person can't go third class; it is too horrible and disgusting there.' 'Yes, sir? Thank you for being so solicitous about decent people's welfare. But in any case, whether it's nasty there or nice, I haven't got five hundred rubles. I didn't loot the Treasury, I didn't exploit the natives, I didn't traffic in contraband, I flogged nobody to death, so judge for yourselves if I have the right to occupy a first class cabin and even to reckon myself among the Russian intelligentsia.' But logic means nothing to them. So I had to resort to fraud. I put on a peasant coat and high boots, I pulled a face so that I looked like a common drunk, and went to the agents: 'Give us a little ticket, your Excellency,' said I—"

"You're not of the gentry, are you?" asked the sailor.

"I come of a clerical family. My father was a priest, and an honest one; he always told the high and mighty the truth to their faces and, as a result, he suffered a great deal."

Pavel Ivanych is exhausted from talking and gasps for breath, but still continues:

"Yes, I always tell people the truth to their faces. I'm not afraid of anyone or anything. In this respect, there is a great difference between me and all of you, men. You are dark people, blind, crushed; you see nothing and what you do see, you don't understand . . . You are told that the wind breaks loose from its chain, that you are beasts, savages, and you believe it; someone gives it to you in the neck—you kiss his hand; some animal in a raccoon coat robs you and then tosses you a fifteen-kopeck tip and you say: 'Let me kiss your hand, sir.' You are outcasts, pitiful wretches. I am different, my mind is clear. I see it all plainly like a hawk or an eagle when it hovers over the earth, and I understand everything. I am protest personified. I see tyranny—I protest. I see a hypocrite—I protest, I see a triumphant swine—I protest. And I cannot be put down, no Spanish Inquisition can silence me. No. Cut out my tongue and I will protest with gestures. Wall me up in a cellar—I will shout so that you will hear me half a mile away, or will starve myself to death, so that they may have another weight on their black consciences. Kill me and I will haunt them. All my acquaintances say to me: 'You are a most insufferable person, Pavel Ivanych.' I am proud of such a reputation. I served three years in the Far East and I shall be remembered there a hundred years. I had rows there with everybody. My friends wrote to me from Russia: 'Don't come back,' but here I am going back to spite them . . . Yes . . . That's life as I understand it. That's what one can call life."

Gusev is not listening; he is looking at the porthole. A junk, flooded with dazzling hot sunshine, is swaying on the transparent turquoise water. In it stand naked Chinamen, holding up cages with canaries in them and calling out: "It sings, it sings!"

Another boat knocks against it; a steam cutter glides past. Then there is another boat: a fat Chinaman sits in it, eating rice with chopsticks. The water sways lazily, white sea gulls languidly hover over it.

"Would be fine to give that fat fellow one in the neck," reflects Gusev, looking at the stout Chinaman and yawning.

He dozes off and it seems to him that all nature is dozing too. Time flies swiftly by. Imperceptibly the day passes. Imperceptibly darkness descends . . . The steamer is no longer standing still but is on the move again.

IV

Two days pass. Pavel Ivanych no longer sits up but is lying down. His eyes are closed, his nose seems to have grown sharper.

"Pavel Ivanych," Gusev calls to him. "Hey, Pavel Ivanych."

Pavel Ivanych opens his eyes and moves his lips.

"Are you feeling bad?"

"No . . . It's nothing . . ." answers Pavel Ivanych gasping for breath. "Nothing, on the contrary . . . I am better . . . You see, I can lie down now . . . I have improved . . ."

"Well, thank God for that, Pavel Ivanych."

"When I compare myself to you, I am sorry for you, poor fellows. My lungs are healthy, mine is a stomach cough . . . I can stand hell, let alone the Red Sea. Besides, I take a critical attitude toward my illness and the medicines. While you— Your minds are dark . . . It's hard on you, very, very hard!"

The ship is not rolling, it is quiet, but as hot and stifling as a Turkish bath; it is hard, not only to speak, but even to listen. Gusev hugs his knees, lays his head on them and thinks of his home. God, in this stifling heat, what a relief it is to think of snow and cold! You're driving in a sleigh; all of a sudden, the horses take fright at something and bolt. Careless of the road, the ditches, the gullies, they tear like mad things right through the village, across the pond, past the pottery, across the open fields. "Hold them!" the pottery hands and the peasants they meet shout at the top of their voices. "Hold them!" But why hold them? Let the keen cold wind beat in your face and bite your hands; let the lumps of snow, kicked up by the horses, slide down your collar, your neck, your chest; let the runners sing, and the traces and the whippletrees break, the devil take them. And what delight when the sleigh upsets and you go flying full tilt into a drift, face right in the snow, and then you get up, white all over with icicles on your mustache, no cap, no gloves, your belt undone . . . People laugh, dogs bark . . .

Pavel Ivanych half opens one eye, fixes Gusev with it and asks softly: "Gusev, did your commanding officer steal?"

"Who can tell, Pavel Ivanych? We can't say, we didn't hear about it."

And after that, a long time passes in silence. Gusev broods, his mind wanders, and he keeps drinking water: it is hard for him to talk and hard for him to listen, and he is afraid of being talked to. An hour passes, a second, a third; evening comes, then night, but he doesn't notice it; he sits up and keeps dreaming of the frost.

There is a sound as though someone were coming into the infirmary, voices are heard, but five minutes pass and all is quiet again.

"The kingdom of Heaven be his and eternal peace," says the soldier with the bandaged arm. "He was an uneasy chap."

"What?" asks Gusev. "Who?"

"He died, they have just carried him up."

"Oh, well," mutters Gusev, yawning, "the kingdom of Heaven be his."

"What do you think, Gusev?" the soldier with the bandaged arm says after a while. "Will he be in the kingdom of Heaven or not?"

"Who do you mean?"

"Pavel Ivanych."

"He will . . . He suffered so long. Then again, he belonged to the clergy and priests have a lot of relatives. Their prayers will get him there."

The soldier with the bandage sits down on Gusev's bunk and says in an undertone:

"You too, Gusev, aren't long for this world. You will never get to Russia."

"Did the doctor or the nurse say so?" asks Gusev.

"It isn't that they said so, but one can see it. It's plain when a man will die soon. You don't eat, you don't drink, you've got so thin it's dreadful to look at you. It's consumption, in a word. I say it not to worry you, but because maybe you would like to receive the sacrament and extreme unction. And if you have any money, you had better turn it over to the senior officer."

"I haven't written home," Gusev sighs. "I shall die and they won't know."

"They will," the sick sailor says in a bass voice. "When you die, they will put it down in the ship's log, in Odessa they will send a copy of the entry to the army authorities, and they will notify your district board or somebody like that."

Such a conversation makes Gusev uneasy and a vague craving begins to torment him. He takes a drink—it isn't that; he drags himself to the porthole and breathes the hot, moist air—it isn't that; he tries to think of home, of the frost—it isn't that . . . At last it seems to him that if he stays in the infirmary another minute, he will certainly choke to death.

"It's stifling, brother," he says. "I'll go on deck. Take me there, for Christ's sake."

"All right," the soldier with the bandage agrees. "You can't walk, I'll carry you. Hold on to my neck."

Gusev puts his arm around the soldier's neck, the latter places his uninjured arm round him and carries him up. On the deck, discharged soldiers and sailors are lying asleep side by side; there are so many of them it is difficult to pass.

"Get down on the floor," the soldier with the bandage says softly. "Follow me quietly, hold on to my shirt."

It is dark, there are no lights on deck or on the masts or anywhere on the sea around. On the prow the seaman on watch stands perfectly still like a statue, and it looks as though he, too, were asleep. The steamer seems to be left to its own devices and to be going where it pleases.

"Now they'll throw Pavel Ivanych into the sea," says the soldier with the bandage, "in a sack and then into the water."

"Yes, that's the regulation."

"At home, it's better to lie in the earth. Anyway, your mother will come to the grave and shed a tear."

"Sure."

There is a smell of dung and hay. With drooping heads, steers stand at the ship's rail. One, two, three—eight of them! And there's a pony. Gusev puts out his hand to stroke it, but it shakes its head, shows its teeth, and tries to bite his sleeve.

"Damn brute!" says Gusev crossly.

The two of them thread their way to the prow, then stand at the rail, peering. Overhead there is deep sky, bright stars, peace and quiet, exactly as at home in the village. But below there is darkness and disorder. Tall waves are making an uproar for no reason. Each one of them as you look at it is trying to rise higher than all the rest and to chase and crush its neighbor; it is thunderously attacked by a third wave that has a gleaming white mane and is just as ferocious and ugly.

The sea has neither sense nor pity. If the steamer had been smaller, not made of thick iron plates, the waves would have crushed it without the slightest remorse, and would have devoured all the people in it without distinguishing between saints and sinners. The steamer's expression was equally senseless and cruel. This beaked monster presses forward, cutting millions of waves in its path; it fears neither darkness nor the wind, nor space, nor solitude—it's all child's play for it, and if the ocean had its population, this monster would crush it, too, without distinguishing between saints and sinners.

"Where are we now?" asks Gusev.

"I don't know. Must be the ocean."

"You can't see land . . ."

"No chance of it! They say we'll see it only in seven days."

The two men stare silently at the white phosphorescent foam and brood. Gusev is first to break the silence.

"There is nothing frightening here," he says. "Only you feel queer as if you were in a dark forest; but if, let's say, they lowered the boat this minute and an officer ordered me to go fifty miles across the sea to catch fish, I'll go. Or, let's say, if a Christian were to fall into the water right now, I'd jump in after him. A German or a Chink I wouldn't try to save, but I'd go in after a Christian."

"And are you afraid to die?"

"I am. I am sorry about the farm. My brother at home, you know, isn't steady; he drinks, he beats his wife for no reason, he doesn't honor his father and mother. Without me everything will go to rack and ruin, and before long it's my fear that my father and old mother will be begging their bread. But my legs won't hold me up, brother, and it's stifling here. Let's go to sleep."

V

Gusev goes back to the infirmary and gets into his bunk. He is again tormented by a vague desire and he can't make out what it is that he wants. There is a weight on his chest, a throbbing in his head, his mouth is so dry that it is difficult for him to move his tongue. He dozes and talks in his sleep and, worn out with nightmares, with coughing and the stifling heat, towards morning he falls into a heavy sleep. He dreams that they have just taken the bread out of the oven in the barracks and that he has climbed into the oven and is having a steam bath there, lashing himself with a besom of birch twigs. He sleeps for two days and on the third at noon two sailors come down and carry him out of the infirmary. He is sewn up in sailcloth and to make him heavier, they put two gridirons in with him. Sewn up in sailcloth, he looks like a carrot or a radish: broad at the head and narrow at the feet. Before sunset, they carry him on deck and put him on a plank. One end of the plank lies on the ship's rail, the other on a box placed on a stool. Round him stand the discharged soldiers and the crew with heads bared.

"Blessed is our God," the priest begins, "now, and ever, and unto ages of ages."

"Amen," three sailors chant.

The discharged men and the crew cross themselves and look off at the waves. It is strange that a man should be sewn up in sailcloth and should soon be flying into the sea. Is it possible that such a thing can happen to anyone?

The priest strews earth upon Gusev and makes obeisance to him. The men sing "Memory Eternal."

The seaman on watch duty raises the end of the plank, Gusev slides off it slowly and then flying, head foremost, turns over in the air and—plop! Foam covers him, and for a moment, he seems to be wrapped in lace, but the instant passes and he disappears in the waves.

He plunges rapidly downward. Will he reach the bottom? At this spot the ocean is said to be three miles deep. After sinking sixty or seventy feet, he begins to descend more and more slowly, swaying rhythmically as though in hesitation, and, carried along by the current, moves faster laterally than vertically.

And now he runs into a school of fish called pilot fish. Seeing the dark body, the little fish stop as though petrified and suddenly all turn round together and disappear. In less than a minute they rush back at Gusev, swift as arrows and begin zigzagging round him in the water. Then another dark body appears. It is a shark. With dignity and reluctance, seeming not to notice Gusev, as it were, it swims under him; then while he, moving downward, sinks upon its back, the shark turns, belly upward, basks in the warm transparent water and languidly opens its jaws with two rows of teeth. The pilot fish are in ecstasy; they stop to see what will happen next. After playing a little with the body, the shark nonchalantly puts his jaws under it, cautiously touches it with his teeth and the sailcloth is ripped the full length of the body, from head to foot; one of the gridirons falls out, frightens the pilot fish and striking the shark on the flank, sinks rapidly to the bottom.

Meanwhile, up above, in that part of the sky where the sun is about to set, clouds are massing, one resembling a triumphal arch, another a lion, a third a pair of scissors. A broad shaft of green light issues from the clouds and reaches to the middle of the sky; a while later, a violet beam appears alongside of it and then a golden one and a pink one . . . The heavens turn a soft lilac tint. Looking at this magnificent enchanting sky, the ocean frowns at first, but soon it, too, takes on tender, joyous, passionate colors for which it is hard to find a name in the language of man.

LOVE

William Faulkner

from THE HAMLET

As winter became spring and the spring itself advanced, he had less and less of darkness to flee through and from. Soon it was dark only when he left the barn, backed carefully, with one down-groping foot, from the harness-room where his quilt-and-straw bed was, and turned his back on the long rambling loom of the house where last night's new drummer-faces snored on the pillows of the beds which he had now learned to make as well as Mrs Littlejohn could; by April it was the actual thin depthless suspension of false dawn itself, in which he could already see and know himself to be an entity solid and cohered in visibility instead of the uncohered all-sentience of fluid and nerve-springing terror alone and terribly free in the primal sightless inimicality. That was gone now. Now the terror existed only during that moment after the false dawn, that interval's second between it and the moment which birds and animals know: when the night at last succumbs to day; and then he would begin to hurry, trot, not to get there quicker but because he must get back soon, without fear and calmly now in the growing visibility, the gradation from gray through primrose to the morning's ultimate gold, to the brow of the final hill, to let himself downward into the creekside mist and lie in the drenched myriad waking life of grasses and listen for her approach.

Then he would hear her, coming down the creekside in the mist. It would not be after one hour, two hours, three; the dawn would be empty, the moment and she would not be, then he would hear her and he would lie drenched in the wet grass, serene and one and indivisible in joy, listening to her approach. He would smell her; the whole mist reeked with her; the same malleate hands of mist which drew along his prone drenched flanks palped her pearled barrel too and shaped them both somewhere in immediate time, already married. He would not move. He would lie amid the waking instant of earth's teeming minute life, the motionless fronds of water-heavy grasses stooping into the mist before his face in black, fixed curves, along each parabola of which the marching drops held in minute magnification the dawn's rosy miniatures, smelling and even tasting the rich, slow, warm barn-reek milk-reek, the flowing immemorial female, hearing the slow planting and the plopping suck of each deliberate cloven mud-spreading hoof, invisible still in the mist loud with its hymeneal choristers.

Then he would see her; the bright thin horns of morning, of sun, would blow the mist away and reveal her, planted, blond, dew-pearled, standing in the parted water of the ford, blowing into the water the thick, warm, heavy, milk-laden breath; and lying in the drenched grasses, his eyes now blind with sun, he would wallow faintly from thigh to thigh, making a faint, thick, hoarse moaning sound. Because he cannot make one with her through the day's morning and noon and evening. It is not that he must return to work. There is no work, no travail, no muscular and spiritual reluctance to overcome, constantly war against; yesterday was not, tomorrow is not, today is merely a placid and virginal astonishment at the creeping ridge of dust and trash in front of the broom, at sheets coming smooth and taut at certain remembered motions of the hands—a routine grooved, irkless; a firm gentle compelling hand, a voice to hold and control him through joy out of kindness as a dog is taught and held.

It is because he can go no further. He tried it. It was the third time he lay and waited for her; the mist blew away and he saw her and this time there was no today even—no beds to return to, no hand, no voice: he repudiated fidelity and even habit. He rose and approached her, speaking to her, his hand extended. She raised her head and looked at him and scrambled up the further bank, out of the water. He followed, stepping gingerly down into the water, and began to cross, lifting his feet high at each step, moaning a little, urgent and concerned yet not to alarm her more. He fell once, at full length into the water, making no effort to catch himself, vanishing completely with one loud cry and rising again, streaming, his breath already indrawn to cry again. But he stopped the cry, speaking to her instead, and climbed out onto the bank and approached her again, his hand extended. This time she ran, rushed on a short distance and turned, her head lowered; she whirled and rushed away again before his hand touched her, he following, speaking to her, urgent and cajoling. Finally she broke back past him and went back to the ford. She ran faster than he could; trotting, moaning, he watched the vain stippling of leaf-shadows as they fled across the intact and escaping shape of love as she recrossed the creek and galloped on up the path for a short way, where once more she stopped to graze.

He ceased to moan. He hurried back to the creek and began to cross it, lifting his feet high out of the water at each step as if he expected each time to find solidity there, or perhaps at each step did not know whether he would or not. This time he did not fall. But as soon as he climbed the bank, she moved again, on up the path, not galloping now but purposefully, so that he once more had to run, once more steadily losing ground, moaning again now with that urgent and now alarmed and bewildered amazement. She was now retracing the path by which she had appeared that morning and all the other mornings. Probably he did not even know it, was paying no attention at all to where he was going, seeing nothing but the cow; perhaps he did not even realise they were in the lot, even when she went on across it and entered the milking shed which she had left less than an hour ago, though he probably knew generally where she would come from each morning, since he knew most of the adjacent countryside and was never disoriented; objects became fluid in darkness but they did not alter in place and juxtaposition. Perhaps he did not even comprehend that she was in her stable, but only that she had stopped at last, ceased to flee at last, because at once he stopped the alarmed and urgent moaning and followed her into the shed, speaking to her again, murmurous, drooling, and touched her with his hand. She whirled; possibly he saw, not that she could not, but only that she did not flee. He touched her again, his hand, his voice, thin and hungry with promise. Then he was lying on his back, her heels were still thudding against the plank wall beside his head and then the dog was standing over him and an instant later the man was hauling him savagely to his feet by the slack of his shirt. Then he was outside the shed while Houston still clutched him by the shirt and cursed in what he could not know was not rage but angry exasperation. The dog stood a few feet away, watching.

"Ike H-mope," he said. "Ike H-mope."

"Ike hell," Houston said, cursing, shaking him. "Go on!" he said. "Git!" He spoke to the dog. "Take him out of here. Easy now." Now the dog shouted at him. It did not move yet, it merely shouted once; it was as if it said "Boo!" and, still moaning, trying now to talk to the man with his blasted eyes, he moved on toward the still-open gate which he had just entered. Now the dog moved too, just behind him. He looked back at the shed, the cow; he tried again to speak to the man with his eyes, moaning, drooling, when the dog shouted at him again, once, taking one pace toward him but no more, whereupon he gave the dog one terrified glance and broke, trotting toward the gate. The dog shouted again, three times in rapid succession, and he cried now, hoarse and abject, running now, the thick reluctant hips working with a sort of abject and hopeless unco-ordination. "Easy, now!" Houston shouted. He did not hear. He heard only the feet of the dog just behind him. He ran heavily, bellowing.

So now he can go no further. He can lie in the grass and wait for her and hear her and then see her when the mist parts, and that is all. So he would rise from the grass and stand, still swaying faintly from side to side and making the faint, hoarse sound. Then he would turn and mount the hill, stumbling a little because his eyes were still full of sun yet. But his bare feet would know the dust of the road, and in it again, he would begin to trot again, hurrying, still moaning, his shadow shortening on the dust ahead and the mounting sun warm on his back and already drying the dust on his damp overalls; and so back to the house, the littered rooms and the unmade beds. Soon he would be sweeping again, stopping only occasionally to make the hoarse sound of bafflement and incredulous grieving, then watching again with peaceful and absorbed astonishment the creeping ridge of dust and trash before the moving broom. Because even while sweeping he would still see her, blond among the purpling shadows of the pasture, not fixed amid the suppurant tender green but integer of spring's concentrated climax, by it crowned, garlanded.

He was upstairs sweeping when he saw the smoke. He knew exactly where it was—the hill, the sedge-and-brier overgrown hill beyond the creek. Although it was three miles away, he can even see her backing away before the flames and hear her bellowing. He began to run where he stood, carrying the broom. He ran blundering at the wall, the high small window through which he had seen the smoke, which he could not have passed through even if he could have taken the eighteen-foot drop to the earth, as a moth or a trapped bird might. Then the corridor door was facing him and without pausing he ran to it and through it, still carrying the broom, and on down the corridor toward the stairs, when Mrs Littlejohn emerged from a second bedroom and stopped him. "You, Isaac," she said. "You, Isaac." She did not raise her voice and she did not touch him, yet he stopped, moaning, the empty eyes striving at her, picking his feet up in turn like a cat standing on something hot. Then she put her hand out and took him by the shoulder and turned him and he went obediently back up the corridor and into the room again, moaning; he even made a stroke or two with the broom before he saw the smoke again through the window. This time he found the corridor door almost at once, though he did not approach it. Instead he stood for a moment, looking at the broom in his hands, whimpering, then at the bed, smooth and neat where he had just made it up, and he stopped whimpering and went to the bed and turned the covers back and put the broom into it, the straw end on the pillow like a face, and drew the covers up smooth again, tucking them about the broom with that paradoxical uncoordinated skill and haste, and left the room.

He made no sound now. He did not move on tiptoe, yet he went down the corridor with astonishing silence and celerity; he had reached the stairs and begun to descend before Mrs Littlejohn could have emerged from the other room. At first, three years ago, he would not try to descend them. He had ascended them alone; nobody ever knew if he had walked or crawled up, or if perhaps he had mounted them without realising he was doing so, altering his position in altitude, depth perception not functioning in reverse. Mrs Littlejohn had gone to the store. Someone passing the house heard him and when she returned there were five or six people in the hall, looking up at where he clung to the rail at the top step, his eyes shut, bellowing. He still clung to the rail, bellowing and tugging back, when she tried to break his grip and draw him downward. He stayed upstairs three days while she carried food to him and people would come in from miles away and say, "Aint you got him down yet?" before she finally coaxed him to attempt to descend. And even then it took several minutes, while faces gathered in the lower hall to watch as the firm, gentle, unremitting hand, the cold, grim, patient voice, drew him, clinging to the rail and bellowing, step by step downward. For a while after that he would fall down them each time he tried to descend. He would know he was going to fall; he would step blindly and already moaning onto nothing and plunge, topple, sprawling and bumping, terrified not by pain but by amazement, to lie at last on the floor of the lower hall, bellowing, his blasted eyes staring aghast and incredulous at nothing.

But at last he learned to negotiate them. Now he merely slowed a little before stepping, not confidently quite but not with alarm, off onto that which at each successive step, was not quite space; was almost nothing but at each advancing instant, not quite was, and hurried on through the lower hall and into the back yard, where he paused again and began to sway from side to side and moan, his empty face now filled with baffled bewilderment. Because he could not see the smoke from here and now all he remembers is the empty dawn-hill from which he will let himself downward into the creekside mist to wait for her, and it is wrong now. Because he stands in sun, visible—himself, earth, trees, house—already cohered and fixed in visibility; no darkness to flee through and from, and this is wrong. So he stood, baffled, moaning and swaying for a time, then he moved again, across the yard to the lot gate. He had learned to open it too. He turned the catch and the gate vanished from between its two posts; he passed through and after a moment he found the gate where it had swung to against the fence and closed it and turned the latch and went on across the sun-glared lot, moaning, and entered the hallway of the stable.

Because of his sun-contracted pupils, he could not see at once. But then, it always was dark when he entered the stable on his way to bed, so at once he ceased to moan and went straight to the door to the harness-room, moving now with actual assurance, and grasped the door-jamb with both hands and raised his foot to the step, and, his down-groping foot already on the ground, he backed out of darkness and into visibility, turning, visibility roaring soundless down about him, establishing him intact and cohered in it and already trotting, running, toward the crest where he will let himself downward into the creekside mist to lie and wait for her, on across the lot and through the spread place in the wire fence. His overalls snagged on the wire but he ripped free, making no sound now, and into the road, running, his thick female thighs working, his face, his eyes, urgent and alarmed.

When he reached the hill three miles away, he was still trotting; when he turned from the road and mounted to the crest of the hill and saw the smoke beyond the creek, he made the hoarse, aghast sound again and ran on down the hill and through the now-dry grass in which at dawn he had lain, and to the creek, the ford. He did not hesitate. He ran full-tilt off the bank and onto the rimpled water, continuing to run even after he began to fall, plunging face-down into the water, completely submerged, and rose, streaming, knee-deep, bellowing. He lifted one foot above the surface and stepped forward as though onto a raised floor and took another step running before he fell. This time his outflung hands touched the further bank and this time when he rose he actually heard the cow's voice, faint and terrified, from beyond the smokepall on the other hill. He raised one foot above the surface and ran again. When he fell this time he lay on dry land. He scrambled up and ran in his sodden overalls, across the pasture and on up the other hill, on whose crest the smokepall lay without wind, grading from blue to delicate mauve and lilac and then copper beneath the meridional sun.

A mile back he had left the rich, broad, flat river-bottom country and entered the hills—a region which topographically was the final blue and dying echo of the Appalachian Mountains. Chicasaw Indians had owned it, but after the Indians it had been cleared where possible for cultivation, and after the Civil War, forgotten save by small peripatetic sawmills which had vanished too now, their sites marked only by the mounds of rotting sawdust which were not only their gravestones but the monuments of a people's heedless greed. Now it was a region of scrubby second-growth pine and oak among which dogwood bloomed until it too was cut to make cotton spindles, and old fields where not even a trace of furrow showed any more, gutted and gullied by forty years of rain and frost and heat into plateaus choked with rank sedge and briers loved of rabbits and quail coveys, and crumbling ravines striated red and white with alternate sand and clay. It was toward one of these plateaus that he now ran, running in ashes without knowing it since the earth here had had time to cool, running among the blackened stubble of last year's sedge dotted with small islands of this year's incombustible green and the blasted heads of tiny blue-and-white daisies, and so onto the crest of the hill, the plateau.

The smoke lay like a wall before him; beyond it he could hear the steady terrified bellowing of the cow. He ran into the smoke and toward the voice. The earth was now hot to his feet. He began to snatch them quickly up; he cried once himself, hoarse and amazed, whereupon, as though in answer, the smoke, the circumambience itself, screamed back at him. The sound was everywhere, above and beneath, funnelling downward at him; he heard the hooves and as he paused, his breath indrawn, the horse appeared, materialised furiously out of the smoke, monstrous and distorted, wild-eyed and with tossing mane, bearing down upon him. He screamed too. For an instant they yelled face to face, the wild eyes, the yellow teeth, the long gullet red with ravening gleeful triumph, stooping at him and then on as the horse swerved without breaking, the wind, the fierce dragon-reek of its passage, blasting at his hair and garments; it was gone. He ran again toward the cow's voice. When he heard the horse behind him again he did not even look back. He did not even scream again. He just ran, running, as again the earth, the smoke, filled and became thunderous with the hard, rapid hoofbeats and again the intolerable voice screamed down at him and he flung both arms about his head and fell sprawling as the wind, the dragon-reek, blasted at him again as the maddened horse soared over his prone body and vanished once more.

He scrambled up and ran. The cow was quite near now and he saw the fire—a tender, rosy, creeping thread low in the smoke between him and the location of the cow's voice. Each time his feet touched the earth now he gave a short shriek like an ejaculation, trying to snatch his foot back before it could have taken his weight, then turning immediately in aghast amazement to the other foot which he had for the moment forgotten, so that presently he was not progressing at all but merely moving in one spot, like a dance, when he heard the horse coming at him again. He screamed. His voice and that of the horse became one voice, wild, furious and without hope, and he ran into and through the fire and burst into air, sun, visibility again, shedding flames which sucked away behind him like a tattered garment. The cow stood at the edge of a ravine about ten feet away, facing the fire, her head lowered, bellowing. He had just time to reach her and turn, his body intervened and his arms about his head, as the frantic horse burst out of the smoke and bore down upon them.

It did not even swerve. It took off almost without gathering, at full stride. The teeth, the wild eyes, the long red gullet, stooped at him, framed out of a swirled rigidity of forelock and mane, the entire animal floating overhead in monstrous deliberation. The air was filled with furious wings and the four crescent-glints of shod hooves as, still screaming, the horse vanished beyond the ravine's lip, sucking first the cow and then himself after it as though by the violent vacuum of its passing. Earth became perpendicular and fled upward—the yawn of void without even the meretricious reassurance of graduated steps. He made no sound as the three of them plunged down the crumbling sheer, at the bottom of which the horse rolled to its feet without stopping and galloped on down the ditch and where he, lying beneath the struggling and bellowing cow, received the violent relaxing of her fear-constricted bowels. Overhead, in the down draft of the ravine, the last ragged flame tongued over the lip, tip-curled, and vanished, swirled off into the windless stain of pale smoke on the sunny sky.

At first he couldn't do anything with her at all. She scrambled to her feet, facing him, her head lowered, bellowing. When he moved toward her, she whirled and ran at the crumbling sheer of the slope, scrambling furiously at the vain and shifting sand as though in a blind paroxysm of shame, to escape not him alone but the very scene of the outragement of privacy where she had been sprung suddenly upon and without warning from the dark and betrayed and outraged by her own treacherous biological inheritance, he following again, speaking to her, trying to tell her how this violent violation of her maiden's delicacy is no shame, since such is the very iron imperishable warp of the fabric of love. But she would not hear. She continued to scrabble at the shifting rise, until at last he set his shoulder to her hams and heaved forward. Striving together, they mounted for a yard or so up the slope, the sand shifting and fleeing beneath their feet, before momentum and strength were spent and, locked together and motionless, they descended once more to the floor of the ditch, planted and fixed ankle-deep in a moving block of sand like two effigies on a float. Again, his shoulder to her hams, they rushed at the precipice and up it for a yard or more before the treacherous footing completely failed. He spoke to her, exhortative: they made a supreme effort. But again the earth fled upward; footing, sand and all plucked violently from beneath them and rushed upward into the pale sky still faintly stained with smoke, and once more they lay inextricable and struggling on the floor of the ravine, he once more underneath, until, bellowing and never ceasing her mad threshing, the cow scrambled up and galloped on down the ditch as the horse had done, vanishing before he could get to his feet to follow.

The ravine debouched onto the creek. Almost at once he was in the pasture again, though possibly he did not realise it, seeing only the cow as she galloped on ahead. Possibly at the moment he did not even recognise the ford at once, even when the cow, slowing, walked down into the water and stopped and drank and he ran up, slowing too, moaning, urgent but not loud, not to send her once more into flight. So he approaches the bank, stilling his voice now, picking his feet up and putting them down again in one spot, his singed and scorched face urgent and tense. But she does not move, and at last he steps down into the water, onto the water, forgetting again that it will give under his weight, crying once again not so much in surprise as in alarm lest he alarm her, and steps again forward onto the receptive solid, and touches her. She does not even stop drinking; his hand has lain on her flank for a second or two before she lifts her dripping muzzle and looks back at him, once more maiden meditant, shame-free.

Houston found them there. He came across the pasture on the horse, bareback, galloping, the hound following, and saw the thick squatting shape in the water behind the cow, clumsily washing her legs with a broken willow branch. "Is she all right?" he shouted, speaking to the horse to slow it since he did not even have a hackamore: "Whoa. Whoa. Ho now. Ho now, damn you.—Why in hell didn't you try to catch the horse?" he shouted. "He might have broke—" Then the other, squatting in the water, turned his scorched face and Houston recognised him. He began to curse, checking the horse with his hand in its mane, already flinging his leg over and sliding down before the horse stopped, cursing with that fretted exasperation which was not anger, rage. He came to the creek, the hound following, and stooped and caught up a dried limb left from last winter's flood water and slashed the cow savagely with it and flung the broken end after her as she sprang forward and scrambled up the further bank. "Git!" Houston shouted. "Git on home, you damn whore!" The cow galloped on a few steps, then stopped and began to graze. "Take her home," Houston said to the dog. Without moving, only raising its head, the hound bayed once. The cow jerked her head up and trotted again, and he in the creek made again his faint hoarse sound, rising too as the hound rose. But the dog did not even cross the creek, it did not even hurry; it merely followed the bank until it came opposite the cow and bayed again, once, contemptuous and peremptory. This time the cow went off at a gallop, back up the creek toward the lot, the hound following on its side of the creek. They went out of sight so. Twice more at intervals the hound bayed, one time, as though it merely shouted "Boo!" each time the cow prepared to stop.

He stood in the water, moaning. Now he actually bellowed himself, not loud, just amazed. When Houston and the dog came up he had looked around, at first at the dog. His mouth had opened to cry then, but instead there had come into his face an expression almost intelligent in its foolish fatuity, which, when Houston began to curse, faded and became one of incredulity, amazement, and which was still incredulous and bereft as he stood in the water, moaning, while Houston on the bank looked at the stained foul front of his overalls, cursing with that baffled exasperation, saying, "Jesus Christ. Jesus Christ.—Come here," he said. "Get out of there"; gesturing his arm savagely. But the other did not move, moaning, looking away up the creek where the cow had gone, until Houston came to the edge and leaned and caught him by the strap of his overalls and drew him roughly out of the water and, his nose wrinkled fiercely and still cursing, unfastened the straps and snatched the overalls down about his hips. "Step out!" Houston said. But he did not move until Houston jerked him, stumbling, out of the overalls, to stand in his shirt and nothing else, moaning faintly, though when Houston picked up the overalls gingerly by the strap and flung them into the creek, he cried again, once, hoarse, abject, not loud. "Go on," Houston said. "Wash them." He made violent washing motions in pantomime. But the other only looked at Houston, moaning, until Houston found another stick and twisted it into the overalls and soused and walloped them violently in the water, cursing steadily, and drew them out, still using the stick, scrubbed them front-down on the grass. "There," he said. "Now git! Home! Home!" he shouted. "Stay there! Let her alone!" He had stopped moaning to watch Houston. Now he began to moan again, drooling, while Houston glared at him in baffled and raging exasperation. Then Houston took a handful of coins from his pocket and chose a fifty-cent piece and came and put it into his shirt pocket and buttoned the flap and went back to the horse, speaking to it until he touched it, grasped it by the mane, and vaulted onto its back. He had stopped moaning now, he just watched as, again without seeming to gather itself, just as when it had soared above him and the cow on the edge of the ravine an hour ago, the horse made two short circles under Houston's hand and then took the creek cleanly, already galloping, and was gone.

Then he began to moan again. He stood for a while, moaning, looking down at the shirt pocket which Houston had buttoned, fumbling at it. Then he looked at his soaked and wadded overalls on the ground beside him. After a while he stooped and picked them up. One leg was turned wrong-side-outward. He tried patiently for a while to put them on so, moaning. Then presently they came straight again and he got into them and fastened the straps and went to the creek and crossed, moving gingerly, raising his foot at each step as if he were mounting onto a raised floor, and climbed out and went back to the place where he had lain at each dawn for three months now, waiting for her. It was the same spot; he would return as exactly to it each time as a piston to its cylinder-head, and he stood there for a time, fumbling at the buttoned pocket, moaning. Then he went on up the hill; his feet knew the dust of the road again though perhaps he himself was unaware of it, possibly it was pure instinct functioning in the desolation of bereavement which carried him back toward the house which he had left that morning, because twice more in the first mile he stopped and fumbled at the buttoned pocket. Apparently he was not trying to unbutton the pocket without being able to do it, because presently he had the coin in his hand, looking at it, moaning. He was standing then on a plank bridge over a narrow, shallow, weed-choked ditch. He made no false motion with the hand which held the coin, he had made no motion of any kind, he was standing perfectly still at the moment, yet suddenly his palm was empty. The coin rang dully once on the dusty planks and perhaps glinted once, then vanished, though who to know what motion, infinitesimal and convulsive, of supreme repudiation there might have been, its impulse gone, vanished with the movement, because he even ceased to moan as he stood looking at his empty palm with quiet amazement, turning the hand over to look at the back, even raising and opening the other hand to look into it. Then—it was an effort almost physical, like childbirth—he connected two ideas, he progressed backward into time and recaptured an image by logical retrogression and fumbled into the shirt pocket again, peering into it, though only for a moment, as if he actually did not expect to find the coin there, though it was doubtless pure instinct which caused him to look down at the dusty planks on which he stood. And he was not moaning. He made no sound at all. He just stood there, looking at the planks, lifting his feet in turn; when he stepped off the bridge and into the ditch, he fell. You could not have told if he did step off intentionally or if he fell off, though it was doubtless a continuation of the instinct, the inherited constant awareness of gravity, which caused him to look under the bridge for the coin—if he were looking for it as he squatted in the weeds, bobbing his head faintly yet still making no sound. From then on he made no sound at all. He squatted for a time, pulling at the weeds, and now even the paradoxical dexterity was missing from his movements, even the dexterity which caused his hands to function at other times as though in spite of him; watching him you would have said he did not want to find the coin. And then you would have said, known, that he did not intend to find it; when after a time a wagon came up the road and crossed the bridge and the driver spoke to him, when he raised his face it was not even empty, it was unfathomable and profoundly quiet; when the man spoke his name, he did not even reply with the one sound which he knew, or at least was ever known to make, and that infallibly when anyone spoke to him.

He did not move until the wagon was out of sight, though he was not watching it. Then he rose and climbed back into the road. He was already trotting, back in the direction from which he had just come, treading his own tracks into the hot dust of the road beneath the May noon, back to where he would leave the road to mount the hill, and crossed the hill again and trotted down the slope to the creek. He passed the place where he would lie in the wet grass each dawn without even looking at it and turned on up the creek, trotting. It was then about two oclock Saturday afternoon. He could not have known that at that hour and day Houston, a childless widower who lived alone with the hound and a Negro man to cook for them both, would already be sitting on the gallery of Varner's store three miles away; he could not have thought that maybe Houston would not be at home. Certainly he did not pause to find out. He entered the lot, trotting, he went straight to the closed door of the shed. There was a halter hanging from a nail beside it. Perhaps he merely put his hand on the halter by chance in fumbling at the latch. But he put it on the cow properly, as he had seen it done.

At six oclock that afternoon they were five miles away. He did not know it was that distance. It did not matter; there is no distance in either space or geography, no prolongation of time for distance to exist in, no muscular fatigue to establish its accomplishment. They are moving not toward a destination in space but a destination in time, toward the pinnacle-keep of evening where morning and afternoon become one; the sleight hand of May shapes them both, not in the immediate, the soon, but in the now as, facing her, braced against the pull of the rope, he speaks to her implacable and compelling while she tugs back, shaking her head against the rope and bellowing. She had been doing this for the last half hour, drawn backward and barnward by the discomfort of her bag. But he held her, slacking the rope gradually until his other hand touched her, first her head then her neck, speaking to her until the resistance went out of her and she moved on again. They were in the hills now, among pines. Although the afternoon wind had fallen, the shaggy crests still made a constant murmuring sound in the high serene air. The trunks and the massy foliage were the harps and strings of afternoon; the barred inconstant shadow of the day's retrograde flowed steadily over them as they crossed the ridge and descended into shadow, into the azure bowl of evening, the windless well of night; the portcullis of sunset fell behind them. At first she would not let him touch her bag at all. Even then she kicked him once, but only because the hands were strange and clumsy. Then the milk came down, warm among his fingers and on his hands and wrists, making a thin sharp hissing on the earth.

There was a moon at that time. It waned nightly westward; juxtaposed to it, each dawn the morning star burned in fierce white period to the night, and he would smell the waking's instant as she would rise, hindquarters first, backing upward out of invisibility, attenuating then disseminating out of the nest-form of sleep, the smell of milk. Then he would rise too and tie the rope-end to a swinging branch and seek and find the basket by the smell of the feed which it contained last night, and depart. From the edge of the woods he would look back. She would be still invisible, but he could hear her; it is as though he can see her—the warm breath visible among the tearing roots of grass, the warm reek of the urgent milk a cohered shape amid the fluid and abstract earth.

The barn is less than a half-mile away. Soon it looms, forthright and square upon the scroll and cryptogram of heaven. The dog meets him at the fence, not barking, furrowing invisibly somewhere between sight and sound, moving completely in neither. On the first morning it rushed at him, yapping furiously. He stopped then. Perhaps he remembered that other dog five miles away, but only for a moment, since such is succeeding's success, such is that about victory which out-odors the betraying stink of all past defeats: so that now it comes up to him already fawning, invisible and fluid about his walking legs, its warm wet limber tongue shaping for him out of invisibility his own swinging hand.

In the ammoniac density of the barn, filled with the waking dawn-sounds of horses and cattle, he cannot even sense space. But he does not hesitate. He finds the crib door and enters; his sightless hand which knows and remembers finds the feed-box. He sets the basket down and begins to fill it, working steadily and fast, spilling half of what his cupped hands raise, as on the two preceding mornings establishing between feed-box and basket the agent of his own betrayal. When he rises and faces the door, he can see it now, gray, lighter in tone yet paradoxically no more luminous, as if a rectangle of opaque glass had been set into nothing's self while his back was turned, to further confound obscurity. And now he becomes aware of the birds. The cattle-sounds are louder now, constant; he can actually see the dog waiting in the stable door and he knows that he should hurry, since he knows that soon someone will come to feed and milk. So he leaves the crib, pausing for a moment in the door before descending as though he were listening, breathing in the reek, the odor of cows and mares as the successful lover does that of a room full of women, his the victor's drowsing rapport with all anonymous faceless female flesh capable of love walking the female earth.

He and the dog recross the lot together in the negative dawn-wash cacophonous and loud with birds. He can see the fence now, where the dog leaves him. He climbs through the fence, hurrying now, carrying the basket awkwardly before him in both arms, leaving in the wet grass a dark fixed wake. Now he watches the recurrence of that which he discovered for the first time three days ago: that dawn, light, is not decanted onto earth from the sky, but instead is from the earth itself suspired. Roofed by the woven canopy of blind annealing grass-roots and the roots of trees, dark in the blind dark of time's silt and rich refuse—the constant and unslumbering anonymous worm-glut and the inextricable known bones—Troy's Helen and the nymphs and the snoring mitred bishops, the saviors and the victims and the kings—it wakes, up-seeping, attritive in uncountable creeping channels: first, root; then frond by frond, from whose escaping tips like gas it rises and disseminates and stains the sleep-fast earth with drowsy insect-murmur; then, still upward-seeking, creeps the knitted bark of trunk and limb where, suddenly louder leaf by leaf and dispersive in diffusive sudden speed, melodious with the winged and jeweled throats, it upward bursts and fills night's globed negation with jonquil thunder. Far below, the gauzy hemisphere treads with herald-cock, and sty and pen and byre salute the day. Vanes on steeples groove the southwest wind, and fields for plowing, since sunset married to the bedded and unhorsed plow, spring into half-furrowed sight like the slumbering half-satiate sea. Then the sun itself: within the half-mile it overtakes him. The silent copper roar fires the drenched grass and flings long before him his shadow prone for the vain eluded treading; the earth mirrors his antic and constant frustration which soars up the last hill and, motionless in the void, hovers until he himself crests over, whereupon it drops an invisible bridge across the ultimate ebb of night and, still preceding him, leaps visible once more across the swale and touches the copse itself, shortening into the nearing leafy wall, head: shoulders: hips: and then the trotting legs, until at last it stands upright upon the mazy whimple of the windy leaves for one intact inconstant instant before he runs into and through it.

She stands as he left her, tethered, chewing. Within the mild enormous moist and pupilless globes he sees himself in twin miniature mirrored by the inscrutable abstraction; one with that which Juno might have looked out with, he watches himself contemplating what those who looked at Juno saw. He sets the basket before her. She begins to eat. The shifting shimmer of incessant leaves gives to her a quality of illusion as insubstantial as the prone negative of his late hurrying, but this too is not so: one blond touch stipulates and affirms both weight and mass out of the flowing shadow-maze; a hand's breadth of contact shapes her solid and whole out of the infinity of hope. He squats beside her and begins to draw the teats.

They eat from the basket together. He has eaten feed before—hulls and meal, and oats and raw corn and silage and pig-swill, never much at one time but more or less constantly while he is awake as birds do, eating not even very much of the filled plate which Mrs Littlejohn would set for him, leaving it less than half-emptied, then an hour later eating something else, anything else, things which the weary long record of shibboleth and superstition had taught his upright kind to call filth, neither liking nor disliking the taste of any thing save that of certain kinds of soil and the lime in old plaster and the dissolved ink in chewed newspapers and the formic acid of stinging ants, making but one discrimination: he is herbivorous, even the life he eats is the life of plants. Then he removed the basket. It was not empty. It contained yet almost to the measured ounce exactly half of the original feed, but he takes it away from her, drags it from beneath the swinging muzzle which continues to chew out of the center of surprise, and hangs it over a limb, who is learning fast now, who has learned success and then precaution and secrecy and how to steal and even providence; who has only lust and greed and bloodthirst and a moral conscience to keep him awake at night, yet to acquire.

They go first to the spring. He found it on the first day—a brown creep of moisture in a clump of alder and beech, sunless, which wandered away without motion among the unsunned roots of other alders and willows. He cleaned it out and scooped a basin for it, which now at each return of light stood full and clear and leaf by leaf repeating until they lean and interrupt the green reflections and with their own drinking faces break each's mirroring, each face to its own shattered image wedded and annealed. Then he rises and takes up the rope, and they go on across the swale, toward the woods, and enter them.

Dawn is now over. It is now bald and forthright day. The sun is well up the sky. The air is still loud with birds, but the cries are no longer the mystery's choral strophe and antistrophe rising vertical among the leafed altars, but are earth-parallel, streaking the lateral air in prosaic busy accompaniment to the prosaic business of feeding. They dart in ceaseless arrowings, tinted and electric, among the pines whose shaggy crests murmur dry and incessant in the high day wind. Now he slacks the rope; from now until evening they will advance only as the day itself advances, no faster. They have the same destination: sunset. They pursue it as the sun itself does and within the compass of one single immutable horizon. They pace the ardent and unheeding sun, themselves unheeding and without ardor among the shadows of the soaring trunks which are the sun-geared ratchet-spokes which wheel the axled earth, powerful and without haste, up out of the caverns of darkness, through dawn and morning and midmorning, and on toward and at last into the slowing neap of noon, the flood, the slack of peak and crown of light garlanding all within one single coronet the fallen and unregenerate seraphim. The sun is a yellow column, perpendicular. He bears it on his back as, stooping with that thick, reluctant uncoordination of thigh and knee, he gathers first the armful of lush grass, then the flowers. They are the bright blatant wild daisies of flamboyant summer's spendthrift beginning. At times his awkward and disobedient hand, instead of breaking the stem, merely shuts about the escaping stalk and strips the flower-head into a scatter of ravished petals. But before he reaches the windless noon-bound shade in which she stands, he has enough of them. He has more than enough; if he had only gathered two of them, there would have been too many: he lays the plucked grass before her, then out of the clumsy fumbling of the hands there emerges, already in dissolution, the abortive diadem. In the act of garlanding, it disintegrates, rains down the slant of brow and chewing head; fodder and flowers become one inexhaustible rumination. From the sidling rhythm of the jaws depends one final blossom.

That afternoon it rained. It came without warning and it did not last long. He watched it for some time and without alarm, wanton and random and indecisive before it finally developed, concentrated, drooping in narrow unperpendicular bands in two or three different places at one time, about the horizon, like gauzy umbilical loops from the bellied cumulae, the sun-belled ewes of summer grazing up the wind from the southwest. It was as if the rain were actually seeking the two of them, hunting them out where they stood amid the shade, finding them finally in a bright intransigent fury. The pine-snoring wind dropped, then gathered; in an anticlimax of complete vacuum the shaggy pelt of earth became overblown like that of a receptive mare for the rampant crash, the furious brief fecundation which, still rampant, seeded itself in flash and glare of noise and fury and then was gone, vanished; then the actual rain, from a sky already breaking as if of its own rich over-fertile weight, running in a wild lateral turmoil among the unrecovered leaves, not in drops but in needles of fiery ice which seemed to be not trying to fall but, immune to gravity, earthless, were merely trying to keep pace with the windy uproad which had begotten and foaled them, striking in thin brittle strokes through his hair and shirt and against his lifted face, each brief lance already filled with the glittering promise of its imminent cessation like the brief bright saltless tears of a young girl over a lost flower; then gone too, fled north and eastward beyond the chromatic arch of its own insubstantial armistice, leaving behind it the spent confetti of its carnival to gather and drip leaf by leaf and twig by twig then blade by blade of grass, to gather in murmuring runnels, releasing in mirrored repetition the sky which, glint by glint of fallen gold and blue, the falling drops had prisoned.

It was over at last. He takes up the rope again and they move out from beneath the tree and go on, moving no faster than before but for the first time since they entered the woods, with purpose. Because it is nearing sunset. Although the rain had not seemed to last long, yet now it is as if there had been something in that illogical and harmless sound and fury which abrogated even the iron schedule of grooved and immutable day as the abrupt unplumbable tantrum of a child, the very violence of which is its own invincible argument against protraction, can somehow seem to set the clock up. He is soaking wet. His overalls are heavy and dank and cold upon him—the sorry refuse, the scornful lees of glory—a lifeless chill which is no kin to the vivid wet of the living water which has carried into and still retains within the very mud, the boundless freedom of the golden air as that same air glitters in the leaves and branches which globe in countless minute repetition the intact and iridescent cosmos. They walk in splendor. Joined by the golden skein of the wet grass rope, they move in single file toward the ineffable effulgence, directly into the sun. They are still pacing it. They mount the final ridge. They will arrive together. At the same moment all three of them cross the crest and descend into the bowl of evening and are extinguished.

The rapid twilight effaces them from the day's tedious recording. Original, in the womb-dimension, the unavoidable first and the inescapable last, eyeless, they descend the hill. He finds the basket by smell and lifts it down from the limb and sets it before her. She nuzzles into it, blowing the sweet breath-reek into the sweetish reek of feed until they become indistinguishable with that of the urgent and unimpatient milk as it flows among and about his fingers, hands, wrists, warm and indivisible as the strong inexhaustible life ichor itself, inherently, of itself, renewing. Then he leaves the invisible basket where he can find it again at dawn, and goes to the spring. Now he can see again. Again his head interrupts, then replaces as once more he breaks with drinking the reversed drinking of his drowned and fading image. It is the well of days, the still and insatiable aperture of earth. It holds in tranquil paradox of suspended precipitation dawn, noon, and sunset; yesterday, today, and tomorrow—star-spawn and hieroglyph, the fierce white dying rose, then gradual and invincible speeding up to and into slack-flood's coronal of nympholept noon. Then ebb's afternoon, until at last the morning, noon, and afternoon flow back, drain the sky and creep leaf by voiceless leaf and twig and branch and trunk, descending, gathering frond by frond among the grass, still creeping downward in drowsy insect murmurs, until at last the complete all of light gathers about that still and tender mouth in one last expiring inhalation. He rises. The swale is constant with random and erratic fireflies. There is the one fierce evening star, though almost at once the marching constellations mesh and gear and wheel strongly on. Blond too in that gathering last of light, she owns no dimension against the lambent and undimensional grass. But she is there, solid amid the abstract earth. He walks lightly upon it, returning, treading lightly that frail inextricable canopy of the subterrene slumber—Helen and the bishops, the kings and the graceless seraphim. When he reaches her, she has already begun to lie down—first the forequarters, then the hinder ones, lowering herself in two distinct stages into the spent ebb of evening, nestling back into the nest-form of sleep, the mammalian attar. They lie down together.

The account of Ike Snopes and the cow has been excerpted from a rather long and complex novel. Although the episode makes excellent reading on its own, certain of its implications can be approached most easily through reference to its context.

Elsewhere in the novel Ike is seen from the outside, from the point of view of the sewing-machine salesman, Ratliff, who looks upon the idiot with pity and outrage and some horror. But here, though Ike still has idiot qualities, we see him differently—partly from the inside and partly from the outside, but without the assumption that our point of view is superior.

The ambivalence he shares with his Snopes kinfolk is important. The clan in general can claim attributes which in gentlemen could be virtues, but which in the redneck Snopeses are often so extreme, so misdirected, or so devoid of counterbalance that they range from the ludicrous to the horrible. I. O. Snopes' pretensions to learning result mostly in garbled axioms, eyeglasses without lenses, professional garb with a paper dickey as shirtfront and false cuffs attached to the coat sleeves. Mink Snopes' intense pride leads him to shoot a man from ambush, stuff him in a hollow tree, and refuse money with which to escape. As I. O. is, in a sense, the caricature of man's pretensions to learning, so Mink is the caricature of man's pretensions to honor. If we wish to be charitable, we might say that I. O. represents "learning" in the wrong person, and that Mink represents pride in the wrong person. Ike, in the same scheme, could be said to represent love in the wrong person.

Mink, we might tell ourselves, shows that pride is possible even in the poorest of white trash, and Ike demonstrates the possibility of love even in an idiot. Certainly, Ike's love story has a genuine beauty seldom approached in fiction. It is largely through language (as opposed to the inherent nature of the chosen events, characters, and places) that Faulkner elevates the passage to the realm of romance, equates it with the highest forms of love in our literature. As in the Benjy section of *The Sound and the Fury,* Faulkner does not limit himself to the words the idiot might use, but employs the full scope of language to express the sensations of the idiot as he might experience them wordlessly. In the case of Ike, however, Faulkner also looks upon him and the cow from the outside as we might see them if we were looking on not literally, but literarily, in the tradition of romantic love.

Love has been known to change a rather plain woman into a vision of irresistible loveliness; it may have happened in a lover's mind, but certainly it has happened on the page. Shakespeare played with the idea in Sonnet 130:

> My mistress' eyes are nothing like the sun;
> Coral is far more red than her lips' red;
> If snow be white, why then her breasts are dun;
> If hairs be wires, black wires grow on her head.
> I have seen roses damask'd, red and white,
> But no such roses see I in her cheeks;
> And in some perfumes is there more delight

Than in the breath that from my mistress reeks.
I love to hear her speak, yet well I know
That music hath a far more pleasing sound:
I grant I never saw a goddess go;
My mistress, when she walks, treads on the ground:
    And yet, by heaven, I think my love as rare
    As any she belied with false compare.

It was in Shakespeare's time a literary tradition to speak of the lady's hair as golden wires, her lips as coral. Faulkner does not use the stock romantic terms, but he is within the same sort of tradition when he describes, for instance, the idiot lying "in the drenched myriad waking life of grasses" waiting for the approach of his bovine lady:

Then he would hear her, coming down the creekside in the mist. . . .[T]he dawn would be empty, the moment and she would not be, then he would hear her and he would lie drenched in the wet grass, serene and one and indivisible in joy, listening to her approach. He would smell her; the whole mist reeked with her; the same malleate hands of mist which drew along his prone drenched flanks palped her pearled barrel too and shaped them both somewhere in immediate time, already married.

After Ike and the cow fall out of the burning field into the ravine, Ike tries to talk to her in terms reminiscent of Marvell in "To His Coy Mistress":

. . . trying to tell her how this violent violation of her maiden's delicacy is no shame, since such is the very iron imperishable warp of the fabric of love.

Faulkner's triumph in the episode is partly that he has captured for us an experience which we can accept as real: This, we say, is the way Ike sees it and feels it. But we also—and this is as much a part of the triumph—are given an experience which we can accept as literary: This, we know at least subconsciously, is the way we have read it, and it may be because we have been taught to experience love this way that we do so experience it. One marvelous passage not only describes the way the lover may actually see the dawn, but insists by means of the quality of the language and by the literary references that the written tradition of romantic love is very much involved:

. . . dawn, light, is not decanted onto earth from the sky, but instead is from the earth itself suspired. Roofed by the woven canopy of blind annealing grass-roots and the roots of trees, dark in the blind dark of time's silt and rich refuse—the constant and unslumbering anonymous worm-glut and the inextricable known bones—Troy's Helen and the nymphs and the snoring mitred bishops, the saviors and the victims and the kings—it wakes, up-seeping, attritive in uncountable creeping channels: first, root; then frond by frond, from whose escaping tips like gas it rises and disseminates and stains the sleep-fast earth with drowsy insect-murmur; then, still upward-seeking, creeps the knitted bark of trunk and limb where, suddenly louder leaf by leaf and dispersive in diffusive sudden speed, melodious with the winged and jeweled throats, it upward bursts and fills night's globed negation with jonquil thunder.

At one point, near the end of the section, Faulkner seems to specify that from the realistic, and even from the personal, point of view at this time, the experience is less than romantic, but that if one moves back and observes through the literary tradition, wet Ike Snopes and his grass rope and the cow take on cosmic, mythic proportions:

He is soaking wet. His overalls are heavy and dank and cold upon him—the sorry refuse, the scornful lees of glory—a lifeless chill which is no kin to the vivid wet of the living water which has carried into and still retains within the very mud, the boundless freedom of the golden air as that same air glitters in the leaves and branches which globe in countless minute repetition the intact and iridescent cosmos. They walk in splendor. Joined by the golden skein of the wet grass rope, they move in single file toward the ineffable effulgence, directly into the sun. They are still pacing it. They mount the final ridge. They will arrive together. At the same moment all three of them cross the crest and descend into the bowl of evening and are extinguished.

The emphasis placed, in this discussion, upon the literary view employed in the idiot-cow section of *The Hamlet* should not be construed as an attempt to limit the passage to such notice. The quotation just above, for instance, may be, among other things, symbolic of the act of love—here glorified though given a hint of reality; later when Ratliff goes with the store-front loungers to watch as Ike actually does make love to the cow, the scene is sordid. No longer is the idiot's love for the cow raised above ordinary human experience by literary means; rather it is lowered to the animal, to what we think of as subhuman and degrading. In both instances, however, our attention is called to the fact of the real humanity involved, to a central point between glory and degradation. Golden Ike in the field has wet overalls; later, at the barn, Ratliff watches him,

and it was as though it were himself inside the stall with the cow, himself looking out of the blasted tongueless face at the row of faces watching him who had been given the wordless passions but not the specious words.

Ike hasn't been given the "specious" words, but Faulkner has given them to us for him—Faulkner and the tradition of literary romantic love. Having become aware through the words that an idiot can be as exalted in his love for a cow as the most literate and noble men in their love for our most beautiful heroines, we are forced to ask if in our own great love poems and stories we have not speciously exalted ourselves. Strip the language away, and do we not have idiots and cows?

The paradox is used neither exclusively to degrade man nor solely to exalt him. With Ratliff, we see ourselves in the "blasted tongueless face," and with Ike, inglorious as we and our ladies may "objectively" be, we experience exaltation. And though the words by which it is expressed may be specious, it is through the words that we come to know and experience our own ambivalence.

J. P. Donleavy

FRANZ F

He lived in Elderberry Street, in the West End of Boston, and had a shop front with a coldwater flat behind. In the basement of the building a man made wine and the fermented smell came up between the floor boards. The kitchen was misshapen, small and dark and whenever Franz turned on the light a lot of roaches would scurry over the sink and disappear in the wall.

The little living room had a built in couch on which Franz slept. Some bookcases around the wall and in a farther tiny room there was another bed. Rattan shades on all the windows to keep out eyes passing in the alley. A big woolly rug on the floor. This was a lonely outpost. Except for the loud fights that went on in the rest of the building and sometimes on both sides of the street.

At six any morning when he could not sleep, Franz stood in the shadow of his doorway to listen to the alarm clocks going off up and down the street, the ringing of these sad timepieces escaping out the open windows. Then taking a shower, and at eight fifty every morning, Monday to Friday, he put particulars in his briefcase, cornflakes inside him, and set off.

Elderberry a narrow street with one or two grotesque trees arching and sneaking their branches between the houses. Empty flats to rent with the price written in white grease on the windows. Some buildings had fallen down and had become vacant lots where cars were parked. Franz F walking toward the river, slinging his briefcase ahead of him, sweeping his free arm across his face at the clouds of flies blossoming off the garbage as he passed. By the river there was a breeze, a brightness of water, and an early-morning green.

Sometimes he went down behind the hospital past a red brick wall with a pair of big dark doors. If these were open, there was an empty trolley waiting by the steps. And certain times a black van from a funeral parlor would pull out, a man preceding it to warn traffic in the narrow street.

Above these large doors were windows Franz could see into from the other side of the road. Shelves around the wall of a large room, rows of bottles and bottles. This is how he went one day.

The hospital extended to the river. And here were grass, trees, and the building's high balconies and curtained windows. Someone sitting in a wheelchair reading. And outside this entrance were always parked several long expensive cars. It gave one heart. Inside, a bright reception desk in the gleaming hall. And elderly women with canes and furs were helped up the steps by their chauffeurs.

On the hottest days there was always freshness here along the river. Young maple trees spreading over the paths. At night the factory buildings across the water shone bright neon lights and rippled and flickered. Saturdays and Sundays the sailboats were out. White one-winged butterflies.

Past the hospital was the jail. Always a little difficult to decide which place would be better to be, hospital or jail. But upon serious consideration of this problem, Franz chose the jail. At least it was near the river and within a stone's throw of Charles Street Station. Nice to know that if you did make it over the wall you were near public transport.

Climbing the steps to the station platform, Franz was a rigid figure, a lonely one in his Victorian suiting. In the train he always offered his seat to a woman. Doing so evoked a feeling that all was well with the world. Often there were tall horse faced girls travelling, who crossed legs largely lean and read books in their laps. If Franz was early for work he went for coffee in Harvard Square. This pleasant time of day, when the college buildings were coming awake with the summery flap of blue sneakers along the pavement. A tremendous change to come out of the enclosed darkness of Elderberry Street to these open spacious buildings. To see the bright smiling teeth of students. His train pulling into this last stop, a new atmosphere in the air. White clean walls of the tunnel. The magazine kiosk. Even the weighing and gum machines had a clean magic about them. And here he weighed one hundred and seventy one pounds and bought his gum.

Franz F worked in a building just off the Square. It had the feeling of a library. There was a reception desk where a young blond woman, her hair tightly back in a bun, nodded her head to him as he came in. He doffed his cap, gave a slight bow, just so. A little frightened that she thought him pretentious. And his clothes a little too old worldly to be honest. He hoped as he rambled by each morning that she might ask him a question because he looked so intelligent. But her face was always neither sad nor glad and her name was Lydia.

Her legs he knew by heart. Neat muscles knotting over long ankles and toes slightly pigeon. In the outside corner of each eye she had put a dark pencil line that gave her face a touch of Chinese beauty. Her silence made him feel she was aloof and slightly censuring. But passing each morning, he felt he wasn't doing too badly.

Climbing up the stairs to his room where two wide windows over-looked the street and opening his briefcase on the long board table. His hands looked such trembling hooks, freckled, tired and grey. This day was like all the rest and might be like all his future. In going to the window, raising it wide, putting elbows on the sill and looking down at the street and the tailor shop across, there was an iota of hope. All through one's life there were myriad days at school while outside was summertime under the skies.

As the mornings grew toward noon, messengers brought sheets of yellow paper with many statistics. He went down line after line with his pencil, checking those which were related and made a list. From this list other lists would be made. And from these, in another room at the top of the building, people who had higher positions would come to a conclusion.

This office was a lonely life. Two or three infrequent acquaintances might stop by, peek through the door, and chat for a minute. There was a feeling, reading these faces, that they were saying, come on and fight. But getting the gimlet eye, they retreated, making a wisecrack, and were off down the hall to more influential people. The uncomfortable feeling descending on Franz that they were going to intrigue him out of his job.

There were bigger problems than losing one's job. Franz had for many years been interested in having an affair with a woman. One of those things where you like me and I like you. Things would start bravely enough. His shirt, underwear, and seersucker had been oven fresh for those light-blue evenings. The girl tall, fragrant, and socially registered perhaps. And to have his invitation accepted was undermining. He thought there was a secret with women, a combination that unlocked the chastity. That when you phoned to ask them to come to the Bach quartet, you sent a flower that afternoon. And often then, calling at her house, the bloom pinned to her dress hung wilted on its stem, a faded three-dollar overture.

On these dates he took a taxi drive with the girl along the grassy banks of the Charles. Sitting stiffly upright, designating points of interest. And amazed at the nice looking clothes the girl had on. So many attempts in his life to arrange a scene of seduction. Cutting family ties, finding the privacy of one's own quarters, roach ridden as they were. No friends who might pay a call casually and thus wreck a wrestle. But his suggestion for coffee after the concert met with a request to be taken home. The dutiful delivery, walking to their front doors, doffing hat, bowing, saying good night. The door closing, walking away, almost feeling her sigh of relief on the back of his neck.

On these nights, the shop in Elderberry Street became a pit of despair. Nothing to lighten the burden of darkness. Maybe run the shower, chase the roaches. Go out past a bar, think of having a drink, see the smoke and the sour menacing men inside and instead buy a quart of beer from the corner store. The man shortchanging him two cents without fail. And they would go through the usual routine of, oh sorry, and a reluctant two pennies would be dropped one at a time into his upward palm.

Saturday mornings after these terrible Fridays, Franz with shirt and tie would saunter toward the river, walking along past the jail to buy a New York Times at the drugstore. Along Charles Street, past the soothing brick, where inside there must be bliss to make the outside look so mellow. Behind the screened windows tall horse faced women whispering out of the shadows to husbands, darling, come and kiss me. Were it he, he would likely slip and break his neck rushing across the polished floor to her mouth.

And this Saturday morning, a balmy breeze dipping in his hair, Franz made for the Public Garden, paper folded under his arm. An oasis of gigantic trees. Spindle shanked women anciently wrapped in Manx rugs reading with magnifying glasses on the benches. The swan boats quietly churning from pond to pond under the bridges.

Today all the benches were taken and Franz made for the circular one around the tree. Two people go by, each with a bulldog. A nannie pushing twins in a baby carriage. Sitting down, crossing his legs, tugging up socks, Franz opened to the obituaries. He read the prominent deads. Not like the hot days in Elderberry Street, where you could see the bald pate of the undertaker gleaming from the upper half of his window as he worked. These deads in the paper did not die in vain.

Franz heard the words, which came from the other side of the tree. He looked up and then back at his paper. He heard the words again and turned around. A girl's foot and ankle jigging up and down, and he went back to his paper. Once more he heard the words and there was a sizzling in his stomach. They were simple ancient words almost without meaning, do you have a match.

Leaning around the tree, Franz said to what he could see of this person, are you talking to me. And she said, yes, well, I think so. Do you have a match. Franz thought that if he did not have a match he would get up and run as fast as he could to the drugstore on the corner of Charles and Beacon Streets, and there get a match and run back with it already lit, holding his hand before the flame. The utter panic of this thought hit Franz and he laughed outright. The girl leaned forward and said, what's the matter. Franz said it was something in his paper. And she said, well, do you have a match.

Grimness spread on Franz's lips. Hands came up to his eyes like cups to catch the tears. He had no match. His voice disappeared as well. The thought of actually making a run for the drugstore was too much. Like all women he had terrorized previously, this one too, would be gone by the time he got back. The hurried trip for the matches he might pass off as a gesture, a new knighthood. Alas, she would think it lunacy. Here he was, rooted to the spot, dying on each heartbeat.

Sitting, his newspaper clutched in one hand, knees wide apart and feet so flat upon the path. Saturday, the hour before lunch. My God, what to say to the other side of the tree. There had been school days like this when teachers sent questions thudding on some dream. And you sat mumchance.

And her voice once more, I'm sorry if I bothered you. He heard her getting up. A foot crushing a cinder. And Franz said, don't go away.

In that public garden Franz sat talking out toward Arlington Street as she talked in the direction of Boylston. An open air confessional. His resonance increasing as the conversation went on. She said she came from the other end of earth. This statement a little scalding for Franz. But the place was New Zealand and he had heard of it before. Another item was, she was married to a Bostonian. He had heard of this too.

She said she did not like America and was sorry she ever came. Her husband was a bore. So Franz told her of the delights of Boston. Beacon Hill, the red brick pavements, T Wharf, and the quiet seclusion of life. And she said that North Station waiting for trains had been enough of Boston for her.

She got up and came to look at him around the other side of the tree. She was smiling at the foolish situation. She lived in Beaver Place. She said she had to meet someone but that he was interesting. Franz thought, O my God, when will the lies begin. And he walked her to the edge of the park, waving to her when she stopped and looked back from the corner of Beacon and Arlington. He had her telephone number. She told him to ring, perhaps next week.

On Sunday, Franz came again to the Public Garden. Sat where he'd been sitting and relived the encounter. Remembering all the pebbles and each leaf of every weed. In joyous confusion he even bowed to one of the old ladies in her Manx rug and she raised an eye brow, what was left of it.

He had scrubbed out his entire flat. And then tramped across Boston City. Through Scollay Square, down State Street, into the thick life of the markets. Waiting to phone her. To invite her up his decrepit street, by his begrimed store window, in the dust of which kids had written, if you're so smart why aren't you rich. Young kids have such clear minds.

And if she came and when she came would she get cold feet as she neared, looking for his address. Get her to go by the library and along the worn dignity of Blossom Street. He could say something at the door, a verbal gallantry. The telephone was polished and placed just outside the kitchen on his octagonal table and perhaps would give dash to these digs.

All this figured out on Sunday. A day when Franz finally sat for hours on the end of T Wharf staring out across Boston harbor. The sights and sounds of when all this was low scrubland, peopled by strange singular Indians. And a truck driver had come up to him and said, this ain't nothing compared to that harbor they got in Frisco. I just finished driving from there.

And Monday through the routine, except for an extra bun and coffee in the morning. The purchase of a new shirt from the tailor across the street at lunchtime, holding it like a book as he passed the receptionist. And that evening back in Elderberry Street, after a shower and half an hour's deliberation, the final desperate writing out the words on a sheet of paper and pinning it to the wall above the phone. Franz dialled her number.

Another girl had to fetch her. A lot of voices in the background. All the people he knew were so brave on the telephone. She said hello and he asked her through his fumbling voice would she come and have a coffee at his apartment. Silence. He said hello. She said hello. He said, what about it. She said no, she didn't think she could. He said, as the emptiness got bigger, oh, you're still listening. You haven't hung up yet. And she said, no, I haven't hung up. Is that all you've got to say. Franz said, no, I've got more. And she said, well, I can't wait all night. And then he said, would you like to see a play. She said, what. Franz said, I don't know, just a play. And she said, what a funny thing to ask me to. I'm sorry but I've got to go now, good-bye.

Franz gently hung up the phone. Standing in his dark shop where once they sold vegetables. He put his hand up to his brow and wiped away the dripping sweat. He closed his arms around his chest and held himself as he wept.

For a whole week Franz spoke to no one. Taking his lunchtime sandwiches to the steps of Widener Library, he publicly tore at the crusts. He kept the door of his office closed and his head bent over the yellow sheets. In the evenings, unable to face the cloistered loneliness of Elderberry Street, he walked the streets of Cambridge. And one night, passing a straightbacked little crowd, he stopped and followed them and bought a ticket to a play.

Teeth tightly clenched in his mouth as he came to work next morning, eyes ahead, and the receptionist stopped him dead in his tracks. She said, hey. And he turned and she came out from behind her counter and told him she had sat behind him last night at the Poet's Theatre. Wearing a hard distant look and nodding his head, he went his way up the stairs and left her standing there.

In the late night in Elderberry Street, Franz lay head on pillow staring at the sounds of feet as they walked on the ceiling above. He avoided the back end of the hospital these days and once he went swimming in the pool at the end of the street. But all were jaws of more loneliness. He had become a conversation piece on the steps of Widener Library.

And then one afternoon, cap square on head, eyes bearing zero, he passed across the reception hall to go home. The receptionist stepped out in front of him and said, God damn it, you're rude. Franz blinked, stepped back, and tried to make it around her. She said, yes, you're God damned rude, and who the hell wants to speak to you anyhow. Franz said, you do, but nobody else does.

That night, after sitting head in hands in the tall reading room of the library off Blossom Street, Franz thought he might turn on the gas and block up his doors and windows. But it would be weeks before they'd find him, and the indignity was too much. He thought of giving up his job. Before, he had always waited until he was fired. Perhaps he could go back to Europe. Instead, he went to the local bakery, down the steps, smelling the moist dough, crusts baking, and this Italian gentleman who always asked him questions.

And tonight this baker said, You know, mister, you always look important to me, and you never say a thing. Aren't you ever going to tell me what you are. Franz said, yes, tonight I'll tell you. I'm a comma. Franz, gathering the two long loaves in his arms, stepped up the steps, and the Italian gentleman shouted after him, hey, you're a comedian.

Franz chopped up a mound of garlic and made a paste with butter. Slathering the long loaves, he put them in the oven. This lonely act of defiance. Reek tomorrow on the train. Pass by Lydia. Such an unlikely name. Perhaps she would tell him he was not only rude but reeking.

Lights out now in Elderberry Street. Twelve o'clock, when at last the voices stop squabbling out the windows in the alley. A quick roach kill and splash of water on the face. To lie back under the sheet and try to close the eyes. A bleary voice entering the alley. A woman with a customer. Franz still on this couch. Hearing her rap on his window. Hey, you in there, why don't you ever talk. Too good for us around here. What are you anyway. Franz said from his cloister, I'm a comedian.

Peals of laughter as she pulled herself up the back stairs, tugging her customer, shouting, did you hear what he said, that bastard in seersucker. He says he's a comedian. What a laugh. He's queer, that's what he is. Never seen him with a woman. You hear me, you God damn bastards in the rest of this house. Think you're too good for me. He's a queer.

In sleep there was an Autumn afternoon in Vermont, with all the woods red red gold. Tennis players and one was Lydia. She took his hand and said, not tonight. And he tiptoed and tiptoed to her door, rapping lightly as she said, you mustn't, you mustn't. Then as he slept she came and laid herself upon him, a smell of musk from her breasts. Waking now, a corner of swift blue high out beyond the alley in Elderberry Street, Franz begged the dream to come back.

All the way to work, he planned it. Walk up to Lydia, brief bow, and say, I want to apologise for my inexcusable rudeness the other day, and also for smelling of garlic this morning. Then spin on the heel and go up the stairs. But entering the open door, Franz passed her by, with a rigid fearful heart. Reaching his room, the bubbling of the water cooler outside the door, he silently pounded his fists on his table.

Each morning he had it planned, the mountain growing bigger and more impossible to climb. When suddenly she said, I don't know why I'm telling you this, but there's a plot to intrigue you out of your job.

As his knees buckled and his face went ashen, Franz sent whispers into his mind saying over and over, play it cool, play it cool. To Lydia he said, why are you telling me this. She said, because you've got no one to help you. Franz said thanks, and so that she wouldn't notice the moisture in his eyes he turned and went up the stairs.

This time always came. Like clockwork. Just when his life ticked temperately, they got together to oust him. Not because he had mixed the statistics. Or infracted a rule. But because he came to work neither late nor soon, that he bowed gently, dressed in his own fashion and regarded life with his gimlet eye. He did what they told him. Sometimes they will kill you for that.

But more than the token terror of dismissal was the curiosity of a woman with fine bones to her face and a gracious body, helping him. She was married and had nothing to fear. Each afternoon, a cartridge bag slung from her shoulder, she stepped up on the electric car and disappeared along Mount Auburn Street away under the trees of Cambridge. To go behind hedges and into a big white house because he had followed her one afternoon.

It seemed they had made peace. For she smiled once and even licked her lips as he smiled back. He could not engage in the battle to save himself because it was just one army after one man. Yours truly. And in these cases one could only skiddoo.

On a Thursday, Franz F packed up. Dusted and polished his office and took down his poem.

When the going
Is too good
To be true
Reverse course
And beat it.

It was a long trip back to Elderberry Street. And inside this address Franz let the roaches run wild. Friday morning he went down the street and straight across to the swimming pool where he clonked into the meter one penny. For an hour he lived like a seal. Some of the kids wanted to know why he wasn't working. Their insolence was amusing.

A letter arrived. His resignation was accepted and herewith two weeks' salary. Franz popped this blue-green check back in an envelope and returned it to that sunny building off Harvard Square. He took a sheet of paper and put down another poem. This he stuck over the sink.

When you've
Beat it
And the going
Is too desperate
To be true
Forge on.

Over the weekend Franz bought beer and let the man cheat him of the two cents. But as he turned out of the store, the man called him back and said, hey, what's the matter. You upset or something. Franz said, no. The man said, don't you know I'm robbing you two cents. Franz said, yes. The man said, I can't help it, it's a habit.

For twenty five cents on Tuesday Franz bought a pound of kidneys. And was frying these in olive oil. A balanced diet for the siege. And standing on a chair fanning smoke out the window, there came a knock on his door. On the steps handing him an envelope was Lydia.

She said, I have this for you. Franz took it and said, thanks. She said, so this is where you live. He said, yes. And she said, well aren't you going to ask me in. Franz saw eyes and faces hanging out the windows. This was news for Elderberry Street. He said, sure, come in if you want.

Franz directed her through the smoke. In the sitting room she sat on his bed. She said, you're such a funny and silly person, you're going to lose all the way through life. Why didn't you put up a fight. They thought they could fire you only because you ate your lunch on the steps of Widener Library. And then to send the check back was so silly.

In the hour evaporating away they had tea. Franz brought out the Peek Frean biscuits. Made a rose of them on a plate. She said, something seemed to have happened to you a while back. Suddenly you stopped talking to everybody. You were so grim. Franz said yes, he was grim. She said, that's why I wanted to make friends with you, and you just snubbed me. Franz said that was true, he had snubbed her. And Lydia had another Peek Frean and rising, said she had to go.

Franz led her sadly into the kitchen. He pulled the light cord and Lydia stopped in the dark. Franz said, I don't want you to see the roaches. She said, I don't mind what I see. And as Franz put his arms around her she whispered, you mustn't, you mustn't. Franz said, you've said that to me before and he pressed his lips on the scent behind her ear. And she said, will you be here next Saturday afternoon. I'll come at three thirty.

Franz took the envelope and check and burned them over the stove. He took a pail of water and washed the store window. The kids crowded around, hey, what's a matter, mister. You trying to make your place look good. Franz rolled a nickel down the street, quietly relishing as the kids wrestled in the gutter.

Each morning rising, beating fists on chest, touching toes, breathing God's air. Tearing open the front door and smiling out into the street. Buy the paper and read it over a coffee and crumb cake in Charles Street. And then militantly to the Public Garden, where there was half an hour's revenge on the circular bench around the tree.

Lydia was light-haired. And she would walk pigeon toed, her body curved in, passing by all the cellar entrances, dark alleys and broken windows and knock on his door. And at twenty past three on this Saturday Franz had changed his underwear twice in the last hour. The weather report was cool. And the world light blue. And his hands trembling. This was a lonely station. A chair by the telephone, eyes glued on the door.

And the phone rang. Picking up this black talking instrument Franz heard a nearby muffled voice that said, this is Lydia's husband, and I've got my gun and I'm coming round to shoot you.

The telephone fell out of Franz's hand and lay on the floor making a gurgling sound. The little words of his office poem. When the going is too good to be true.

Franz got up and unlocked the door, leaving it slightly ajar. He returned to his chair, having made his decision. The afternoon was deep red. Save him the trouble of knocking. And now after all these years it would be a curious justice that would put him down. Franz sitting slumped forward facing the door, hanging his head and hands. Perhaps he would have the dignity of being shot by a college graduate.

As the door opened Franz F closed his eyes and turning his head aside, raised his hands to block the bullets. The steps came near and a hand touched him on the hair and Lydia said, oh my God I phoned you as a joke.

Joyce Carol Oates

ACCOMPLISHED DESIRES

There was a man she loved with a violent love, and she spent much of her time thinking about his wife.

No shame to it, she actually followed the wife. She followed her to Peabody's Market, which was a small, dark, crowded store, and she stood in silence on the pavement as the woman appeared again and got into her station wagon and drove off. The girl, Dorie, would stand as if paralyzed and even her long, fine, blonde hair seemed paralyzed with thought—her heart pounded as if it too were thinking, planning—and then she would turn abruptly as if executing one of the steps in her modern dance class and cross through Peabody's alley and out to the Elks' Club parking lot and so up toward the campus, where the station wagon was bound.

Hardly had the station wagon pulled into the driveway when Dorie, out of breath, appeared a few houses down and watched. How that woman got out of a car—you could see the flabby expanse of her upper leg, white flesh that should never be exposed—and then turned and leaned in, probably with a grunt, to get shopping bags out of the backseat. Two of her children ran out to meet her, without coats or jackets. They had nervous, darting bodies—Dorie felt sorry for them—and their mother rose, straightening, a stout woman in a colorless coat, either scolding them or teasing them, one bag in either muscular arm, and so the mother and children went into the house and Dorie stood with nothing to stare at except the battered station wagon, and the small, snowy wilderness that was the Arbers' front yard, and the house itself. It was a large, ugly, peeling Victorian home in a block of similar homes, most of which had been fixed up by the faculty members who rented them. Dorie, who had something of her own mother's shrewd eye for hopeless, cast-off things, believed that the house could be remodeled and made presentable—but as long as he remained married to *that woman* it would be slovenly and peeling and ugly.

She loved that woman's husband with a fierce love that was itself a little ugly. Always a rather stealthy girl, thought to be simply quiet, she had entered his life by no accident—had not appeared in his class by accident—but every step of her career, like every outfit she wore and every expression on her face, was planned and shrewd and desperate. Before her twenties she had not thought much about herself; now she thought about herself continuously. She was leggy, long-armed, slender, and had a startled look, but the look was stylized now, and attractive. Her face was denuded of makeup and across her soft skin a galaxy of freckles glowed with health. She looked like a girl about to bound onto the tennis courts—and she did play tennis, though awkwardly. She played tennis with *him*. But so confused with love was she that the game of tennis, the relentless slamming of the ball back and forth, had seemed to her a disguise for something else the way everything in poetry or literature was a disguise for something else—for love?—and surely he must know, or didn't he know? Didn't he guess? There were many other girls he played tennis with, so that was nothing special, and her mind worked and worked while she should have slept, planning with the desperation of youth that has never actually been young—planning how to get him, how to get him, for it seemed to her that she would never be able to overcome her desire for this man.

The wife was as formidable as the husband. She wrote narrow volumes of poetry Dorie could not understand and he, the famous husband, wrote novels and critical pieces. The wife was a big, energetic, high-colored woman; the husband, Mark Arber, was about her size though not so high-colored, his complexion was rather putty-colored, rather melancholy. Dorie thought about the two of them all the time, awake or asleep, and she could feel the terrible sensation of blood flowing through her body, a flowing of desire that was not just for the man but somehow for the woman as well, a desire for her accomplishments, her fame, her children, her ugly house, her ugly body, her very life. She had light, frank blue eyes and people whispered that she drank; Dorie never spoke of her.

The college was a girls' college, exclusive and expensive, and every girl who remained there for more than a year understood a peculiar, even freakish kinship with it—as if she had always been there and the other girls, so like herself with their sleepy unmade-up faces, the skis in winter and the bicycles in good weather, the excellent expensive professors and the excellent air—everything, everything had always been there, had existed for centuries. They were stylish and liberal in their cashmere sweaters with soiled necks; their fingers were stained with ballpoint ink; and like them Dorie understood that most of the world was wretched and would never come to this college, never, would be kept back from it by armies of helmeted men. She, Dorie Weinheimer, was not wretched but supremely fortunate, and she must be grateful always for her good luck, for there was no justification for her existence any more than there was any justification for the wretched lots of the world's poor. And there would flash to her mind's eye a confused picture of dark-faced starving mobs, or emaciated faces out of an old-fashioned Auschwitz photograph, or something—some dreary horror from The New York *Times'* one hundred neediest cases at Christmastime. She had, in the girls' soft, persistent manner, an idealism-turned pragmatism under the influence of the college faculty, who had all been idealists at Harvard and Yale as undergraduates but who were now in their forties, and as impatient with normative values as they were with their students' occasional lockets-shaped-into-crosses; Mark Arber was the most disillusioned and the most eloquent of the Harvard men.

In class he sat at the head of the seminar table, leaning back in his leather-covered chair. He was a rather stout man. He had played football once in a past Dorie could not quite imagine, though she wanted to imagine it, and he had been in the war—one of the wars—she believed it had been World War II. He had an ugly, arrogant face and discolored teeth. He read poetry in a raspy, hissing, angry voice. "Like Marx I believe that poetry has had enough of love; the hell with it. Poetry should now cultivate the whip," he would say grimly, and Dorie would stare at him to see if he were serious. There were four senior girls in this class and they sometimes asked him questions, or made observations of their own, but there was no consistency in his reaction. Sometimes he seemed not to hear, sometimes he nodded enthusiastically and indifferently, sometimes he opened his eyes and looked at them, not distinguishing between them, and said: "A remark like that is quite characteristic." So she sat and stared at him and her heart seemed to turn to stone, wanting him, hating his wife and envying her violently, and the being that had been Dorie Weinheimer for twenty-one years changed gradually through the winter into another being, obsessed with jealousy. She did not know what she wanted most, this man or the victory over his wife.

She was always bringing poems to him in his office. She borrowed books from him and puzzled over every annotation of his. As he talked to her he picked at his fingernails, settled back in his chair, and he talked on in his rushed, veering, sloppy manner, as if Dorie did not exist or were a crowd, or a few intimate friends, it hardly mattered, as he raved about frauds in contemporary poetry, naming names, "that bastard with his sonnets," "that cow with her daughter-poems," and getting so angry that Dorie wanted to protest, No, no, why are you angry? Be gentle. Love me and be gentle.

When he failed to come to class six or seven times that winter the girls were all understanding. "Do you think he really is a genius?" they asked. His look of disintegrating, decomposing recklessness, his shiny suits and bizarre loafer shoes, his flights of language made him so different from their own fathers that it was probable he was a genius; these were girls who believed seriously in the existence of geniuses. They had been trained by their highly paid, verbose professors to be vaguely ashamed of themselves, to be silent about any I.Q. rated under 160, to be uncertain about their talents within the school and quite confident of them outside it—and Dorie, who had no talent and only adequate intelligence, was always silent about herself. Her talent perhaps lay in her faithfulness to an obsession, her cunning patience, her smile, her bared teeth which were a child's teeth and yet quite sharp. . . .

One day Dorie had been waiting in Dr. Arber's office for an hour, with some new poems for him. He was late but he strode into the office as if he had been hurrying all along, sitting heavily in the creaking swivel chair, panting; he looked a little mad. He was the author of many reviews in New York magazines and papers and in particular the author of three short, frightening novels, and now he had a burned-out, bleached-out look. Like any of the girls at this college, Dorie would have sat politely if one of her professors set fire to himself, and so she ignored his peculiar stare and began her rehearsed speech about—but what did it matter what it was about? The poems of Emily Dickinson or the terrible yearning of Shelley or her own terrible lust, what did it matter?

He let his hand fall onto hers by accident. She stared at the hand, which was like a piece of meat—and she stared at him and was quite still. She was pert and long-haired in the chair facing him, an anonymous student and a minor famous man, and every wrinkle of his sagging, impatient face was bared to her in the winter sunlight from the window—and every thread of blood in his eyes—and quite calmly and politely she said, "I guess I should tell you, Dr. Arber, that I'm in love with you. I've felt that way for some time."

"You what, you're what?" he said. He gripped her feeble hand as if clasping it in a handshake. "What did you say?" He spoke with an amazed, slightly irritated urgency, and so it began.

His wife wrote her poetry under an earlier name, Barbara Scott. Many years ago she had had a third name, a maiden name—Barbara Cameron—but it belonged to another era about which she never thought except under examination from her analyst. She had a place cleared in the dirty attic of her house and she liked to sit up there, away from the children, and look out the small octagon of a window, and think. People she saw from her attic window looked bizarre and helpless to her. She herself was a hefty, perspiring woman, and all her dresses—especially her expensive ones—were stained under the arms with great lemon-colored half-moons no dry cleaner could remove. Because she was so large a woman she was quick to see imperfections in others, as if she used a magnifying glass. Walking by her window on an ordinary morning were an aged, tottering woman, an enormous Negro woman—probably someone's cleaning lady—and a girl from the college on aluminum crutches, poor brave thing, and the white-blonde child from up the street who was precocious and demonic. Her own children were precocious and only slightly troublesome. Now two of them were safe in school and the youngest, the three-year-old, was asleep somewhere.

Barbara Scott had won the Pulitzer Prize not long before with an intricate sonnet series that dealt with the "voices" of many people; her energetic, coy line was much imitated. This morning she began a poem which her agent was to sell, after Barbara's death, to *The New Yorker: What awful wrath / what terrible betrayal / and these aluminum crutches, rubber-tipped* . . . She had such a natural talent that she let words take her anywhere. Her decade of psychoanalysis had trained her to hold nothing back; even when she had nothing to say the very authority of her technique carried her on. So she sat that morning at her big, nicked desk—over the years the children had marred it with sharp toys—and stared out the window and waited for more inspiration. She felt the most intense kind of sympathy when she saw someone deformed—she was anxious, in a way, to see deformed people because it released such charity in her. But apart from the girl on the crutches she saw nothing much. Hours passed and she realized that her husband had not come home; already school was out and her two boys were running across the lawn.

When she descended the two flights of stairs to the kitchen, she saw that the three-year-old, Geoffrey, had opened a white plastic bottle of ammonia and had spilled it on the floor and on himself; the stench was sickening. The two older boys bounded in the back door as if spurred on by the argument that ranged between them, and Barbara whirled upon them and began screaming. The ammonia had spilled onto her slacks. The boys ran into the front room and she remained in the kitchen, screaming. She sat down heavily on one of the kitchen chairs. After half an hour she came to herself and tried to analyze the situation. Did she hate these children, or did she hate herself? Did she hate Mark? Or was her hysteria a form of love, or was it both love and hate together? She put the ammonia away and made herself a drink.

When she went into the front room she saw that the boys were playing with their mechanical inventors' toys and had forgotten about her. Good. They were self-reliant. Slight, cunning children, all of them dark like Mark and prematurely aged, as if by the burden of their prodigious intelligences, they were not always predictable: they forgot things, lost things, lied about things, broke things, tripped over themselves and each other, mimicked classmates, teachers, and their parents, and often broke down into pointless tears. And yet sometimes they did not break down into tears when Barbara punished them, as if to challenge her. She did not always know what she had given birth to: they were so remote, even in their struggles and assaults, they were so fictional, as if she had imagined them herself. It had been she who'd imagined them, not Mark. Their father had no time. He was always in a hurry, he had three aged typewriters in his study and paper in each one, an article or a review or even a novel in progress in each of the machines, and he had no time for the children except to nod grimly at them or tell them to be quiet. He had been so precocious himself, Mark Arber, that after his first, successful novel at the age of twenty-four he had had to whip from place to place, from typewriter to typewriter, in a frantic attempt to keep up with—he called it keeping up with his "other self," his "real self," evidently a kind of alter ego who was always typing and creating, unlike the real Mark Arber. The real Mark Arber was now forty-five and he had made the transition from "promising" to "established" without anything in between, like most middle-aged critics of prominence.

Strachey, the five-year-old, had built a small machine that was both a man and an automobile, operated by the motor that came with the set of toys. "This is a modern centaur," he said wisely, and Barbara filed that away, thinking perhaps it would do well in a poem for a popular, slick magazine. . . . She sat, unbidden, and watched her boys' intense work with the girders and screws and bolts, and sluggishly she thought of making supper, or calling Mark at school to see what had happened. . . .

That morning he had left the house in a rage and when she went into his study, prim and frowning, she had discovered four or five crumpled papers in his wastebasket. It was all he had accomplished that week.

Mark had never won the Pulitzer Prize for anything. People who knew him spoke of his slump, familiarly and sadly; if they disliked Mark they praised Barbara, and if they disliked Barbara they praised Mark. They were "established," but it did not mean much; younger writers were being discovered all the time who had been born in the mid- or late Forties, strangely young, terrifyingly young, and people the Arbers' age were being crowded out, hustled toward the exits. . . . Being "established" should have pleased them, but instead it led them to long spiteful bouts of eating and drinking in the perpetual New England winter.

She made another drink and fell asleep in the chair. Sometime later her children's fighting woke her and she said, "Shut up," and they obeyed at once. They were playing in the darkened living room, down at the other end by the big brick fireplace, which was never used. Her head ached. She got to her feet and went out to make another drink.

Around one o'clock Mark came in the back door. He stumbled and put the light on. Barbara, in her plaid bathrobe, was sitting at the kitchen table. She had a smooth, shiny, bovine face, heavy with fatigue. Mark said, "What the hell are you doing here?"

She attempted a shrug of her shoulders. Mark stared at her. "I'm getting you a housekeeper," he said. "You need more time for yourself, for your work," he said, twisting his mouth at the word to show what he thought of it. "You shouldn't neglect your poetry, so we're getting in a housekeeper, not to do any heavy work, just to sort of watch things—in other words—a kind of external consciousness. You should be freed from ordinary considerations."

He was not drunk, but he had the appearance of having been drunk, hours before, and now his words were muddled and dignified with the air of words spoken too early in the morning. He wore a dirty tweed overcoat, the same coat he'd had when they were married, and his necktie had been pulled off and stuffed somewhere, and his puffy, red face looked mean. Barbara thought of how reality was too violent for poetry, and how poetry, and the language itself, shimmered helplessly before the confrontation with living people and their demands. "The housekeeper is here. She's outside," Mark said. "I'll go get her."

He returned with a college girl who looked like a hundred other college girls. "This is Dorie, this is my wife Barbara, you've met no doubt at some school event, here you are," Mark said. He was carrying a suitcase which must have belonged to the girl. "Dorie has requested room and board with a faculty family. The Dean of Women arranged it. Dorie will baby-sit or something—we can put her in the spare room. Let's take her up."

Barbara had not yet moved. The girl was pale and distraught; she looked about sixteen. Her hair was disheveled. She stared at Barbara and seemed about to speak.

"Let's take her up, you want to sit there all night?" Mark snarled.

Barbara indicated with a motion of her hand that they should go up without her. Mark, breathing heavily, stomped up the back steps and the girl followed at once. There was no indication of her presence because her footsteps were far too light on the stairs, she said nothing, and only a slight change in the odor of the kitchen indicated something new—a scent of cologne, hair scrubbed clean, a scent of panic. Barbara sat listening to her heart thud heavily inside her and she recalled how, several years ago, Mark had left her and had turned up at a friend's apartment in Chicago—he'd been beaten up by someone on the street, an accidental event—and how he had blackened her eye once in an argument over the worth of Samuel Richardson, and how—there were many other bitter memories—and of course there had been other women, some secret and some known—and now this. . . .

So she sat thinking with a small smile of how she would have to dismiss this when she reported it to their friends: *Mark has had this terrible block for a year now, with his novel, and so. . . .*

She sat for a while running through phrases and explanations, and when she climbed up the stairs to bed she was grimly surprised to see him in their bedroom, asleep, his mouth open and his breath raspy and exhausted. At the back of the house, in a small oddly shaped maid's room, slept the girl; in their big dormer room slept the three boys, or perhaps they only pretended to sleep; and only she, Barbara, stood in the dark and contemplated the bulk of her own body, wondering what to do and knowing that there was nothing she would do, no way for her to change the process of events any more than she could change the heavy fact of her body itself. There was no way to escape what the years had made her.

From that time on they lived together like a family. Or, it was as Mark put it: "Think of a baby-sitter here permanently. Like the Lunt girl, staying on here permanently to help, only we won't need that one anymore." Barbara made breakfast for them all, and then Mark and Dorie drove off to school and returned late, between six and six-thirty, and in the evenings Mark worked hard at his typewriters, going to sit at one and then the next and then the next, and the girl Dorie helped Barbara with the dishes and odd chores and went up to her room, where she studied . . . or did something, she must have done something.

Of the long afternoons he and the girl were away Mark said nothing. He was evasive and jaunty; he looked younger. He explained carefully to Dorie that when he and Mrs. Arber were invited somewhere she must stay home and watch the children, that she was not included in these invitations; and the girl agreed eagerly. She did so want to help around the house! She had inherited from her background a dislike for confusion—so the mess of the Arber house upset her and she worked for hours picking things up, polishing tarnished objects Barbara herself had forgotten were silver, cleaning, arranging, fixing. As soon as the snow melted she was to be seen outside, raking shyly through the flower beds. How to explain her to the neighbors? Barbara said nothing.

"But I didn't think we lived in such a mess. I didn't think it was so bad," Barbara would say to Mark in a quiet, hurt voice, and he would pat her hand and say, "It isn't a mess, she just likes to fool around. *I* don't think it's a mess."

It was fascinating to live so close to a young person. Barbara had never been young in quite the way Dorie was young. At breakfast—they ate crowded around the table—everyone could peer into everyone else's face, there were no secrets, stale mouths and bad moods were inexcusable, all the wrinkles of age or distress that showed on Barbara could never be hidden, and not to be hidden was Mark's guilty enthusiasm, his habit of saying, *"We* should go to . . .", *"We* are invited . . ." and the "we" meant either him and Barbara, or him and Dorie, but never all three; he had developed a new personality. But Dorie was fascinating. She awoke to the slow grey days of spring with a panting, wondrous expectation, her blonde hair shining, her freckles clear as dabs of clever paint on her heartbreaking skin, her teeth very, very white and straight, her pert little lips innocent of lipstick and strangely sensual . . . yes, it was heart-breaking. She changed her clothes at least twice a day while Barbara wore the same outfit—baggy black slacks and a black sweater—for weeks straight. Dorie appeared downstairs in cashmere sweater sets that were the color of birds' eggs, or of birds' fragile legs, and white trim blouses that belonged on a genteel hockey field, and bulky pink sweaters big as jackets, and when she was dressed casually she wore stretch slacks that were neatly secured by stirrups around her long, narrow, white feet. Her eyes were frankly and emptily brown, as if giving themselves up to every observer. She was so anxious to help that it was oppressive; "No, I can manage, I've been making breakfast for eight years by myself," Barbara would say angrily, and Dorie, a chastised child, would glance around the table not only at Mark but at the children for sympathy. Mark had a blackboard set up in the kitchen so that he could test the children's progress in languages, and he barked out commands for them—French or Latin or Greek words—and they responded with nervous glee, clacking out letters on the board, showing off for the rapt, admiring girl who seemed not to know if they were right or wrong.

"Oh, how smart they are—how wonderful everything is," Dorie breathed.

Mark had to drive to Boston often because he needed his prescription for tranquilizers refilled constantly, and his doctor would not give him an automatic refill. But though Barbara had always looked forward to these quick trips, he rarely took her now. He went off with Dorie, now his "secretary," who took along a notebook decorated with the college's insignia to record his impressions in, and since he never gave his wife warning she could not get ready in time, and it was such an obvious trick, so crudely cruel, that Barbara stood in the kitchen and wept as they drove out. . . . She called up friends in New York, but never exactly told them what was going on. It was so ludicrous, it made her seem such a fool. Instead she chatted and barked with laughter; her conversations with these people were always so witty that nothing, nothing seemed very real until she hung up the receiver again; and then she became herself, in a drafty college-owned house in New England, locked in this particular body.

She stared out the attic window for hours, not thinking. She became a state of being, a creature. Downstairs the children fought, or played peacefully, or rifled through their father's study, which was forbidden, and after a certain amount of time something would nudge Barbara to her feet and she would descend slowly, laboriously, as if returning to the real world where any ugliness was possible. When she slapped the boys for being bad they stood in meek defiance and did not cry. "Mother, you're out of your mind," they said. "Mother, you're losing control of yourself."

"It's your father who's out of his mind!" she shouted.

She had the idea that everyone was talking about them, everyone. Anonymous worthless people who had never published a line gloated over her predicament; high-school baton twirlers were better off than Barbara Scott, who had no dignity. Dorie, riding with Mark Arber on the expressway to Boston, was at least young and stupid, anonymous though she was, and probably she too had a slim collection of poems which Mark would manage to get published . . . and who knew what would follow, who could tell? Dorie Weinheimer was like any one of five hundred or five thousand college girls and was no one, had no personality, and yet Mark Arber had somehow fallen in love with her so perhaps everyone would eventually fall in love with her? Barbara imagined with panic the parties she knew nothing about, to which Mark and his new girl went: Mark in his slovenly tweed suits, looking like his own father in the Thirties, and Dorie chic as a *Vogue* model in her weightless bones and vacuous face.

"Is Dorie going to stay here long?" the boys kept asking.

"Why, don't you like her?"

"She's nice. She smells nice. Is she going to stay long?"

"Go ask your father that," Barbara said angrily.

The girl was officially boarding with them; it was no lie. Every year certain faculty families took in a student or two, out of generosity or charity, or because they themselves needed the money, and the Arbers themselves had always looked down upon such hearty liberalism. But now they had Dorie, and in Peabody's Market Barbara had to rush up and down the aisles with her shopping cart, trying to avoid the wives of other professors who were sure to ask her about the new boarder; and she had to buy special things for the girl, spinach and beets and artichokes, while Barbara and Mark liked starches and sweets and fat, foods that clogged up the blood vessels and strained the heart and puffed out the stomach. While Barbara ate and drank hungrily Dorie sat chaste with her tiny forkfuls of food, and Barbara could eat three platefuls to Dorie's one; her appetite increased savagely just in the presence of the girl. (The girl was always asking politely, "Is it the boys who get the bathroom all dirty?" or, "Could I take the vacuum cleaner down and have it fixed?" and these questions, polite as they were, made Barbara's appetite increase savagely.)

In April, after Dorie had been boarding with them three and a half months, Barbara was up at her desk when there was a rap on the plywood door. Unused to visitors, Barbara turned clumsily and looked at Mark over the top of her glasses. "Can I come in?" he said. "What are you working on?"

There was no paper in her typewriter. "Nothing," she said.

"You haven't shown me any poems lately. What's wrong?"

He sat on the window ledge and lit a cigarette. Barbara felt a spiteful satisfaction to see how old he looked—he hadn't her fine, fleshed-out skin, the smooth complexion of an overweight woman; he had instead the bunched, baggy complexion of an overweight man whose weight keeps shifting up and down. Good. Even his fingers shook as he lit the cigarette.

"This is the best place in the house," he said.

"Do you want me to give it up to Dorie?"

He stared at her. "Give it up—why? Of course not."

"I thought you might be testing my generosity."

He shook his head, puzzled. Barbara wondered if she hated this man, or if she felt a writer's interest in him. Perhaps he was insane. Or perhaps he had been drinking again; he had not gone out to his classes this morning and she'd heard him arguing with Dorie. "Barbara, how old are you?" he said.

"Forty-three. You know that."

He looked around at the boxes and other clutter as if coming to an important decision. "Well, we have a little problem here."

Barbara stared at her blunt fingernails and waited.

"She got herself pregnant. It seems on purpose."

"She what?"

"Well," Mark said uncomfortably, "she did it on purpose."

They remained silent. After a while, in a different voice he said, "She claims she loves children. She loves our children and wants some of her own. It's a valid point, I can't deny her her rights . . . but still. . . . I thought you should know about it in case you agree to help."

"What do you mean?"

"Well, I have something arranged in Boston," he said, not looking at her, "and Dorie has agreed to it . . . though reluctantly . . . and, unfortunately, I don't think I can drive her, myself . . . you know I have to go to Chicago. . . ."

Barbara did not look at him.

"I'm on this panel at the University of Chicago, with John Ciardi. You know, it's been set up for a year, it's on the state of contemporary poetry—you know—I can't possibly withdraw from it now."

"And so?"

"If you could drive Dorie in—"

"If I could drive her in?"

"I don't see what alternative we have," he said slowly.

"Would you like a divorce so you can marry her?"

"I have never mentioned that," he said.

"Well, would you?"

"I don't know."

"Look at me. Do you want to marry her?"

A nerve began to twitch in his eye. It was a familiar twitch—it had been with him for two decades. "No, I don't think so. I don't know—you know how I feel about disruption."

"Don't you have any courage?"

"Courage?"

"If you want to marry her, go ahead. I won't stop you."

"Do you want a divorce, yourself?"

"I'm asking you. It's up to you. Then Dorie can have her baby and fulfill herself," Barbara said with a deathly smile, "she can assert her rights as a woman twenty years younger than I. She can become the third Mrs. Arber and become automatically envied. Don't you have the courage for it?"

"I had thought," Mark said with dignity, "that you and I had an admirable marriage. It was different from the marriages of other people we know—part of it is that we don't work in the same area, yes, but the most important part lay in our understanding of each other. It has taken a tremendous generosity on your part, Barbara, over the last three months and I appreciate it," he said, nodding slowly, "I appreciate it and I can't help asking myself whether . . . whether I would have had the strength to do what you did, in your place. I mean, if you had brought in—"

"I know what you mean."

"It's been an extraordinary marriage. I don't want it to end on an impulse, anything reckless or emotional," he said vaguely. She thought that he did look a little mad, but quietly mad; his ears were very red. For the first time she began to feel pity for the girl who was, after all, nobody, who had no personality, and who was waiting in the ugly maid's room for her fate to be decided.

"All right, I'll drive her to Boston," Barbara said.

Mark had to leave the next morning for Chicago. He would be gone, he explained, about a week—there was not only the speaking appearance but other things as well. The three of them had a kind of farewell party the night before. Dorie sat with her frail hand on her flat, child's stomach and drank listlessly, while Barbara and Mark argued about the comparative merits of two English novelists—their literary arguments were always witty, superficial, rapid, and very enjoyable. At two o'clock Mark woke Dorie to say good-bye and Barbara, thinking herself admirably discreet, went upstairs alone.

She drove Dorie to Boston the next day. Dorie was a mother's child, the kind of girl mothers admire—clean, bright, neat, passive—and it was a shame for her to be so frightened. Barbara said roughly, "I've known lots of women who've had abortions. They lived."

"Did you ever have one?"

"No," Barbara answered quickly but in a softer voice.

Dorie turned away as if in reproach.

"I've had children and that's harder, maybe. It's thought to be harder," Barbara said, as if offering the girl something.

"I would like children, maybe three of them," Dorie said.

"Three is a good number, yes."

"But I'd be afraid . . . I wouldn't know what to do. . . . I don't know what to do now. . . ."

She was just a child herself, Barbara thought with a rush of sympathy;

of all of them it was Dorie who was most trapped. The girl sat with a scarf around her careless hair, staring out the window. She wore a camel's hair coat like all the girls and her fingernails were colorless and uneven, as if she had been chewing them.

"Stop thinking about it. Sit still."

"Yes," the girl said listlessly.

They drove on. Something began to weigh at Barbara's heart, as if her flesh were aging moment by moment. She had never liked her body. Dorie's body was so much more prim and chaste and stylish, and her own body belonged to another age, a hearty nineteenth century where fat had been a kind of virtue. Barbara thought of her poetry, which was light and sometimes quite clever, the poetry of a girl, glimmering with half-seen visions and echoing with peculiar off-rhymes—and truly it ought to have been Dorie's poetry and not hers. She was not equal to her own writing. And, on the highway like this, speeding toward some tawdry destination, she had the sudden terrible conviction that language itself did not matter and that nothing mattered ultimately except the body, the human body and the bodies of other creatures and objects: what else existed?

Her own body was the only real fact about her. Dorie, huddled over in her corner, was another real fact and they were going to do something about it, defeat it. She thought of Mark already in Chicago, at a cocktail party, the words growing like weeds in his brain and his wit moving so rapidly through the brains of others that it was, itself, a kind of lie. It seemed strange to her that the two of them should move against Dorie, who suffered because she was totally real and helpless and gave up nothing of herself to words.

They arrived in Boston and began looking for the street. Barbara felt clumsy and guilty and did not dare to glance over at the girl. She muttered aloud as they drove for half an hour, without luck. Then she found the address. It was a small private hospital with a blank grey front. Barbara drove past it and circled the block and approached it again. "Come on, get hold of yourself," she said to Dorie's stiff profile, "this is no picnic for me either."

She stopped the car and she and Dorie stared out at the hospital, which looked deserted. The neighborhood itself seemed deserted. Finally Barbara said, with a heaviness she did not yet understand, "Let's find a place to stay tonight, first. Let's get that settled." She took the silent girl to a motel on a boulevard and told her to wait in the room, she'd be back shortly. Dorie stared in a drugged silence at Barbara, who could have been her mother—there flashed between them the kind of camaraderie possible only between mother and daughter—and then Barbara left the room. Dorie remained sitting in a very light chair of imitation wood and leather. She sat so that she was staring at the edge of the bureau; occasionally her eye was attracted by the framed picture over the bed, of a woman in a red evening gown and a man in a tuxedo observing a waterfall by moonlight. She sat like this for quite a while, in her coat. A nerve kept twitching in her thigh but it did not bother her; it was a most energetic, thumping twitch, as if her very flesh were doing a dance. But it did not bother her. She remained there for a while, waking to the morning light, and it took her several panicked moments to remember where she was and who had brought her here. She had the immediate thought that she must be safe—if it was morning she must be safe—and someone had taken care of her, had seen what was best for her and had carried it out.

And so she became the third Mrs. Arber, a month after the second one's death. Barbara had been found dead in an elegant motel across the city, the Paradise Inn, which Mark thought was a brave, cynical joke; he took Barbara's death with an alarming, rhetorical melodrama, an alcoholic melancholy Dorie did not like. Barbara's "infinite courage" made Dorie resentful. The second Mrs. Arber had taken a large dose of sleeping pills and had died easily, because of the strain her body had made upon her heart; so that was that. But somehow it wasn't—because Mark kept talking about it, speculating on it, wondering: "She did it for the baby, to preserve life. It's astonishing, it's exactly like something in a novel," he said. He spoke with a perpetual guilty astonishment.

She married him and became Mrs. Arber, which surprised everyone. It surprised even Mark. Dorie herself was not very surprised, because a daydreamer is prepared for most things and in a way she had planned even this, though she had not guessed how it would come about. Surely she had rehearsed the second Mrs. Arber's suicide and funeral already a year before, when she'd known nothing, could have guessed nothing, and it did not really surprise her. Events lost their jagged edges and became hard and opaque and routine, drawing her into them. She was still a daydreamer, though she was Mrs. Arber. She sat at the old desk up in the attic and leaned forward on her bony elbows to stare out the window, contemplating the hopeless front yard and the people who strolled by, some of them who—she thought—glanced toward the house with a kind of amused contempt, as if aware of her inside. She was almost always home.

The new baby was a girl, Carolyn. Dorie took care of her endlessly, and she took care of the boys; she hadn't been able to finish school. In the evening when all the children were at last asleep Mark would come out of his study and read to her in his rapid, impatient voice snatches of his new novel, or occasionally poems of his late wife's, and Dorie would stare at him and try to understand. She was transfixed with love for him and yet—and yet she was unable to locate this love in this particular man, unable to comprehend it. Mark was invited everywhere that spring; he flew all the way out to California to take part in a highly publicized symposium with George Steiner and James Baldwin, and Dorie stayed home. Geoffrey was seeing a psychiatrist in Boston and she had to drive him in every other day, and there was her own baby, and Mark's frequent visitors who arrived often without notice and stayed a week—sleeping late, staying up late, drinking, eating, arguing—it was exactly the kind of life she had known would be hers, and yet she could not adjust to it. Her baby was somehow mixed up in her mind with the other wife, as if it had been that woman's and only left to her, Dorie, for safekeeping. She was grateful that her baby was a girl because wasn't there always a kind of pact or understanding between women?

In June two men arrived at the house to spend a week, and Dorie had to cook for them. They were long, lean, grey-haired young men who were undefinable, sometimes very fussy, sometimes reckless and hysterical with wit, always rather insulting in a light, veiled manner Dorie could not catch. They were both vegetarians and could not tolerate anyone eating meat in their presence. One evening at a late dinner Dorie began to cry and had to leave the room, and the two guests and Mark and even the children were displeased with her. She went up to the attic and sat mechanically at the desk. It did no good to read Barbara Scott's poetry because she did not understand it. Her understanding had dropped to tending the baby and the boys, fixing meals, cleaning up, and shopping, and taking the station wagon to the garage perpetually . . . and she had no time to go with the others to the tennis courts, or to accompany Mark to New York . . . and around her were human beings whose lives consisted of language, the grace of language, and she could no longer understand them. She felt strangely cheated, a part of her murdered, as if the abortion had taken place that day after all and something had been cut permanently out of her.

In a while Mark climbed the stairs to her. She heard him coming, she heard his labored breathing. "Here you are," he said, and slid his big beefy arms around her and breathed his liquory love into her face, calling her his darling, his beauty. After all, he did love her, it was real and his arms were real, and she still loved him although she had lost the meaning of that word. "Now will you come downstairs and apologize, please?" he said gently. "You've disturbed them and it can't be left like this. You know how I hate disruption."

She began weeping again, helplessly, to think that she had disturbed anyone, that she was this girl sitting at a battered desk in someone's attic, and no one else, no other person who might confidently take upon herself the meaning of this man's words—she was herself and that was a fact, a final fact she'd never overcome.

FAITH

Flannery O'Connor

THE ARTIFICIAL NIGGER

Mr. Head awakened to discover that the room was full of moonlight. He sat up and stared at the floor boards—the color of silver—and then at the ticking on his pillow, which might have been brocade, and after a second, he saw half of the moon five feet away in his shaving mirror, paused as if it were waiting for his permission to enter. It rolled forward and cast a dignifying light on everything. The straight chair against the wall looked stiff and attentive as if it were awaiting an order and Mr. Head's trousers, hanging to the back of it, had an almost noble air, like the garment some great man had just flung to his servant; but the face on the moon was a grave one. It gazed across the room and out the window where it floated over the horse stall and appeared to contemplate itself with the look of a young man who sees his old age before him.

Mr. Head could have said to it that age was a choice blessing and that only with years does a man enter into that calm understanding of life that makes him a suitable guide for the young. This, at least, had been his own experience.

He sat up and grasped the iron posts at the foot of his bed and raised himself until he could see the face on the alarm clock which sat on an overturned bucket beside the chair. The hour was two in the morning. The alarm on the clock did not work but he was not dependent on any mechanical means to awaken him. Sixty years had not dulled his responses; his physical reactions, like his moral ones, were guided by his will and strong character, and these could be seen plainly in his features. He had a long tube-like face with a long rounded open jaw and a long depressed nose. His eyes were alert but quiet, and in the miraculous moonlight they had a look of composure and of ancient wisdom as if they belonged to one of the great guides of men. He might have been Vergil summoned in the middle of the night to go to Dante, or better, Raphael, awakened by a blast of God's light to fly to the side of Tobias. The only dark spot in the room was Nelson's pallet, underneath the shadow of the window.

Nelson was hunched over on his side, his knees under his chin and his heels under his bottom. His new suit and hat were in the boxes that they had been sent in and these were on the floor at the foot of the pallet where he could get his hands on them as soon as he woke up. The slop jar, out of the shadow and made snow-white in the moonlight, appeared to stand guard over him like a small personal angel. Mr. Head lay back down, feeling entirely confident that he could carry out the moral mission of the coming day. He meant to be up before Nelson and to have the breakfast cooking by the time he awakened. The boy was always irked when Mr. Head was the first up. They would have to leave the house at four to get to the railroad junction by five-thirty. The train was to stop for them at five forty-five and they had to be there on time for this train was stopping merely to accommodate them.

This would be the boy's first trip to the city though he claimed it would be his second because he had been born there. Mr. Head had tried to point out to him that when he was born he didn't have the intelligence to determine his whereabouts but this had made no impression on the child at all and he continued to insist that this was to be his second trip. It would be Mr. Head's third trip. Nelson had said, "I will've already been there twict and I ain't but ten."

Mr. Head had contradicted him.

"If you ain't been there in fifteen years, how you know you'll be able to find your way about?" Nelson had asked. "How you know it hasn't changed some?"

"Have you ever," Mr. Head had asked, "seen me lost?"

Nelson certainly had not but he was a child who was never satisfied until he had given an impudent answer and he replied, "It's nowhere around here to get lost at."

"The day is going to come," Mr. Head prophesied, "when you'll find you ain't as smart as you think you are." He had been thinking about this trip for several months but it was for the most part in moral terms that he conceived it. It was to be a lesson that the boy would never forget. He was to find out from it that he had no cause for pride merely because he had been born in a city. He was to find out that the city is not a great place. Mr. Head meant him to see everything there is to see in a city so that he would be content to stay at home for the rest of his life. He fell asleep thinking how the boy would at last find out that he was not as smart as he thought he was.

He was awakened at three-thirty by the smell of fatback frying and he leaped off his cot. The pallet was empty and the clothes boxes had been thrown open. He put on his trousers and ran into the other room. The boy had a corn pone on cooking and had fried the meat. He was sitting in the half-dark at the table, drinking cold coffee out of a can. He had on his new suit and his new gray hat pulled low over his eyes. It was too big for him but they had ordered it a size large because they expected his head to grow. He didn't say anything but his entire figure suggested satisfaction at having arisen before Mr. Head.

Mr. Head went to the stove and brought the meat to the table in the skillet. "It's no hurry," he said. "You'll get there soon enough and it's no guarantee you'll like it when you do neither," and he sat down across from the boy whose hat teetered back slowly to reveal a fiercely expressionless face, very much the same shape as the old man's. They were grandfather and grandson but they looked enough alike to be brothers and brothers not too far apart in age, for Mr. Head had a youthful expression by daylight, while the boy's look was ancient, as if he knew everything already and would be pleased to forget it.

Mr. Head had once had a wife and daughter and when the wife died, the daughter ran away and returned after an interval with Nelson. Then one morning, without getting out of bed, she died and left Mr. Head with sole care of the year-old child. He had made the mistake of telling Nelson that he had been born in Atlanta. If he hadn't told him that, Nelson couldn't have insisted that this was going to be his second trip.

"You may not like it a bit," Mr. Head continued. "It'll be full of niggers."

The boy made a face as if he could handle a nigger.

"All right," Mr. Head said. "You ain't ever seen a nigger."

"You wasn't up very early," Nelson said.

"You ain't ever seen a nigger," Mr. Head repeated. "There hasn't been a nigger in this county since we run that one out twelve years ago and that was before you were born." He looked at the boy as if he were daring him to say he had ever seen a Negro.

"How you know I never saw a nigger when I lived there before?" Nelson asked. "I probably saw a lot of niggers."

"If you seen one you didn't know what he was," Mr. Head said, completely exasperated. "A six-month-old child don't know a nigger from anybody else."

"I reckon I'll know a nigger if I see one," the boy said and got up and straightened his slick sharply creased gray hat and went outside to the privy.

They reached the junction some time before the train was due to arrive and stood about two feet from the first set of tracks. Mr. Head carried a paper sack with some biscuits and a can of sardines in it for their lunch. A coarse-looking orange-colored sun coming up behind the east range of mountains was making the sky a dull red behind them, but in front of them it was still gray and they faced a gray transparent moon, hardly stronger than a thumbprint and completely without light. A small tin switch box and a black fuel tank were all there was to mark the place as a junction; the tracks were double and did not converge again until they were hidden behind the bends at either end of the clearing. Trains passing appeared to emerge from a tunnel of trees and, hit for a second by the cold sky, vanish terrified into the woods again. Mr. Head had had to make special arrangements with the ticket agent to have this train stop and he was secretly afraid it would not, in which case, he knew Nelson would say, "I never thought no train was going to stop for you." Under the useless morning moon the tracks looked white and fragile. Both the old man and the child stared ahead as if they were awaiting an apparition.

Then suddenly, before Mr. Head could make up his mind to turn back, there was a deep warning bleat and the train appeared, gliding very slowly, almost silently around the bend of trees about two hundred yards down the track, with one yellow front light shining. Mr. Head was still not certain it would stop and he felt it would make an even bigger idiot of him if it went by slowly. But he and Nelson, however, were prepared to ignore the train if it passed them.

The engine charged by, filling their noses with the smell of hot metal and then the second coach came to a stop exactly where they were standing. A conductor with the face of an ancient bloated bulldog was on the step as if he expected them, though he did not look as if it mattered one way or the other to him if they got on or not. "To the right," he said.

Their entry took only a fraction of a second and the train was already speeding on as they entered the quiet car. Most of the travelers were still sleeping, some with their heads hanging off the chair arms, some stretched across two seats, and some sprawled out with their feet in the aisle. Mr. Head saw two unoccupied seats and pushed Nelson toward them. "Get in there by the winder," he said in his normal voice which was very loud at this hour of the morning. "Nobody cares if you set there because it's nobody in it. Sit right there."

"I heard you," the boy muttered. "It's no use in you yelling," and he sat down and turned his head to the glass. There he saw a pale ghost-like face scowling at him beneath the brim of a pale ghost-like hat. His grandfather, looking quickly too, saw a different ghost, pale but grinning, under a black hat.

Mr. Head sat down and settled himself and took out his ticket and started reading aloud everything that was printed on it. People began to stir. Several woke up and stared at him. "Take off your hat," he said to Nelson and took off his own and put it on his knee. He had a small amount of white hair that had turned tobacco-colored over the years and this lay flat across the back of his head. The front of his head was bald and creased. Nelson took off his hat and put it on his knee and they waited for the conductor to come ask for their tickets.

The man across the aisle from them was spread out over two seats, his feet propped on the window and his head jutting into the aisle. He had on a light blue suit and a yellow shirt unbuttoned at the neck. His eyes had just opened and Mr. Head was ready to introduce himself when the conductor came up from behind and growled, "Tickets."

When the conductor had gone, Mr. Head gave Nelson the return half of his ticket and said, "Now put that in your pocket and don't lose it or you'll have to stay in the city."

"Maybe I will," Nelson said as if this were a reasonable suggestion.

Mr. Head ignored him. "First time this boy has ever been on a train," he explained to the man across the aisle, who was sitting up now on the edge of his seat with both feet on the floor.

Nelson jerked his hat on again and turned angrily to the window.

"He's never seen anything before," Mr. Head continued. "Ignorant as the day he was born, but I mean for him to get his fill once and for all."

The boy leaned forward, across his grandfather and toward the stranger. "I was born in the city," he said. "I was born there. This is my second trip." He said it in a high positive voice but the man across the aisle didn't look as if he understood. There were heavy purple circles under his eyes.

Mr. Head reached across the aisle and tapped him on the arm. "The thing to do with a boy," he said sagely, "is to show him all it is to show. Don't hold nothing back."

"Yeah," the man said. He gazed down at his swollen feet and lifted the left one about ten inches from the floor. After a minute he put it down and lifted the other. All through the car people began to get up and move about and yawn and stretch. Separate voices could be heard here and there and then a general hum. Suddenly Mr. Head's serene expression changed. His mouth almost closed and a light, fierce and cautious both, came into his eyes. He was looking down the length of the car. Without turning, he caught Nelson by the arm and pulled him forward. "Look," he said.

A huge coffee-colored man was coming slowly forward. He had on a light suit and a yellow satin tie with a ruby pin in it. One of his hands rested on his stomach which rode majestically under his buttoned coat, and in the other he held the head of a black walking stick that he picked up and set down with a deliberate outward motion each time he took a step. He was proceeding very slowly, his large brown eyes gazing over the heads of the passengers. He had a small white mustache and white crinkly hair. Behind him there were two young women, both coffee-colored, one in a yellow dress and one in a green. Their progress was kept at the rate of his and they chatted in low throaty voices as they followed him.

Mr. Head's grip was tightening insistently on Nelson's arm. As the procession passed them, the light from a sapphire ring on the brown hand that picked up the cane reflected in Mr. Head's eye, but he did not look up nor did the tremendous man look at him. The group proceeded up the rest of the aisle and out of the car. Mr. Head's grip on Nelson's arm loosened. "What was that?" he asked.

"A man," the boy said and gave him an indignant look as if he were tired of having his intelligence insulted.

"What kind of a man?" Mr. Head persisted, his voice expressionless.

"A fat man," Nelson said. He was beginning to feel that he had better be cautious.

"You don't know what kind?" Mr. Head said in a final tone.

"An old man," the boy said and had a sudden foreboding that he was not going to enjoy the day.

"That was a nigger," Mr. Head said and sat back.

Nelson jumped up on the seat and stood looking backward to the end of the car but the Negro had gone.

"I'd of thought you'd know a nigger since you seen so many when you was in the city on your first visit," Mr. Head continued. "That's his first nigger," he said to the man across the aisle.

The boy slid down into the seat. "You said they were black," he said in an angry voice. "You never said they were tan. How do you expect me to know anything when you don't tell me right?"

"You're just ignorant is all," Mr. Head said and he got up and moved over in the vacant seat by the man across the aisle.

Nelson turned backward again and looked where the Negro had disappeared. He felt that the Negro had deliberately walked down the aisle in order to make a fool of him and he hated him with a fierce raw fresh hate; and also, he understood now why his grandfather disliked them. He looked toward the window and the face there seemed to suggest that he might be inadequate to the day's exactions. He wondered if he would even recognize the city when they came to it.

After he had told several stories, Mr. Head realized that the man he was talking to was asleep and he got up and suggested to Nelson that they walk over the train and see the parts of it. He particularly wanted the boy to see the toilet so they went first to the men's room and examined the plumbing. Mr. Head demonstrated the ice-water cooler as if he had invented it and showed Nelson the bowl with the single spigot where the travelers brushed their teeth. They went through several cars and came to the diner.

This was the most elegant car in the train. It was painted a rich egg-yellow and had a wine-colored carpet on the floor. There were wide windows over the tables and great spaces of the rolling view were caught in miniature in the sides of the coffee pots and in the glasses. Three very black Negroes in white suits and aprons were running up and down the aisle, swinging trays and bowing and bending over the travelers eating breakfast. One of them rushed up to Mr. Head and Nelson and said, holding up two fingers, "Space for two!" but Mr. Head replied in a loud voice, "We eaten before we left!"

The waiter wore large brown spectacles that increased the size of his eye whites. "Stan' aside then please," he said with an airy wave of the arm as if he were brushing aside flies.

Neither Nelson nor Mr. Head moved a fraction of an inch. "Look," Mr. Head said.

The near corner of the diner, containing two tables, was set off from the rest by a saffron-colored curtain. One table was set but empty but at the other, facing them, his back to the drape, sat the tremendous Negro. He was speaking in a soft voice to the two women while he buttered a muffin. He had a heavy sad face and his neck bulged over his white collar on either side. "They rope them off," Mr. Head explained. Then he said, "Let's go see the kitchen," and they walked the length of the diner but the black waiter was coming fast behind them.

"Passengers are not allowed in the kitchen!" he said in a haughty voice. "Passengers are NOT allowed in the kitchen!"

Mr. Head stopped where he was and turned. "And there's good reason for that," he shouted into the Negro's chest, "because the cockroaches would run the passengers out!"

All the travelers laughed and Mr. Head and Nelson walked out, grinning. Mr. Head was known at home for his quick wit and Nelson felt a sudden keen pride in him. He realized the old man would be his only support in the strange place they were approaching. He would be entirely alone in the world if he were ever lost from his grandfather. A terrible excitement shook him and he wanted to take hold of Mr. Head's coat and hold on like a child.

As they went back to their seats they could see through the passing windows that the countryside was becoming speckled with small houses and shacks and that a highway ran alongside the train. Cars sped by on it, very small and fast. Nelson felt that there was less breath in the air than there had been thirty minutes ago. The man across the aisle had left and there was no one near for Mr. Head to hold a conversation with so he looked out the window, through his own reflection, and read aloud the names of the buildings they were passing. "The Dixie Chemical Corp!" he announced. "Southern Maid Flour! Dixie Doors! Southern Belle Cotton Products! Patty's Peanut Butter! Southern Mammy Cane Syrup!"

"Hush up!" Nelson hissed.

All over the car people were beginning to get up and take their luggage off the overhead racks. Women were putting on their coats and hats. The conductor stuck his head in the car and snarled, "Firstoppppppmry," and Nelson lunged out of his sitting position, trembling. Mr. Head pushed him down by the shoulder.

"Keep your seat," he said in dignified tones. "The first stop is on the edge of town. The second stop is at the main railroad station." He had come by this knowledge on his first trip when he had got off at the first stop and had had to pay a man fifteen cents to take him into the heart of town. Nelson sat back down, very pale. For the first time in his life, he understood that his grandfather was indispensable to him.

The train stopped and let off a few passengers and glided on as if it had never ceased moving. Outside, behind rows of brown rickety houses, a line of blue buildings stood up, and beyond them a pale rose-gray sky faded away to nothing. The train moved into the railroad yard. Looking down, Nelson saw lines and lines of silver tracks multiplying and criss-crossing. Then before he could start counting them, the face in the window stared out at him, gray but distinct, and he looked the other way. The train was in the station. Both he and Mr. Head jumped up and ran to the door. Neither noticed that they had left the paper sack with the lunch in it on the seat.

They walked stiffly through the small station and came out of a heavy door into the squall of traffic. Crowds were hurrying to work. Nelson didn't know where to look. Mr. Head leaned against the side of the building and glared in front of him.

Finally Nelson said, "Well, how do you see what all it is to see?"

Mr. Head didn't answer. Then as if the sight of people passing had given him the clue, he said, "You walk," and started off down the street. Nelson followed, steadying his hat. So many sights and sounds were flooding in on him that for the first block he hardly knew what he was seeing. At the second corner, Mr. Head turned and looked behind him at the station they had left, a putty-colored terminal with a concrete dome on top. He thought that if he could keep the dome always in sight, he would be able to get back in the afternoon to catch the train again.

As they walked along, Nelson began to distinguish details and take note of the store windows, jammed with every kind of equipment—

hardware, drygoods, chicken feed, liquor. They passed one that Mr. Head called his particular attention to where you walked in and sat on a chair with your feet upon two rests and let a Negro polish your shoes. They walked slowly and stopped and stood at the entrances so he could see what went on in each place but they did not go into any of them. Mr. Head was determined not to go into any city store because on his first trip here, he had got lost in a large one and had found his way out only after many people had insulted him.

They came in the middle of the next block to a store that had a weighing machine in front of it and they both in turn stepped up on it and put in a penny and received a ticket. Mr. Head's ticket said, "You weigh 120 pounds. You are upright and-brave and all your friends admire you." He put the ticket in his pocket, surprised that the machine should have got his character correct but his weight wrong, for he had weighed on a grain scale not long before and knew he weighed 110. Nelson's ticket said, "You weigh 98 pounds. You have a great destiny ahead of you but beware of dark women." Nelson did not know any women and he weighed only 68 pounds but Mr. Head pointed out that the machine had probably printed the number upsidedown, meaning the 9 for a 6.

They walked on and at the end of five blocks the dome of the terminal sank out of sight and Mr. Head turned to the left. Nelson could have stood in front of every store window for an hour if there had not been another more interesting one next to it. Suddenly he said, "I was born here!" Mr. Head turned and looked at him with horror. There was a sweaty brightness about his face. "This is where I come from!" he said.

Mr. Head was appalled. He saw the moment had come for drastic action. "Lemme show you one thing you ain't seen yet," he said and took him to the corner where there was a sewer entrance. "Squat down," he said, "and stick your head in there," and he held the back of the boy's coat while he got down and put his head in the sewer. He drew it back quickly, hearing a gurgling in the depths under the sidewalk. Then Mr. Head explained the sewer system, how the entire city was underlined with it, how it contained all the drainage and was full of rats and how a man could slide into it and be sucked along down endless pitchblack tunnels. At any minute any man in the city might be sucked into the sewer and never heard from again. He described it so well that Nelson was for some seconds shaken. He connected the sewer passages with the entrance to hell and understood for the first time how the world was put together in its lower parts. He drew away from the curb.

Then he said, "Yes, but you can stay away from the holes," and his face took on that stubborn look that was so exasperating to his grandfather. "This is where I come from!" he said.

Mr. Head was dismayed but he only muttered, "You'll get your fill," and they walked on. At the end of two more blocks he turned to the left, feeling that he was circling the dome; and he was correct for in a half-hour they passed in front of the railroad station again. At first Nelson did not notice that he was seeing the same stores twice but when they passed the one where you put your feet on the rests while the Negro polished your shoes, he perceived that they were walking in a circle.

"We done been here!" he shouted. "I don't believe you know where you're at!"

"The direction just slipped my mind for a minute," Mr. Head said and they turned down a different street. He still did not intend to let the dome get too far away and after two blocks in their new direction, he turned to the left. This street contained two- and three-story wooden dwellings. Anyone passing on the sidewalk could see into the rooms and Mr. Head, glancing through one window, saw a woman lying on an iron bed, looking out, with a sheet pulled over her. Her knowing expression shook him. A fierce-looking boy on a bicycle came driving down out of nowhere and he had to jump to the side to keep from being hit. "It's nothing to them if they knock you down," he said. "You better keep closer to me."

They walked on for some time on streets like this before he remembered to turn again. The houses they were passing now were all unpainted and the wood in them looked rotten; the street between was narrower. Nelson saw a colored man. Then another. Then another. "Niggers live in these houses," he observed.

"Well come on and we'll go somewhere else," Mr. Head said. "We didn't come to look at niggers," and they turned down another street but they continued to see Negroes everywhere. Nelson's skin began to prickle and they stepped along at a faster pace in order to leave the neighborhood as soon as possible. There were colored men in their undershirts standing in the doors and colored women rocking on the sagging porches. Colored children played in the gutters and stopped what they were doing to look at them. Before long they began to pass rows of stores with colored customers in them but they didn't pause at the entrances of these. Black eyes in black faces were watching them from every direction. "Yes," Mr. Head said, "this is where you were born—right here with all these niggers."

Nelson scowled. "I think you done got us lost," he said.

Mr. Head swung around sharply and looked for the dome. It was nowhere in sight. "I ain't got us lost either," he said. "You're just tired of walking."

"I ain't tired, I'm hungry," Nelson said. "Give me a biscuit."

They discovered then that they had lost the lunch.

"You were the one holding the sack," Nelson said. "I would have kepaholt of it."

"If you want to direct this trip, I'll go on by myself and leave you right here," Mr. Head said and was pleased to see the boy turn white. However, he realized they were lost and drifting farther every minute from the station. He was hungry himself and beginning to be thirsty and since they had been in the colored neighborhood, they had both begun to sweat. Nelson had on his shoes and he was unaccustomed to them. The concrete sidewalks were very hard. They both wanted to find a place to sit down but this was impossible and they kept on walking, the boy muttering under his breath, "First you lost the sack and then you lost the way," and Mr. Head growling from time to time, "Anybody wants to be from this nigger heaven can be from it!"

By now the sun was well forward in the sky. The odor of dinners cooking drifted out to them. The Negroes were all at their doors to see them pass. "Whyn't you ast one of these niggers the way?" Nelson said. "You got us lost."

"This is where you were born," Mr. Head said. "You can ast one yourself if you want to."

Nelson was afraid of the colored men and he didn't want to be laughed at by the colored children. Up ahead he saw a large colored woman leaning in a doorway that opened onto the sidewalk. Her hair stood straight out from her head for about four inches all around and she was resting on bare brown feet that turned pink at the sides. She had on a pink dress that showed her exact shape. As they came abreast of her, she lazily lifted one hand to her head and her fingers disappeared into her hair.

Nelson stopped. He felt his breath drawn up by the woman's dark eyes. "How do you get back to town?" he said in a voice that did not sound like his own.

After a minute she said, "You in town now," in a rich low tone that made Nelson feel as if a cool spray had been turned on him.

"How do you get back to the train?" he said in the same reed-like voice.

"You can catch you a car," she said.

He understood she was making fun of him but he was too paralyzed even to scowl. He stood drinking in every detail of her. His eyes traveled up from her great knees to her forehead and then made a triangular path from the glistening sweat on her neck down and across her tremendous bosom and over her bare arm back to where her fingers lay hidden in her hair. He suddenly wanted her to reach down and pick him up and draw him against her and then he wanted to feel her breath on his face. He wanted to look down and down into her eyes while she held him tighter and tighter. He had never had such a feeling before. He felt as if he were reeling down through a pitchblack tunnel.

"You can go a block down yonder and catch you a car take you to the railroad station, Sugarpie," she said.

Nelson would have collapsed at her feet if Mr. Head had not pulled him roughly away. "You act like you don't have any sense!" the old man growled.

They hurried down the street and Nelson did not look back at the woman. He pushed his hat sharply forward over his face which was already burning with shame. The sneering ghost he had seen in the train window and all the foreboding feelings he had on the way returned to him and he remembered that his ticket from the scale had said to beware of dark women and that his grandfather's had said he was upright and brave. He took hold of the old man's hand, a sign of dependence that he seldom showed.

They headed down the street toward the car tracks where a long yellow rattling trolley was coming. Mr. Head had never boarded a streetcar and he let that one pass. Nelson was silent. From time to time his mouth trembled slightly but his grandfather, occupied with his own problems, paid him no attention. They stood on the corner and neither looked at the Negroes who were passing, going about their business just as if they had been white, except that most of them stopped and eyed Mr. Head and

Nelson. It occurred to Mr. Head that since the streetcar ran on tracks, they could simply follow the tracks. He gave Nelson a slight push and explained that they would follow the tracks on into the railroad station, walking, and they set off.

Presently to their great relief they began to see white people again and Nelson sat down on the sidewalk against the wall of a building. "I got to rest myself some," he said. "You lost the sack and the direction. You can just wait on me to rest myself."

"There's the tracks in front of us," Mr. Head said. "All we got to do is keep them in sight and you could have remembered the sack as good as me. This is where you were born. This is your old home town. This is your second trip. You ought to know how to do," and he squatted down and continued in this vein but the boy, easing his burning feet out of his shoes, did not answer.

"And standing there grinning like a chim-pan-zee while a nigger woman gives you directions. Great Gawd!" Mr. Head said.

"I never said I was nothing but born here," the boy said in a shaky voice. "I never said I would or wouldn't like it. I never said I wanted to come. I only said I was born here and I never had nothing to do with that. I want to go home. I never wanted to come in the first place. It was all your big idea. How you know you ain't following the tracks in the wrong direction?"

This last had occurred to Mr. Head too. "All these people are white," he said.

"We ain't passed here before," Nelson said. This was a neighborhood of brick buildings that might have been lived in or might not. A few empty automobiles were parked along the curb and there was an occasional passerby. The heat of the pavement came up through Nelson's thin suit. His eyelids began to droop, and after a few minutes his head tilted forward. His shoulders twitched once or twice and then he fell over on his side and lay sprawled in an exhausted fit of sleep.

Mr. Head watched him silently. He was very tired himself but they could not both sleep at the same time and he could not have slept anyway because he did not know where he was. In a few minutes Nelson would wake up, refreshed by his sleep and very cocky, and would begin complaining that he had lost the sack and the way. You'd have a mighty sorry time if I wasn't here, Mr. Head thought; and then another idea occurred to him. He looked at the sprawled figure for several minutes; presently he stood up. He justified what he was going to do on the grounds that it is sometimes necessary to teach a child a lesson he won't forget, particularly when the child is always reasserting his position with some new impudence. He walked without a sound to the corner about twenty feet away and sat down on a covered garbage can in the alley where he could look out and watch Nelson wake up alone.

The boy was dozing fitfully, half conscious of vague noises and black forms moving up from some dark part of him into the light. His face worked in his sleep and he had pulled his knees up under his chin. The sun shed a dull dry light on the narrow street; everything looked like exactly what it was. After a while Mr. Head, hunched like an old monkey on the garbage can lid, decided that if Nelson didn't wake up soon, he would make a loud noise by bamming his foot against the can. He looked at his watch and discovered that it was two o'clock. Their train left at six and the possibility of missing it was too awful for him to think of. He kicked his foot backwards on the can and a hollow boom reverberated in the alley.

Nelson shot up onto his feet with a shout. He looked where his grandfather should have been and stared. He seemed to whirl several times and then, picking up his feet and throwing his head back, he dashed down the street like a wild maddened pony. Mr. Head jumped off the can and galloped after but the child was almost out of sight. He saw a streak of gray disappearing diagonally a block ahead. He ran as fast as he could, looking both ways down every intersection, but without sight of him again. Then as he passed the third intersection completely winded, he saw about half a block down the street a scene that stopped him altogether. He crouched behind a trash box to watch and get his bearings.

Nelson was sitting with both legs spread out and by his side lay an elderly woman, screaming. Groceries were scattered about the sidewalk. A crowd of women had already gathered to see justice done and Mr. Head distinctly heard the old woman on the pavement shout, "You've broken my ankle and your daddy'll pay for it! Every nickel! Police! Police!" Several of the women were plucking at Nelson's shoulder but the boy seemed too dazed to get up.

Something forced Mr. Head from behind the trash box and forward, but only at a creeping pace. He had never in his life been accosted by a policeman. The women were milling around Nelson as if they might suddenly all dive on him at once and tear him to pieces, and the old woman continued to scream that her ankle was broken and to call for an officer. Mr. Head came on so slowly that he could have been taking a backward step after each forward one, but when he was about ten feet away, Nelson saw him and sprang. The child caught him around the hips and clung panting against him.

The women all turned on Mr. Head. The injured one sat up and shouted, "You sir! You'll pay every penny of my doctor's bill that your boy has caused. He's a juvenile delinquent! Where is an officer? Somebody take this man's name and address!"

Mr. Head was trying to detach Nelson's fingers from the flesh in the back of his legs. The old man's head had lowered itself into his collar like a turtle; his eyes were glazed with fear and caution.

"Your boy has broken my ankle!" the old woman shouted. "Police!"

Mr. Head sensed the approach of the policeman from behind. He stared straight ahead at the women who were massed in their fury like a solid wall to block his escape. "This is not my boy," he said. "I never seen him before."

He felt Nelson's fingers fall out of his flesh.

The women dropped back, staring at him with horror, as if they were so repulsed by a man who would deny his own image and likeness that they could not bear to lay hands on him. Mr. Head walked on, through a space they silently cleared, and left Nelson behind. Ahead of him he saw nothing but a hollow tunnel that had once been the street.

The boy remained standing where he was, his neck craned forward and his hands hanging by his sides. His hat was jammed on his head so that there were no longer any creases in it. The injured woman got up and shook her fist at him and the others gave him pitying looks, but he didn't notice any of them. There was no policeman in sight.

In a minute he began to move mechanically, making no effort to catch up with his grandfather but merely following at about twenty paces. They walked on for five blocks in this way. Mr. Head's shoulders were sagging and his neck hung forward at such an angle that it was not visible from behind. He was afraid to turn his head. Finally he cut a short hopeful glance over his shoulder. Twenty feet behind him, he saw two small eyes piercing into his back like pitchfork prongs.

The boy was not of a forgiving nature but this was the first time he had ever had anything to forgive. Mr. Head had never disgraced himself before. After two more blocks, he turned and called over his shoulder in a high desperately gay voice, "Let's us go get us a Co' Cola somewheres!"

Nelson, with a dignity he had never shown before, turned and stood with his back to his grandfather.

Mr. Head began to feel the depth of his denial. His face as they walked on became all hollows and bare ridges. He saw nothing they were passing but he perceived that they had lost the car tracks. There was no dome to be seen anywhere and the afternoon was advancing. He knew that if dark overtook them in the city, they would be beaten and robbed. The speed of God's justice was only what he expected for himself, but he could not stand to think that his sins would be visited upon Nelson and that even now, he was leading the boy to his doom.

They continued to walk on block after block through an endless section of small brick houses until Mr. Head almost fell over a water spigot sticking up about six inches off the edge of a grass plot. He had not had a drink of water since early morning but he felt he did not deserve it now. Then he thought that Nelson would be thirsty and they would both drink and be brought together. He squatted down and put his mouth to the nozzle and turned a cold stream of water into his throat. Then he called out in the high desperate voice, "Come on and getcher some water!"

This time the child stared through him for nearly sixty seconds. Mr. Head got up and walked on as if he had drunk poison. Nelson, though he had not had water since some he had drunk out of a paper cup on the train, passed by the spigot, disdaining to drink where his grandfather had. When Mr. Head realized this, he lost all hope. His face in the waning afternoon light looked ravaged and abandoned. He could feel the boy's steady hate, traveling at an even pace behind him and he knew that (if by some miracle they escaped being murdered in the city) it would continue just that way for the rest of his life. He knew that now he was wandering into a black strange place where nothing was like it had ever been before, a long old age without respect and an end that would be welcome because it would be the end.

As for Nelson, his mind had frozen around his grandfather's treachery as if he were trying to preserve it intact to present at the final judgment.

He walked without looking to one side or the other, but every now and then his mouth would twitch and this was when he felt, from some remote place inside himself, a black mysterious form reach up as if it would melt his frozen vision in one hot grasp.

The sun dropped down behind a row of houses and hardly noticing, they passed into an elegant suburban section where mansions were set back from the road by lawns with birdbaths on them. Here everything was entirely deserted. For blocks they didn't pass even a dog. The big white houses were like partially submerged icebergs in the distance. There were no sidewalks, only drives and these wound around and around in endless ridiculous circles. Nelson made no move to come nearer to Mr. Head. The old man felt that if he saw a sewer entrance he would drop down into it and let himself be carried away; and he could imagine the boy standing by, watching with only a slight interest, while he disappeared.

A loud bark jarred him to attention and he looked up to see a fat man approaching with two bulldogs. He waved both arms like someone shipwrecked on a desert island. "I'm lost!" he called. "I'm lost and can't find my way and me and this boy have got to catch this train and I can't find the station. Oh Gawd I'm lost! Oh help me Gawd I'm lost!"

The man, who was bald-headed and had on golf knickers, asked him what train he was trying to catch and Mr. Head began to get out his tickets, trembling so violently he could hardly hold them. Nelson had come up to within fifteen feet and stood watching.

"Well," the fat man said, giving him back the tickets, "you won't have time to get back to town to make this but you can catch it at the suburb stop. That's three blocks from here," and he began explaining how to get there.

Mr. Head stared as if he were slowly returning from the dead and when the man had finished and gone off with the dogs jumping at his heels, he turned to Nelson and said breathlessly, "We're going to get home!"

The child was standing about ten feet away, his face bloodless under the gray hat. His eyes were triumphantly cold. There was no light in them, no feeling, no interest. He was merely there, a small figure, waiting. Home was nothing to him.

Mr. Head turned slowly. He felt he knew now what time would be like without seasons and what heat would be like without light and what man would be like without salvation. He didn't care if he never made the train and if it had not been for what suddenly caught his attention, like a cry out of the gathering dusk, he might have forgotten there was a station to go to.

He had not walked five hundred yards down the road when he saw, within reach of him, the plaster figure of a Negro sitting bent over on a low yellow brick fence that curved around a wide lawn. The Negro was about Nelson's size and he was pitched forward at an unsteady angle because the putty that held him to the wall had cracked. One of his eyes was entirely white and he held a piece of brown watermelon.

Mr. Head stood looking at him silently until Nelson stopped at a little distance. Then as the two of them stood there, Mr. Head breathed,

"An artificial nigger!"

It was not possible to tell if the artificial Negro were meant to be young or old; he looked too miserable to be either. He was meant to look happy because his mouth was stretched up at the corners but the chipped eye and the angle he was cocked at gave him a wild look of misery instead.

"An artificial nigger!" Nelson repeated in Mr. Head's exact tone.

The two of them stood there with their necks forward at almost the same angle and their shoulders curved in almost exactly the same way and their hands trembling identically in their pockets. Mr. Head looked like an ancient child and Nelson like a miniature old man. They stood gazing at the artificial Negro as if they were faced with some great mystery, some monument to another's victory that brought them together in their common defeat. They could both feel it dissolving their differences like an action of mercy. Mr. Head had never known before what mercy felt like because he had been too good to deserve any, but he felt he knew now. He looked at Nelson and understood that he must say something to the child to show that he was still wise and in the look the boy returned he saw a hungry need for that assurance. Nelson's eyes seemed to implore him to explain once and for all the mystery of existence.

Mr. Head opened his lips to make a lofty statement and heard himself say, "They ain't got enough real ones here. They got to have an artificial one."

After a second, the boy nodded with a strange shivering about his mouth, and said, "Let's go home before we get ourselves lost again."

Their train glided into the suburb stop just as they reached the station and they boarded it together, and ten minutes before it was due to arrive at the junction, they went to the door and stood ready to jump off if it did not stop; but it did, just as the moon, restored to its full splendor, sprang from a cloud and flooded the clearing with light. As they stepped off, the sage grass was shivering gently in shades of silver and the clinkers under their feet glittered with a fresh black light. The treetops, fencing the junction like the protecting walls of a garden, were darker than the sky which was hung with gigantic white clouds illuminated like lanterns.

Mr. Head stood very still and felt the action of mercy touch him again but this time he knew that there were no words in the world that could name it. He understood that it grew out of agony, which is not denied to any man and which is given in strange ways to children. He understood it was all a man could carry into death to give his Maker and he suddenly burned with shame that he had so little of it to take with him. He stood appalled, judging himself with the thoroughness of God, while the action of mercy covered his pride like a flame and consumed it. He had never thought himself a great sinner before but he saw now that his true depravity had been hidden from him lest it cause him despair. He realized that he was forgiven for sins from the beginning of time, when he had conceived in his own heart the sin of Adam, until the present, when he had denied poor Nelson. He saw that no sin was too monstrous for him to claim as his own, and since God loved in proportion as He forgave, he felt ready at that instant to enter Paradise.

Nelson, composing his expression under the shadow of his hat brim, watched him with a mixture of fatigue and suspicion, but as the train glided past them and disappeared like a frightened serpent into the woods, even his face lightened and he muttered, "I'm glad I've went once, but I'll never go back again!"

ANALYSIS

Flannery O'Connor's "The Artificial Nigger" is an unusually successful fusion of allegory and realism. Unlike such relatively pure allegories as *Pilgrim's Progress* and *Everyman,* the story can be read as the actual experience of its characters in a real setting—grandfather and grandson going from their home in the backwoods of Georgia into Atlanta and back again. But even the least practiced of readers must be struck by the ending, where the issue of *mercy* emerges from some substratum of the story and takes on cosmic proportions. Mr. Head's denial of Nelson becomes the last in a long line of sins "from the beginning of time, when he had conceived in his own heart the sin of Adam." And the forgiveness becomes not only that of Nelson, but that of God: "and since God loved in proportion as He forgave, [Mr. Head] felt ready at that instant to enter Paradise."

However subtly, the allegorical elements have been there throughout the story, growing out of and adding dimension to its physical aspects. Mr. Head (whose name is significant) represents "will and strong character" and "ancient wisdom"—those virtues of man without salvation, without a living soul. Nelson is in a sense his alter ego, the soul which must be spiritually born into Man. One may look upon the grandfather and grandson as a single person—they are identified with each other consistently—and the salvation at the end of the story brings "them together in their common defeat. They could feel it dissolving their differences like an action of mercy." The two separate parts of man become one "whole." In most Christian doctrine, the child, though born in sin, must reach an age at which he is capable of a realization of his sin, including that original sin inherited from Adam, before he can be saved or "born again." Until then the child is in a state of innocence similar to that of Eden; after salvation he is back in a "sinless" state, but now through a realization of the mercy of God. Man must leave his Eden and go into the world of the flesh, of sin, must recognize that he is lost, and must come to Christ before he can be saved.

Nelson was born in Atlanta, which, in the story, represents the sinful world, and now that he is ten years old it is necessary for him to realize what he was born into. As "the soul" he is as yet unborn. If we take Mr. Head and Nelson as, together, Man, we may say that Man has been to the world, but as a "soul-less" observer. In his Head he knows that the world is not the place for him, but in his soul he knows that it is his home. The Head believes that, by his will and strong character and his worldly wisdom, he will be able to guide the Man, of which he is part, safely in the world, and that by experience and "calm understanding" Man will be able to withhold himself henceforth from the world, remaining in a state of innocence.

Thus it is that Mr. Head awakes in the moonlight believing himself to be a "suitable guide to the young." The moonlight, at the first of the story, is "miraculous" in that it shows things in a state of innocence, as Mr. Head sees them—it casts "a dignifying light on everything." It makes Mr. Head seem to be a great man and "one of the great guides of men." It is miraculous because it is a partial light, a merciful light—unlike the sun by which one sees things as, in worldly terms, they are. Nelson, lying as if in the womb, is not touched by the moonlight: "The only dark spot in the room was Nelson's pallet . . . Nelson was hunched over on his side, his knees under his chin and his heels under his bottom." Though Mr. Head is the part of Man with experience, he has "a youthful expression by daylight, while the boy's look was ancient, as if he knew everything already and would be pleased to forget it." The soul is born into the flesh already knowing, though not realizing, the sin-and-salvation which the Head cannot know alone.

When Mr. Head and Nelson reach the train tracks they are at the outer edge of their Eden, where the morning moon is "useless." The sky, it appears from later allusions, is God's—the moonlight itself with all its comforting falsification part of God's grace—and the train is identified as the serpent, in effect, which took Eve and Adam into sin and now takes the grandfather and grandson into the tunnel which becomes a symbol for the pathway to hell. "Trains passing appeared to emerge from a tunnel of trees and, hit for a second by the cold sky, vanish terrified into the woods again."

Much as in Melville's "Benito Cereno," Negroes are used in this story as symbols of sin. Here the realistic aspect is sound enough: The Negroes were segregated or used as servants in the Georgia of the time, and Atlanta certainly had its Negrotown. "The Artificial Nigger" is not a story about race, however, and one should not demand of it a message about civil rights. The story is allegorical, and in its Southern setting the Negro was in such a position that he could be used to represent sin-which-is-apparent by virtue of color, in the same way that the train could be used to represent the serpent. Nelson has never seen a Negro, and when he sees his first one he does not recognize him as a Negro. Sin is represented as "black," by moralists like Mr. Head, and the borning soul may not recognize the actual thing because it is not black: "The boy slid down into the seat. 'You said they were black,' he said in an angry voice. 'You never said they were tan. How do you expect me to know anything when you don't tell me right?'" In Mr. Head's moonlight abstractions, Negroes are black; in the world of "reality," which the two begin to enter at the train tracks, abstractions are nonfunctional.

In spite of the danger of getting lost and of such worldly deceptions as that of the weighing machine, the soul of man has a longing, a perverse desire for the world, the flesh, and the devil. Nelson is fascinated:

[He] could have stood in front of every store window for an hour if there had not been another more interesting one next to it. Suddenly he said, "I was born here!" Mr. Head turned and looked at him with horror. There was a sweaty brightness about his face. "This is where I come from!" he said.

Mr. Head takes "drastic action." He shows Nelson the sewer, holding the boy by his coat.

Then Mr. Head explained the sewer system, how the entire city was underlined with it, how it contained all the drainage and was full of rats and how a man could slide into it and be sucked along down endless pitchblack tunnels. At any minute any man in the city might be sucked into the sewer and never heard from again. He described it so well that Nelson was for some seconds shaken. He connected the sewer passages with the entrance to hell and understood for the first time how the world was put together in its lower parts.

As the two get lost, they first encounter apparent unsymbolic sin—the prostitute lying in bed, the boy who nearly runs them down—and then they arrive at the poorer section of the city, where the wood of the houses looks "rotten"; they are thoroughly lost now, in the Negro section. Mr. Head, whose sin is not of the flesh, not of love for the world, tells Nelson that, "Anybody wants to be from this nigger heaven can be from it!" Nelson, however, is drawn to the Negro woman of whom he asks directions. The effect is that of one caught by the desires of the flesh, mesmerized by the "earth" which is the mother of men and which is their death.

He suddenly wanted her to reach down and pick him up and draw him against her and then he wanted to feel her breath on his face. He wanted to look down and down into her eyes while she held him tighter and tighter. He had never had such a feeling before. He felt as if he were reeling down through a pitchblack tunnel.

Nelson has reached his depth of sin here, and at the entrance to the "pitchblack tunnel" into hell (although he has said, "Yes, but you can stay away from the holes") he "would have collapsed at her feet if Mr. Head had not pulled him roughly away."

Certain Christian concepts must be kept in mind: Sin is inherent in man, and he naturally responds to the sinful world. He is incapable of saving himself. And he must often reach the depths before he can be "found."

Here composite Man is restrained by his will from total collapse, but the will is not invulnerable either. Soon Nelson drops off to sleep in the white section, which is, though less obviously sinful, still in the city. Nelson, susceptible to the flesh, has been tempted in the fleshly-sin section of the world; Mr. Head's temptation comes in the white section, where pride, not desire, is the deadly sin. As Nelson sleeps, "black forms" move "up from some dark part of him into the light"; Mr. Head is awake in a peculiar light. The sun has been described earlier, when the moonlight waned, as "coarse-looking" and "orange-colored"; as the man and the boy wandered through the Negro section "the sun was well forward in the sky": now "everything looked like exactly what it was." Mr. Head's abstractions, it has been said, do not work in the world. Now with all worldly reality perfectly clear to him, Mr. Head makes his crucial error.

After his disastrous trick on Nelson, Mr. Head denies him. Not only is the denial reminiscent of Peter's denial of Jesus, and of Judas' turning Jesus over to the authorities for trial (the "policeman" behind him is what most frightens Mr. Head), but it is so obviously a denial of a part of himself, his soul, that even the worldly women are shocked. Perhaps some parallel should be pointed out, though any single instance is too narrow to be taken literally: A "scientific" approach to Man, via the head, is likely to leave out those things not seen when, in the light of examination, everything looks like exactly what it is—and the soul, not apparent, is denied.

Now this Man is totally lost, separated not only from God but from the potential of God in himself. Nelson's desire for the "pitchblack tunnel" has been appropriately a perverse, sinful, earth-bound desire for spiritual death. Mr. Head, the intellectual part of Man, now walks down "a hollow tunnel that had once been the street." His efforts on his own to bring about a reconciliation fail, and he expects God's justice for himself, but cannot "stand to think that his sins would be visited upon Nelson and that even now, he was leading the boy to his doom." From the time before the denial when everything looked like exactly what it was, Mr. Head has come a long way: "He knew that now he was wandering into a black strange place where nothing was like it had ever been before, a long old age without respect and an end that would be welcome because it would be the end."

As for Nelson, his mind had frozen around his grandfather's treachery as if he were trying to preserve it intact to present at the final judgment. . . . [H]e felt, from some remote place inside himself, a black mysterious form reach up as if it would melt his frozen vision in one hot grasp.

The "black mysterious form" is the realization of sin and the subsequent, in part consequent, forgiveness. It will soon be objectified and will melt the "frozen vision" which sees the "big white houses" as "partially submerged icebergs," and which holds the treachery intact for final judgment. Mr. Head feels now that he "would drop down into" a sewer entrance if one were available, "and let himself be carried away."

With no hope, Mr. Head loses his pride and admits that he himself is lost—a necessary step toward salvation. "Oh Gawd I'm lost! Oh help me Gawd I'm lost!" The man with the dogs cannot save them, but can give them directions to the train. Mr. Head says, "We're going to get home!" But Nelson does not respond:

his face [was] bloodless under the gray hat. His eyes were triumphantly cold. There was no light in them, no feeling, no interest. He was merely there, a small figure, waiting. Home was nothing to him.

Denied, the soul is inoperative; it awaits judgment or salvation, but it cannot return on its own to the former state of innocence. Home, the place one lives, is now a kind of hell: "Mr. Head . . . felt he knew now what time would be like without seasons and what heat would be like without light and what man would be like without salvation."

Salvation does come, however, as Mr. Head and Nelson are drawn together in contemplation of the artificial Negro. The plaster figure is the symbol of sin, the depiction of Man as he is without God, the ultimate in defeat. In it Mr. Head and Nelson see their own image, their own sin symbolized, but as conquered, standing as the crucifix stands for the expiation of the sins of the world, the death of death. They stand in awe before the great mystery of the mercy of God:

> The Negro was about Nelson's size and he was pitched forward at an unsteady angle because the putty that held him to the wall had cracked. One of his eyes was entirely white and he held a piece of brown watermelon. . . .
>
> It was not possible to tell if the artificial Negro were meant to be young or old; he looked too miserable to be either. He was meant to look happy because his mouth was stretched up at the corners but the chipped eye and the angle he was cocked at gave him a wild look of misery instead.
>
> "An artificial nigger!" Nelson repeated in Mr. Head's exact tone.
>
> The two of them stood there with their necks forward at almost the same angle and their shoulders curved in almost exactly the same way and their hands trembling identically in their pockets. Mr. Head looked like an ancient child and Nelson like a miniature old man. They stood gazing at the artificial Negro as if they were faced with some great mystery, some monument to another's victory that brought them together in their common defeat. They could feel it dissolving their differences like an action of mercy.

In taking upon himself defeat and death, Jesus took with Him the sins of all mankind; He rose again, but they didn't; through defeat and death He achieved victory and life. The artificial Negro, somewhat like the cross, is a monument not to sin, or death, but to "another's victory that" brings "them together in their common defeat." It is through "defeat" that the individual comes to mercy, much as through defeat Christ came to victory. Man can look upon all the sins in the world (all the "real ones") without achieving mercy, just as he may look upon death without attaining life. Yet through the symbolic representation of death's defeat, the cross, he is said to receive life. And by the symbolic representation of the defeat of sin—the artificial Negro—Mr. Head and Nelson receive mercy. When Mr. Head opens his "lips to make a lofty statement," he hears himself say something that, like the Apostle Paul's "foolishness of preaching," comes out not lofty—it is humorous in its effect—but true: "They ain't got enough real ones here. They got to have an artificial one." In Christian terms, all the real death in the world will not make for victory over death; we must have a supernatural death which carries with it all sin from which death derives. And then we must have it presented to us in terms that we can appropriate, by means of a symbol, an artificial "real one."

Sin, defeat, and death express the limited condition of Man, the fact that he is not complete, perfect, whole; but mercy may bring together the two nonphysical elements of Man, mind and soul. Given spiritual wholeness, Man is capable of perceiving things hidden from him in his limitation.

Together, Mr. Head and Nelson go home where just as the train stops the moon, restored to its full splendor, sprang from a cloud and flooded the clearing with light. . . . The treetops, fencing the junction like the protecting walls of a garden, were darker than the sky which was hung with gigantic white clouds illuminated like lanterns.

Before, the miraculous moonlight mercifully gave Mr. Head his own partial view—the only view he could stand without despairing. Now, just as far from the city sunlight which makes everything look like exactly what it is, the moonlight allows Mr. Head to contemplate, with eyes no longer limited to external reality or prideful abstractions, the enormity of his own sin and the greatness of God's mercy. And the train disappears "like a frightened serpent into the woods."

Frank O'Connor

FIRST CONFESSION

All the trouble began when my grandfather died and my grandmother—my father's mother—came to live with us. Relations in the one house are a strain at the best of times, but, to make matters worse, my grandmother was a real old countrywoman and quite unsuited to the life in town. She had a fat, wrinkled old face, and, to Mother's great indignation, went round the house in bare feet—the boots had her crippled, she said. For dinner she had a jug of porter and a pot of potatoes with—sometimes—a bit of salt fish, and she poured out the potatoes on the table and ate them slowly, with great relish, using her fingers by way of a fork.

Now, girls are supposed to be fastidious, but I was the one who suffered most from this. Nora, my sister, just sucked up to the old woman for the penny she got every Friday out of the old-age pension, a thing I could not do. I was too honest, that was my trouble; and when I was playing with Bill Connell, the sergeant-major's son, and saw my grandmother steering up the path with the jug of porter sticking out from beneath her shawl I was mortified. I made excuses not to let him come into the house, because I could never be sure what she would be up to when we went in.

When Mother was at work and my grandmother made the dinner I wouldn't touch it. Nora once tried to make me, but I hid under the table from her and took the bread-knife with me for protection. Nora let on to be very indignant (she wasn't, of course, but she knew Mother saw through her, so she sided with Gran) and came after me. I lashed out at her with the bread-knife, and after that she left me alone. I stayed there till Mother came in from work and made my dinner, but when Father came in later Nora said in a shocked voice: "Oh, Dadda, do you know what Jackie did at dinnertime?" Then, of course, it all came out; Father gave me a flaking; Mother interfered, and for days after that he didn't speak to me and Mother barely spoke to Nora. And all because of that old woman! God knows, I was heart-scalded.

Then, to crown my misfortunes, I had to make my first confession and communion. It was an old woman called Ryan who prepared us for these. She was about the one age with Gran; she was well-to-do, lived in a big house on Montenotte, wore a black cloak and bonnet, and came every day to school at three o'clock when we should have been going home, and talked to us of hell. She may have mentioned the other place as well, but that could only have been by accident, for hell had the first place in her heart.

She lit a candle, took out a new half-crown, and offered it to the first boy who would hold one finger—only one finger!—in the flame for five minutes by the school clock. Being always very ambitious I was tempted to volunteer, but I thought it might look greedy. Then she asked were we afraid of holding one finger—only one finger!—in a little candle flame for five minutes and not afraid of burning all over in roasting hot furnaces for all eternity. "All eternity! Just think of that! A whole lifetime goes by and it's nothing, not even a drop in the ocean of your sufferings." The woman was really interesting about hell, but my attention was all fixed on the half-crown. At the end of the lesson she put it back in her purse. It was a great disappointment; a religious woman like that, you wouldn't think she'd bother about a thing like a half-crown.

Another day she said she knew a priest who woke one night to find a fellow he didn't recognize leaning over the end of his bed. The priest was a bit frightened—naturally enough—but he asked the fellow what he wanted, and the fellow said in a deep, husky voice that he wanted to go to confession. The priest said it was an awkward time and wouldn't it do in the morning, but the fellow said that last time he went to confession, there was one sin he kept back, being ashamed to mention it, and now it was always on his mind. Then the priest knew it was a bad case, because the fellow was after making a bad confession and committing a mortal sin. He got up to dress, and just then the cock crew in the yard outside, and—lo and behold!—when the priest looked round there was no sign of the fellow, only a smell of burning timber, and when the priest looked at his bed didn't he see the print of two hands burned in it? That was because the fellow had made a bad confession. This story made a shocking impression on me.

But the worst of all was when she showed us how to examine our conscience. Did we take the name of the Lord, our God, in vain? Did we honour our father and our mother? (I asked her did this include grandmothers and she said it did.) Did we love our neighbours as ourselves? Did we covet our neighbour's goods? (I thought of the way I felt about the penny that Nora got every Friday.) I decided that, between one thing and another, I must have broken the whole ten commandments, all on account of that old woman, and so far as I could see, so long as she remained in the house I had no hope of ever doing anything else.

I was scared to death of confession. The day the whole class went I let on to have a toothache, hoping my absence wouldn't be noticed; but at three o'clock, just as I was feeling safe, along comes a chap with a message from Mrs. Ryan that I was to go to confession myself on Saturday and be at the chapel for communion with the rest. To make it worse, Mother couldn't come with me and sent Nora instead.

Now, that girl had ways of tormenting me that Mother never knew of. She held my hand as we went down the hill, smiling sadly and saying how sorry she was for me, as if she were bringing me to the hospital for an operation.

"Oh, God help us!" she moaned. "Isn't it a terrible pity you weren't a good boy? Oh, Jackie, my heart bleeds for you! How will you ever think of all your sins? Don't forget you have to tell him about the time you kicked Gran on the shin."

"Lemme go!" I said, trying to drag myself free of her. "I don't want to go to confession at all."

"But sure, you'll have to go to confession, Jackie," she replied in the same regretful tone. "Sure, if you didn't, the parish priest would be up to the house, looking for you. 'Tisn't, God knows, that I'm not sorry for you. Do you remember the time you tried to kill me with the bread-knife under the table? And the language you used to me? I don't know what he'll do with you at all, Jackie. He might have to send you up to the bishop."

I remember thinking bitterly that she didn't know the half of what I had to tell—if I told it. I knew I couldn't tell it, and understood perfectly why the fellow in Mrs. Ryan's story made a bad confession; it seemed to me a great shame that people wouldn't stop criticizing him. I remember that steep hill down to the church, and the sunlit hillsides beyond the valley of the river, which I saw in the gaps between the houses like Adam's last glimpse of Paradise.

Then, when she had maneuvered me down the long flight of steps to the chapel yard, Nora suddenly changed her tone. She became the raging malicious devil she really was.

"There you are!" she said with a yelp of triumph, hurling me through the church door. "And I hope he'll give you the penitential psalms, you dirty little caffler."

I knew then I was lost, given up to eternal justice. The door with the coloured-glass panels swung shut behind me, the sunlight went out and gave place to deep shadow, and the wind whistled outside so that the silence within seemed to crackle like ice under my feet. Nora sat in front of me by the confession box. There were a couple of old women ahead of her, and then a miserable-looking poor devil came and wedged me in at the other side, so that I couldn't escape even if I had the courage. He joined his hands and rolled his eyes in the direction of the roof, muttering aspirations in an anguished tone, and I wondered had he a grandmother too. Only a grandmother could account for a fellow behaving in that heartbroken way, but he was better off than I, for he at least could go and confess his sins; while I would make a bad confession and then die in the night and be continually coming back and burning people's furniture.

Nora's turn came, and I heard the sound of something slamming, and then her voice as if butter wouldn't melt in her mouth, and then another slam, and out she came. God, the hypocrisy of women! Her eyes were lowered, her head was bowed, and her hands were joined very low down on her stomach, and she walked up the aisle to the side altar looking like a saint. You never saw such an exhibition of devotion; and I remembered the devilish malice with which she had tormented me all the way from our door, and wondered were all religious people like that, really. It was my turn now. With the fear of damnation in my soul I went in, and the confessional door closed of itself behind me.

It was pitch-dark and I couldn't see priest or anything else. Then I really began to be frightened. In the darkness it was a matter between God and me, and He had all the odds. He knew what my intentions were before I even started; I had no chance. All I had ever been told about confession got mixed up in my mind, and I knelt to one wall and said: "Bless me, father, for I have sinned; this is my first confession." I waited for a few minutes, but nothing happened, so I tried it on the other wall. Nothing happened there either. He had me spotted all right.

It must have been then that I noticed the shelf at about one height with my head. It was really a place for grown-up people to rest their elbows, but in my distracted state I thought it was probably the place you were supposed to kneel. Of course, it was on the high side and not very deep, but I was always good at climbing and managed to get up all right. Staying up was the trouble. There was room only for my knees, and nothing you could get a grip on but a sort of wooden moulding a bit above it. I held on to the moulding and repeated the words a little louder, and this time something happened all right. A slide was slammed back; a little light entered the box, and a man's voice said: "Who's there?"

"'Tis me, father," I said for fear he mightn't see me and go away again. I couldn't see him at all. The place the voice came from was under the moulding, about level with my knees, so I took a good grip of the moulding and swung myself down till I saw the astonished face of a young priest looking up at me. He had to put his head on one side to see me, and I had to put mine on one side to see him, so we were more or less talking to one another upside-down. It struck me as a queer way of hearing confessions, but I didn't feel it my place to criticize.

"Bless me, father, for I have sinned; this is my first confession," I rattled off all in one breath, and swung myself down the least shade more to make it easier for him.

"What are you doing up there?" he shouted in an angry voice, and the strain the politeness was putting on my hold of the moulding, and the shock of being addressed in such an uncivil tone, were too much for me. I lost my grip, tumbled, and hit the door an unmerciful wallop before I found myself flat on my back in the middle of the aisle. The people who had been waiting stood up with their mouths open. The priest opened the door in the middle box and came out, pushing his biretta back from his forehead; he looked something terrible. Then Nora came scampering down the aisle.

"Oh, you dirty little caffler!" she said. "I might have known you'd do it. I might have known you'd disgrace me. I can't leave you out of my sight for one minute."

Before I could even get to my feet to defend myself she bent down and gave me a clip across the ear. This reminded me that I was so stunned I had even forgotten to cry, so that people might think I wasn't hurt at all, when in fact I was probably maimed for life. I gave a roar out of me.

"What's all this about?" the priest hissed, getting angrier than ever and pushing Nora off me. "How dare you hit the child like that, you little vixen?"

"But I can't do my penance with him, father," Nora cried, cocking an outraged eye up at him.

"Well, go and do it, or I'll give you some more to do," he said, giving me a hand up. "Was it coming to confession you were, my poor man?" he asked me.

"'Twas, father," said I with a sob.

"Oh," he said respectfully, "a big hefty fellow like you must have terrible sins. Is this your first?"

"'Tis, father," said I.

"Worse and worse," he said gloomily. "The crimes of a lifetime. I don't know will I get rid of you at all today. You'd better wait now till I'm finished with these old ones. You can see by the looks of them they haven't much to tell."

"I will, father," I said with something approaching joy.

The relief of it was really enormous. Nora stuck out her tongue at me from behind his back, but I couldn't even be bothered retorting. I knew from the very moment that man opened his mouth that he was intelligent above the ordinary. When I had time to think, I saw how right I was. It only stood to reason that a fellow confessing after seven years would have more to tell than people that went every week. The crimes of a lifetime, exactly as he said. It was only what he expected, and the rest was the cackle of old women and girls with their talk of hell, the bishop, and the penitential psalms. That was all they knew. I started to make my examination of conscience, and barring the one bad business of my grandmother it didn't seem so bad.

The next time, the priest steered me into the confession box himself and left the shutter back the way I could see him get in and sit down at the further side of the grille from me.

"Well, now," he said, "what do they call you?"

"Jackie, father," said I.

"And what's a-trouble to you, Jackie?"

"Father," I said, feeling I might as well get it over while I had him in good humour, "I had it all arranged to kill my grandmother."

He seemed a bit shaken by that, all right, because he said nothing for quite a while.

"My goodness," he said at last, "that'd be a shocking thing to do. What put that into your head?"

"Father," I said, feeling very sorry for myself, "she's an awful woman."

"Is she?" he asked. "What way is she awful?"

"She takes porter, father," I said, knowing well from the way Mother talked of it that this was a mortal sin, and hoping it would make the priest take a more favourable view of my case.

"Oh, my!" he said, and I could see he was impressed.

"And snuff, father," said I.

"That's a bad case, sure enough, Jackie," he said.

"And she goes round in her bare feet, father," I went on in a rush of self-pity, "and she knows I don't like her, and she gives pennies to Nora and none to me, and my da sides with her and flakes me, and one night I was so heart-scalded I made up my mind I'd have to kill her."

"And what would you do with the body?" he asked with great interest.

"I was thinking I could chop that up and carry it away in a barrow I have," I said.

"Begor, Jackie," he said, "do you know you're a terrible child?"

"I know, father," I said, for I was just thinking the same thing myself. "I tried to kill Nora too with a bread-knife under the table, only I missed her."

"Is that the little girl that was beating you just now?" he asked.

"'Tis, father."

"Someone will go for her with a bread-knife one day, and he won't miss her," he said rather cryptically. "You must have great courage. Between ourselves, there's a lot of people I'd like to do the same to but I'd never have the nerve. Hanging is an awful death."

"Is it, father?" I asked with the deepest interest—I was always very keen on hanging. "Did you ever see a fellow hanged?"

"Dozens of them," he said solemnly. "And they all died roaring."

"Jay!" I said.

"Oh, a horrible death!" he said with great satisfaction. "Lots of the fellows I saw killed their grandmothers too, but they all said 'twas never worth it."

He had me there for a full ten minutes talking, and then walked out the chapel yard with me. I was genuinely sorry to part with him, because he was the most entertaining character I'd ever met in the religious line. Outside, after the shadow of the church, the sunlight was like the roaring of waves on a beach; it dazzled me; and when the frozen silence melted and I heard the screech of trams on the road my heart soared. I knew now I wouldn't die in the night and come back, leaving marks on my mother's furniture. It would be a great worry to her, and the poor soul had enough.

Nora was sitting on the railing, waiting for me, and she put on a very sour puss when she saw the priest with me. She was mad jealous because a priest had never come out of the church with her.

"Well," she asked coldly, after he left me, "what did he give you?"

"Three Hail Marys," I said.

"Three Hail Marys," she repeated incredulously. "You mustn't have told him anything."

"I told him everything," I said confidently.

"About Gran and all?"

"About Gran and all."

(All she wanted was to be able to go home and say I'd made a bad confession.)

"Did you tell him you went for me with the bread-knife?" she asked with a frown.

"I did to be sure."

"And he only gave you three Hail Marys?"

"That's all."

She slowly got down from the railing with a baffled air. Clearly, this was beyond her. As we mounted the steps back to the main road she looked at me suspiciously.

"What are you sucking?" she asked.

"Bullseyes."

"Was it the priest gave them to you?"

"'Twas."

"Lord God," she wailed bitterly, "some people have all the luck! 'Tis no advantage to anybody trying to be good. I might just as well be a sinner like you."

Isaac Bashevis Singer

GIMPEL THE FOOL

I

I am Gimpel the fool. I don't think myself a fool. On the contrary. But that's what folks call me. They gave me the name while I was still in school. I had seven names in all: imbecile, donkey, flax-head, dope, glump, ninny, and fool. The last name stuck. What did my foolishness consist of? I was easy to take in. They said, "Gimpel, you know the rabbi's wife had been brought to childbed?" So I skipped school. Well, it turned out to be a lie. How was I supposed to know? She hadn't had a big belly. But I never looked at her belly. Was that really so foolish? The gang laughed and hee-hawed, stomped and danced and chanted a good-night prayer. And instead of the raisins they give when a woman's lying in, they stuffed my hand full of goat turds. I was no weakling. If I slapped someone he'd see all the way to Cracow. But I'm really not a slugger by nature. I think to myself: Let it pass. So they take advantage of me.

I was coming home from school and heard a dog barking. I'm not afraid of dogs, but of course I never want to start up with them. One of them may be mad, and if he bites there's not a Tartar in the world who can help you. So I made tracks. Then I looked around and saw the whole market place wild with laughter. It was no dog at all but Wolf-Leib the Thief. How was I supposed to know it was he? It sounded like a howling bitch.

When the pranksters and leg-pullers found that I was easy to fool, every one of them tried his luck with me. "Gimpel, the Czar is coming to Frampol; Gimpel, the moon fell down in Turbeen; Gimpel, little Hodel Furpiece found a treasure behind the bathhouse." And I like a golem believed everyone. In the first place, everything is possible, as it is written in the Wisdom of the Fathers, I've forgotten just how. Second, I had to believe when the whole town came down on me! If I ever dared to say, "Ah, you're kidding!" there was trouble. People got angry. "What do you mean! You want to call everyone a liar?" What was I to do? I believed them, and I hope at least that did them some good.

I was an orphan. My grandfather who brought me up was already bent toward the grave. So they turned me over to a baker, and what a time they gave me there! Every woman or girl who came to bake a batch of noodles had to fool me at least once. "Gimpel, there's a fair in heaven; Gimpel, the rabbi gave birth to a calf in the seventh month; Gimpel, a cow flew over the roof and laid brass eggs." A student from the yeshiva came once to buy a roll, and he said, "You, Gimpel, while you stand here scraping with your baker's shovel the Messiah has come. The dead have arisen." "What do you mean?" I said. "I heard no one blowing the ram's horn!" He said, "Are you deaf?" And all began to cry, "We heard it, we heard!" Then in came Rietze the Candle-dipper and called out in her hoarse voice, "Gimpel, your father and mother have stood up from the grave. They're looking for you."

To tell the truth, I knew very well that nothing of the sort had happened, but all the same, as folks were talking, I threw on my wool vest and went out. Maybe something had happened. What did I stand to lose by looking? Well, what a cat music went up! And then I took a vow to believe nothing more. But that was no go either. They confused me so that I didn't know the big end from the small.

I went to the rabbi to get some advice. He said, "It is written, better to be a fool all your days than for one hour to be evil. You are not a fool. They are the fools. For he who causes his neighbor to feel shame loses Paradise himself." Nevertheless the rabbi's daughter took me in. As I left the rabbinical court she said, "Have you kissed the wall yet?" I said, "No; what for?" She answered, "It's the law; you've got to do it after every visit." Well, there didn't seem to be any harm in it. And she burst out laughing. It was a fine trick. She put one over on me, all right.

I wanted to go off to another town, but then everyone got busy matchmaking, and they were after me so they nearly tore my coat tails off. They talked at me and talked until I got water on the ear. She was no chaste maiden, but they told me she was virgin pure. She had a limp, and they said it was deliberate, from coyness. She had a bastard, and they told me the child was her little brother. I cried, "You're wasting your time. I'll never marry that whore." But they said indignantly, "What a way to talk! Aren't you ashamed of yourself? We can take you to the rabbi and have you fined for giving her a bad name." I saw then that I wouldn't escape them so easily and I thought: They're set on making me their butt. But when you're married the husband's the master, and if that's all right with her it's agreeable to me too. Besides, you can't pass through life unscathed, nor expect to.

I went to her clay house, which was built on the sand, and the whole gang, hollering and chorusing, came after me. They acted like bear-baiters. When we came to the well they stopped all the same. They were afraid to start anything with Elka. Her mouth would open as if it were on a hinge, and she had a fierce tongue. I entered the house. Lines were strung from wall to wall and clothes were drying. Barefoot she stood by the tub, doing the wash. She was dressed in a worn hand-me-down gown of plush. She had her hair put up in braids and pinned across her head. It took my breath away, almost, the reek of it all.

Evidently she knew who I was. She took a look at me and said, "Look who's here! He's come, the drip. Grab a seat."

I told her all; I denied nothing. "Tell me the truth," I said, "are you really a virgin, and is that mischievous Yechiel actually your little brother? Don't be deceitful with me, for I'm an orphan."

"I'm an orphan myself," she answered, "and whoever tries to twist you up, may the end of his nose take a twist. But don't let them think they can take advantage of me. I want a dowry of fifty guilders, and let them take up a collection besides. Otherwise they can kiss my you-know-what." She was very plainspoken. I said, "It's the bride and not the groom who gives a dowry." Then she said, "Don't bargain with me. Either a flat 'yes' or a flat 'no'—Go back where you came from."

I thought: No bread will ever be baked from this dough. But ours is not a poor town. They consented to everything and proceeded with the wedding. It so happened that there was a dysentery epidemic at the time. The ceremony was held at the cemetery gates, near the little corpse-washing hut. The fellows got drunk. While the marriage contract was being drawn up I heard the most pious high rabbi ask, "Is the bride a widow or a divorced woman?" And the sexton's wife answered for her, "Both a widow and divorced." It was a black moment for me. But what was I to do, run away from under the marriage canopy?

There was singing and dancing. An old granny danced opposite me, hugging a braided white *chalah.* The master of revels made a "God 'a mercy" in memory of the bride's parents. The schoolboys threw burrs, as on Tishe b'Av fast day. There were a lot of gifts after the sermon: a noodle board, a kneading trough, a bucket, brooms, ladles, household articles galore. Then I took a look and saw two strapping young men carrying a crib. "What do we need this for?" I asked. So they said, "Don't rack your brains about it. It's all right, it'll come in handy." I realized I was going to be rooked. Take it another way though, what did I stand to lose? I reflected: I'll see what comes of it. A whole town can't go altogether crazy.

II

At night I came where my wife lay, but she wouldn't let me in. "Say, look here, is this what they married us for?" I said. And she said, "My monthly has come." "But yesterday they took you to the ritual bath, and that's afterward, isn't it supposed to be?" "Today isn't yesterday," said she, "and yesterday's not today. You can beat it if you don't like it." In short, I waited.

Nor four months later she was in childbed. The townsfolk hid their laughter with their knuckles. But what could I do? She suffered intolerable pains and clawed at the walls. "Gimpel," she cried, "I'm going. Forgive me!" The house filled with women. They were boiling pans of water. The screams rose to the welkin.

The thing to do was to go to the House of Prayer to repeat Psalms, and that was what I did.

The townsfolk liked that, all right. I stood in a corner saying Psalms and prayers, and they shook their heads at me. "Pray, pray!" they told me.

"Prayer never made any woman pregnant." One of the congregation put a straw to my mouth and said, "Hay for the cows." There was something to that too, by God!

She gave birth to a boy. Friday at the synagogue the sexton stood up before the Ark, pounded on the reading table, and announced, "The wealthy Reb Gimpel invites the congregation to a feast in honor of the birth of a son." The whole House of Prayer rang with laughter. My face was flaming. But there was nothing I could do. After all, I *was* the one responsible for the circumcision honors and rituals.

Half the town came running. You couldn't wedge another soul in. Women brought peppered chick-peas, and there was a keg of beer from the tavern. I ate and drank as much as anyone, and they all congratulated me. Then there was a circumcision, and I named the boy after my father, may he rest in peace. When all were gone and I was left with my wife alone, she thrust her head through the bed-curtain and called me to her.

"Gimpel," said she, "why are you silent? Has your ship gone and sunk?"

"What shall I say?" I answered. "A fine thing you've done to me! If my mother had known of it she'd have died a second time."

She said, "Are you crazy, or what?"

"How can you make such a fool," I said, "of one who should be the lord and master?"

"What's the matter with you?" she said. "What have you taken it into your head to imagine?"

I saw that I must speak bluntly and openly. "Do you think this is the way to use an orphan?" I said. "You have borne a bastard."

She answered, "Drive this foolishness out of your head. The child is yours."

"How can he be mine?" I argued. "He was born seventeen weeks after the wedding."

She told me then that he was premature. I said, "Isn't he a little too premature?" She said, she had had a grandmother who carried just as short a time and she resembled this grandmother of hers as one drop of water does another. She swore to it with such oaths that you would have believed a peasant at the fair if he had used them. To tell the plain truth, I didn't believe her; but when I talked it over next day with the schoolmaster he told me that the very same thing had happened to Adam and Eve. Two they went up to bed, and four they descended.

"There isn't a woman in the world who is not the granddaughter of Eve," he said.

That was how it was; they argued me dumb. But then, who really knows how such things are?

I began to forget my sorrow. I loved the child madly, and he loved me too. As soon as he saw me he'd wave his little hands and want me to pick him up, and when he was colicky I was the only one who could pacify him. I bought him a little bone teething ring and a little gilded cap. He was forever catching the evil eye from someone, and then I had to run to get one of those abracadabras for him that would get him out of it. I worked like an ox. You know how expenses go up when there's an infant in the house. I don't want to lie about it; I didn't dislike Elka either, for that matter. She swore at me and cursed, and I couldn't get enough of her. What strength she had! One of her looks could rob you of the power of speech. And her orations! Pitch and sulphur, that's what they were full of, and yet somehow also full of charm. I adored her every word. She gave me bloody wounds though.

In the evening I brought her a white loaf as well as a dark one, and also poppyseed rolls I baked myself. I thieved because of her and swiped everything I could lay hands on: macaroons, raisins, almonds, cakes. I hope I may be forgiven for stealing from the Saturday pots the women left to warm in the baker's oven. I would take out scraps of meat, a chunk of pudding, a chicken leg or head, a piece of tripe, whatever I could nip quickly. She ate and became fat and handsome.

I had to sleep away from home all during the week, at the bakery. On Friday nights when I got home she always made an excuse of some sort. Either she had heartburn, or a stitch in the side, or hiccups, or headaches. You know what women's excuses are. I had a bitter time of it. It was rough. To add to it, this little brother of hers, the bastard, was growing bigger. He'd put lumps on me, and when I wanted to hit back she'd open her mouth and curse so powerfully I saw a green haze floating before my eyes. Ten times a day she threatened to divorce me. Another man in my place would have taken French leave and disappeared. But I'm the type that bears it and says nothing. What's one to do? Shoulders are from God, and burdens too.

One night there was a calamity in the bakery; the oven burst, and we almost had a fire. There was nothing to do but go home, so I went home. Let me, I thought, also taste the joy of sleeping in bed in mid-week. I didn't want to wake the sleeping mite and tiptoed into the house. Coming in, it seemed to me that I heard not the snoring of one but, as it were, a double snore, one a thin enough snore and the other like the snoring of a slaughtered ox. Oh, I didn't like that! I didn't like it at all. I went up to the bed, and things suddenly turned black. Next to Elka lay a man's form. Another in my place would have made an uproar, and enough noise to rouse the whole town, but the thought occurred to me that I might wake the child. A little thing like that—why frighten a little swallow, I thought. All right then, I went back to the bakery and stretched out on a sack of flour and till morning I never shut an eye. I shivered as if I had had malaria. "Enough of being a donkey," I said to myself. "Gimpel isn't going to be a sucker all his life. There's a limit even to the foolishness of a fool like Gimpel."

In the morning I went to the rabbi to get advice, and it made a great commotion in the town. They sent the beadle for Elka right away. She came, carrying the child. And what do you think she did? She denied it, denied everything, bone and stone! "He's out of his head," she said. "I know nothing of dreams or divinations." They yelled at her, warned her, hammered on the table, but she stuck to her guns: it was a false accusation, she said.

The butchers and the horse-traders took her part. One of the lads from the slaughterhouse came by and said to me, "We've got our eye on you,

you're a marked man." Meanwhile the child started to bear down and soiled itself. In the rabbinical court there was an Ark of the Covenant, and they couldn't allow that, so they sent Elka away.

I said to the rabbi, "What shall I do?"

"You must divorce her at once," said he.

"And what if she refuses?" I asked.

He said, "You must serve the divorce. That's all you'll have to do."

I said, "Well, all right, Rabbi. Let me think about it."

"There's nothing to think about," said he. "You mustn't remain under the same roof with her."

"And if I want to see the child?" I asked.

"Let her go, the harlot," said he, "and her brood of bastards with her."

The verdict he gave was that I mustn't even cross her threshold—never again, as long as I should live.

During the day it didn't bother me so much. I thought: It was bound to happen, the abscess had to burst. But at night when I stretched out upon the sacks I felt it all very bitterly. A longing took me, for her and for the child. I wanted to be angry, but that's my misfortune exactly, I don't have it in me to be really angry. In the first place—this was how my thoughts went—there's bound to be a slip sometimes. You can't live without errors. Probably that lad who was with her led her on and gave her presents and what not, and women are often long on hair and short on sense, and so he got around her. And then since she denies it so, maybe I was only seeing things? Hallucinations do happen. You see a figure or a mannikin or something, but when you come up closer it's nothing, there's not a thing there. And if that's so, I'm doing her an injustice. And when I got so far in my thoughts I started to weep. I sobbed so that I wet the flour where I lay. In the morning I went to the rabbi and told him that I had made a mistake. The rabbi wrote on with his quill, and he said that if that were so he would have to reconsider the whole case. Until he had finished I wasn't to go near my wife, but I might send her bread and money by messenger.

III

Nine months passed before all the rabbis could come to an agreement. Letters went back and forth. I hadn't realized that there could be so much erudition about a matter like this.

Meanwhile Elka gave birth to still another child, a girl this time. On the Sabbath I went to the synagogue and invoked a blessing on her. They called me up to the Torah, and I named the child for my mother-in-law—may she rest in peace. The louts and loudmouths of the town who came into the bakery gave me a going over. All Frampol refreshed its spirits because of my trouble and grief. However, I resolved that I would always believe what I was told. What's the good of *not* believing? Today it's your wife you don't believe; tomorrow it's God Himself you won't take stock in.

By an apprentice who was her neighbor I sent her daily a corn or a wheat loaf, or a piece of pastry, rolls or bagels, or, when I got the chance, a slab of pudding, a slice of honeycake, or wedding strudel—whatever came my way. The apprentice was a goodhearted lad, and more than once he added something on his own. He had formerly annoyed me a lot, plucking my nose and digging me in the ribs, but when he started to be a visitor to my house he became kind and friendly. "Hey, you, Gimpel," he said to me, "you have a very decent little wife and two fine kids. You don't deserve them."

"But the things people say about her," I said.

"Well, they have long tongues," he said, "and nothing to do with them but babble. Ignore it as you ignore the cold of last winter."

One day the rabbi sent for me and said, "Are you certain, Gimpel, that you were wrong about your wife?"

I said, "I'm certain."

"Why, but look here! You yourself saw it."

"It must have been a shadow," I said.

"The shadow of what?"

"Just of one of the beams, I think."

"You can go home then. You owe thanks to the Yanover rabbi. He found an obscure reference in Maimonides that favored you."

I seized the rabbi's hand and kissed it.

I wanted to run home immediately. It's no small thing to be separated for so long a time from wife and child. Then I reflected: I'd better go back to work now, and go home in the evening. I said nothing to anyone, although as far as my heart was concerned it was like one of the Holy Days. The women teased and twitted me as they did every day, but my thought was: Go on, with your loose talk. The truth is out, like the oil upon the water. Maimonides says it's right, and therefore it is right!

At night, when I had covered the dough to let it rise, I took my share of bread and a little sack of flour and started homeward. The moon was full and the stars were glistening, something to terrify the soul. I hurried onward, and before me darted a long shadow. It was winter, and a fresh snow had fallen. I had a mind to sing, but it was growing late and I didn't want to wake the householders. Then I felt like whistling, but I remembered that you don't whistle at night because it brings the demons out. So I was silent and walked as fast as I could.

Dogs in the Christian yards barked at me when I passed, but I thought: Bark your teeth out! What are you but mere dogs? Whereas I am a man, the husband of a fine wife, the father of promising children.

As I approached the house my heart started to pound as though it were the heart of a criminal. I felt no fear, but my heart went thump! thump! Well, no drawing back. I quietly lifted the latch and went in. Elka was asleep. I looked at the infant's cradle. The shutter was closed, but the moon forced its way through the cracks. I saw the newborn child's face and loved it as soon as I saw it—immediately—each tiny bone.

Then I came nearer to the bed. And what did I see but the apprentice lying there beside Elka. The moon went out all at once. It was utterly black, and I trembled. My teeth chattered. The bread fell from my hands, and my wife waked and said, "Who is that, ah?"

I muttered, "It's me."

"Gimpel?" she asked. "How come you're here? I thought it was forbidden."

"The rabbi said," I answered and shook as with a fever.

"Listen to me, Gimpel," she said, "go out to the shed and see if the goat's all right. It seems she's been sick." I have forgotten to say that we had a goat. When I heard she was unwell I went into the yard. The nannygoat was a good little creature. I had a nearly human feeling for her.

With hesitant steps I went up to the shed and opened the door. The goat stood there on her four feet. I felt her everywhere, drew her by the horns, examined her udders, and found nothing wrong. She had probably eaten too much bark. "Good night, little goat," I said. "Keep well." And the little beast answered with a "Maa" as though to thank me for the good will.

I went back. The apprentice had vanished.

"Where," I asked, "is the lad?"

"What lad?" my wife answered.

"What do you mean?" I said. "The apprentice. You were sleeping with him."

"The things I have dreamed this night and the night before," she said, "may they come true and lay you low, body and soul! An evil spirit has taken root in you and dazzles your sight." She screamed out, "You hateful creature! You moon calf! You spook! You uncouth man! Get out, or I'll scream all Frampol out of bed!"

Before I could move, her brother sprang out from behind the oven and struck me a blow on the back of the head. I thought he had broken my neck. I felt that something about me was deeply wrong, and I said, "Don't make a scandal. All that's needed now is that people should accuse me of raising spooks and *dybbuks.*" For that was what she had meant. "No one will touch bread of my baking."

In short, I somehow calmed her.

"Well," she said, "that's enough. Lie down, and be shattered by wheels."

Next morning I called the apprentice aside. "Listen here, brother!" I said. And so on and so forth. "What do you say?" He stared at me as though I had dropped from the roof or something.

"I swear," he said, "you'd better go to an herb doctor or some healer. I'm afraid you have a screw loose, but I'll hush it up for you." And that's how the thing stood.

To make a long story short, I lived twenty years with my wife. She bore me six children, four daughters and two sons. All kinds of things happened, but I neither saw nor heard. I believed, and that's all. The rabbi recently said to me, "Belief in itself is beneficial. It is written that a good man lives by his faith."

Suddenly my wife took sick. It began with a trifle, a little growth upon the breast. But she evidently was not destined to live long; she had no years. I spent a fortune on her. I have forgotten to say that by this time I had a bakery of my own and in Frampol was considered to be something of a rich man. Daily the healer came, and every witch doctor in the neighborhood was brought. They decided to use leeches, and after that to try cupping. They even called a doctor from Lublin, but it was too late. Before she died she called me to her bed and said, "Forgive me, Gimpel."

I said, "What is there to forgive? You have been a good and faithful wife."

"Woe, Gimpel!" she said. "It was ugly how I deceived you all these years. I want to go clean to my Maker, and so I have to tell you that the children are not yours."

If I had been clouted on the head with a piece of wood it couldn't have bewildered me more.

"Whose are they?" I asked.

"I don't know," she said. "There were a lot . . . but they're not yours." And as she spoke she tossed her head to the side, her eyes turned glassy, and it was all up with Elka. On her whitened lips there remained a smile.

I imagined that, dead as she was, she was saying, "I deceived Gimpel. That was the meaning of my brief life."

IV

One night, when the period of mourning was done, as I lay dreaming on the flour sacks, there came the Spirit of Evil himself and said to me, "Gimpel, why do you sleep?"

I said, "What should I be doing? Eating *kreplach?*"

"The whole world deceives you," he said, "and you ought to deceive the world in your turn."

"How can I deceive all the world?" I asked him.

He answered, "You might accumulate a bucket of urine every day and at night pour it into the dough. Let the sages of Frampol eat filth."

"What about the judgment in the world to come?" I said.

"There is no world to come," he said. "They've sold you a bill of goods and talked you into believing you carried a cat in your belly. What nonsense!"

"Well then," I said, "and is there a God?"

He answered, "There is no God either."

"What," I said, "*is* there, then?"

"A thick mire."

He stood before my eyes with a goatish beard and horn, long-toothed, and with a tail. Hearing such words, I wanted to snatch him by the tail, but I tumbled from the flour sacks and nearly broke a rib. Then it happened that I had to answer the call of nature, and, passing, I saw the risen dough, which seemed to say to me, "Do it!" In brief, I let myself be persuaded.

At dawn the apprentice came. We kneaded the bread, scattered caraway seeds on it, and set it to bake. Then the apprentice went away, and I was left sitting in the little trench by the oven, on a pile of rags. Well, Gimpel, I thought, you've revenged yourself on them for all the shame they've put on you. Outside the frost glittered, but it was warm beside the oven. The flames heated my face. I bent my head and fell into a doze.

I saw in a dream, at once, Elka in her shroud. She called to me, "What have you done, Gimpel?"

I said to her, "It's all your fault," and started to cry.

"You fool!" she said. "You fool! Because I was false is everything false too? I never deceived anyone but myself. I'm paying for it all, Gimpel. They spare you nothing here."

I looked at her face. It was black; I was startled and waked, and remained sitting dumb. I sensed that everything hung in the balance. A false step now and I'd lose Eternal Life. But God gave me His help. I seized the long shovel and took out the loaves, carried them into the yard, and started to dig a hole in the frozen earth.

My apprentice came back as I was doing it. "What are you doing boss?" he said, and grew pale as a corpse.

"I know what I'm doing," I said, and I buried it all before his very eyes.

Then I went home, took my hoard from its hiding place, and divided it among the children. "I saw your mother tonight," I said. "She's turning black, poor thing."

They were so astounded they couldn't speak a word.

"Be well," I said, "and forget that such a one as Gimpel ever existed." I put on my short coat, a pair of boots, took the bag that held my prayer shawl in one hand, my stock in the other, and kissed the *mezzuzah*. When people saw me in the street they were greatly surprised.

"Where are you going?" they said.

I answered, "Into the world." And so I departed from Frampol.

I wandered over the land, and good people did not neglect me. After many years I became old and white; I heard a great deal, many lies and falsehoods, but the longer I lived the more I understood that there were really no lies. Whatever doesn't really happen is dreamed at night. It happens to one if it doesn't happen to another, tomorrow if not today, or a century hence if not next year. What difference can it make? Often I heard tales of which I said, "Now this is a thing that cannot happen." But before a year had elapsed I heard that it actually had come to pass somewhere.

Going from place to place, eating at strange tables, it often happens that I spin yarns—improbable things that could never have happened—about devils, magicians, windmills, and the like. The children run after me, calling, "Grandfather, tell us a story." Sometimes they ask for particular stories, and I try to please them. A fat young boy once said to me, "Grandfather, it's the same story you told us before." The little rogue, he was right.

So it is with dreams too. It is many years since I left Frampol, but as soon as I shut my eyes I am there again. And whom do you think I see? Elka. She is standing by the washtub, as at our first encounter, but her face is shining and her eyes are as radiant as the eyes of a saint, and she speaks outlandish words to me, strange things. When I wake I have forgotten it all. But while the dream lasts I am comforted. She answers all my queries, and what comes out is that all is right. I weep and implore, "Let me be with you." And she consoles me and tells me to be patient. The time is nearer than it is far. Sometimes she strokes and kisses me and weeps upon my face. When I awaken I feel her lips and taste the salt of her tears.

No doubt the world is entirely an imaginary world, but it is only once removed from the true world. At the door of the hovel where I lie, there stands the plank on which the dead are taken away. The gravedigger Jew has his spade ready. The grave waits and the worms are hungry; the shrouds are prepared—I carry them in my beggar's sack. Another *shnorrer* is waiting to inherit my bed of straw. When the time comes I will go joyfully. Whatever may be there, it will be real, without complication, without ridicule, without deception. God be praised: there even Gimpel cannot be deceived.

Translated by Saul Bellow